ANALOG AND DIGITAL HOLOGRAPHY WITH MATLAB®

ANALOG AND DIGITAL HOLOGRAPHY WITH MATLAB®

Georges Nehmetallah

Rola Aylo

Logan Williams

SPIE PRESS
Bellingham, Washington USA

Library of Congress Cataloging-in-Publication Data

Nehmetallah, Georges T., author.
 Analog and digital holography with MATLAB / Georges T. Nehmetallah, Rola
Aylo, and Logan A. Williams.
     pages cm
 Includes bibliographical references and index.
 ISBN 978-1-62841-692-3
 1. Holography—Data processing.   2. Image processing—Digital techniques.
 3. MATLAB. I. Aylo, Rola, 1981- author. II. Williams, Logan A., 1977-
author. III. Title.
 TA1540.N46 2015
 621.36'75028553—dc23

                                                              2015008134

Published by

SPIE
P.O. Box 10
Bellingham, Washington 98227-0010 USA
Phone: + 1 360.676.3290
Fax: + 1 360.647.1445
Email: Books@spie.org
Web: http://spie.org

Printed in the United States of America.
First printing

Table of Contents

Preface

Although the concept of holography has been known for decades, the field has seen significant development due to the availability of moderately priced lasers in the market for holographic applications. Also due to the advances in computer technology and computational processes, gathering and processing the experimental data has become much more tangible. Holography is a useful technique because it is the only truly three-dimensional imaging method available. It is used in a plethora of fields, such as 3D nonintrusive testing of cracks and fatigue in equipment, high-axial and lateral-resolution 3D topography of surfaces, 3D particle image velocimetry, 3D stress and deformation measurement, 3D microscopy of transparent phase objects for biomedical imaging, and holographic displays for the entertainment industry, just to name a few. For these reasons, digital and analog holography, along with their many variations (i.e., holographic interferometry, holographic microscopy, holographic tomography, multiwavelength digital holography, phase-shifting holography, compressive holography, coherence holography, computer-generated holography, etc.) have become the methods of choice for various metrological applications in 3D imaging.

This book begins with a brief introduction of the history of holography, types of holograms, and materials used for hologram recording, followed by a discussion of the basic principles of analog and digital holography and an in-depth explanation of some of the most famous fringe-deciphering techniques for holographic interferometry. Besides the traditional topics already mentioned, other related topics are discussed—dynamic holography, non-Bragg orders, and compressive holographic tomography—as well as a nonholographic technique for 3D visualization, i.e., transportation of intensity imaging. Furthermore, the latest topics in the field of holography are discussed for the first time here: compressive holography, coherence holography, nonlinear holography, and polarization holography. The last chapter is dedicated to the progress in holographic and nonholographic 3D display technologies.

Multiple holographic techniques are presented, and readers may master their basic concepts through in-depth theory and applications. This book is a comprehensive study in the sense that traditional and up-to-date topics concerning holographic imaging and displays are presented. The focus is not so much the theory of these 3D imaging techniques, which exists in many references and will be briefly mentioned in this book, but rather the programming side, namely, the exact code that is needed to perform complex mathematical and physical operations. The code associated with each section help the reader grasp the mathematical concepts better through changing and adapting the parameters. Programming these complex equations is tedious and not straightforward; supplying the code with the text makes it easier for students and experienced researchers to concentrate on performing the experiment and simply changing the parameters in the code to get their results.

Because MATLAB® has become the programming language of choice for engineering and physics students, we decided to use this fantastic tool for our code examples. A few authors suggest the use of MATLAB for optics-oriented books, but none is adequate for use in practical situations. There are many books about analog and digital holography, but this book is more practical in terms of MATLAB code and examples because it includes all of the different techniques and codes in a single volume. A supplemental CD-ROM is included, which has a detailed version of the code and functions, as well as typical test images, so that readers do not need to perform the experiment to use the code in the book.

Special thanks to Dr. Partha Banerjee, Dr. Joe Haus, and Dr. Andrew Sarangan, Dr. John Loomis, and Dr. Russel Hardie from the University of Dayton. Also, special thanks to those who contributed to some of the original code in this book, namely, Mr. Thanh Nguyen (CUA), Dr. D. J. Brady (Duke University), Dr. J. Antonio Quiroga (The University of Madrid), Drs. J. Bioucas-Dias and G. Valadão (the Instituto Superior Técnico, Lisboa, Portugal), Dr. Munther Gdeisat [the General Engineering Research Institute (GERI) at Liverpool John Moores University], Dr. Miguel Arevallilo Herraez (the Mediterranean University of Science and Technology, Valencia, Spain), Dr. Justin Romberg (Georgia Tech.), Mr. Peyman Soltani (University of Zanjan, Iran), Dr. Jeny Rajan (the National Institute of Technology, Karnataka Surathkal, Mangalore, India), Dr. Wei Wang (the Heriot–Watt University, Edinburgh), Dr. Laura Waller (UC Berkeley), and Drs. Lei Tian and George Barbastathis (the Department of Mechanical Engineering at MIT). We offer special thanks to our parents, for without them this work would not have been possible.

Georges Nehmetallah
Rola Aylo
Logan Williams
June 2015

List of Acronyms and Abbreviations

2D-SRNCP	Sorting by reliability, following a non-continuous path
AgBr	Silver bromide
AgCl	Silver chloride
AgH	Silver halide
AgI	Silver iodide
AH	Analog holography
AHI	Analog holographic interferometry
AO	Acousto-optic
AOM	Acousto-optic modulator
API	Application program interface
AR	Active retarder
AS	Angular spectrum
$BaTiO_3$	Barium titanate
BC	Branch cuts
BLU	Backlight unit
BMA	Block-matching algorithm
BS	Beamsplitter
BSO	Bismuth silicon oxide
CAD	Computer-aided design
CCD	Charge-coupled device
CGH	Computer-generated holography
CH	Coherence holography
CL	Collimating lens
CO_2	Carbon dioxide
CPAS	Compensated phase-added stereogram
CRS	Cathode ray sphere
CRT	Coherent raytrace
CRTs	Cathode ray tubes
CS	Compressive sensing
CsH	Compressive holography
DBS	Direct binary search

DC	direct current (zero order)
DCT/IDCT	Discrete cosine transform/inverse discrete cosine transform
DFD	Depth-fused display
DFT	Discrete Fourier transform
DH	Digital holography
DHI	Digital holographic interferometry
DHI-SM	Digital holographic interferometry with spatial multiplexing
DHM	Digital holographic microscopy
DHT	Digital holographic tomography
DL	Delay line
DLP	Digital light processing
DMD	Digital micromirror device
DND	Diffractive nanodevice
DOE	Diffractive optical element
DPSI	Digital phase shifting interferometry
DS	Diffraction specific
DSCP	Diffraction-specific coherent panoramagram
EASLM	Electrically addressable spatial light modulator
EBL	E-beam lithography
ED	Error diffusion
ESPI	Electronic speckle pattern interferometry
fft	Fast Fourier transform
FK	Fresnel–Kirchhoff
FOV	Field of view
FP	Full parallax
FPA	Focal plane array
FPGA	Field programmable gate array
FZP	Fresnel zone plate
GLV	Grating light valve
GPU	Graphical processing unit
GS	Gerchberg and Saxton
GVF	Gradient vector field
GWS	Guided wave scanner
H&D	Hurter–Driffield
HC	Holocamera
HDTV	High-definition TV
HMD	Head-mounted display
HOE	Holographic optical element
HORN	Holographic reconstruction
HPO	Horizontal parallax only
HTh	Hard thresholding
HWP	Half-wave plate
IR	Infrared
ITO	Indium tin oxide

$KNbO_3$	Potassium niobate
LCD	Liquid crystal display
LCOS	Liquid crystal on silicon
LCP	Left circularly polarized light
LED	Light-emitting diode
LEM	Lumped-element model
LID	Laser induced damage
$LiNbO_3$, LN	Lithium niobate
LP	Linear polarizer
LUT	Look-up table
MAC	Multiplication and accumulation
MEMS	Microelectromechanical systems
MO	Microscope Objective
MWDH	Multi-wavelength digital holography
MWDH-SH	Multi-wavelength digital holography with spatial heterodyning
MWDHM	Multi-wavelength digital holographic microscopy
MWDHM-SH	Multi-wavelength digital holographic microscopy with spatial heterodyning
Nd:YAG	Neodymium-doped yttrium aluminium garnet
NLS	Nonlinear Schrödinger
NMRS	Numerical mean square error
OALCD	Optically addressed LCD
OL/ETL	Offset diverging lens and electrically tunable lens
OPEN-GL	Open Graphics Library
OR	Orthoscopic
PAS	Phase-added stereogram
PBS	Polarized beamsplitter
PC	Phase conjugate
PDLC	Polymer-dispersed liquid crystal
PE	Phase enhanced
PMMA	Poly(methyl methacrylate)
POCS	Projection onto constrained sets
PP	Ping-pong
PR	Photorefractive
PR	Patterned retarder
PS	Pseudoscopy
PSDH	Phase-shifting digital holography
PSDH-WP	Phase-shifting digital holography using a wave plate
PSF	Point spread function
PSH	Phase-shifting holography
PTP	Photothermoplastic
PUMA	Phase unwrapping via maximum flow/min-cut
PZT	Piezoelectric transducer

QWT   Quarter-wave plate
RCP   Right circularly polarized light
RGB   Red, green, and blue
RHS   Right hand side
RIP   Restricted isometry propoerty
RMSE   Root-mean-square error
ROACH   Referenceless on-axis complex hologram
RPT   Regularized phase tracking
RS   Rayleigh–Sommerfeld
SADBS   Simulated annealing direct binary search
SAW   Surface acoustic wave
SBN   Strontium–barium niobate
SCF   Spatial coherence function
SF   Spatial filter
SHOT   Single-beam holographic tomography
SHOT-MT   Single-beam holographic tomography using a multiplicative
             technique
SHOT-RTT   Single-beam holographic tomography using a Radon
             transform technique
SIP   Shutter in panel
SLM   Spatial light modulator
SMV   Super multiview
SNR   Signal-to-noise ratio
SOP   State of polarization
SVEA   Slowly varying envelope approximation
TCH   Tomographic compressive holography
TCH-MT   Tomographic compressive holography using a
             multiplicative technique
TeO_2 Tellurium dioxide
TIE   Transport of intensity equation
TIR   Total internal reflection
TMP   Tree-matching pursuit
TV   Total variation
TWIST   Two-step iterative shrinkage thresholding
USAF   United States Air Force
UV   Ultraviolet
VA   Visual acuity
VPO   Vertical parallax only
VR   Virtual reality
VW   Viewing window
WRPM   Wavefront recording plane method

ANALOG AND DIGITAL
HOLOGRAPHY
WITH MATLAB®

Chapter 1
Introduction and Preliminaries

1.1 History of Holography

1.1.1 Introduction

The word "holography" aptly means "entire recording" and originates from the Greek words "holos" ("whole") and "gramma" ("message"). "Entire" refers to the recording of both the intensity and the phase of the object, as opposed to conventional photography, where only the intensity profile of the object is recorded.[1] It is the *phase* (which contains the information of depth or the information about how an object may have changed over time) that ordinary imaging lacks. Holography provides a way to ascertain the phase through comparison with the "known" phase of a reference beam.

Holography is capable of forming what may be termed a "3D" image from a 2D recording because it contains the optical phase information needed to stimulate the human visual system's depth cues. Other techniques, such as stereoscopic, autostereoscopic, and volumetric imaging, are deficient in some depth cues or may even produce conflicting cues.[2] For example, in a stereoscopic display system, convergence (i.e., the angular convergence between each eye's line of sight when directed at the same point) and accommodation (focusing) depth cues may conflict, which may result in the viewer experiencing discomfort, especially after long-term use.[2] However, holography does not actually record the complete 3D information content of an object; only the "3D" information that can be recorded in a given field of view (i.e., the holographic recording would not contain information about the *back* of an object if recorded only from the front). Complete 3D information can be obtained with tomographic techniques, including holographic tomography.

The ability to perform phase retrieval is crucial in many applications, such as surface reconstruction (i.e., topography), microscopy, location detection, and depth measurements. Is holography the only way to retrieve the phase information?

1

- **Yes**, if the intensity profile can be monitored at only *one* particular distance during the propagation of the object field (and reference field).
- **No**, if the object field intensity can be monitored at *various* distances of propagation or by using phase diversity.

Note that holographic techniques typically require a temporally and spatially coherent laser/light source, although there are some exceptions. The theory of conventional holography, including hologram recording and reconstruction using photographic film, can be found in numerous books, including Goodman.[1] Familiarity with the principles of holography is recommended before venturing into the realm of digital holography.

1.1.2 Types of holograms

The theory of holography, first introduced by Dennis Gabor in 1947, was developed in an attempt to improve the resolution of electron microscopes;[3] however, advancement in this field was stifled during the 1950s, primarily because light sources were generally not coherent. Temporally coherent light is light that is monochromatic (consisting of a single wavelength), whereas spatially coherent light is light with highly uniform/smooth phase fronts. In 1960, the invention of the laser overcame this difficulty by providing highly coherent optical sources, thus leading to renewed interest in holography. Gabor's original concept for holographic recording and reconstruction uses a single illumination wave to generate both the object and references waves using the scattered and unscattered light passing through/around the object. This type of recording setup is usually referred to as the Gabor setup, or on-axis setup, as shown in Fig. 1.1. However, this method has the disadvantage of placing both the real and virtual image along the same axis during reconstruction.

In 1962, Emmett Leith and Juris Upatnieks realized that holography could be used as a 3D visualization medium.[4] They developed a more practical recording method by using an off-axis reference beam, as opposed to Gabor's inline setup, as shown in Fig. 1.2. This beam allows the real image to be separated from the virtual image during reconstruction, thus creating a

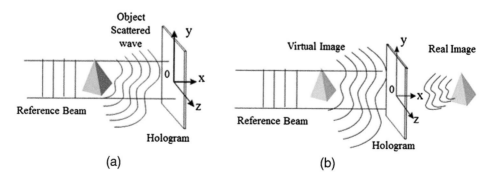

Figure 1.1   (a) On-axis recording and (b) on-axis reconstruction.

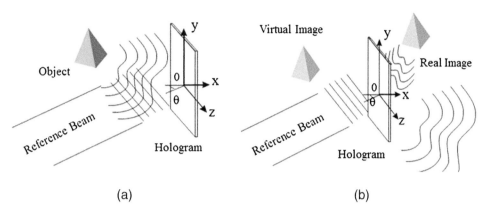

Figure 1.2 (a) Off-axis hologram recording setup and (b) off-axis reconstruction.

Figure 1.3 "Train and Bird," by Leith and Upatnieks, is the first hologram ever made with a laser using the off-axis technique, only four years after the invention of the laser.

clearer 3D visualization. Leith and Upatnieks created the first optical hologram in history using laser illumination: a toy train and bird, shown in Fig. 1.3.

Later in 1962, Yuri Denisyuk combined holography with Nobel Laureate (1908) Gabriel Lippmann's work in natural color photography to record a "reflection" hologram using coherent light that could then be viewed (i.e., reconstructed) using the white light from an incandescent light bulb.[5] He proved that it is possible to record a hologram using an object beam and reference beam that are incident on the photographic film from opposite sides, where the angle between beams can be as much as 180 deg, as shown in Fig. 1.4. These holograms can be reconstructed by illuminating them with

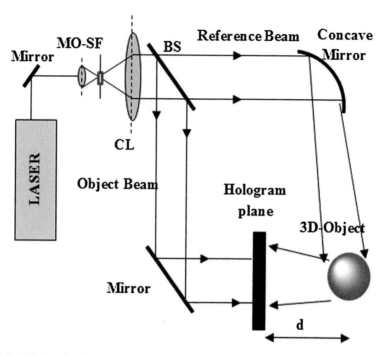

Figure 1.4 "Reflection" hologram recording setup, with a collimating lens (CL), microscope objective–spatial filter (MO-SF), and beamsplitter (BS).

spatially coherent white light (i.e., viewed some distance from a white-light point source) to obtain a "3D" image of good quality.[6] This development led to a new category of hologram, known as "reflection" holograms. Reflection holograms are viewed in a manner similar to common photographs, using white light reflected from the surface of the hologram. Prior to this development, most holograms were "transmission" holograms, which are viewed from the front by illuminating the back of the hologram with a coherent light source.[5]

Throughout this book, the off-axis setup shown in Fig. 1.2 will be used exclusively for reflective objects. The reason will become clear later while discussing digital holography, in which the relatively large pixel size (relative to the film-grain size) of the CCD camera limits the angle between the reference and the object beams to only a few degrees, making "reflection" holograms of the Denisyuk variety impossible to record. Note that future references to "transmission" or "reflection" recording configurations, as well as "transmission" and "reflection" holograms, will depend on whether the *object* is transmissive or reflective, not the manner of viewing. Therefore, the off-axis reflection setup (Fig. 1.2) is typically used for reflective objects, and the on-axis setup (Fig. 1.1) is used for transmissive objects.

The invention of the pulsed-ruby laser in 1960 made it possible to create holograms of high-speed objects, leading to the first hologram of a person in 1967.

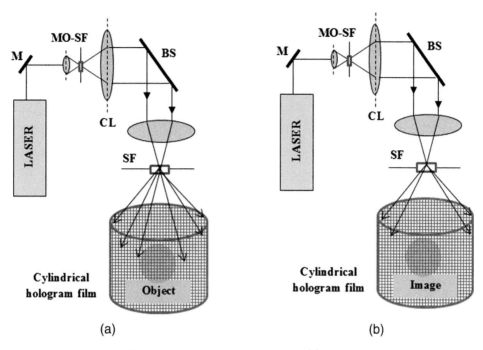

Figure 1.5 (a) Recording of a full-view hologram setup[6,8] and (b) reconstruction of the image.

The holograms discussed thus far have a limited viewing angle, or field of view (FOV). The first attempt to acquire a full 360-deg view of an object was performed using the setup shown in Fig. 1.5(a) by wrapping a photographic film around the inner surface of a cylinder, which surrounds the object.[7,8] The figure illustrates how part of the illumination beam will fall on the cylinder, directly constituting the reference beam, and part of it will be scattered from the central object onto the cylinder where the film is located, constituting the object beam. The interference of these two beams forms a hologram that encompasses a full 360-deg (lateral) view. For reconstruction, the same reference beam is used with the film mounted in its original position, as shown in Fig. 1.5(b).

The integral hologram (i.e., holographic stereogram or multiplex hologram), invented by Lloyd Cross in 1972, combines white-light transmission holography with conventional cinematography to produce moving 3D objects.[9,10] This technique uses 2D motion-picture footage of a rotating subject recorded on holographic film. Typically, three movie frames are recorded for each degree of rotation;[7] a schematic is shown in Fig. 1.6. The image is reconstructed by illuminating the integral hologram with white light, and it appears to be "3D" when viewed. However, this holographic technique exhibits only horizontal parallax and lacks vertical parallax, is monochromatic, and will change color when observers move their viewpoint up or down (similar to the rainbow holograms discussed next).[6] A typical integral hologram is shown in Fig. 1.6(d).[11]

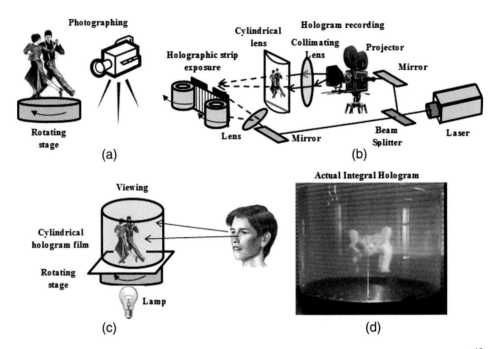

Figure 1.6 Integral (multiplex) hologram recording and reconstruction setup:[10] (a) photographing stage, (b) hologram recording setup, (c) hologram viewing (reconstruction) with white light, and (d) actual integral stereogram hologram.[11]

Another breakthrough in display holography occurred in 1968 when Stephen A. Benton invented white-light transmission holography while researching holographic television at Polaroid Research Laboratories.[7,12] These holograms are often called rainbow holograms and are a type of transmission hologram capable of reconstructing a monochromatic image when illuminated with white light. This type of hologram can be viewed in ordinary white light by creating a "rainbow" image from the various white light color components. This form of holography is significant because it paved the way for the mass production of holograms via embossing, invented by Michael Foster in 1974 and by Steve McGreww in 1979. The holograms are printed by stamping the interference pattern onto plastic using an embossing mold, a process that can be inexpensively duplicated in large quantities. These holograms are now widely used in publishing, advertising, banking, and security industries, and are commonly found on credit cards as a proof of authenticity.

Figure 1.7 shows the steps needed to create such a hologram. Figure 1.7(a) shows the recording of a regular hologram, and Fig. 1.7(b) shows the reconstruction of the real image by the conjugate of the reference beam. In Figs. 1.7(c) and (d), a horizontal slit is placed over the holographic plate, and a second hologram is recorded using another converging reference in the vertical direction. The second holographic plate is placed at the same location where the reconstructed image from the first hologram is located. Therefore, the second

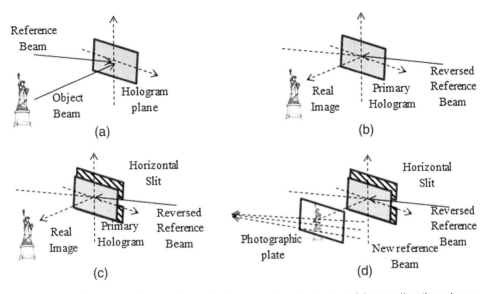

Figure 1.7 Sequence of steps for producing a rainbow hologram: (a) recording the primary hologram, (b) projecting the real image, (c) the real image with no vertical parallax, (d) and recording the final hologram. Reprinted from Hariharan[6] with permission.

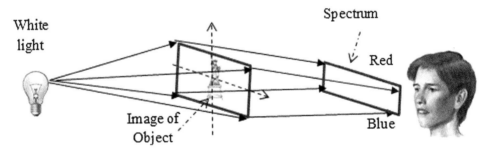

Figure 1.8 Image reconstruction of a rainbow hologram using white light. Reprinted from Hariharan[6] and Hariharan et al.[13] with permission.

hologram is recorded using the reconstructed optical field of the first hologram and the new reference beam. Finally, because the slit image is dispersed in the vertical direction, a white-light source may be used to reconstruct the rainbow hologram to form a continuous spectrum. The observer will then see the reconstructed 3D image in different colors depending on the viewing angle, as shown in Fig. 1.8. Figure 1.9 shows a typical rainbow hologram. Many of the early pioneers in the field of holography are shown in Figure 1.10.

1.1.3 Holographic recording media

A. Photographic materials

Photographic plates and films were the first materials used to record holograms. They are still widely used due to their high resolution and ability

Figure 1.9 A typical rainbow hologram.

Figure 1.10 Major figures in holography (from left): D. Gabor, E. Leith, J. Upatnieks, Y. Denisyuk, S. Benton, and L. Cross.

to be customized with a dye to match the wavelength of laser illumination. *Photographic film* consists of a transparent material with a coating of a photosensitive emulsion of silver halide (usually abbreviated as AgH, e.g., AgCl, AgBr and AgI) on top. When recording the hologram, the film is exposed to light, which changes the AgH to metallic silver. Silver is opaque at optical frequencies, so this process creates an amplitude type of hologram. The process of developing and fixing the film causes areas of unexposed AgH to dissolve and become transparent, yielding the negative image (transparent for dark regions). This process is shown in Fig. 1.11.

The intensity transmittance can be defined as:[14]

$$T_n(x,y) = \left\langle \frac{I_{Transmitted}(x,y)}{I_{Incident}(x,y)} \right\rangle. \tag{1.1}$$

Note that $T_n(x,y)$ decreases with exposure, defined as $E = I_{Incident}(x,y) \times Time$. The photographic density in the linear region is defined as

$$D = \log_{10}\left(\frac{1}{T_n(x,y)}\right) => T_n(x,y) = 10^{-D}. \tag{1.2}$$

This photographic density is typically supplied by the manufacturer of a particular film and is typically represented by a plot similar to that shown in

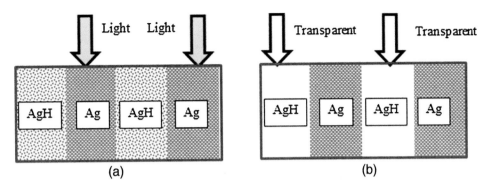

Figure 1.11 Photographic film (a) during exposure and (b) after fixing.

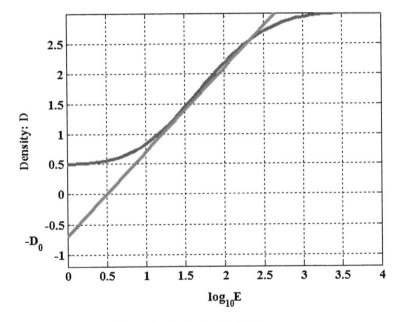

Figure 1.12 Hurter–Driffield curve.

Fig. 1.12. These types of curves are called Hurter–Driffield (H&D) curves. The region of interest is the linear region shown as a red line. The slope of this line determines the contrast and is denoted by α_{n1} (the subscript is for negative film). In the linear region,

$$D = \alpha_{n1} \log_{10} E - D_0 = \alpha_{n1} \log_{10}(I_{Incident} \times Time) - D_0. \qquad (1.3)$$

Plugging Eq. (1.3) into Eq. (1.2) produces the following:

$$T_n(x,y) = 10^{D_0} \, Time^{-\alpha_{n1}} I_{Incident}^{-\alpha_{n1}}(x,y) = \beta_{n1} I_{Incident}^{-\alpha_{n1}}(x,y), \qquad (1.4)$$

where $\beta_{n1} = 10^{D_0} Time^{-\alpha_{n1}}$. If a photograph is taken of the first negative to obtain a positive transparency that mimics the object, then the final intensity transmittance is

$$T_p(x,y) = \beta_{n2}[\beta_{n1}I_{Incident}^{-\alpha_{n1}}(x,y)]^{-\alpha_{n2}} = \beta_p I_{Incident}^{\alpha_p \approx 2}(x,y). \qquad (1.5)$$

It is desirable to have $\alpha_p = \alpha_{n1}\alpha_{n2} \approx 2$. Finally, the amplitude transmittance of the positive transparency is proportional to the intensity of the light incident on the film:

$$t_p(x,y) \propto I_{Incident}(x,y). \qquad (1.6)$$

B. Photothermoplastic film device

Photothermoplastic (PTP) films are often discussed in connection with the storage and retrieval of holograms and with holographic interferometry. PTP film consists of four layers: (1) glass substrate, (2) doped tin or indium oxide (a transparent conductor), (3) polyvinyl carbazole sensitized with trinitro-9-fluorenone (a photoconductive organic polymer) and (4) Stabelite® Ester 10 (a thermoplastic substance, a resin). A PTP device works as follows (see Fig. 1.13):[15]

1. **Charging:** The thermoplastic resin is first positively charged in the dark by a corona discharge device that uniformly moves over the thermoplastic plate at a constant distance. A uniform negative charge is thus induced on the photoconductive coating on the surface.
2. **Exposure:** The plate is then exposed to the holographic interference pattern, which alters the conductivity of the conductive layer. Electrons travel through the conductive layer and are attracted to the positively charged plate; however, they cannot pass through the thermoplastic even though they neutralize part of the charge from step 1.
3. **Recharging:** The electrostatic field is further increased by recharging the surface (after blocking the light) again with the corona discharge mentioned in the first step. The charge pattern creates a spatially varying static electric field of $\sim 1 - 10$ V/cm^2, and thus a latent image.

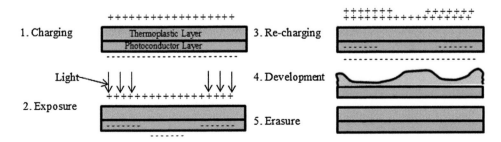

Figure 1.13 Steps for recording a hologram using a PTP device.[15,16]

4. **Development:** The film is developed by passing a current through the conductive layer, heating the plate nearly to its melting point, and softening the thermoplastic film. The softened film deforms under the static electric field (illuminated area), becoming thicker in the unexposed areas and thinner at the illuminated areas. As the film cools to room temperature, the thickness variation is frozen, resulting in a phase surface-relief hologram.

5. **Erasure:** The plate can be erased by flooding it with light and passing a current pulse through the conductive layer, which heats the thermoplastic layer and re-softens it with surface tension. Before the next exposure, the plate is blasted with compressed air or dry nitrogen to cool the thermoplastic layer to room temperature.

The complete charging, exposing, and developing cycle takes less than a minute, and the PTP material typically has high sensitivity over the entire visible spectrum.

C. Photorefractive materials

Photorefractive (PR) materials have been used over the last three decades in various optical applications, such as beam amplification, phase conjugation, holography, optical image processing, etc.[1] A PR material is an electro-optic material doped with electron (or hole) donors that can be photoexcited. When two coherent plane waves of light intersect in a PR material, they form an intensity interference pattern comprising bright and dark regions (see Fig. 1.14). Assuming that the PR material is predominantly *n*-doped, the electrons migrate from bright regions to dark regions, thus creating an approximately sinusoidal charge distribution. This *nonlocal* diffusion-controlled PR effect, in turn, creates an electrostatic space-charge field that is ideally 90 deg phase shifted from the intensity pattern and modulates the refractive index of the crystal via the electro-optic effect (see Fig. 1.14). It can be shown that the induced refractive index in this case depends on the gradient of the intensity pattern. The incident plane waves are, in turn, diffracted by the grating such that one wave may have constructive recombination and the other may encounter a destructive recombination. This effect leads to energy coupling between the beams through what is commonly referred to as the two-beam-coupling effect. Typical examples of PR crystals are $BaTiO_3$, $LiNbO_3$, SBN, $KNbO_3$, BSO, etc., and a typical dopant is Fe^{2+}.

In some PR materials, such as $LiNbO_3$, there is a second contribution to the space-charge field through the photovoltaic effect. In this case, the photocurrent depends on the *local* intensity of the illumination, resulting in a refractive index profile that can be shown to be proportional to the intensity and in phase with the intensity pattern. Therefore, the total index of refraction due to both effects can be expressed as

$$\Delta n_{Total} = c_1 I + c_2 \nabla I = (\Delta n)_{PV} + (\Delta n)_{DIFF} = -\frac{1}{2} n_e^3 \gamma_{33} (E_{PV} + E_{DIFF}), \quad (1.7)$$

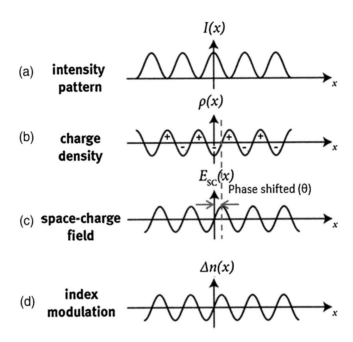

Figure 1.14 Schematic of the PR effect: (a) when two beams interfere on a PR material, they create fringes, where the electrons migrate from bright to dark regions; (b) the sinusoidal charge distribution due to electron migration; (c) an electrostatic space-charge field that is ideally 90-deg phase shifted (pure diffusion case) from the intensity pattern is created due to the nonlocal diffusion-controlled PR effect; and (d) the refractive index of the crystal is modulated via the electro-optic effect.

where E_{PV} is the photovoltaic field, E_{DIFF} is the diffusion field, n_e is the extraordinary refractive index, and γ_{33} is the relevant electro-optic coefficient. Although this local effect modulates the refractive index, it only leads to phase coupling between the two interacting waves.

In other PR materials, such as BSO, SBN, etc., a bias field is introduced through the application of an external voltage across the material. The bias field adds to the existing space-charge field and determines the overall current through the material. The combined effects of diffusion, drift, and the photovoltaic effect are incorporated in the material equations for a PR material, called the Kukhtarev equations. The Kukhtarev equations are a well-established model for charge generation, transport, and recombination, and the resulting electrostatic field due to incident illumination in PR materials.[17] They include the continuity equation, the rate equation for ionized donor (or acceptor) concentration, the current equation, and Gauss' law. (See Yeh[18] for further details.) This set of coupled equations is further coupled to the optical wave equation and must be simultaneously solved to yield the exact profiles of the optical field and the space-charge field in the PR material.

The Kukhtarev equations are often linearized in order to determine approximate solutions for the space-charge field (and thus the induced refractive index). The space-charge field can be written as

$$E_{sc} = m \frac{E_0 + E_{PV} + jE_{DIFF}}{\left(1 + \frac{E_{DIFF}}{E_q}\right) - j\left(\frac{E_0}{E_q} + \frac{N_a E_{PV}}{N_d E_q}\right)}, \tag{1.8}$$

where m is the intensity modulation index, E_0 is the applied field, E_q is the saturation field, and N_a and N_d represent the acceptor and donor concentrations, respectively. The diffusion and saturation fields depend on the material parameters, and their definitions and the derivation of Eq. (1.8) can be found in Yeh.[18] It is important to note that in the absence of an applied field and the photovoltaic effect, only the nonlocal effect of diffusion exists; the space-charge field is out of phase with the intensity modulation by 90 deg. Although this is the case for $BaTiO_3$, in a material such as $LiNbO_3$ both the nonlocal and local contribution exist (due to the photovoltaic effect), and the phase shift between the induced refractive index and the intensity distribution is no longer 90 deg. The phase shift is also different than 90 deg if drift and diffusion are present, as is the case in PR materials such as BSO and SBN.

Doped polymeric composites (as opposed to inorganic crystals) can be used as an alternative PR media. The properties of these materials can be optimized simultaneously and independently to enhance the PR effect to a degree not possible with inorganic materials. The advantages of the multicomponent composite (chromophore: photoconductor: plasticizer: photosensitizer) approach include

(a) convenient engineering of the molecular structures of the components to optimize charge generation, transport, and trapping;
(b) easy manipulation of energetics using dopants with suitable ionization energy;
(c) ability to process polymeric materials into different device forms;
(d) easy processing and reproducibility; and
(e) lower cost and fabrication time.

The reorientation of the chromophores in the PR polymer (operating close to the glass temperature) is due to the total electrostatic field, which includes the externally applied bias field E_0 and the optically induced space-charge field E_s. The chromophore reorientation, along with the electro-optic effect, modulates the refractive index in the PR polymer. Holes, rather than electrons, are the predominant mobile carriers in common PR polymers.[19] A typical PR polymer used in holographic displays is PATPD/CAAN:FDCST: ECZ:PCBM (49.5:30:20:0.5 wt%).[20–22]

D. Photopolymer materials

Thickness and refractive-index variations can also be produced using organic photopolymers activated by a photosensitizer, through a photopolymerization process.[6] Commercial photopolymer products exist from DuPont (Omni-Dex) and are used for volume phase holograms with high diffraction efficiency and high angular selectivity. Photopolymer materials can be improved by adding dichromated gelatine and photoresine to produce surface-relief gratings with the embossing technique, which is widely used in the industry. Two recent photopolymer films for volume holography have been developed by Bayer Material Science (Bayfol® HX self-developing photopolymer film) and by the National Chiao Tung University, Taiwan (PQ-doped PMMA photopolymer film).

1.2 Scalar Theory of Diffraction

1.2.1 Maxwell's equations

The following are Maxwell's equations in differential form:

$$\vec{\nabla} \times \vec{E} = -\frac{\partial \vec{B}}{\partial t}, \tag{1.9}$$

$$\vec{\nabla} \times \vec{H} = \vec{J} = \vec{J}_c + \frac{\partial \vec{D}}{\partial t}, \tag{1.10}$$

$$\vec{\nabla} \cdot \vec{D} = \rho, \tag{1.11}$$

$$\vec{\nabla} \cdot \vec{B} = 0, \tag{1.12}$$

where the operator $\vec{\nabla} = [\partial/(\partial x), \partial/(\partial y), \partial/(\partial z)]$, $\vec{D}$ is the electric flux density-electric flux density (C/m^2), ρ is the density of the electric charges of the source (C/m^3), $\vec{B}$ is the magnetic flux density (Wb/m^2), $\vec{E}$ is the electric field (V/m), $\vec{H}$ is the magnetic field strength (A/m), and $\vec{J}$ is the current density (A/m^2), which is the summation of the source current density and the displacement current.

Due to the continuity equation $\vec{\nabla} \cdot \vec{J}_c + (\partial \rho)/(\partial t) = 0$ and the vector relation $\vec{\nabla} \cdot (\vec{\nabla} \times \vec{A}) = 0$, Eqs. (1.9) and (1.10) are dependent on Eqs. (1.11) and (1.12). However, $\vec{E}$ and $\vec{H}$ are vectors, and thus Eqs. (1.9) and (1.10) are actually six equations with twelve unknown (x, y, z) components of $\vec{E}$, $\vec{H}$, $\vec{B}$, and $\vec{B}$. Therefore, six additional equations must be introduced that come from the constitutive relationships:

$$\vec{D} = \bar{\varepsilon} \vec{E}, \tag{1.13}$$

$$\vec{B} = \bar{\mu} \vec{H}, \tag{1.14}$$

$$\vec{J} = \bar{\sigma} \vec{E}, \tag{1.15}$$

where $\bar{\sigma}(\Omega^{-1}/m)$ is the conductivity, $\bar{\varepsilon}$ is the permittivity (F/m), and $\bar{\mu}$ is the permeability (H/m) of the medium. In general, $\bar{\sigma}$, $\bar{\varepsilon}$, and $\bar{\mu}$ are tensors;

however, for a linear (not a function of $|E|^n$), homogeneous [not a function of position (x,y,z)], and isotropic (no polarization effect) medium, they are effectively reduced to scalar quantities.

Thus, for a given $\vec{J}_c$ and ρ, one can solve for the above equations to find the components of the electric field $\vec{E}$. If the medium is assumbed to be free of sources ($\vec{J}_c = \rho = 0$), Maxwell's equations can be rewritten as follows:

$$\vec{\nabla} \times \vec{E} = -\frac{\partial \vec{B}}{\partial t}, \tag{1.16}$$

$$\vec{\nabla} \times \vec{H} = \frac{\partial \vec{D}}{\partial t}. \tag{1.17}$$

$$\vec{\nabla} \cdot \vec{D} = 0, \tag{1.18}$$

$$\vec{\nabla} \cdot \vec{B} = 0. \tag{1.19}$$

Taking the curl of Eq. (1.16) produces

$$\vec{\nabla} \times \vec{\nabla} \times \vec{E} = \vec{\nabla} \times \left(-\frac{\partial \vec{B}}{\partial t}\right) = -\mu \vec{\nabla} \times \left(\frac{\partial \vec{H}}{\partial t}\right) = -\mu \frac{\partial}{\partial t}(\vec{\nabla} \times \vec{H}). \tag{1.20}$$

Substituting Eqs. (1.17) and (1.13) in Eq. (1.20) yields

$$\vec{\nabla} \times \vec{\nabla} \times \vec{E} = -\mu \varepsilon \frac{\partial \vec{E}}{\partial t}. \tag{1.21}$$

By using the identity

$$\vec{\nabla} \times \vec{\nabla} \times \vec{E} = \vec{\nabla}(\vec{\nabla} \cdot \vec{E}) - \vec{\nabla}^2 \vec{E} \tag{1.22}$$

[where $\vec{\nabla}^2 \vec{E} = \vec{\nabla} \cdot (\vec{\nabla}\vec{E})$ is the vector Laplacian operator defined as $\vec{\nabla}^2 = \Delta E_x \hat{a}_x + \Delta E_y \hat{a}_y + \Delta E_z \hat{a}_z$, and $\Delta = [(\partial^2)/(\partial x^2),(\partial^2)/(\partial y^2),(\partial^2)/(\partial z^2)]$ is the scalar Laplacian operator, combined with Eq. (1.18), $\vec{\nabla} \cdot \vec{D} = \vec{\nabla} \cdot (\varepsilon \vec{E}) = \varepsilon(\vec{\nabla} \cdot \vec{E}) = 0$ for homogeneous media], Eq. (1.22) becomes

$$\vec{\nabla} \times \vec{\nabla} \times \vec{E} = -\vec{\nabla}^2 \vec{E}, \tag{1.23}$$

and Eq. (1.21) becomes

$$\vec{\nabla}^2 \vec{E} = \mu \varepsilon \frac{\partial^2 \vec{E}}{\partial t^2}, \tag{1.24}$$

where $v = 1/\sqrt{\mu\varepsilon}$ is the velocity of the wave in the medium. The same process can be used to deduce a similar wave equation for $\vec{H}$.

Let ψ be one component of the field $\vec{E}$ or $\vec{H}$, such that Eq. (1.24) can be written as

$$\nabla^2\psi = \mu\varepsilon\frac{\partial^2\psi}{\partial t^2}. \tag{1.25}$$

The solution for Eq. (1.25) is found according to D'Alembert[14] to be

$$\psi(x,y,z,t) = c_+ f_+(\omega_0 t - k_{0x}x - k_{0y}y - k_{0z}z)$$
$$+ c_- f_-(\omega_0 t + k_{0x}x + k_{0y}y + k_{0z}z), \tag{1.26}$$

where $\omega_0^2/(k_{0x}^2 + k_{0y}^2 + k_{0z}^2) = \omega_0^2/k_0^2 = v^2$, k_0 is the propagation constant, ω_0 is the angular frequency, $c_\pm$ are two constants, and $f_\pm$ are the forward- and backward-traveling waves. Equation (1.26) can also be written as

$$\psi(x,y,z,t) = c_+ f_+(\omega_0 t - \vec{k}_0 \cdot \vec{r}) + c_- f_-(\omega_0 t + \vec{k}_0 \cdot \vec{r}), \tag{1.27}$$

which is the superposition of two waves traveling in opposite directions, where $\vec{k}_0 = k_{0x}\hat{a}_x + k_{0y}\hat{a}_y + k_{0z}\hat{a}_z$, $\vec{r} = x\hat{a}_x + y\hat{a}_y + z\hat{a}_z$.

Note that ψ is constant when $\omega_0 t - \vec{k}_0 \cdot \vec{r}$ is constant, or $\vec{k}_0 \cdot \vec{r} = \omega_0 t + c$, which is the equation of a plane perpendicular to $\vec{k}_0$, where c is a constant and t is a parameter (hence the name "plane wave solution to the wave equation"). Equation (1.27) can be written as

$$\psi(\vec{r},t) = \mathrm{Re}[\psi_0 e^{j(\omega_0 t - \vec{k}_0 \cdot \vec{r})}]. \tag{1.28}$$

The wavefronts, defined as the surfaces joining all points of equal phase $\omega_0 t \pm \vec{k}_0 \cdot \vec{r}$ are planar, as shown in Fig. 1.15.

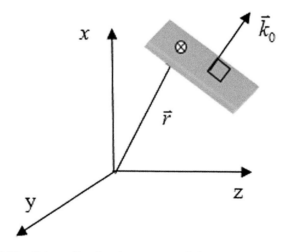

Figure 1.15 Schematic of a plane wave solution to the wave equation.

1.2.2 Spatial frequency transfer function and Fresnel diffraction

Equation (1.25) can be written as

$$\frac{\partial^2 \psi}{\partial x^2} + \frac{\partial^2 \psi}{\partial y^2} + \frac{\partial^2 \psi}{\partial z^2} = \frac{1}{v^2}\frac{\partial^2 \psi}{\partial t^2},\qquad(1.29)$$

where ψ is the scalar wave function. This can be written in phasor notation to divide the spatial dependence from the temporal dependence:

$$\psi(x,y,z,t) = \mathrm{Re}\{\psi_p(x,y,z)e^{j\omega t}\},\qquad(1.30)$$

where $\psi_p(x,y,z)$ is the complex spatial amplitude, and $e^{j\omega t}$ is the temporal carrier. Substituting Eq. (1.30) into Eq. (1.29) produces what is known as the Helmholtz equation:

$$\frac{\partial^2 \psi_p}{\partial x^2} + \frac{\partial^2 \psi_p}{\partial y^2} + \frac{\partial^2 \psi_p}{\partial z^2} + k_0^2\psi_p = 0,\qquad(1.31)$$

where $k_0 = \omega_0/v$. We can denote $\tilde{\Psi}_p(k_x,k_y;z)$ to be the Fourier transform of $\psi_p(x,y,z)$ with respect to the transverse spatial coordinates (x,y). The Fourier transform is defined as

$$\tilde{\Psi}_p(k_x,k_y;z) = \Im_{x,y}[\psi_p(x,y;z)] = \int_{-\infty}^{\infty}\int_{-\infty}^{\infty} \psi_p(x,y;z)\exp[j(k_x x + k_y y)]dxdy.\qquad(1.32)$$

Equation (1.31) can be solved using the Fourier transform technique. Employing the Fourier transform property $\Im_{x,y}[(\partial^2\psi_p)/(\partial(x,y)^2)] = (jk_{(x,y)})^2\tilde{\Psi}_p$ produces

$$\frac{d^2\tilde{\Psi}_p}{dz^2} + k_0^2\left(1 - \frac{k_x^2}{k_0^2} - \frac{k_y^2}{k_0^2}\right)\tilde{\Psi}_p = 0.\qquad(1.33)$$

Equation (1.33) is a second-order, homogeneous, linear ordinary differential equation with constant coefficients. The solution of this equation, which is easily found using the characteristic equation technique, is

$$\tilde{\Psi}_p(k_x,k_y;z) = \tilde{\Psi}_p(k_x,k_y,z=0)\exp\left[-jk_0z\sqrt{1 - \frac{k_x^2}{k_0^2} - \frac{k_y^2}{k_0^2}}\right].\qquad(1.34)$$

If $\tilde{G}(k_x,k_y;z) = \exp\left(-jk_0z\sqrt{1 - (k_x^2/k_0^2) - (k_y^2/k_0^2)}\right)$ is defined as the spatial frequency transfer function of propagation and $\tilde{\Psi}_{p0}(k_x,k_y) = \tilde{\Psi}_p(k_x,k_y,z=0)$, then Eq. (1.34) can be written as

$$\tilde{\Psi}_p(k_x,k_y;z) = \tilde{\Psi}_{p0}(k_x,k_y)\tilde{G}(k_x,k_y;z).\qquad(1.35)$$

Also, if $k_x^2 + k_y^2 \ll k_0^2$ or $\varepsilon = \frac{k_x^2}{k_0^2} + \frac{k_y^2}{k_0^2} \ll 1$ is assumed (paraxial approximation), the spatial frequency transfer function becomes

$$\tilde{G}(k_x,k_y;z) = \exp(-jk_0 z(1-\varepsilon)^{1/2}) = \exp(-jk_0 z(1-\varepsilon/2)). \qquad (1.36)$$

By using the binomial approximation $(1+\varepsilon)^n = 1 + n\varepsilon - (n(n-1)/2!)\varepsilon^2 + \ldots$, Eq. (1.36) becomes

$$\tilde{G}(k_x,k_y;z) = \exp(-jk_0 z)\exp\left(j\frac{(k_x^2 + k_y^2)}{2k_0}z\right). \qquad (1.37)$$

The impulse response of propagation is defined as $g(x,y;z) = \mathfrak{S}_{x,y}^{-1}\{\tilde{G}(k_x,k_y;z)\}$ and can be computed as

$$g(x,y;z) = (jk_0/2\pi z)\exp(-jk_0 z)\exp\left(-\frac{jk_0(x^2+y^2)}{2z}\right). \qquad (1.38)$$

To revert back to the space domain, the inverse Fourier transform of Eq. (1.35) gives

$$\psi_p(x,y;z) = \psi_{p0}(x,y) * g(x,y;z), \qquad (1.39)$$

where

$$\psi_p(x,y;z) = \exp(-jk_0 z) \times (jk_0/2\pi z) \times \iint \psi_{p0}(x',y')$$
$$\times \exp\{-(jk_0/2z)[(x-x')^2 + (y-y')^2]\}dx'dy'. \qquad (1.40)$$

This equation is called the *Fresnel diffraction* formula.

Figure 1.16 illustrates the impulse response function that transfers the field at point $P(x',y')$ on the input plane to point $P(x,y)$ on the output plane. Table 1.1 shows the Fresnel diffraction of a rectangular aperture. The sample code in the table produces Fig. 1.17.

1.2.3 Fraunhofer diffraction

The range of applicability of the Fresnel diffraction formula spans the near field of the object to the far field. However, Fresnel's formula is not always easy to compute. If only the far-field diffraction pattern is of interest, another approximation can be made to yield the Fraunhofer diffraction formula, which is often simpler to compute. Under the Fraunhofer approximation, it is assumed that, when viewed from a sufficiently large distance (i.e., the far

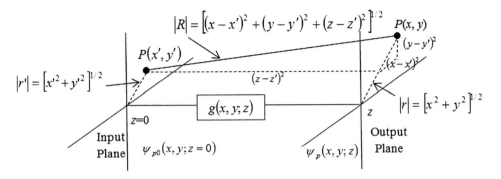

Figure 1.16 Schematic showing the impulse response of propagation between an input and output plane. Reprinted from Poon and Banerjee[14] with permission.

Table 1.1 MATLAB code "my_Fresnel.m" for Fresnel diffraction of a rectangular aperture (see Fig. 1.17).

```
1   %%
2   clc
3   clear all
4   N=2^9;                                      %Number of grid points
5   L=sqrt(N);                                  %Dimension of the image in mm
6   h = L/N;                                    %Space step
7   n =[-N/2:1:N/2-1]';                         %Indices
8   x = n*h;                                    %Grid points in mm
9   y=x;
10  w0=L/10;                        %Width of the rectangular aperture in mm
11  M=floor(N*w0/L);                %M dimension of rectangle aperture
12                                  %should be less than N/2;
13  lambda=0.5*10^-3;                           %Wavelength in mm
14  k0=2*pi/lambda;                             %Wavenumber
15  zr=k0*w0^2/2;                               %Rayleigh range
16  z=zr/100;                                   %Propagation distance in the
17                                              %Fresnel region
18  a=pi/h;                         %Maximum frequency in radians/mm
19  [X,Y]=meshgrid(x,y);            %Create a spatial 2D grid
20  f=zeros(N,N);
21  f(N/2-M:N/2+M,N/2-M:N/2+M)=1;               %Create the rectangular
22                                              %aperture
23                              %Plot the initial amplitude and phase
24  figure
25  subplot(1,2,1)
26  mesh(x,y,f)
27  xlabel('x(mm)')
28  ylabel('y(mm)')
29  title('Initial Pattern: Amplitude')
30  view(2)
31  subplot(1,2,2)
32  mesh(x,y,angle(f))
33  view(2)
34  title('Inital Pattern: Phase')
```

(continued)

Table 1.1 (*Continued*)

```
35  xlabel('x(mm)')
36  ylabel('y(mm)')
37  kx=[-a:2*a/N:a-2*a/N]';          %Create the spatial frequency
38                                    %arrays
39  ky=kx;
40  [KX,KY]=meshgrid(kx,ky);          %Create 2D frequency grid
41  KK=(KX.^2+KY.^2);
42  F0=fftshift(fft2(f));             %Fourier transform of object.
43                                    %Start propagating distance z.
44  F=exp(i*KK*z/(2*k0)).*F0;         %Create the transfer function
45                                    %of propagation
46  f_f=ifft2(fftshift(F));
47  m_abs=max(abs(f_f(:)));
48  I=find(abs(f_f)<m_abs/100);        %Eliminate regions where the
49                                     %amplitude is small to avoid
50                                     %phase errors
51  phi_f_f=angle(f_f);
52  phi_f_f(I)=0;
53                          %Plot results after propagating a distance z
54  figure
55  subplot(1,2,1)
56  mesh(X,Y,abs(f_f))
57  view(2)
58  title('Fresnel Diffraction: Amplitude')
59  xlabel('x(mm)')
60  ylabel('y(mm)')
61  subplot(1,2,2)
62  mesh(X,Y,phi_f_f)
63  view(2)
64  title('Fresnel Diffraction: Phase')
65  xlabel('x(mm)')
66  ylabel('y(mm)')
67  figure
68  plot(x,abs(f(N/2,:)),x,abs(f_f(N/2,:)),'r')
69  xlabel('x(mm)')
70  title('Slice of the Fresnel Diffraction: Amplitude')
71  grid on
```

field), the quadratic phase distribution across the diffracting aperture is approximately unity. To differentiate between the near and far field, the Fresnel number is usually defined as

$$Fr = \left[\frac{k_0 r'^2}{2z} \right]. \tag{1.41}$$

According to Fig. 1.16, if the Fresnel diffraction number $Fr = [(k_0 r'^2)/2z] \geq 1$, we are in the Fresnel regime and must use the Fresnel diffraction formula. When $Fr = [(k_0 r'^2)/2z] \approx 0.01 \ll 1$, we are in the Fraunhofer diffraction regime, where the Fraunhofer diffraction formula will

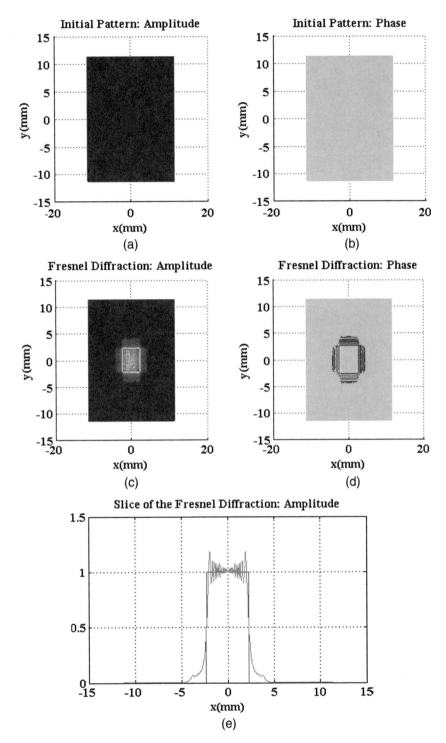

Figure 1.17 Example of Fresnel diffraction from a rectangular aperture: (a, b) Initial pattern amplitude and phase, (c, d) Fresnel diffraction amplitude and phase, and (e) slice of the Fresnel diffraction amplitude.

yield reasonably accurate results. Thus, the Fresnel number can be re-written as

$$\left[\frac{k_0(x'^2 + y'^2)}{2z}\right]_{max} = \frac{z_R}{z},$$

where z_R is defined as the Rayleigh range. The Rayleigh range of the object is simply the range at which the Fresnel number is equal to $1/\pi$. If $z \gg z_R$, the Fraunhofer approximation can be used, and Eq. (1.40) becomes

$$\psi_p(x,y,z) = \exp(-jk_0 z)\left(j\frac{k_0}{2\pi z}\right)\exp\left(-j\frac{k_0}{2z}(x^2 + y^2)\right)$$

$$\times \iint \psi_{p0}(x',y')\exp\left(j\frac{k_0}{z}(xx' + yy')\right)dx'dy'. \qquad (1.42)$$

According to the definition of the Fourier transform defined in Eq. (1.32),

$$\psi_p(x,y,z) = e^{-jk_0 z}j\frac{k_0}{2\pi z}e^{-j\frac{k_0}{2z}(x^2+y^2)} \times \mathfrak{I}_{x,y}\{\psi_{p0}(x,y)\}\Big|_{k_x = \frac{k_0 x}{z}, k_y = \frac{k_0 y}{z}}. \qquad (1.43)$$

Equation (1.43) is called the Fraunhofer diffraction formula. For example, given a red light ($\lambda \approx 0.6$ μm) with a 1-mm maximum dimension on the input plane (or object aperture), then $z_R = (2\pi \times 10^{-6})/(2 \times 0.6 \times 10^{-6}) \approx 5$ m, so z should be much greater (5 m) to be in the Fraunhofer regime. Table 1.2 shows the Fraunhofer diffraction of a rectangular aperture; the sample code produces Fig. 1.18.

1.2.4 Fourier transform property of an ideal lens

Consider a point source located at an initial plane labeled 1. Mathematically, a point source can be expressed as a Dirac delta function $\psi_{p0}(x,y) = \delta(x)\delta(y)$. The point source will diffract as it propagates according to Fresnel diffraction [Eq. (1.40)] as

$$\psi_p(x,y;z) = \delta(x)\delta(y) * g(x,y;z) = h(x,y;z)$$

$$= \frac{jk_0}{2\pi z}\exp(-jk_0 z)\exp\left(-jk_0\frac{(x^2+y^2)}{2z}\right). \qquad (1.44)$$

Using the reverse of the binomial approximation

$$R = (z^2 + r^2)^{1/2} = z\left(1 + \frac{r^2}{z^2}\right)^{1/2} \approx z\left(1 + \frac{r^2}{2z^2}\right) = z + \frac{x^2 + y^2}{2z},$$

Eq. (1.44) can be approximated as

$$\psi_p(x,y;z) = j\frac{k_0}{2\pi z}\exp\left[-jk_0\left(z + \frac{x^2+y^2}{2z}\right)\right]j\frac{k_0}{2\pi R}\exp(-jk_0 R),$$

Table 1.2 MATLAB code "my_Fraunhofer.m" for Fraunhofer diffraction of a rectangular aperture (see Fig. 1.18).

```
1    %%Fraunhofer diffraction of a rectangular aperture
2    clc
3    clear all
4    N=2^9;                              %Number of grid points
5    L=sqrt(N);                          %Dimension of the image in mm
6    h = L/N;                            %Space step
7    n = [-N/2:1:N/2-1]';                %Indices
8    x = n*h;                            %Grid points in mm
9    y=x;
10   w0=L/20;                            %Width of the rectangular
11                                       %aperture in mm
12   M=floor(N*w0/L);                    %M should be less than N/2;
13   lambda=0.5*10^-3;                   %Wavelength in mm
14   k0=2*pi/lambda;                     %Wavenumber
15   zr=k0*w0^2/2;                       %Rayleigh range
16   z=5*zr;                             %Propagation distance in the
                                         %Fraunhofer region
17   a=pi/h;                             %Maximum frequency in rad/mm
18   [X,Y]=meshgrid(x,y);                %Create spatial 2D grid
19   f=zeros(N,N);
20   f(N/2-M:N/2+M,N/2-M:N/2+M)=1;              %Create the rectangular
21                                              %aperture
22                                       %Plot the initial amplitude
23   figure
24                                       %mesh(x,y,f)
25   colormap(gray(256))
26   imagesc(x,y,f)
27   xlabel('x(mm)')
28   ylabel('y(mm)')
29   title('Initial Pattern: Amplitude')
30   view(2)
31   F=abs(fftshift(fft2(f)));
32   kx=[-a:2*a/N:a-2*a/N]';             %Create the spatial frequency
33                                       %arrays
34   ky=kx;
35   [KX,KY]=meshgrid(kx,ky);            %Create 2D frequency grid
36   figure
37   %mesh(X,Y,F)
38   %view(2)
39   mylogim(x,y,F,2)                    %Function mylogim is used for contrast
40                                       %enhancement
41   title('Fraunhofer Diffraction')
42   xlabel('x(mm)')
43   ylabel('y(mm)')
```

which is a diverging spherical wave, as expected from a point source. Therefore, the Fresnel impulse response is a paraxial approximation to a spherical wave. Figure 1.19 shows the diffraction of a point source from an initial plane 1 to a final plane 2.

Consider a point source diverging from plane 1 located at a distance d_0 before a converging lens. A point source should be recovered at the image

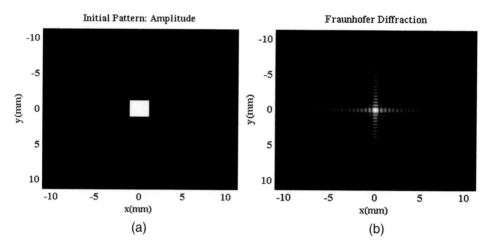

Figure 1.18 Example of Fraunhofer diffraction from a rectangular aperture: (a) initial profile and (b) in the far field.

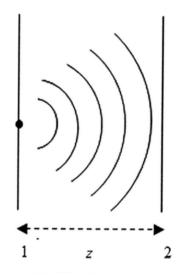

Figure 1.19 Diffraction of a point source.

plane d_i. Figure 1.20 shows the geometry of this setup. According to Eq. (1.44), the wavefront just before the lens can be expressed as

$$\psi_{12} = A \exp\left[-j\frac{k_0}{2d_0}(x^2 + y^2)\right] = A \exp\left(-j\frac{k_0}{2d_0}r^2\right), \qquad (1.45)$$

where $A = [(jk_0)/(2\pi z)] \exp(-jk_0 z)$. The wavefront just after lens (the wave traveling in the negative direction) is given by

$$\psi_{23} = A \exp\left[+j\frac{k_0}{2d_i}(x^2 + y^2)\right] = A \exp\left(+j\frac{k_0}{2d_i}r^2\right). \qquad (1.46)$$

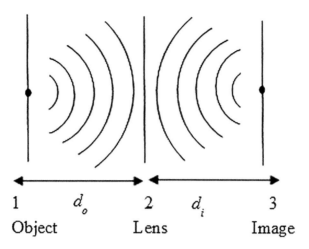

Figure 1.20 Lens transfer function.

Therefore, the lens itself has generated the following transformation:

$$\psi_{23} = L(r)\psi_{12} \Rightarrow \exp\left(+j\frac{k_0}{2d_i}r^2\right) = L(r)\exp\left(-j\frac{k_0}{2d_0}r^2\right)$$

$$\Rightarrow L(r) = \exp\left[j\frac{k_0 r^2}{2}\left(\frac{1}{d_0}+\frac{1}{d_i}\right)\right] = \exp\left(j\frac{k_0}{2f}r^2\right),$$

where $(1/f) = (1/d_i) + (1/d_0)$. Therefore, for an ideal lens of focal length f, its phase transformation function can be expressed as

$$t_f(x,y) = \exp\left(j\frac{k_0}{2f}(x^2+y^2)\right). \tag{1.47}$$

1.2.5 Gaussian beam optics

This section examines the Fresnel diffraction of a Gaussian beam. Consider a Gaussian beam

$$\psi_{p0}(x,y) = \exp\left[-\left(\frac{x^2+y^2}{w_0^2}\right)\right] = \exp\left(-\frac{r^2}{w_0^2}\right), \tag{1.48}$$

where w_0 is the half waist of the Gaussian beam, where the field amplitude has fallen to $1/e$, as shown in Fig. 1.21.

The Fourier transform of Eq. (1.48) is also Gaussian, given by

$$\Psi_{p0}(k_x,k_y) = \pi w_0^2 \exp\left[-\frac{w_0^2}{4}(k_x^2+k_y^2)\right]. \tag{1.49}$$

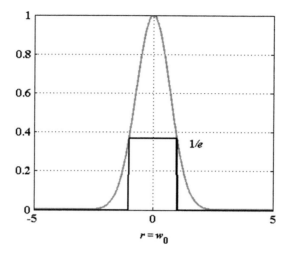

Figure 1.21   One-dimensional Gaussian beam.

Using Eq. (1.37), after propagating a distance z, Eq. (1.49) becomes

$$\Psi_p(k_x,k_y;z) = \Psi_{p0}(k_x,k_y) \exp(-jk_0 z) \exp\left[j(k_x^2 + k_y^2)\frac{z}{2k_0}\right]$$

$$= \pi w_0^2 \exp\left(-(k_x^2 + k_y^2)\frac{w_0^2}{4}\right) \exp(-jk_0 z) \exp\left(j(k_x^2 + k_y^2)\frac{z}{2k_0}\right)$$

$$= \pi w_0^2 \exp(-jk_0 z) \exp\left[j(k_x^2 + k_y^2)\frac{q}{2k_0}\right], \tag{1.50}$$

where q is the q-parameter of the Gaussian beam, defined as

$$q = z + jz_R, \tag{1.51}$$

where $z_R = (k_0 w_0^2)/2$ is the Rayleigh range of a Gaussian beam.
   Performing the inverse Fourier transform on Eq. (1.51) produces

$$\psi_p(x,y;z) = \exp(-jk_0 z)\left(j\frac{k_0 w_0^2}{2q}\right) \exp[-jk_0(x^2 + y^2)/2q]. \tag{1.52}$$

After considerable algebra, the Eq. (1.52) reduces to[14]

$$\psi_p(x,y;z) = \frac{w_0}{w(z)} \exp\left[-\frac{(x^2 + y^2)}{w^2(z)}\right] \exp\left[-\frac{jk_0(x^2 + y^2)}{2R(z)}\right]$$

$$\times \exp(-j\phi(z)) \exp(-jk_0 z), \tag{1.53}$$

where

$$w^2(z) = w_0^2 \left[1 + \left(\frac{z}{z_R} \right)^2 \right],$$ (1.54a)

$$R(z) = \frac{(z^2 + z_R^2)}{z},$$ (1.54b)

$$\phi(z) = -\tan^{-1} \left(\frac{z}{z_R} \right),$$ (1.54c)

where $w(z)$ is monotonically increasing with z (at $z = z_R$, $w = \sqrt{2}w_0$), $\phi(z)$ is a slowly varying phase, and $R(z)$ is the radius of curvature of the phase fronts, with a minimum at $\frac{dR}{dz}\big|_{\min} = 2z^2 - (z^2 + z_R^2) = 0$, $z = z_R$. The beamwidth, radius of curvature, and phase (w, R, ϕ) are shown in Figs. 1.22(a–c), respectively. Table 1.3 provides the code that produces Fig. 1.22.

1.2.6 *q*-transformation of Gaussian beams

The q-parameter of a Gaussian beam is conveniently used to track an arbitrary Gaussian beam during its propagation through an optical system. Three cases are considered here: propagation, lens transformation, and the general case.

A. Propagation

If the Gaussian beam propagates a distance d, using the Fresnel transfer function, then

$$\begin{aligned}
\tilde{\Psi}_p(k_x, k_y, z + d) &= \tilde{\Psi}_{p0}(k_x, k_y; z) \exp\left[j(k_x^2 + k_y^2) \frac{d}{2k_0} \right] \\
&= \pi w_0^2 \exp\left[j(k_x^2 + k_y^2) \frac{q}{2k_0} \right] \exp\left[j(k_x^2 + k_y^2) \frac{d}{2k_0} \right] \\
&= \pi w_0^2 \exp\left[j(k_x^2 + k_y^2) \frac{q_d}{2k_0} \right],
\end{aligned}$$ (1.55)

where

$$q_d = q + d.$$ (1.56)

B. Lens transformation

If the Gaussian beam travels through a lens with a focal length f, using the lens transformation function from Eq. (1.47), then the beam before the lens is expressed as

$$\psi_{p(Before)}(x, y; z) = \exp(-jk_0 z) \left(j \frac{k_0 w_0^2}{2q} \right) \exp[-jk_0(x^2 + y^2)/2q].$$

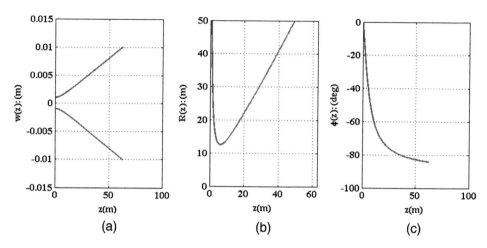

Figure 1.22   (a) Gaussian beamwidth, (b) radius of curvature, and (c) phase.

Table 1.3   MATLAB code "fig 1_22.m" for Gaussian beam parameters (see Fig. 1.22).

```
1    %Gaussian beam parameters
2    clc
3    clear all
4    w0=10^-3;                        %Initial waist
5    lambda0 = 0.5*10^-6;             %Wavelength in microns
6    k0=2*pi/lambda0;                 %Wavenumber
7    zr=k0*w0^2/2                     %Rayleigh length
8    z=linspace(0,10*zr,2000);          %Propagation distance
9    w1=sqrt(w0^2*(1+(z/zr).^2));        %Gaussian beamwidth
10                                       %formula
11   w2=-sqrt(w0^2*(1+(z/zr).^2));
12   R=z+zr^2./z;                     %Radius of curvature formula
13   phi=-atan(z/zr)*180/pi;          %Phase shift formula
14   %Plot the results
15   figure
16   subplot(131)
17   plot(z,w1,z,w2,'b')
18   xlabel('z(m)')
19   ylabel('w(z):(m)')
20   grid on
21   subplot(132)
22   plot(z,R)
23   axis([0 max(z) 0 50])
24   xlabel('z(m)')
25   ylabel('R(z):(m)')
26   grid on
27   subplot(133)
28   plot(z,phi)
29   xlabel('z(m)')
30   ylabel('\phi(z):(deg)')
31   grid on
```

The beam just after the lens is computed by multiplying the transformation function of the lens:

$$\Psi_{p(After)}(x,y;z) \propto \exp\left(-j\frac{k_0(x^2+y^2)}{2q}\right)\exp\left[\frac{jk_0(x^2+y^2)}{2f}\right]$$

$$= \exp\left[-j\frac{k_0}{2q_L}(x^2+y^2)\right], \qquad (1.57)$$

where

$$\frac{1}{q_L} = \frac{1}{q} - \frac{1}{f}, \qquad (1.58)$$

C. General case

In general, the q-parameter transformation parameter can be expressed as

$$q' = \frac{Aq+B}{Cq+D}; \qquad (1.59)$$

- for the translation case, $\begin{pmatrix} A & B \\ C & D \end{pmatrix} = \begin{pmatrix} 1 & d \\ 0 & 1 \end{pmatrix}$ and $q' = q+d$;

- for the lens case, $\begin{pmatrix} A & B \\ C & D \end{pmatrix} = \begin{pmatrix} 1 & 0 \\ -1/f & 1 \end{pmatrix}$ and $(1/q') = (1/q) - (1/f)$.

Because $q = z + jz_R$, then $1/q = [1/(z+jz_R)] = [z/(z^2+z_R^2)] - j[z_R/(z^2+z_R^2)]$. However, from Eq. (1.54b), $(1/R) = [z/(z^2+z_R^2)]$. On the other hand, from Eq. (1.54a), $w^2(z) = w_0^2[1+(z/z_R)^2] = (2/k_0)[(z_R^2+z^2)/z_R]$. Therefore,

$$\frac{1}{q} = \frac{1}{R} + \frac{1}{jk_0w^2(z)/2}. \qquad (1.60)$$

1.2.7 Focusing a Gaussian beam

Based on the q-transformation of a Gaussian beam, consider the focusing of a Gaussian beam by a lens, as shown in Fig. 1.23.

For a Gaussian beam of initial waist w_0, if the q-parameter $q = q_0 = jz_R = j[(k_0w_0^2)/2]$ is purely imaginary, then the phase curvature will be identical to a plane wave, such that

$$\tilde{\Psi}_p(k_x,k_y;z=0) = \pi r_0^2 \exp\left(j(k_x^2+k_y^2)\frac{q}{2k_0}\right) = \pi r_0^2 \exp\left[-(k_x^2+k_y^2)\frac{w_0^2}{4}\right].$$

The inverse Fourier transform of the previous equation is a Gaussian function: $\exp[-(x^2+y^2)/w_0^2]$. The q-parameter transformation due to

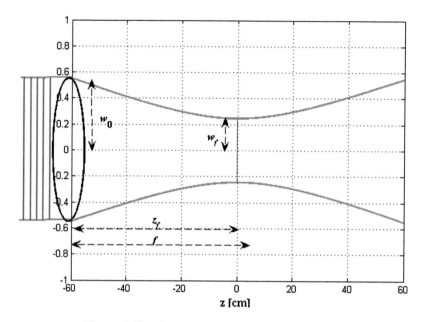

Figure 1.23   Gaussian beam focusing by a lens.

propagating through a lens of focal length f and due to propagation of a distance z_f, where the beam is refocused, is given by

$$q(z_f) = \frac{f q_0}{f - q_0} + z_f = j p(z_f) = j \frac{k_0}{2} w_f^2. \tag{1.61}$$

The final q-parameter is purely imaginary because the beam at the focus has a planar wavefront. Replacing the value of q_0 in Eq. (1.61) produces

$$\frac{j f z_R}{f - j z_R} + z_f = j \frac{f^2 z_R}{f^2 + z_R^2} + \underbrace{\left(z_f - \frac{f z_R^2}{f^2 + z_R^2} \right)}_{=0} = j p(z_f).$$

Therefore, the focusing distance is found to be

$$z_f = \frac{f z_R^2}{f^2 + z_R^2}. \tag{1.62}$$

If z_R is much larger than f, then $z_f \approx f$, and

$$w_f^2 = \frac{w_0^2 f^2}{f^2 + z_R^2}; \tag{1.63}$$

Table 1.4 MATLAB code "Gaussian_beam_schematic.m" for Gaussian beam shape and field curvature (see Fig. 1.24).

```
1   %This program shows a schematic of 1D Gaussian beam
2   %propagation
3   clc; clear all
4   w0=0.5;                          %Initial waist
5   ZR=1;                            %Normalized Rayleigh range
6   z=linspace(-5*ZR,5*ZR,101);      %Propagation distance
7   w = w0*sqrt((z/ZR).^2+1);        %Gaussian beamwidth formula
8   figure
9   plot(z,w);hold on;
10  plot(z,-w);hold on
11  z2 = linspace(-5*ZR,5*ZR,9);     %Specific values of Z where
12                                   %we evaluate the wavefronts
13  w2 = w0*sqrt((z2/ZR).^2+1);      %Gaussian beamwidth at
14                                   %these specific values of Z
15  R2 = (z2.^2+ZR^2)./z2;           %Gaussian beam radius of
16                                   %curvature at these
17                                   %specific values of Z
18  R2(ceil(length(R2)/2)) = 1000;   %Limits the maximum value
19                                   %of the radius of curvature
20  theta=linspace(-pi/2,pi/2,100);  %Range of angle that the
21                       %wavefront will be drawn between.
22  %This part draws the wavefronts
23  for i=1:length(z2).
24  x=R2(i)*cos(theta);              %Because the wavefront is part
25                                   %of a circle, this will
26  y=R2(i)*sin(theta);              %determine x and y.
27  I1=find(abs(y)<w2(i));
28  if R2(i)==1000
29  plot(zeros(100),linspace(-w2(i),w2(i),100),...
30          'k','LineWidth',1.5)
31  hold on
32  end
33  y2=y(I1);
34  x2=x(I1);
35  plot(x2,y2,'k','LineWidth',1.5);   %Plots the wavefront
36  hold on
37  end
38  hold off
39  xlabel('z');ylabel('beam size');
```

[also for small $\lambda(f \ll z_R)$ and $w_f \approx (w_0 f)/z_R = (\lambda f)/(\pi w_0)$, e.g., if $w_0 = 3$ mm, $\lambda_0 = 633$ nm, $f = 10$ cm, and $w_f \approx 6.7$ μm]. Table 1.4 provides the code that produces Fig. 1.24.

1.3 Example 1: MATLAB Code for Calculating Diffraction with the Fast Fourier Transform

This section shows typical code for 1D and 2D Gaussian beam propagation using MATLAB's fast Fourier transform (fft) function. Table 1.5 provides the code that produces Fig. 1.25.

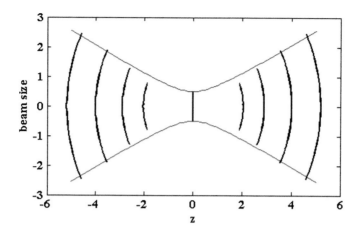

Figure 1.24   Gaussian beam shape and field curvature.

Table 1.5   MATLAB code "Example1.m" for diffraction of 1D and 2D Gaussian beams (see Fig. 1.25).

```
1    %%Example 1: 1D Gaussian Beam Propagation----------
2    clc
3    clear all
4    N=1024;                              %Number of transverse spatial points
5    L=sqrt(N);                           %Spatial dimension of the beam
6    delz=0.01;                           %Step size in propagation direction
7    M=100;                               %Number of steps
8    J=10;                                %Number of planes shown for plotting
9    h = L/N                              %Transverse space step
10   n =[-N/2:1:N/2-1]';                  %Indices
11   x = n*h;                             %Transverse grid points
12   u=exp(-x.^2);                        %Initial Gaussian beam
13   U = u;                               %Compute initial condition,
14                                        %save it in U.
15   kx2 = -4*n.*n*pi*pi/L/L;             %Squares of wavenumbers
16   E=sum(u.^2)*h            %Track energy for computation verification
17   up =fftshift(fft(u));                %Take Fourier transform
18   EFo=sum(abs(up).^2)*h/N              %Verify if energy is conserved
19   %Create a video.
20   aviobj=avifile('beamprop.avi','compression','none');
21   figure
22   for m = 1:1:M                        %Start time evolution
23   up = fftshift(fft(u));               %Take Fourier transform
24   up = exp(delz*i*kx2).*up;            %Advance in Fourier space
25   u = ifft(fftshift(up));              %Return to physical space
26   if rem(m,J) == 0                     %Save output every J steps
27   U =[U u];
28   plot(x,abs(u));
29   MM(m)=getframe;                      %Capture the frames
30   aviobj=addframe(aviobj,MM(m));
31   end
32   end
33   figure
34   S=size(U);                           %Display with mesh(abs(U))
```

Table 1.5 *(Continued)*

```
35  y=linspace(0,M*delz,S(2));
36  [X,Y]=meshgrid(x,y);
37  mesh(X,Y,abs(U'));
38  xlabel('x')
39  ylabel('z:Propagation');
40  zlabel('Beam Amplitude')
41  Ef=sum(abs(u).^2)*h                    %Check energy
42  aviobj = close(aviobj);
43  %%2D Gaussian Beam Propagation----------------
44  clc
45  clear all
46  close all
47  w0=2;                                  %Initial waist in mm
48  lambda=0.5*10^-3;                      %Wavelength in mm
49  k0=2*pi/lambda;                        %Wavenumber
50  Zr=(w0^2*k0)/2;                        %Rayleigh range
51  N=256;                           %Number of transverse spatial points
52  L=30;                                  %Spatial dimension of the beam
53  delz=1000;                       %Step size in propagation direction
54  M=100;                                 %Number of steps
55  J=10;                            %Number of planes shown for plotting
56  h = L/N                                %Transverse space step
57  n =[-N/2:1:N/2-1]';                    %Indices
58  x = n*h;                               %Grid points
59  y=x;
60  [X,Y]=meshgrid(x,y);                   %2D grid
61  u0=exp((-X.^2-Y.^2)/w0^2);             %Initial Gaussian beam
62  u=u0;
63  a=pi/h;
64  kx=[-a:2*a/N:a-2*a/N]';                %Spatial frequency vector
65  ky=kx;
66  [Kx,Ky]=meshgrid(kx,ky);               %2D frequency grid
67  Num=-(Kx.^2+Ky.^2);
68  Den=i*2*k0;
69  P=Num./Den;  %Create the transfer function of propagation
70  M*delz
71  %aviobj=avifile('beamprop2.avi','compression','none');
72  %fig=figure;
73  vidObj=VideoWriter('beamprop1.avi','Motion JPEG AVI');
74  open(vidObj)
75  figure('Renderer','zbuffer')
76  %subplot(2,1,1)
77  %imagesc(abs(u0));
78  %subplot(2,1,2)
79  surf(X,Y,abs(u0));
80  axis tight manual
81  set(gca,'NextPlot','replaceChildren');
82  for m = 1:1:M                          %Start time evolution
83  up = fftshift(fft2(u));                %Take Fourier transform
84  up = exp(delz*P).*up;                  %Advance in Fourier space
85  u = ifft2(fftshift(up));               %Return to physical space
86  %subplot(2,1,1)
87  %imagesc(abs(u));
88  %subplot(2,1,2)
89  surf(X,Y,abs(u));
```

(continued)

Table 1.5 (*Continued*)

```
90   %F= getframe(fig);
91   %aviobj = addframe(aviobj,F);
92   currFrame = getframe;
93   writeVideo(vidObj,currFrame);
94   end
95   %close(fig)
96   %aviobj = close(aviobj);
97   close(vidObj);
98   figure
99   subplot(2,1,1)
100  mesh(X,Y,abs(u0));
101  title('Initial Beam')
102  xlabel('x')
103  ylabel('y');
104  zlabel('Beam Amplitude')
105  subplot(2,1,2)
106  mesh(X,Y,abs(u));
107  title('Beam after propagation')
108  xlabel('x')
109  ylabel('y');
110  zlabel('Beam Amplitude')
```

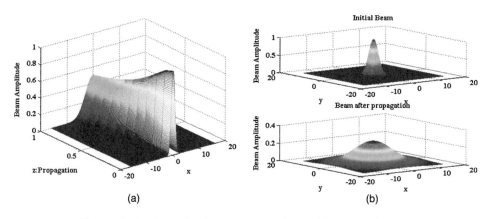

Figure 1.25 Gaussian beam propagation in (a) 1D and (b) 2D.

1.4 Example 2: MATLAB Code for Calculating Forward and Backward Gaussian Beam Propagation

Table 1.6 provides the code that produces Fig. 1.26.

1.5 Example 3: MATLAB Code for Gaussian Beam Propagation through a Lens

Assume a Gaussian beam propagating in air with an initial plane wavefront and waist w_0 at a distance d_0 in front of a converging lens of focal length f, similar to Fig. 1.23. Using the beam propagation method, the code in

Table 1.6 MATLAB code "Example2.m" for forward and backward Gaussian beam propagation (see Fig. 1.26).

```
1    %%Forward and backward propagation of a Gaussian beam.
2    %All units are in mm.
3    clc
4    clear all
5    N=512;                     %Number of points
6    w0=3;                      %Inital waist
7    lambda=.543e-3;            %HeNe laser-green
8    zr=pi*w0^2./lambda         %Rayleigh range
9    z0=zr;                        %Chose propagation distance as Zr
10   k0=2*pi/lambda;            %Wavenumber
11   L=sqrt(N);                 %%%Spatial dimension unit is in mm
12   dx=L/N;                    %Sampling spacing
13   n=[-N/2:1:N/2-1];
14   x=linspace(-L/2,L/2,N);    %Spatial vector
15   y=x;
16   [X,Y]=meshgrid(x,y);
17   a=pi./dx;                  %Maximum frequency
18   kx=[-a:2*a/N:a-2*a/N];     %Frequency vector
19   ky=kx;
20   [KX,KY]=meshgrid(kx,ky);   %2D frequency grid
21   KK=KX.^2+KY.^2;
22   %Initial Gaussian beam
23   a=0;b=0;
24   u0=exp(-((X-a).^2+(Y-b).^2)/w0^2);     %Inital beam
25   phi0=0;%(X-a).^2+(Y-b).^2;  %Inital phase is plane wave
26   e0=u0.*exp(i*phi0);
27   %Plot the inital beam amplitude and phase
28   figure
29   subplot(3,2,1)
30   mesh(X,Y,abs(e0))
31   view(0,90)
32   axis square
33   axis tight
34   title('Intensity at distance z=0 mm')
35   subplot(3,2,2)
36   mesh(X,Y,angle(e0))
37   view(0,90)
38   axis square
39   axis tight
40   title('Phase at distance z=0 mm')
41   f_e0=fftshift(fft2(e0));  %Fourier transform of object.
42   %Start propagating.
43   U=exp(i*KK*z0/(2*k0)).*f_e0; %Multiply with the transfer
44                               %function
45   u_f=ifft2(fftshift(U));   %Go back to the space domain
46   abs_u_f=abs(u_f);
47   phase_u_f=angle(u_f);
48   subplot(3,2,3)
49   mesh(X,Y,abs_u_f)
50   title('Intensity at distance z=zr mm')
51   view(0,90);axis square;axis tight
52   subplot(3,2,4)
53   mesh(X,Y,phase_u_f)
```

(continued)

Table 1.6 *(Continued)*

```
54  title('Phase at distance z=zrmm')
55  view(0,90);axis square;axis tight
56  %Start back-propogating
57  f_u_f=fftshift(fft2(u_f));
58  Ub=exp(-i*KK*z0/(2*k0)).*f_u_f;
59  u_02=ifft2(fftshift(Ub));
60  abs_u_02=abs(u_02);
61  phase_u_02=angle(u_02);
62  subplot(3,2,5)
63  mesh(X,Y,abs_u_02)
64  title('Intensity at distance z=0 mm')
65  view(0,90);axis square;axis tight
66  subplot(3,2,6)
67  mesh(X,Y,phase_u_02)
68  title('Phase at distance z=0mm')
69  view(0,90);axis square;axis tight
```

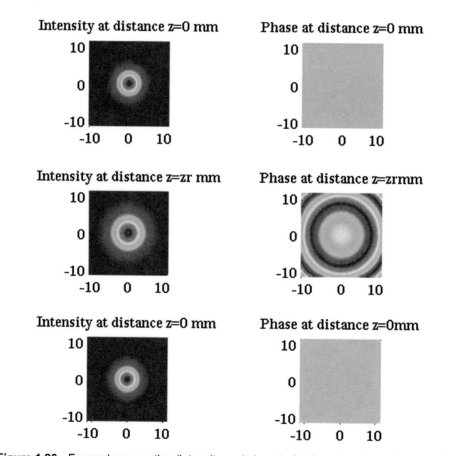

Figure 1.26 Forward propagation (intensity and phase) of a Gaussian beam from $z = 0$ to $z = z_R$, and then back from $z = z_R$ to $z = 0$.

Table 1.7 simulates the propagation of the beam through air, through a lens, then finally to the focus point again.

1.6 Generalized Diffraction Example via the Fresnel Transform

The code in Table 1.8 simulates the diffraction from a user-defined aperture. The diffraction calculation is based on the Fresnel transform, which will be discussed in detail in Chapter 4. In this example, a plane wave incident upon a

Table 1.7 MATLAB code "Example3.m" for Gaussian beam propagation through a lens (see Fig. 1.27).

```
1    %%------------------------Gaussian beam prop-------------------
2    clc
3    clear all
4    N=2^8;                              %Number of samples
5    L=sqrt(N);                          %Spatial length in mm
6    h = L/N;                            %Spatial sampling
7    n = [-N/2:1:N/2-1]';                %Indices
8    x = n*h;                            %Grid points
9    y=x;
10   w0=1;                               %Inital beam waist in mm
11   lambda=0.5*10^-3;                   %Wavelength in mm
12   k0=2*pi/lambda;                     %Wavenumber
13   Zr=(w0^2*k0)/2                      %Rayleigh range
14   a=pi/h;                             %Maximum frequency
15   f=Zr;     %First propagation distance is the focal length
16             %of the lens
17   [X,Y] =meshgrid(x,y);
18   u0=exp(-(X.^2+Y.^2)/w0^2);                  %Inital Gaussian beam.
19   %Plot inital beam amplitude and phase.
20   figure
21   mesh(X,Y,abs(u0));
22   E0=h^2*sum(sum(abs(u0).^2))          %Energy is used to check
                                          %validity of propagation
23   view(90,0)
24   xlabel('x');ylabel('y');zlabel('|u_0(x,y)|')
25   title ('Initial Beam Profile')
26   grid on
27   m_abs=max(abs(u0(:)));
28   I=find(abs(u0)<m_abs/100);            %Manually set the phase of
29                                         %small amplitudes to zero
30   ph_u0=angle(u0);
31   ph_u0(I)=0;
32   figure
33   mesh(X,Y,ph_u0);
34   view(0,90)
35   xlabel('x');ylabel('y');zlabel('|u(x,y)|')
36   title ('Initial Beam Phase Profile')
37   grid on
38   %%Just verify ifft technique works and takes you back
```

(continued)

Table 1.7 (*Continued*)

```
39   %to initial beam
40   UI=fftshift(fft2((u0)));
41   %figure
42   %mesh(abs(UI))
43   uf=ifft2(fftshift(UI));
44   figure
45   mesh(X,Y,abs(uf));
46   xlabel('x');ylabel('y');zlabel('|u_f(x,y)|')
47   title ('Final Beam Profile')
48   grid on
49   m_abs=max(abs(uf(:)));
50   I=find(abs(uf)<m_abs/100);
51   ph_uf=angle(uf);
52   ph_uf(I)=0;
53   figure
54   mesh(X,Y,ph_uf);
55   xlabel('x');ylabel('y');zlabel('|u(x,y)|')
56   title ('Final Beam Phase Profile')
57   %%---------Field just before lens
58   u=u0;
59   kx=[-a:2*a/N:a-2*a/N]';             %Frequency vector
60   ky=kx;
61   [Kx,Ky]=meshgrid(kx,ky);
62   Num=-(Kx.^2+Ky.^2);
63   Den=i*2*k0;
64   P=Num./Den;                         %Exponent of transfer function
65   up=fftshift(fft2(u));
66   %figure
67   %mesh(X,Y,abs(up))
68   up2 = exp(f*P).*up;                 %Propagation is performed by
69                                       %multiplying by transfer function
70   u =ifft2(fftshift(up2));
71   %Plot amplitude and phase just before lens
72   figure
73   mesh(X,Y,abs(u));
74   view(90,0)
75   xlabel('x');ylabel('y');zlabel('|u(x,y)|')
76   title ('Beam Profile before the Lens')
77   grid on
78   m_abs=max(abs(u(:)));
79   I=find(abs(u)<m_abs/100);
80   ph_u=angle(u);
81   ph_u(I)=0;
82   figure
83   mesh(X,Y,ph_u);
84   view(0,90)
85   xlabel('x');ylabel('y');zlabel('|u(x,y)|')
86   title ('Beam Phase Profile before the Lens')
87   grid on
88   Ef1=h^2*sum(sum(abs(u).^2))
89   %%Field just after lens
90   t_lens=exp(i*k0/(2*f)*(X.^2+Y.^2));   %Lens transfer
91                                         %function
```

(continued)

Table 1.7 (*Continued*)

```
92   u_after=u.*t_lens;                    %Multiply Gaussian beam with
93                                          %lens transfer function.
94   %Plot amplitude and phase just after lens.
95   figure
96   mesh(X,Y,abs(u_after));
97   view(90,0)
98   xlabel('x');ylabel('y');zlabel('|u_f(x,y)|')
99   title ('Beam Profile just after the Lens')
100  grid on
101  m_abs=max(abs(u_after(:)));
102  I=find(abs(u_after) < m_abs/100);
103  ph_u_after=angle(u_after);
104  ph_u_after(I)=0;
105  figure
106  mesh(X,Y,ph_u_after);
107  view(0,90)
108  xlabel('x');
109  ylabel('y');
110  zlabel('|u(x,y)|')
111  title ('Beam Phase Profile just after the Lens')
112  grid on
113  %%Field at a distance f after the lens
114  d=f;
115  up = fftshift(fft2(u_after));
116  up = exp(d*P).*up;
117  u_final = ifft2(fftshift(up));
118  figure
119  mesh(X,Y,abs(u_final));
120  view(90,0);
121  xlabel('x');
122  ylabel('y');
123  zlabel('|u_f(x,y)|')
124  title ('Beam Profile at a Distance f after the Lens')
125  grid on
126  m_abs=max(abs(u_final(:)));
127  I=find(abs(u_final)<m_abs/100);
128  ph_ufinal=angle(u_final);
129  ph_ufinal(I)=0;
130  figure
131  mesh(X,Y,ph_ufinal);
132  view(0,90);
133  xlabel('x');
134  ylabel('y');
135  zlabel('|u(x,y)|')
136  title ({ 'Beam Phase Profile at a Distance f',...
137  'after the Lens'})
138  grid on
```

circular lens (with a 1.6-mm diameter) of focal length $f = 20$ cm is propagated a distance of 50 cm from the lens. In this case, diffraction through the lens will reveal the focusing effect of the lens, including the depth of focus and subsequent diffraction of the beam. The user can specify any

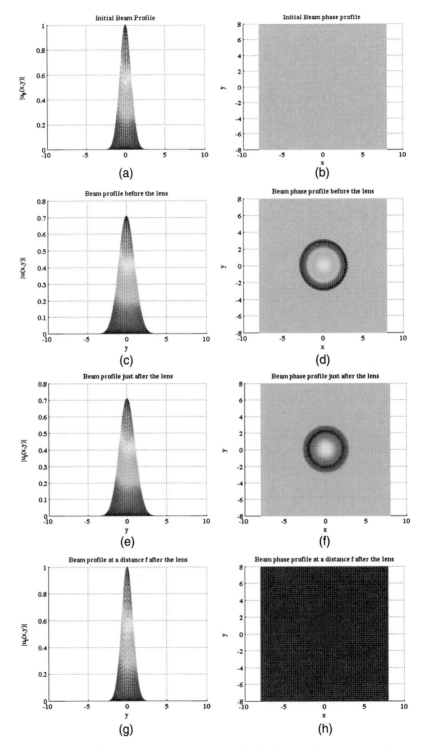

Figure 1.27 Using the beam propagation method, the amplitude and phase of the Gaussian beam (a, b) at initial beam, (c, d) just before the lens, (e, f) just after the lens, and (g, h) at the back focal plane of the lens.

Table 1.8 MATLAB code "Example4_chapter1_3D_Visualizations.m" for diffraction through a circular lens (see Figs. 1.28 and 1.29).

```
1  %Chapter 1, Example 4.
2  %This example will demonstrate diffraction propagation
3  %via Fresnel transform of a circular lens aperture.
4  format compact
5  clear all;close all
6  %Draw the circular aperture with the following
7  %parameters:
8  Bitmap_size = 301;                      %Odd bitmap sizes will keep
9                                          %the patterns centered
10 radius = 81;
11 shift_x = 0;shift_y = 0;
12 %Either input an aperture bitmap or create one
13 Aperture = ...
14 myDrawCircle(Bitmap_size,radius,shift_x,shift_y);
15 %Aperture = myDrawRectangle(Bitmap_size,radius,radius);
16 %In this case, let the aperture be a circular lens with
17 %the following parameters:
18 focal_length = 0.2;                     %20-cm focal length
19 wavelength = 633e-9;                    %Illumination wavelength
20 dx = 10e-6;                             %Assumes this is the physical dimension
21                                         %of a pixel in the aperture plane.
22 %Create the lens phase.
23 Phase = ...
24 myLensPhase_f(Bitmap_size,focal_length,wavelength,dx);
25 %Phase = 0;                             %Set phase angle to zero if
26                                         %none is desired
27 Aperture = Aperture.*exp(1i.*Phase);      %Multiply the phase
28                                         %onto the aperture.
29 %Propagate the diffraction pattern from the aperture
30 %using the following parameters (all units in SI units):
31 Propagation_distance = 0.5;              %50 cm
32 Increment = 0.01;                       %Distance between calculated
33                                         %diffraction planes
34 [Dr,Dr_phase,Slice,Slice_phase,Vol,Vol_phase] = ...
35 myDiffraction(Aperture,Propagation_distance,...
36 wavelength,dx,Increment,0,0,true);
37 %%Display the diffraction volume with different methods.
38 %Loft the volume to be a perfect cube --> easier to use
39 %plotting functions.
40 Vol2 = myLoftAndRotate(Vol);            %Loft along z axis into a
41                                         %cube
42 Vol2 = permute(Vol2,[2 3 1]);           %Correct permutation is
43                                         %[2 3 1]
44 Vol2 = myFast_Rigid3D(Vol2,0,180,0,0,0,0);        %Rotate
45                                         %right-side-up
46 figure(6)
47 myDisplay3d(Vol2,.1,3,.2)               %Display using transparent
48                                         %isosurface
49 view(-15,15); grid on
50 title('Diffraction Volume (displayed using isoSurface)')
51 %%Display the volume using slice planes.
52 %This follows/modifies an example found on the
53 %Mathworks website:
54 %http://www.mathworks.com/help/matlab/visualize/
```

(continued)

Table 1.8 (*Continued*)

```
55  %exploring-volumes-with-slice-planes.html.
56  v = double(Vol2);                      %Double precision required for the
57                                          %next functions
58  Vsize = size(v);
59  %Define the size of the meshgrid for the volume
60  [x,y,z] = meshgrid(1:Vsize(1), 1:Vsize(2), 1:Vsize(3));
61  xmin = min(x(:)); ymin = min(y(:)); zmin = min(z(:));
62  xmax = max(x(:)); ymax = max(y(:)); zmax = max(z(:));
63  %Now generate the slice at a 45-deg angle within the
64  %volume
65  figure(7)
66  theta=45;                              %Rotation angle keeps slice centered at
67                                         %0 and 45, but not other angles
68  %The ymax value is modified in anticipation of rotation
69  %by 45 deg.
70  hslice = surf(linspace(xmin,xmax,Vsize(1)),...
71  linspace(ymin,ymax*(1/cosd(theta)),Vsize(2)),...
72  zeros(Vsize(1),Vsize(2)));
73  origin = ([0 0 0]);                    %No need to change origin
74                                         %because ymax was changed
75  rotate(hslice,[1,0,0],theta,origin)
76  %rotate(hslice,[0,0,-1],-45)
77  xd = get(hslice,'XData');yd = get(hslice,'YData');
78  zd = get(hslice,'ZData');
79  xlabel('x');ylabel('y');zlabel('z')
80  %Delete the slice after viewing/verifying correct
81  %location
82  delete(hslice)
83  %Draw the slice plane with the volume data v
84  %superposed
85  h = slice(x,y,z,v,xd,yd,zd);
86  set(h,'FaceColor','interp','EdgeColor','none',...
87  'DiffuseStrength',.8)
88  %Draw the endcaps of the volume with the data v
89  %superposed
90  hold on
91  hx = slice(x,y,z,v,xmax,[],[]);
92  set(hx,'FaceColor','interp','EdgeColor','none')
93  hy = slice(x,y,z,v,[],ymax,[]);
94  set(hy,'FaceColor','interp','EdgeColor','none')
95  hz = slice(x,y,z,v,[],[],zmin);
96  set(hz,'FaceColor','interp','EdgeColor','none')
97  axis tight;box on
98  axis([xmin xmax ymin ymax zmin zmax])
99  view(-15,15)
100 %%Display with different colormaps to better
101 %visualize data
102 colormap hot
```

aperture shape by defining an input bitmap in which the aperture opening consists of 1s against a background of 0s. Plane waves are assumed to be incident upon the aperture, although the aperture bitmap may include a complex phase to simulate propagation through lenses, prism tilt effects, etc.

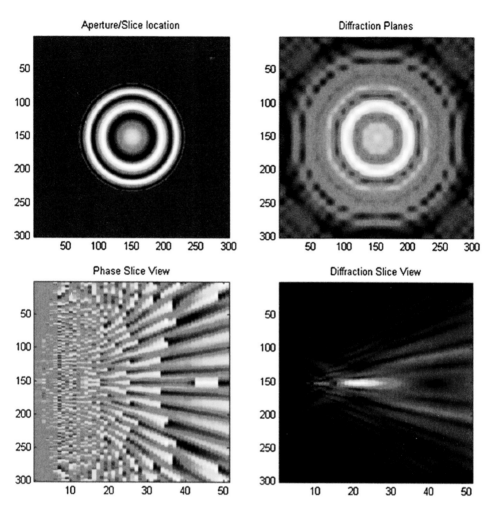

Figure 1.28 Diffraction simulation of a plane wave incident on a circular lens with focal length $f = 20$ cm and size $= 1.62$ mm. The original aperture, with phase modulo 2π, is shown in the upper left; the final diffraction pattern at $z = 50$ cm is shown in the upper right. A central side-view slice of the beam phase is illustrated at lower left, while the side-view slice of the intensity is shown at lower right. Note that the beam focuses at approximately 20 cm, with a depth of focus of a few centimeters.

To assist intuitive visualization, a side-view of the diffraction pattern is also plotted. The user may define the location of the side-view slice, although a central location will generally be most intuitive. As the software runs, the user may view each diffraction plane as it is calculated, with the final diffraction plane displayed in the figure. Table 1.8 provides the code that produces Figs. 1.28 and 1.29. See Appendix 1 for additional functions used in this example.

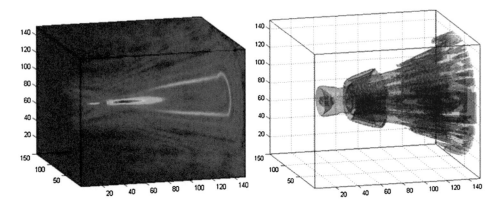

Figure 1.29 Two alternate 3D reconstructions of the diffraction pattern of Fig. 1.28 using MATLAB. The reconstruction on the left uses volumetric slice plots with an alternative (jet) colormap to visualize the overall intensity distribution within a chosen slice; the reconstruction on the right uses the isosurface function to visualize surfaces of constant intensity within the 3D volume.

References

1. J. W. Goodman, *Introduction to Fourier Optics*, 3rd Ed., Roberts & Co., Englewood, CO (1996).
2. C. Slinger, C. Cameron, and M. Stanley, "Computer-generated holography as a generic display technology," *Computer* **38**(8), 47–53 (2005).
3. D. Gabor, "A new microscopic principle," *Nature* **161**(4098), 777–778 (1948).
4. E. N. Leith and J. Upatnieks, "Reconstructed wavefronts and communication theory," *J. Opt. Soc. Am.* **52**(10), 1123–1130 (1962).
5. Y. Denisyuk, "Photographic reconstruction of the optical properties of an object in its own scattered radiation field," *Soviet Physics-Doklady* **7**, 543–545 (1962).
6. P. Hariharan, *Basics of Holography*, Cambridge University Press, Cambridge, UK (2002).
7. S. A. Benton, "Holographic displays—a review," *Opt. Eng.* **14**(5), 402–407 (1975).
8. T. H. Jeong, "Cylindrical holography and some proposed applications," *J. Opt. Soc. Am.* **57**(11), 1396–1398 (1967).
9. L. Cross, "Multiplex holography," *Annual meeting of the SPIE*, San Diego, CA (August, 1977).
10. S. F. Johnston, *Holographic Visions: A History of New Science*, Oxford University Press, Oxford, UK (2006).
11. zarathustrawild, "holograms, Japan," footage from HODIC meeting, https://www.youtube.com/watch?v=Wdl-P5yBKBk (uploaded Mar. 2008).
12. S. A. Benton and V. M. Bove, Jr., "White-Light Transmission 'Rainbow' Holography," Chapter 14 in *Holographic Imaging*, Wiley Interscience, Hoboken, NJ (2008).

13. P. Hariharan, W. H. Steel, and Z. S. Hegedus, "Multicolor holographic imaging with a white-light source," *Opt. Lett.* **1**(1), 8–9 (1977).

14. T.-C. Poon and P. P. Banerjee, *Contemporary Optical Image Processing with MATLAB®*, Elsevier Science, Amsterdam (2001).

15. R. J. Parker, "A quarter century of thermoplastic holography," *Int. Conf. Hologram Interferometry Speckle Metrol.*, K. Stetson and R. Pryputniewicz, eds., 217–224 (1990).

16. T. Kreis, *Holographic Interferometry: Principles and Methods*, Akademie Verlag, Berlin (1996).

17. N. V. Kukhtarev, V. B. Markov, S. G. Odoulov, and M. S. Soskin, "Holographic storage in electrooptic crystals," *Ferroelectrics* **22**, 949–964 (1979).

18. P. Yeh, *Introduction to Photorefractive Nonlinear Optics, John Wiley & Sons*, New York (1993).

19. B. L. Volodin, B. Kippelen, K. Meerholz, N. V. Kukhtarev, H. J. Caulfield, and N. Peyghambarian, "Non-Bragg orders in dynamic self-diffraction on thick phase gratings in a photorefractive polymer," *Opt. Lett.* **21**(7), 519–521 (1996).

20. S. Tay et al., "An updatable holographic three-dimensional display," *Nature* **451**(7179), 694–698 (2008).

21. P. A. Blanche et al., "Holographic three-dimensional telepresence using large-area photorefractive polymer," *Nature* **468**(7320), 80–83 (2010).

22. O. Ostroverkhova and W. E. Moerner, "Organic photorefractives: mechanism, materials and applications," *Chem. Rev.* **104**(7), 3267–3314 (2004).

Chapter 2
Analog Holography, Holographic Interferometry, and Phase-Shifting Holographic Interferometry

2.1 Fourier Optics Theory

Because the objective of holography is to perform phase retrieval from a recorded hologram, this chapter discusses how this can be achieved using analog holographic techniques. Conventional analog holography entails physical re-illumination of the hologram of the object with a reading beam and finding the 3D real or virtual image. Numerical phase retrieval methods are also addressed that unwrap the computed (and thus always modulo 2π) phase to determine the exact phase change of the image. In holographic interferometry and phase-shifting holographic interferometry, the phases from different states of an object can be compared to yield information about the 3D deformation of the object.

Propagation of optical fields (amplitudes and phases) is the central theme behind phase retrieval and reconstruction of the 3D image, and so the derivation of the nonparaxial Fresnel diffraction formula (contrary to the paraxial approximation in Chapter 1) will be briefly summarized for the sake of completeness. The starting point is the Helmholtz equation for the time-harmonic optical field (phasor) $E(x, y, z)$, which can be expressed as

$$\nabla^2 E(x, y, z) + k_0^2 E(x, y, z) = 0, \qquad (2.1)$$

where $k_0 = 2\pi/\lambda$ is the propagation constant, with λ representing the wavelength. Assuming z to be the nominal direction of propagation and x, y

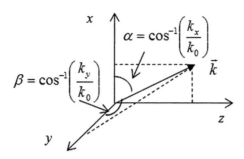

Figure 2.1 Wavevector $\vec{k}$.

to be transverse coordinates, Eq. (2.1) can be Fourier transformed with respect to x, y to yield

$$\frac{d^2 \tilde{E}(k_x,k_y;z)}{dz^2} + k_0^2[1 - (k_x/k_0)^2 - (k_y/k_0)^2]\tilde{E}(k_x,k_y;z) = 0, \qquad (2.2)$$

where $\tilde{E}(k_x,k_y;z)$ is the Fourier transform of $E(x,y,z)$, defined as

$$\tilde{E}(k_x,k_y;z) = \mathfrak{I}_{x,y}[E(x,y;z)] = \int\limits_{-\infty}^{\infty}\int\limits_{-\infty}^{\infty} E(x,y;z)\exp j(k_x x + k_y y)dxdy \qquad (2.3)$$

and called the *angular plane wave spectrum*, and k_x, k_y are the spatial angular frequencies (rad/m) defined as $k_x = k_0 \cos\alpha$, $k_y = k_0 \cos\beta$, where α, β are the angles that the propagation vector $\vec{k}$ makes with the x, y axes respectively (see Fig. 2.1).

The solution to Eq. (2.2) for waves propagating nominally along $+z$ is

$$\tilde{E}(k_x,k_y;z) = \tilde{E}(k_x,k_y;0)\exp\left\{-jk_0\sqrt{[1-(k_x/k_0)^2-(k_y/k_0)^2]}z\right\}$$

$$\equiv \tilde{E}(k_x,k_y;0)\tilde{G}_{PSF}(k_x,k_y;z), \qquad (2.4)$$

so that the solution in spatial coordinates becomes

$$E(x,y;z) = E(x,y;0) * g_{PSF}(x,y;z), \qquad (2.5)$$

where $*$ denotes convolution, and

$$g_{PSF}(x,y;z) = \mathfrak{I}_{x,y}^{-1}\left\{\exp\left\{-jk_0\sqrt{[1-(k_x/k_0)^2-(k_y/k_0)^2]}z\right\}\right\}$$

$$= jk_0\left(\frac{z}{\rho}\right)\cdot\left(1+\frac{1}{jk_0\rho}\right)\frac{\exp(-jk_0\rho)}{2\pi\rho}, \qquad (2.6)$$

with $\rho = \sqrt{x^2+y^2+z^2}$.

In most cases, $k_0\rho \gg 1$ (i.e., the observation plane distance is much larger than a wavelength: $z \gg \lambda$). The term $z/\rho = \cos\Phi = Q \approx 1$ is called the obliquity factor, and Φ is the angle between the positive z axis and the line passing through the origin of coordinates.[1,2] With the approximations discussed earlier,

$$g_{PSF}(x, y; z) \approx jk_0 \frac{\exp(-jk_0\rho)}{2\pi\rho}, \qquad (2.7)$$

where g_{PSF} is often referred to as the *impulse response of propagation* and denotes the diverging spherical waves from a point source, thereby justifying the subscript PSF for *point spread function*. Equation (2.5), along with Eq. (2.7), is the well-known Fresnel–Kirchhoff (FK) or Rayleigh–Sommerfeld (RS) integral[2,3] and is an essential relation that will be used in Chapter 4 to develop numerical algorithms for the propagation of optical fields from a hologram illuminated with a reading beam for digital holographic reconstruction of an image. An alternative approach to analyzing diffraction starts from the Helmholtz equation and derives the eikonal equations or, equivalently, the transport of intensity equations, which are discussed in Chapter 10.

2.2 Analog Holography Theory and Setups

As mentioned in Chapter 1, a hologram is the recording of the intensity profile of the interference at *one* particular distance during the propagation of the object field and the reference. Holograms can be off-axis [as in a Leith–Upatneiks type, see Fig. 2.2(a)] or on-axis [as in a Gabor-type, see Fig. 2.2(b)]. The inline setup is primarily used to analyze transparent (phase) objects or small particle distribution, where the reference wave is the light passing unaffected between particles, and the object wave is the field scattered by the particles [see Fig. 2.2(b)].[4] The main disadvantage of such a technique comes from the fact that during reconstruction, the reading beam and the twin (defocused) image appear within the same line of sight (i.e., on-axis) as the original image. In the Leith–Upatnieks off-axis setup shown in Fig. 2.2(a), where a nonzero offset angle is introduced between the reference beam and the

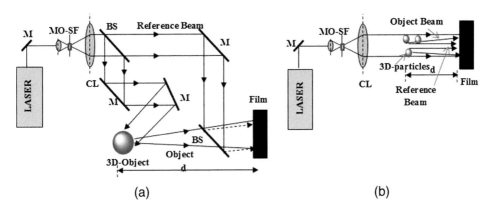

(a)　　　　　　　　　　　　　　　　　(b)

Figure 2.2 (a) Off-axis setup and (b) on-axis setup, with a microscope objective-spatial filter (MO-SF), beamsplitter (BS), mirror (M), collimating lens (CL), and distance between the object and film (d).

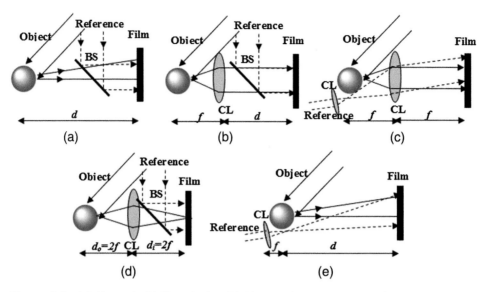

Figure 2.3 (a) Fresnel, (b) Fraunhofer, (c) Fourier, (d) image, and (e) lensless Fourier hologram. The focal length of the lens is f; d_o, d_i are the object and image distance, respectively, from the lens; BS is the beamsplitter; and CL is the converging lens.

object beam, there will be no overlap between the reconstructed virtual and real images and the reading beam. If the angle between the object wave and the reference is nominally zero, an inline hologram can again be obtained.

Holograms can be divided into five general classes:

- Fresnel,
- Fraunhofer,
- Fourier,
- image, and
- lensless Fourier.

A hologram is of the Fresnel type if the recording plane lies within the region of Fresnel diffraction for the illuminated object (i.e., the distance between the object and hologram is much greater than the lateral dimensions of the object, such that the Fresnel number is approximately 1 but not necessarily much less than 1), as shown in Fig. 2.3(a). The hologram is a Fraunhofer type if the transformation from the object to the hologram plane (film) is best described by the Fraunhofer diffraction equation, which means that either the lateral dimensions of the object are small with respect to the distance between the object and the film (i.e., the Fresnel number is much less than 1) or the object is at the focus of a lens, as shown in Fig. 2.3(b). In this case, the hologram is recorded on the back focal plane of the lens, which contains the Fourier transform or Fraunhofer diffraction of the object. If there is a thin object, the Fourier transform of the object and the reference fields can be recorded on the film, thus producing a Fourier transform hologram like that shown in Fig. 2.3(c). The resolution requirements on the recording medium of such a setup are fewer.

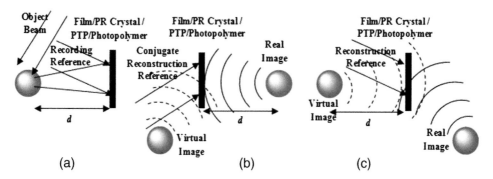

Figure 2.4 Analog holography: (a) optical recording, (b) optical reconstruction where the conjugate of the reference beam generates a real image, and (c) optical reconstruction where the original reference beam generates a virtual image.

If a hologram is recorded in an image plane, it is called an image hologram. Thus, the object is focused on the hologram plane (CCD), and the real image of the object is recorded instead of the wave field scattered by the object, as shown in Fig. 2.3(d). The advantage of this setup is that image holograms can be reconstructed by an incoherent source. Lensless Fourier transform holography occurs when the object and reference sources are at finite, equal distances from the film or the CCD. Here, the effect of the spherical phase factor associated with the near-field Fresnel diffraction pattern is eliminated by the spherical reference wave with the same curvature as that shown in Fig. 2.3(e). The Fourier transform and lensless Fourier transform holograms make the most efficient use of the space bandwidth product of the hologram. Nevertheless, the Fresnel holograms are the most general (and common) type of hologram.[2,4]

In analog holography (AH), the conventional recording of light scattered from an object (along with a reference wave) is recorded on an analog recording medium, such as a silver halide film,[2,4] PTP film (also called holocamera, see Chapter 1),[5] PR material such as lithium niobate (LN), PR polymer (see Chapter 1), and, recently, photopolymer films (e.g., Bayer Bayfol® HX film and the PQ-doped PMMA film) [see Fig. 2.4(a)]. Reconstruction of the recording, also called a hologram, is achieved by physically shining a read-out or reconstruction beam of light on the hologram.[5]

The holographic process can be described mathematically as follows. The complex amplitude from the object wave on the plane of the recording medium can be written as[2]

$$E_O(x, y) = a_O(x, y) \exp[-j\phi_O(x, y)], \qquad (2.8)$$

where $a_O(x, y)$ is the object amplitude, and $\phi_O(x, y)$ is the object phase. Also, the complex amplitude of the reference wave on the recording medium can be expressed as

$$E_R(x, y) = a_R(x, y) \exp[-j\phi_R(x, y)], \qquad (2.9)$$

where $a_R(x,y)$ is the reference amplitude, and $\phi_R(x,y)$ is the reference phase. When both waves interfere at a recording medium, the intensity is given by

$$I(x,y) = |E_O(x,y) + E_R(x,y)|^2. \qquad (2.10)$$

Mathematically, a real image of the original object can be found by multiplying Eq. (2.10) with the conjugate of the reference beam $E_R^*(x,y)$ (also called the reading or reconstruction beam):

$$
\begin{aligned}
I(x,y)E_R^*(x,y) &= |E_O(x,y) + E_R(x,y)|^2 E_R^*(x,y) \\
&= [E_O(x,y)E_O^*(x,y) + E_R(x,y)E_R^*(x,y) \\
&\quad + E_O(x,y)E_R^*(x,y) + E_O^*(x,y)E_R(x,y)]E_R^*(x,y) \\
&= |E_O(x,y)|^2 E_R^*(x,y) + |E_R(x,y)|^2 E_R^*(x,y) \\
&\quad + E_O(x,y)E_R^{*2}(x,y) + |E_R(x,y)|^2 E_O^*(x,y).
\end{aligned}
\qquad (2.11)
$$

The only term that has the information about the real image is the fourth term on the right side of Eq. (2.11). Multiplication by the conjugate of the reference beam removes any phase contribution from the reference. The schematic shown in Fig. 2.4(b) is a reconstruction technique in AH involving actual physical illumination of the hologram by the reconstruction beam. Reconstruction of the virtual image also happens simultaneously and can be traced to the third term on the right side of Eq. (2.11). Finally, Fig. 2.4(c) shows the case when the reconstruction beam is the same as the original reference beam.

2.3 Analog Holographic Interferometry Theory and Setups

As mentioned earlier, a hologram with amplitude transmittance $h(x,y)$ is the record of the interference between the object field and a reference, which, in turn, is also a record of the 3D information of the object. Therefore, although holography is useful in reconstructing the 3D shape of an object, it is often also useful to accurately determine a change in shape over time. *Holographic interferometry* is an oft-used technique for this and can give accurate information about transverse deformation on the scale of the wavelength of light and axial deformation on the order of a few nanometers.[6,7] The idea here is to compare the phases of the object at two different states. For instance, if the stored hologram at one state, formed by a reference and light from the object, is stored (through "fixing") in an *analog* device, such as PTP or a PR material (e.g., LN), and then read by the optical fields from the reference and light from the object at a different state, the pertinent interference pattern can be recorded (e.g., on a CCD camera) and analyzed to determine the phase difference. This process is called *analog holographic interferometry* (AHI). Non-Bragg orders are noticeable in this type of holographic read-out and can

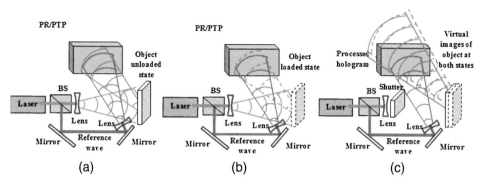

Figure 2.5 (a, b) Recording and (c) reconstruction of a double-exposure holographic interferogram. Reprinted from Kreis[4] with permission.

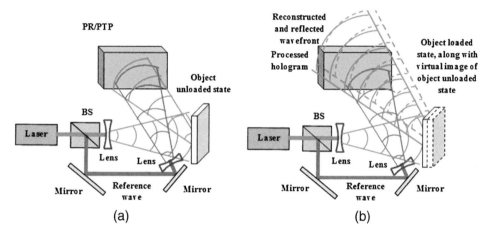

Figure 2.6 (a) Recording and (b) reconstruction of a real-time holographic interferogram. Reprinted from Kreis[4] with permission.

show phase conjugation as well as phase doubling of the recorded object upon reconstruction. The resolution of the analog holographic recording medium used in AHI can be comparable to that of conventional films and is generally higher than that of digital cameras that are used in digital holographic interferometry (DHI, discussed later).

Although AH can reconstruct the 3D shape of the object, AHI can monitor the change in shape very accurately—up to a fraction of the wavelength of light.[6] There exist two major techniques in AHI: double exposure and real time. In *double-exposure AHI*,[4,6–8] the hologram of an object is first recorded and fixed on a recording device [Fig. 2.5(a)], followed by a second hologram of the displaced or deformed object [loaded state, see Fig. 2.5(b)]. During reconstruction, the two holograms produce two sets of diffracted optical fields that interfere, thereby producing a composite image with interference patterns superposed on it [Fig. 2.5(c)]. A variation of this process is *real-time AHI*, where the hologram [Fig. 2.6(a)] is recorded and then read out soon thereafter (or in "real-time") by the displaced object and the reference [Fig. 2.6(b)].[4] The recording can be done with either PTP films or PR LN crystals.[9–12]

The following simplified mathematical description is valid for both double-exposure and real-time AHI. Let the initial- and final-state object wave be denoted by

$$E_{O(1,2)}(x, y) = a_O(x, y)e^{-j\varphi_{O(1,2)}(x,y)}, \qquad (2.12)$$

where $\phi_{O2}(x, y) = \phi_{O1}(x, y) + \Delta\phi(x, y)$, and the amplitude is considered to be unchanged for small deformations. Thus, the intensity of the interference pattern resulting from the "interference" of the optical fields upon holographic reconstruction can be expressed as

$$I(x, y) = |E_{O1}(x, y) + E_{O2}(x, y)|^2 = 2|a_O|^2(1 + \cos(\Delta\phi)). \qquad (2.13)$$

The fringe pattern generally has the following form:

$$I(x, y) = I_0(x, y) + I_1(x, y) \cos[\Delta\phi(x, y)]. \qquad (2.14)$$

Let us define the path difference as $\delta = (\overline{SP_1} + \overline{P_1D}) - (\overline{SP_2} + \overline{P_2D}) = (\overrightarrow{SP_1}\vec{s}_1 + \overrightarrow{P_1D}\vec{o}_1) - (\overrightarrow{SP_2}\vec{s}_2 + \overrightarrow{P_2D}\vec{o}_2)$. If the source is far from the object and significantly larger than the small deformation, then $\vec{s}_1 \approx s_2 = \vec{s}$ and $\vec{o}_1 \approx \vec{o}_2 = \vec{o}$. Because $\vec{p} = (\overrightarrow{P_1D} - \overrightarrow{P_2D}) = (\overrightarrow{SP_2} - \overrightarrow{SP_1})$, then $\delta = (\vec{o} - \vec{s})\vec{d}$. If the sensitivity vector is $\vec{S} = (2\pi/\lambda)(\vec{o} - \vec{s})$, then the deformation is found to be $\Delta\phi = (2\pi/\lambda)\delta = \vec{d} \cdot \vec{S}$. Three interferograms of the same surface with linear, independent sensitivity vectors are necessary to determine the displacement. In practice, the total 3D displacement is not necessary—only the deformation perpendicular to the surface is needed. This *out-of-plane* deformation can be measured with a setup that has parallel illumination and observation directions; thus, $\vec{S} = (2\pi/\lambda)(0, 0, 2) = (4\pi/\lambda)$. In reflection mode, the deformation profile (perpendicular to the surface) is[4,5]

$$d_z(x, y) = [\lambda/(4\pi)]\Delta\phi(x, y). \qquad (2.15)$$

An example of AHI has been applied to determine the pitch, yaw, and roll angles of a model aircraft. Referring to the setup shown in Fig. 2.8, the recorded AH of the aircraft model on PTP is illuminated with light from the reference and the light scattered from the displaced/deformed object.[8] In one of the diffracted orders behind the AH, the "image" of the original object is recreated along with superposed interference fringes that contain the information about the displacement/deformation (see Fig. 2.9). The image, along with the superposed fringes, is recorded by a CCD camera and electronically analyzed by computational tools to quantify the displacement/deformation, as shown in Fig. 2.10.[8] Incidentally, higher diffracted orders are also present and can yield additional information about the object, as will be discussed in Section 2.6.

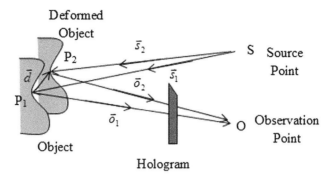

Figure 2.7   Schematic of deformation calculation. Reprinted from Kreis[4] with permission.

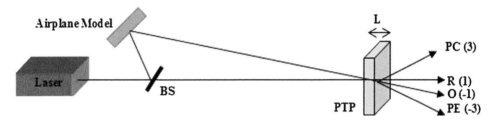

Figure 2.8   Experimental setup for holographic interferometry of a diffuse object (model aircraft) to determine the attitude deformation (pitch, yaw, and roll).

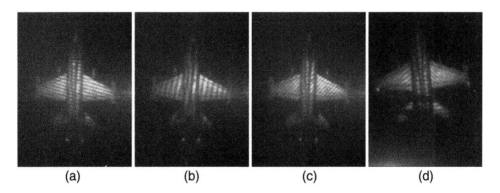

Figure 2.9   (a–c) Interferograms superposed on the image for different amounts of pitch and roll, respectively. (d) Interferogram superposed on the image for pitch and yaw.

2.4 Phase Unwrapping in 1D and 2D

Based on the earlier examples of object intensity profiles, it is clear that the phase (or depth information) can also be retrieved from the reconstruction of the hologram. However, numerically reconstructed phases can only vary by modulo 2π. Phase unwrapping is therefore used to decipher wrapped-phase maps computed by the arctan function which are in the interval between $-\pi$ and π in order to derive the absolute phase or, equivalently, the depth information. Also, for holographic interferometry, the interference phase

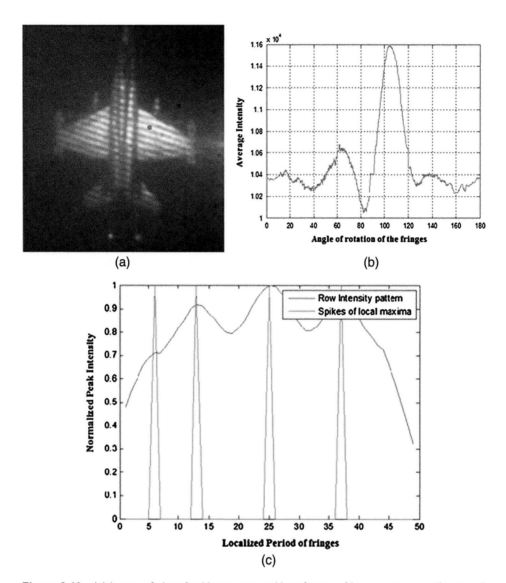

(a)   (b)

(c)

Figure 2.10   (a) Image of aircraft with superposed interference fringes corresponding to roll and pitch [from Fig. 2.9(a)]. (b) Plot of the averaged localized intensity around the red dot in (a) along the vertical direction versus the angle by which the picture in (a) is rotated. When the fringes become vertical for a particular rotation angle, the maximum intensity should be detected. The amount of imparted rotation should yield information about the original angle of the fringes. (c) Local period of the fringes around the red dot, found after appropriate rotation as described in (b). This information is used to determine the roll and pitch of the aircraft to be $\Delta\theta = 0.5188$ deg, $\Delta\psi = -2.0962$ deg.[8]

(which gives information about object deformation) is a wrapped-phase map, and thus phase unwrapping becomes indispensable in order to reconstruct the absolute phase (or deformation) unambiguously.

The MATLAB code used to create Fig. 2.11 is shown in Table 2.1. Figure 2.11(a) shows both the 1D wrapped phase that is between $-\pi$ and π

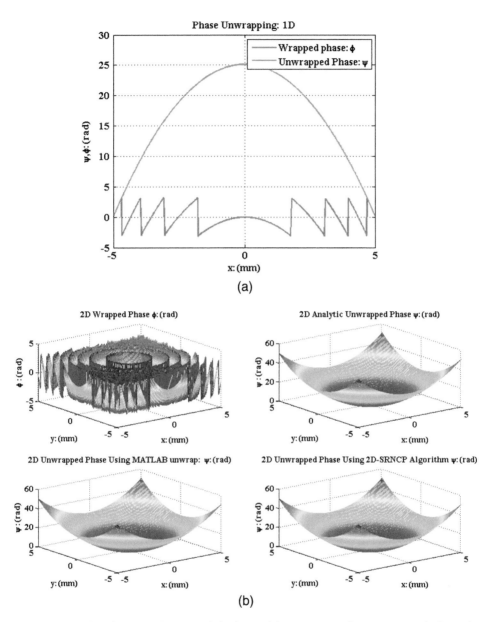

Figure 2.11 Interference phase modulo 2π and its corresponding unwrapped phase in both (a) 1D and (b) 2D: (upper left) wrapped phase, (upper right) analytic unwrapped phase, (lower left) 2D unwrapping using the 1D MATLAB unwrap function, and (lower right) 2D unwrapping using the "sorting by reliability, following a non-continuous path" (2D-SRNCP) method. Reprinted from Arevalillo Herráez et al.[13] with permission.

and the unwrapped phase using various unwrapping schemes. The upper-left image in Fig. 2.11(b) illustrates a 2D wrapped phase that is between $-\pi$ and π. In this example, the analytical phase is known beforehand, as shown in the upper right of Fig. 2.11(b). The 2D phase unwrapping is a more difficult problem to solve than its 1D counterpart, especially when noise and

Table 2.1   MATLAB code "unwrapping1D_and2D.m" for phase unwrapping (see Fig. 2.11).

```
1   %%1D phase unwrapping: method 1
2   clc
3   clear all
4   x=-5:.01:5;
5   z=exp(-j*x.^2);            %1D parabolic phase example
6   phase2=phase(z);,          %Use MATLAB phase function to
7                              %do phase unwrapping
8   phase1=angle(z);
9   figure
10  plot(x,phase1,'r',x,phase2,'g')
11  grid on
12  title('Phase Unwrapping: 1D')
13  legend('Wrapped phase:\phi','Unwrapped Phase:\psi')
14  ylabel('\psi,\phi:(rad)')
15  xlabel('x:(mm)')
16  %%1D phase unwrapping: method 2
17  clc
18  clear all
19  x=-5:.01:5;
20  z=exp(-j*x.^2);            %1D parabolic phase example
21  phase1=angle(z);
22  phase2=unwrap(phase1);     %Use MATLAB unwrap function to
23                             %do phase unwrapping
24  figure
25  plot(x,phase1,'r',x,phase2,'g')
26  grid on
27  title('Phase Unwrapping: 1D')
28  legend('Wrapped phase:\phi','Unwrapped Phase:\psi')
29  ylabel('\psi,\phi:(rad)')
30  xlabel('x:(mm)')
31  %%----Example showing the difference between a wrapped
32  %and unwrapped 2D image
33  clc
34  clear all
35  x=-5:.05:5;
36  [X,Y]=meshgrid(x,x);
37                             %Original phase
38  phase1=(X.^2+Y.^2);        %2D parabolic phase example
39  Z=exp(j*phase1);
40  phase2=angle(Z);
41  figure
42  subplot(2,2,1)
43  mesh(X,Y,phase2);
44  grid on
45  title('2D Wrapped Phase \phi:(rad)')
46  ylabel('y:(mm)')
47  xlabel('x:(mm)')
48  zlabel('\phi:(rad)')
49  subplot(2,2,2)
50  mesh(X,Y,phase1);
51  grid on
52  title('2D Analytic Unwrapped Phase \psi:(rad)')
53  ylabel('y:(mm)')
54  xlabel('x:(mm)')
```

(continued)

Table 2.1   *(Continued)*

```
55   zlabel('\psi: (rad)')
56   %Unwrapped phase using MATLAB unwrap function applied
57   %sequentially
58   phase2_col=unwrap(phase2,[],1);   %Unwrapping columns
59   phase3=unwrap(phase2_col,[],2);   %Unwrapping rows
60   min_phase3=min(phase3(:));
61   subplot(2,2,3)
62   mesh(X,Y,phase3-min_phase3);
63   grid on
64   title({ '2D Unwrapped Phase Using',...
65   'MATLAB unwrap: \psi:(rad)'})
66   ylabel('y:(mm)')
67   xlabel('x:(mm)')
68   zlabel('\psi: (rad)')
69   %%%-Unwrapping using the 2D_SRNCP algorithm:
70   %http://www.ljmu.ac.uk/GERI/90225.htm
71   %Instructions:
72   %Install the Microsoft Windows SDK 7.1
73   %mex -setup
74   %Follow instructions: type Y then 1 then Y.
75   %Call the 2D phase unwrapper from C language.
76   %To compile the C code: in MATLAB command window, you
77   %have to run
78   mex Miguel_2D_unwrapper.cpp
79   %This file has to be in the same directory as the
80   %script to work.
81   WrappedPhase=phase2;         %Read the wrapped phase
82   mex Miguel_2D_unwrapper.cpp
83   %The wrapped phase should have the single (float in C)
84   %data type
85   WrappedPhase = single(WrappedPhase);
86   UnwrappedPhase = Miguel_2D_unwrapper(WrappedPhase);
87   UnwrappedPhase=double(UnwrappedPhase);
88   min_UnwrappedPhase=min(UnwrappedPhase(:));
89   subplot(2,2,4)
90   mesh(X,Y,UnwrappedPhase-min_UnwrappedPhase);
91   grid on
92   title('2D Unwrapped Phase Using 2D-SRNCP \psi:(rad)')
93   ylabel('y:(mm)')
94   xlabel('x:(mm)')
95   zlabel('\psi: (rad)')
```

```
96   function PHI=phase(G)
97   %PHASE Computes the phase of a complex vector
98   %PHI=phase(G)
99   %G is a complex-valued row vector, and PHI is returned
100  %as its phase (in radians), with an effort made to
101  %keep it continuous over the pi-borders.
102  %L. Ljung 10-2-86
103  %Copyright 1986-2004 The MathWorks, Inc.
104  %$Revision: 1.5.4.2 $ $Date: 2004/07/31 23:24:49
105  %PHI = unwrap(angle(G));
106  [nr,nc] = size(G);
107  if min(nr,nc) > 1
```

(continued)

Table 2.1 (*Continued*)

```
108   error(sprintf([ 'PHASE applies only to row or' ...
109   'column vectors.' ...
110   '\nFor matrices you have to decide along' ...
111   'which dimension the' ...
112   '\nphase should be continuous.']))
113   end
114   if nr>nc
115   G = G.' ;
116   end
117   PHI=atan2(imag(G),real(G));
118   N=length(PHI);
119   DF=PHI(1:N-1)-PHI(2:N);
120   I=find(abs(DF)>3.5);
121   for i=I
122   if i~=0,
123   PHI=PHI+2*pi*sign(DF(i))*[zeros(1,i) ones(1,N-i)];
124   end
125   end
126   if nr>nc
127   PHI = PHI.' ;
128   end
```

discontinuities plague the phase image. For a noiseless wrapped-phase image, the MATLAB 1D built-in function can be used successively on the columns and rows of a wrapped-phase image to unwrap the phase, as shown in the lower left of Fig. 2.11(b). The lower-right image in Fig. 2.11(b) shows the unwrapped phase with the "sorting by reliability, following a noncontinuous path" (2D-SRNCP) method.[13] This section illustrates the use of a class of unwrapping techniques based on minimum-norm methods (least-square phase unwrapping).

For phase unwrapping, there are many widely used techniques.[14] Most of these algorithms begin with the measured gradient of the phase field, which is subsequently integrated to recover the unwrapped phases. The earliest approaches in interferometric applications incorporated residue identification and cuts to limit the possible integration paths,[15] whereas a second class of approaches using least-squares techniques was developed in the 1990s.[14] The approaches that rely on the residue-cut algorithms are quite accurate but do not produce good estimates in regions of moderate phase noise.[16] The least-squares methods yield complete coverage but at the cost of distortion in the recovered phase field. Another synthesis approach, combining the two approaches, offers greater spatial coverage with less distortion in many instances.[16]

This section discusses the least-squares technique because it is the one used throughout this chapter. In least-squares methods, the vector gradient of the phase field is determined and then integrated, subject to the constraint of a smooth solution as determined by weighted or unweighted least-squared-difference criteria, and finally solved using the direct cosine transform (DCT).

Consider a sampled wrapped-phase function $\phi(i,j)$, evaluated at discrete points i, j corresponding to the row and column locations, respectively, of a 2D data matrix. The objective is to determine a smooth, unwrapped-phase function $\psi(i,j)$ that minimizes the difference between the gradients calculated from the wrapped phase and the presumed smooth, unwrapped phase. It has been shown that these two may be related by a matrix-vector equation[16]

$$\mathbf{S} = \mathbf{P}\psi + n, \tag{2.16}$$

where $\mathbf{S}$ is derived from the measured row and column phase differences of ϕ, $\mathbf{P}$ is a matrix containing 1s, -1s, and 0s describing row- and column-differencing operations, ψ is the unwrapped-phase field, and n is a vector representing measurement noise. The least-squares solution is

$$\psi = (\mathbf{P}^{\mathrm{T}}\mathbf{P})^{-1}\mathbf{P}^{\mathrm{T}}\mathbf{S}, \tag{2.17}$$

where T stands for the transpose operator. The solution $\psi_{i,j}$ that minimizes the following function:

$$\arg \min_{\psi(i,j)} \left\{ \sum_{i=0}^{M-2} \sum_{j=0}^{N-1} \left[\underbrace{(\psi(i+1,j) - \psi(i,j))}_{\text{unwrapped phase}} - \underbrace{(\phi(i+1,j) - \phi(i,j))}_{\text{wrapped phase }(-\pi, \pi)} \right]^2 \right.$$

$$\left. + \sum_{i=0}^{M-1} \sum_{j=0}^{N-2} \left[\underbrace{(\psi(i,j+1) - \psi(i,j))}_{\text{unwrapped phase}} - \underbrace{(\phi(i,j+1) - \phi(i,j))}_{\text{wrapped phase }(-\pi, \pi)} \right]^2 \right\},$$

is the least-squares solution. The least-squared-error solution is obtained by differentiating Eq. (2.18) with respect to $\psi(i,j)$ and setting the result equal to zero such that[14]

$$[\psi(i+1,j) + \psi(i-1,j) + \psi(i,j+1) + \psi(i,j-1) - 4\psi_{i,j}]$$

$$= [(\phi(i+1,j) - \phi(i,j)) - (\phi(i,j) - \phi(i-1,j))]$$

$$+ [(\phi(i,j+1) - \phi(i,j)) - (\phi(i,j) - \phi(i,j-1))]. \tag{2.19}$$

Equation (2.19) gives the relationship between the wrapped phase differences and the unwrapped phase values in the least-squares-error sense. It can be rewritten as

$$[\psi(i+1,j) - 2\psi_{i,j} + \psi(i-1,j)] + [\psi(i,j+1) - 2\psi_{i,j} + \psi(i,j-1)] = \rho(i,j), \tag{2.20a}$$

where

$$\rho(i,j) = [(\phi(i+1,j) - \phi(i,j)) - (\phi(i,j) - \phi(i-1,j))]$$

$$+ [(\phi(i,j+1) - \phi(i,j)) - (\phi(i,j) - \phi(i,j-1))]. \tag{2.20b}$$

Equation (2.20a) is a discrete form of the Poisson equation and can be written as

$$\frac{\partial^2}{\partial x^2}\psi(x,y) + \frac{\partial^2}{\partial y^2}\psi(x,y) = \rho(x,y).\tag{2.21}$$

Let us define

$$\Delta^x_{i,j} = \begin{cases} (\phi(i+1,j) - \phi(i,j)), & i=0,\dots,M-2, j=0,\dots,N-1 \\ 0 & \text{otherwise,} \end{cases}\tag{2.22a}$$

$$\Delta^y_{i,j} = \begin{cases} (\phi(i,j+1) - \phi(i,j)), & i=0,\dots,M-1, j=0,\dots,N-2 \\ 0 & \text{otherwise.} \end{cases}\tag{2.22b}$$

Equation (2.21) must be solved with the following boundary conditions:

$$\Delta^x_{-1,j} = \Delta^x_{M-1,j} = 0, \quad j=0,\dots,N-1,$$
$$\Delta^y_{i,-1} = \Delta^y_{i,N-1} = 0, \quad i=0,\dots,M-1.\tag{2.23}$$

Equation (2.20a) can be solved using the discrete cosine transform (DCT).[14] Let us define the DCT pair as

$$C_{m,n} = \begin{cases} \sum_{i=0}^{M-1}\sum_{j=0}^{N-1} 4x_{i,j} \cos\left[\frac{\pi}{2M}m(2i+1)\right]\cos\left[\frac{\pi}{2N}n(2j+1)\right] & \begin{array}{l} 0 \le m \le M-1 \\ 0 \le n \le N-1 \end{array} \\ 0 & \text{otherwise,} \end{cases}$$

$$\tag{2.24a}$$

$$x_{i,j} = \begin{cases} \frac{1}{MN}\sum_{m=0}^{M-1}\sum_{n=0}^{N-1} w_1(m)w_2(n)C_{m,n} & \begin{array}{l} 0 \le i \le M-1 \\ 0 \le j \le N-1 \end{array} \\ \times \cos\left[\frac{\pi}{2M}m(2i+1)\right]\cos\left[\frac{\pi}{2N}n(2j+1)\right] \\ 0 & \text{otherwise,} \end{cases}\tag{2.24b}$$

where

$$w_1(m) = \begin{cases} 1/2, & m=0 \\ 1 & 1 \le m \le M-1, \end{cases} \qquad w_2(m) = \begin{cases} 1/2, & n=0 \\ 1 & 1 \le n \le N-1. \end{cases}$$

Expressing the solution of Eq. (2.20) in the form expressed in Eq. (2.24) produces

$$\psi_{i,j} = \frac{1}{MN}\sum_{m=0}^{M-1}\sum_{n=0}^{N-1} w_1(m)w_2(n)\hat\psi_{m,n} \cos\left[\frac{\pi}{2M}m(2i+1)\right]\cos\left[\frac{\pi}{2N}n(2j+1)\right].$$

$$\tag{2.25}$$

Substituting Eq. (2.25) in Eq. (2.20a) and performing some algebra arrives at the exact solution in the DCT domain:

$$\hat{\psi}_{i,j} = \frac{\hat{\rho}_{i,j}}{2\left(\cos\left(\frac{\pi i}{M}\right) + \cos\left(\frac{\pi j}{N}\right) - 2\right)}. \qquad (2.26)$$

The unwrapped phase $\psi_{i,j}$ is obtained by performing the inverse discrete transform (IDCT) of Eq. (2.26). The algorithm works as follows:

1. Perform the 2D forward DCT [using Eq. (2.24a)] of the array of values $\rho_{i,j}$, computed by Eq. (2.20b), to yield the 2D DCT values $\hat{\rho}_{i,j}$.
2. Modify the values $\hat{\rho}_{i,j}$ according to Eq. (2.26) to obtain $\hat{\psi}_{i,j}$.
3. Perform the 2D inverse DCT [using Eq. (2.24b)] of $\hat{\psi}_{i,j}$ to obtain the least-squares unwrapped-phase values $\psi_{i,j}$.

A relatively new phase-unwrapping algorithm using a max-flow/min-cut technique based on energy minimization has been proposed, with accompanying MATLAB software, by J. Bioucas-Dias and G. Valadão.[17] The performance of the phase-unwrapping max-flow/min-cut algorithm (PUMA) is comparable to other state-of-the-art algorithms, and it performs well even in the presence of noise (in-depth consideration of this technique is beyond the scope of this book). The included CD contains examples of PUMA unwrapping in the "PUMA demos" directory, included with the Chapter 2 code. As an example for how to use the software, simply refer to the code in Table 2.2. For the 2D unwrapping that employs the 2D-SRNCP method,[13] also refer to the code (subsection) in Table 2.2 and the corresponding result shown in Fig. 2.12(d). Note that the built-in MATLAB unwrap function does not always yield correct results for 2D arrays, as demonstrated by the introduction of noise [Figure 2.12(b)] in the phase reconstruction. The PUMA result is shown in Fig. 2.12(c). Finally, results for the branch-cut (BC)[15] and DCT methods[14] explained in this section are shown in Figs. 2.12(e) and (f), respectively. To use BC and DCT, simply refer to the code in Table 2.2 and the related MATLAB functions included in the CD.

2.5 Application of Phase Unwrapping in Holographic Interferometry

This section discusses a typical application of real-time AHI in nondestructive testing, how to decipher the fringes using frequency techniques, and how to unwrap the phase using the techniques discussed in the previous section. In this method, the initial state of the object is holographically recorded, as shown in Fig. 2.13. For the second state, a deformation is introduced and diffraction is observed with both recording beams present (with possible attenuation to avoid rapid erasure). While recording the grating in a PR LN

Table 2.2 MATLAB code "PUMADemo_SRNCP_BC_DCT.m" for phase unwrapping (see Fig. 2.12).

```
1    %PUMA (Phase Unwrapping via MAxflow)
2    %demo1 - High-phase-rate Gaussian surface
3    %For further details about using PUMA, please see
4    %puma_ho.m file.
5    %See also: J. Bioucas-Dias and G. Valadão, "Phase
6    %Unwrapping via Graph Cuts,"
7    %IEEE Transactions Image Processing (2007).
8    %Data generation:
9    clc
10   clear all
11   M=100;
12   N=100;
13   z1=gaussele(M,N,14*pi,10,15);
14   %Generate insar pair according to model (2002, TIP,
15   %vol. 11, no 4.)
16   co=0.95;         %Noise (coherence: co = 1 => no noise;
17                    %co = 0 => only noise (no signal))
18   [x1 x2] = insarpair_v2(ones(M), co*ones(M), z1, 0);
19   %Compute interferogram
20   wrapped_phase = angle(x1.*conj(x2));
21   xx = 1:100;
22   yy = xx;
23   hold off
24   colormap(gray);
25   imagesc(xx,yy,wrapped_phase)
26   title('Wrapped Phase');
27   drawnow;
28   %%Unwrapped phase using MATLAB unwrap function applied
29   %sequentially
30   phase2_col=unwrap(wrapped_phase,[],1);    %Unwrapping
31                                             %columns
32   UnwrappedPhase=unwrap(phase2_col,[],2);   %Unwrapping rows
33   figure;
34   surfl(UnwrappedPhase);shading interp; colormap(gray);
35   title('Matlab unwrap function solution');
36   %-----------Input the phase of your image here--------
37   %%PUMA processing
38   p=2;                      %Clique potential exponent
39   figure;
40   [UnwrappedPhase,iter,erglist] =puma_ho(wrapped_phase,p);
41   figure;
42   surfl(UnwrappedPhase);shading interp; colormap(gray);
43   title('Puma solution');
44   %-----------Input the phase of your image here------
45   %%%—Unwrapping using the 2D_SRNCP algorithm:
46   %http://www.ljmu.ac.uk/GERI/90225.htm
47   %Instructions:
48   %Install the Microsoft Windows SDK 7.1.
49   mex -setup
50   %Follow instructions: type Y then 1 then Y.
51   %Call the 2D phase unwrapper from C language.
52   %To compile the C code: in MATLAB command window, you
```

(*continued*)

Table 2.2   (*Continued*)

```
53  %have to run
54  %mex Miguel_2D_unwrapper.cpp
55  %This file has to be in the same directory as the
56  %script to work.
57  mex Miguel_2D_unwrapper.cpp
58  %The wrapped phase should have the single (float in C)
59  %data type
60  WrappedPhase = single(wrapped_phase);
61  UnwrappedPhase = Miguel_2D_unwrapper(WrappedPhase);
62  UnwrappedPhase=double(UnwrappedPhase);
63  figure(2)
64  colormap(gray(256))
65  surfl(UnwrappedPhase);
66  shading interp; colormap(gray);
67  title('2D-SRNCP solution');
68  %%%- Unwrapping using the branch-cut algorithm:
69  %Instructions for branch-cut method:
70  %Install the Microsoft Windows SDK 7.1.
71  mex -setup
72  %Follow instructions: type Y then 1 then Y.
73  %Call the 2D phase unwrapper from C language.
74  %For the code to work, the directory Branch_cut has to
75  %be in the MATLAB path.
76  clc
77  clear all
78  M=100;
79  N=100;
80  z1=gaussele(M,N,14*pi,10,15);
81  %Generate insar pair according to model (2002, TIP,
82  %vol. 11, no 4.)
83  co=0.95;      %Noise (coherence: co = 1 => no noise;
84                %co = 0 => only noise (no signal))
85  [x1 x2] = insarpair_v2(ones(M), co*ones(M), z1, 0);
86  %Compute interferogram
87  wrapped_phase = angle(x1.*conj(x2));
88  xx = 1:M;
89  yy = xx;
90  figure
91  colormap(gray);
92  imagesc(xx,yy,wrapped_phase)
93  title('Interferogram');
94  drawnow;
95  UnwrappedPhase=...
96  double(my_phase_unwrap_BC(wrapped_phase,500));
97  figure;
98  surfl(UnwrappedPhase);shading interp; colormap(gray);
99  title('Matlab Branch-Cut Solution');
100 %%%-Unwrapping using the DCT algorithm:
101 %Instructions for DCT method:
102 %Install the Microsoft Windows SDK 7.1.
103 mex -setup
104 %Follow instructions: type Y then 1 then Y.
105 %Call the 2D phase unwrapper from C language.
```

(*continued*)

Table 2.2 (*Continued*)

```
106  %For the code to work, the directory DCT has to be in
107  %the MATLAB path.
108  %Note that M and N has to be 2^n+1 for this software
109  %to work.
110  clc
111  clear all
112  %The input has to be 2^n+1 for this algorithm to
113  %work
114  n=7;
115  M=2^n+1;              %This software only works for
116                        %M=2^n+1, where n is an integer
117  N=2^n+1;              %This software only works for
118                        %N=2^n+1, where n is an integer
119  z1=gaussele(M,N,14*pi,10,15);
120  %Generate insar pair according to model (2002, TIP,
121  %vol. 11, no 4.)
122  co=0.95;        %Noise (coherence: co = 1 => no noise;
123                  %co = 0 => only noise (no signal))
124  [x1 x2] = insarpair_v2(ones(M), co*ones(M), z1, 0);
125  %Compute interferogram
126  wrapped_phase = angle(x1.*conj(x2));
127  xx = 1:M;
128  yy = xx;
129  figure
130  colormap(gray);
131  imagesc(xx,yy,wrapped_phase)
132  title('Interferogram');
133  drawnow;
134  UnwrappedPhase= ...
135  double(my_phase_unwrap_DCT(wrapped_phase,500));
136  UnwrappedPhase2=UnwrappedPhase(floor(M/2)-50:...
137  floor(M/2)+49, floor(M/2)-50:floor(M/2)+49);
138  figure;
139  surfl(UnwrappedPhase2);shading interp;
140  colormap(gray);
141  title('MATLAB DCT solution');
```

crystal, for example, photoinduced changes of the refractive index are developed in real time, and recording beams (amplitudes, phases, and polarizations) may also be changed by self-diffraction. Another laser source is used to heat an object (e.g., a CD-ROM) [Fig. 2.13(a)]. Figure 2.13(b) is the lab setup. In the experiment we show that we can record a hologram and reconstruct the "fast" 3D deformation due to the heating effect from the focused (blue) laser source on the CD-ROM target. Figure 2.14(a) shows the reconstructed hologram after heating for a predetermined time with a focused laser source. Figure 2.14(b) shows a cropped region of interest of (a). The advantage of the phase-conjugated image over the Bragg "image" is that the latter is a propagated version of the object and can result in the object's diffraction pattern, especially if the object size is small. Furthermore, the phase-conjugated image offers the opportunity to monitor different

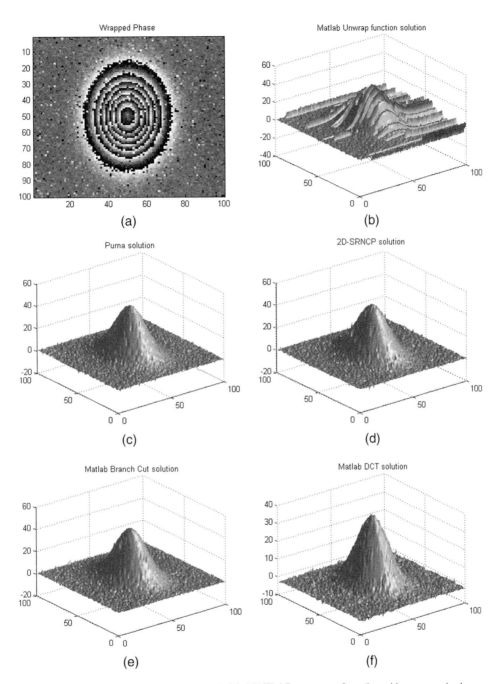

Figure 2.12 (a) Wrapped phase and (b) MATLAB unwrap function. Unwrapped phase using: (c) PUMA, (d) 2D_SRNCP, (e) branch-cut, and (f) DCT techniques.

longitudinal planes in the object because these planes image at different phase-conjugate image planes. Although this example only used the -1 order for our analysis, other orders, as explained later, can also be used to decipher object deformation information.

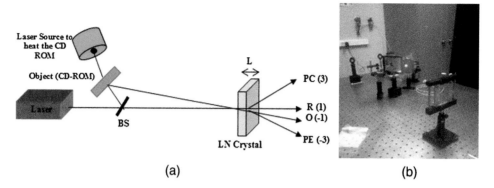

Figure 2.13 (a) Schematic of the dynamic hologram recording in LN with object O (−1) and reference R (+1) waves, along with generation of the first non-Bragg orders, e.g., phase-conjugate PC (+3) and phase-enhanced PE (−3). (b) Lab setup.

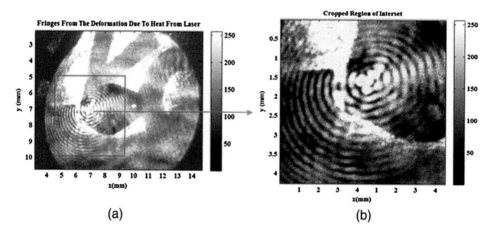

Figure 2.14 (a) Fringes resulting from reading out the stored hologram of the original object (CD-ROM) in LN by the reference and light from the deformed object after heating with a focused laser source; (b) a cropped region of interest of (a), where the pixel size of the camera is 5 μm.

The measured interferometric intensity distribution $I(x, y)$ can be written as

$$I(x,y) = I_0(x,y) + I_1(x,y)\cos[\phi(x,y)], \qquad (2.27)$$

where $I_0(x,y)$ is the background variation, and $I_1(x,y)$ is related to the local contrast of the pattern. In other words, $I_0(x,y)$ carries the additive and $I_1(x,y)$ carries the multiplicative disturbances, respectively. $\phi(x,y)$ is the interference phase to be computed from $I(x,y)$. Equation (2.27) can be written as[18]

$$I(x,y) = I_0(x,y) + I_{1c}(x,y) + I_{1c}^*(x,y), \qquad (2.28)$$

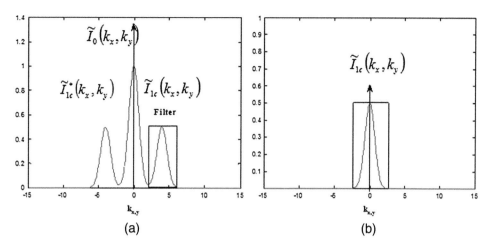

Figure 2.15 Schematic of the process (a) before and (b) after filtering, and shifting to the origin.

where $I_{1c}(x,y) = (I_1(x,y)/2)\exp[j\phi(x,y)]$. The Fourier transform of Eq. (2.28) produces

$$\tilde{I}(k_x,k_y) = \tilde{I}_0(k_x,k_y) + \tilde{I}_{1c}(k_x,k_y) + \tilde{I}_{1c}^*(k_x,k_y). \qquad (2.29)$$

Assuming that the background intensity $I_0(x,y)$ is slowly varying compared to the fringe spacing, the amplitude spectrum $\tilde{I}(k_x,k_y)$ will be a trimodal function with $\tilde{I}_0(k_x,k_y)$ broadening the zero peak and $\tilde{I}_{1c}$, $\tilde{I}_{1c}^*$ placed symmetrically with respect to the origin. The next step is to get rid of the DC term and one of the sidebands $\tilde{I}_{1c}$, $\tilde{I}_{1c}^*$. Therefore, the spectrum is no longer symmetric, and the space-domain function is no longer real but complex. Equation (2.29) thus becomes

$$\tilde{I}'(k_x,k_y) = \tilde{I}_{1c}(k_x,k_y), \qquad (2.30)$$

which is the new filtered spectrum. The inverse Fourier transform is performed on Eq. (2.30) to obtain

$$I'(x,y) = I_{1c}(x,y) = \frac{1}{2}I_1(x,y)\exp[j\phi(x,y)]. \qquad (2.31)$$

Figures 2.15(a) and (b) illustrate the process.

Figure 2.16(a) is the 2D FFT of Fig. 2.14(b). Figs. 2.16(b) and (c) are the filtered versions, as suggested by Eq. (2.31). The following operation is performed to find the wrapped phase:

$$\phi(x,y) = \arctan\left(\frac{\text{Im}[I_{1c}(x,y)]}{\text{Re}[I_{1c}(x,y)]}\right). \qquad (2.32)$$

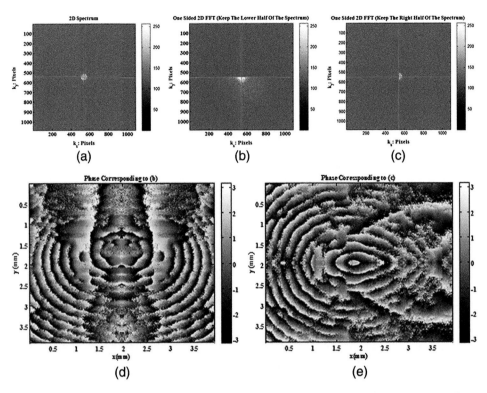

Figure 2.16 (a) The absolute value of the 2D FFT of Fig. 2.15; (b)–(c) filtered versions [see Eq. (2.30)]; (d)–(e) are the wrapped, reconstructed phase diagrams (pixel size of the camera is 5 μm).

Figures 2.16(d) and (e) are the wrapped, reconstructed phase diagrams, as suggested by Eq. (2.32). The unwrapped 3D deformation due to heating of the target is shown in Fig. 2.17.

An alternative formulation of the previous technique for 1D signals works as follows: define a 1D spatial function $I_+(k_x)$ to be

$$I_+(x) \xrightarrow{\mathfrak{I}} \tilde{I}_+(k_x) = \tilde{I}(k_x)U(k_x) \equiv \frac{1}{2}\tilde{I}(k_x)[1 + \text{sgn}(k_x)]$$

$$= \frac{1}{2}\tilde{I}(k_x) + \frac{1}{2}\tilde{I}(k_x)\,\text{sgn}(k_x), \tag{2.33}$$

where $I_+(k_x)$ is the upper side band of the Fourier transform of $I(x)$ and is the Fourier transform of $I_+(k_x)$. Let us define

$$I_+(x) = \frac{1}{2}[I(x) + jI_h(x)]; \tag{2.34}$$

a comparison with Eq. (2.33) produces

$$\frac{1}{2}jI_h(x) \xrightarrow{\mathfrak{I}} \frac{1}{2}j\tilde{I}_h(k_x) = \frac{1}{2}\tilde{I}(k_x)\text{sgn}(k_x). \tag{2.35}$$

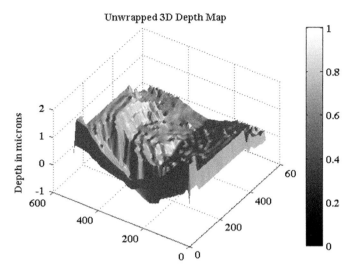

Figure 2.17   3D deformation of the crater formed due to heating.

If a linear system with an input $I(x)$ and a spatial impulse response is defined as

$$h(x) = \frac{1}{\pi x} \xrightarrow{\mathfrak{F}} H(k_x) = -j\,\mathrm{sgn}(k_x),\qquad(2.36)$$

then the output $I_h(x)$ is the Hilbert transform of $I(x)$:

$$I_h(x) = I(x) * \frac{1}{\pi x} = \frac{1}{\pi} \int_{-\infty}^{\infty} \frac{I(\alpha)}{x - \alpha}\, d\alpha \xrightarrow{\mathfrak{F}} \tilde{I}(k_x)[-j\,\mathrm{sgn}(k_x)] = \tilde{I}_h(k_x).\quad(2.37)$$

Therefore, $I(x)$ and $I_h(x)$ are Hilbert transform pairs. The transfer function of the system can be defined as

$$H(k_x) = -j\,\mathrm{sgn}(k_x) = \begin{cases} -j = 1e^{-j\pi/2} & k_x > 0, \\ j = 1e^{j\pi/2} & k_x < 0. \end{cases}\qquad(2.38)$$

The transfer function of a Hilbert transform system is shown in Fig. 2.18. A Hilbert transform is an ideal phase shifter that shifts the phase of every spectral component by $\pm\pi/2$. Thus, an equivalent procedure to the filter method

(a) eliminates the DC term,
(b) computes the Hilbert transform $I_h(x)$ of $I(x)$,
(c) computes $I_+(x) = \frac{1}{2}[I(x) + jI_h(x)]$ according to Eq. (2.34), and
(d) computes the wrapped phase $\phi(x, y) = \arctan[I_h(x)/I(x)]$.

A similar procedure employing Hilbert transforms to determine phase images of highly transparent biological samples (e.g., blood cells) using off-axis holography has been introduced by Ikeda et al.[18] Finally, the Hilbert transform technique for 2D phase demodulation will be discussed in Chapter 3. Table 2.3 illustrates the method used in this section.

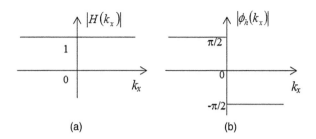

Figure 2.18 Hilbert transform transfer function.

Table 2.3 MATLAB code "chap2_2_5.m" for phase unwrapping (see Figs. 2.16 and 2.17).

```
1   %%This program takes an interferogram that doesn't have
2   %a carrier
3   %and tries to decipher the phase with bandpass filters.
4   clc
5   clear all
6   close all
7   lambda=0.514;                    %In microns
8   load IMG_crop.mat                %Input interferogram
9   colormap(gray(256));
10  imagesc(I)
11  %Fourier transform domain
12  I1F=(fft2(fftshift(I)));
13  I1F_s=fftshift(I1F);
14  abs_I1F_s=abs(I1F_s).^2;
15  %Use bandpass filters in the x and y directions (as
16  %explained in text
17  figure
18  mylogim2(abs_I1F_s,8)        %This is used for contrast
19                               %enhancement only
20  [Ro,Co]=size(I1F);
21  I1F_c1=zeros(Ro,Co);
22  line([ceil(Co/2)+1 ceil(Co/2)+1],[0 ceil(Ro)])
23  line([0 ceil(Co)],[ceil(Ro/2)+1 ceil(Ro/2)+1])
24  Dim=5;
25  I1F_c1(1:end,round(Co/2)+Dim:end)=...
26  I1F_s(1:end,round(Co/2)+Dim:end);
27  abs_I1F_c1=abs(I1F_c1).^2;
28  figure
29  mylogim2(abs_I1F_c1,8)
30  line([ceil(Co/2)+1 ceil(Co/2)+1],[0 ceil(Ro)])
31  line([0 ceil(Co)],[ceil(Ro/2)+1 ceil(Ro/2)+1])
32  figure
33  mylogim2(abs_I1F_s,8)
34  I1F_c2=zeros(Ro,Co);
35  line([ceil(Co/2)+1 ceil(Co/2)+1],[0 ceil(Ro)])
36  line([0 ceil(Co)],[ceil(Ro/2)+1 ceil(Ro/2)+1])
37  I1F_c2(round(Ro/2)+Dim:end,1:end)=...
38  I1F_s(round(Ro/2)+Dim:end,1:end);
39  figure
40  mylogim2(abs_I1F_c2,8)
41  [Ro,Co]=size(abs_I1F_c2);
```

(*continued*)

Table 2.3 (*Continued*)

```
42  line([ceil(Co/2)+1 ceil(Co/2)+1],[0 ceil(Ro)])
43  line([0 ceil(Co)],[ceil(Ro/2)+1 ceil(Ro/2)+1])
44  %Calculate the two wrapped phases
45  I21=fftshift(ifft2(fftshift(I1F_c1)));
46  [ro,co]=size(I21);
47  I2_phase1=atan2(imag(I21),real(I21));
48  I22=fftshift(ifft2(fftshift(I1F_c2)));
49  I2_phase2=atan2(imag(I22),real(I22));
50  if mod(Co,2)==0
51  rr1=round(Co/2):-1:1;
52  rr2=round(Co/2)+1:Co;
53  else
54  rr1=round(Co/2):-1:1;
55  rr2=round(Co/2):Co;
56  end
57  I2_phase1(:,rr2)=I2_phase1(:,rr1);
58  if mod(Co,2)==0
59  rr1=round(Ro/2):-1:1;
60  rr2=round(Ro/2)+1:Ro;
61  else
62  rr1=round(Ro/2):-1:1;
63  rr2=round(Ro/2):Ro;
64  end
65  I2_phase2(rr1,:)=I2_phase2(rr2,:);
66  figure
67  imagesc(I2_phase1)
68  figure
69  imagesc(I2_phase2)
70  %%
71  %%%—Unwrapping using the 2D_SRNCP algorithm:
72  %http://www.ljmu.ac.uk/GERI/90225.htm
73  %Call the 2D phase unwrapper from C language.
74  %To compile the C code: in MATLAB command window, type
75  %Miguel_2D_unwrapper.cpp. The file has to be in the same
76  %directory as the script to work.
77  WrappedPhase=I2_phase1;
78  mex Miguel_2D_unwrapper.cpp
79  %The wrapped phase should have the single (float in C)
80  %data type
81  WrappedPhase = single(WrappedPhase);
82  UnwrappedPhase = Miguel_2D_unwrapper(WrappedPhase);
83  UnwrappedPhase=double(UnwrappedPhase);
84  h = fspecial('average',15);
85  eta1 = imfilter(UnwrappedPhase,h);
86  figure;
87  surfl(eta1/(4*pi)*lambda);shading interp;
88  colormap(gray);
89  title('Unwrapped 3D Depth Map');
90  zlabel('Depth in microns')
91  WrappedPhase=I2_phase2;
92  mex Miguel_2D_unwrapper.cpp
93  %The wrapped phase should have the single (float in C)
94  %data type
95  WrappedPhase = single(WrappedPhase);
```

(*continued*)

Table 2.3 *(Continued)*

```
96   UnwrappedPhase = Miguel_2D_unwrapper(WrappedPhase);
97   UnwrappedPhase=double(UnwrappedPhase);
98   h = fspecial('average',15);
99   eta2 = imfilter(UnwrappedPhase,h);
100  figure;
101  surfl(eta2/(4*pi)*lambda);shading interp;
102  colormap(gray);
103  title('Unwrapped 3D Depth Map');
104  zlabel('Depth in microns')
```

2.6 Phase-Shifting Holography through Dynamic Holography and Self-Diffraction

Phase-shifting holography is another technique used to visualize 3D objects or measure object deformation through multiple recordings of the interference patterns between the object beam and the reference beam. In each recording, the reference beam is shifted with respect to the object beam using several techniques that will be discussed in detail in Chapter 5. A CCD is usually used in phase-shifting holography instead of a PTP or PR crystal to sequentially record the different interference patterns and subsequently deduce the phase of the object. The traditional phase-shifting holography setup is shown in Fig. 2.19.

In the case of an off-axis hologram, the angle between the object wave and the reference wave causes additional fringes due to what is called the "carrier" spatial frequency (discussed in Chapter 3). For inline holograms, the Fresnel transformation provides superposed real and virtual images (as well as the DC term), and filtering is often required to separate them. A way to find the Fresnel-propagated complex object wave on the plane of the recording medium (and thereby reconstruct the complex object) without the complications of the carrier frequency (for off-axis holograms) and superposition of real and virtual images (for inline holograms) is to sequentially record multiple intensity patterns by changing the phase of the reference wave by a predetermined quantity, as in phase-shifting holography (PSH). The minimum number of required phase shifts is typically three, whereas the mathematical relationship for the phase resulting from four predetermined

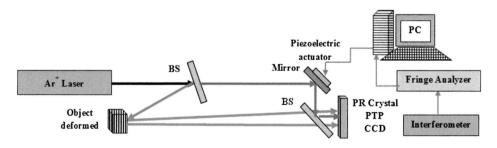

Figure 2.19   19 Phase-shifting holographic interferometry setup.

shifts is rather easy to use. To see this, consider the typical relation for the recorded intensity on the CCD camera, given by

$$I(x, y; \phi_R) = a_R^2 + a_O^2(x, y) + 2a_R a_O(x, y) \cos[\phi_R - \phi_O(x, y)], \qquad (2.39)$$

where a_R, ϕ_R denote the amplitude and phase of the reference, respectively, and $a_O(x, y)$, $\phi_O(x, y)$ denote the propagated amplitude and phase of the object at the recording plane. Upon changing ϕ_R through the values of 0, $\pi/2$, π, $3\pi/2$ and recording the holograms $I(x, y; 0)$, $I(x, y; \pi/2)$, $I(x, y; \pi)$, $I(x, y; 3\pi/2)$, it is possible to conveniently calculate $\phi_O(x, y)$ using the following relation:[4]

$$\phi_O(x, y) = \arctan \left\{ \frac{I(x, y; 3\pi/2) - I(x, y; \pi/2)}{I(x, y; 0) - I(x, y; \pi)} \right\}. \qquad (2.40)$$

With the phase determined, the amplitude $a_O(x, y)$ can be directly found by detecting the intensity $a_O^2(x, y)$ on the detector with the reference beam blocked. With knowledge of the amplitude and phase at the recording plane, the Fresnel integral can be used to back-propagate the field to yield the original object. The disadvantage of this traditional phase-shifting digital holography, however, is that different phase shifts of the reference are required, which may be impractical for objects that change in time faster than the required images can be captured.

This section describes an alternate and novel method to perform PSH through dynamic holography and self-diffraction in higher orders. The recording material can either involve volume gratings in lithium niobate (LN) crystals or a holocamera (HC), e.g., utilizing surface-relief gratings in PTP film. Two-beam coupling in LN is a nonlinear process,[9] where two laser beams are employed to record a holographic grating by modulating the refractive index and simultaneously diffract on this grating—thus the name "self-diffraction."

Dynamic holography is motivated by the fact that the phases in the different diffracted orders from gratings are generally different. For instance, in Raman–Nath diffraction pertinent to "thin" gratings, the complex amplitudes of diffracted orders m vary according to $j^m J_m$, where J_m represent Bessel functions of the first kind of order m, implying phase difference multiples of $\pi/2$. Monitoring the various diffracted intensities can therefore provide a single-shot means of getting all of the required intensities for PSH and reconstruction of the object phase.

Besides the well-known effects of energy and phase transformation in the Bragg beams, the first non-Bragg diffraction orders may appear even for volume (thick) gratings. It is shown that forward phase conjugation and phase doubling occur in non-Bragg orders. In coherent beam combining, all four beams (2 Bragg and 2 non-Bragg) are sensitive to phase modulation as well as to the type of nonlinear mechanism of grating recording. Therefore, the advantage of this technique over the conventional PSH is that multiple phase shifts can be obtained in one shot—hence the ability to decipher the phase or the 3D information of fast and dynamic events, contrary to traditional PSH, where at least three sequential phase shifts are necessary to unambiguously decipher the fringes.

PTPs are widely used in holography because they are reusable and there is no need for a wet chemical process for developing, as in traditional films. The PTP material repeatedly softens and hardens when heated and cooled.[19] The hologram is recorded as a surface-relief grating in the material. On the other hand, PR materials such as LN or polymers, which are used in dynamic holography, record the hologram as an induced refractive-index grating. The refractive-index grating is created as a result of photoexcited charge transport due to diffusion, drift, and the photovoltaic effect, thus creating a space-charge field that modulates the refractive index through the electro-optic effect.

The differential equations of the two-beam coupling and self-diffraction process in LN crystals is described next.[20] Starting from the Helmholtz equation

$$\nabla^2 E_p + k^2 E_p = 0, \tag{2.41}$$

substitute

$$k = nk_0 = (n_0 + \Delta n)k_0 = (1 + \Delta n)k_0, \tag{2.42}$$

where

$$\Delta n = c_1 I + c_2 \nabla I \tag{2.43}$$

represents the refractive-index change due to photovoltaic (c_1) and diffusive (c_2) effects, respectively. For simplicity, it is assumed that $n_0 = 1$.

First, consider the writing (recording) process. Assume that the reference and the object fields are in phase and can be written as

$$E_1 e^{j(K/2)x}, \quad E_{-1} e^{-j(K/2)x}, \tag{2.44}$$

where $K = k_0 \sin(\theta/2)$, k_0 is the propagation constant, and θ is the angle between the object and reference waves [see Fig. 2.20(a)]. Assuming that there is only diffractive coupling due to the photovoltaic effect, Eq. (2.43) becomes $\Delta n = c_1 I + c_2 \nabla I = cI$, and

$$I = |E_1 e^{-j(K/2)x} + E_{-1} e^{j(K/2)x}| = |E_1|^2 + |E_{-1}|^2 + E_1^* E_{-1} e^{jKx} + E_{-1}^* E_1 e^{-jKx},$$

then

$$\Delta n \approx C(I_1 + I_{-1}) + 2C\sqrt{I_1 I_{-1}} \cos Kx. \tag{2.45}$$

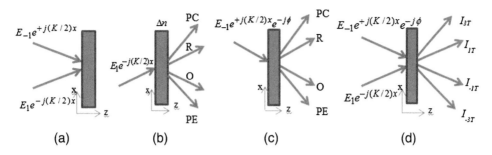

Figure 2.20 (a) Hologram recording with an object beam and a reference beam; (b)–(c) hologram reconstruction with the same reference beam and with the deformed object beam; and (d) different intensities at the different orders at the exit plane of the PR crystal.[21]

Assume, for simplicity, that the reading waves are the same as writing waves, except that E_{-1} has an additional phase ϕ radians. This example will use the *thin* grating approximation and assume illumination at *oblique* incidence by each wave. For the reading process, consider the effect of the reference wave $E_1 e^{-j(K/2)x}$ alone and then the deformed object wave $E_{-1} e^{j(K/2)x} e^{-j\phi}$ alone. The phase hologram can be found to be a summation of a Bessel series as follows:[21]

$$e^{-jk_0 \Delta nL} = e^{-jk_0 c(I_1 + I_{-1})L} e^{-jk_0 2c\sqrt{I_1 I_{-1}} L \cos Kx}$$

$$= e^{-jk_0 c(I_1 + I_{-1})L} \sum_{m=-\infty}^{\infty} (-j)^m J_m\left(k_0 2c\sqrt{I_1 I_{-1}} L\right) e^{-jmKx}, \qquad (2.46)$$

which uses the Jacobi–Anger formula

$$e^{-jz \cos \theta} = \sum_{m=-\infty}^{\infty} (-j)^m J_m(z) e^{-jm\theta}.$$

Therefore, for the first case, reading with the reference beam provides the following Bragg and first non-Bragg terms:

$$(\text{PC}) \propto -jE_1 e^{-j(3K/2)x} J_1(\bullet) e^{-j\Delta KL}, \qquad (2.47\text{a})$$

$$(\text{R}) \propto E_1 e^{-j(K/2)x} J_0(\bullet), \qquad (2.47\text{b})$$

$$(\text{O}) \propto jE_1 e^{+j(K/2)x} J_{-1}(\bullet), \qquad (2.47\text{c})$$

$$(\text{PE}) \propto -E_1 e^{+j(3K/2)x} J_{-2}(\bullet) e^{j\Delta KL}, \qquad (2.47\text{d})$$

where $(\bullet) = (k_0 2C\sqrt{I_1 I_{-1}} L)$ [see Fig. 2.20(b)].

For the second case, reading with the deformed object beam provides the following terms:

$$(\text{PC}) \propto -E_{-1}e^{-j(3K/2)x}e^{-j\phi}J_2(\bullet)e^{j\Delta KL}, \tag{2.48a}$$

$$(\text{R}) \propto -jE_{-1}e^{-j(K/2)x}e^{-j\phi}J_1(\bullet), \tag{2.48b}$$

$$(\text{O}) \propto E_{-1}e^{+j(K/2)x}e^{-j\phi}J_0(\bullet), \tag{2.48c}$$

$$(\text{PE}) \propto jE_{-1}e^{+j(3K/2)x}e^{-j\phi}J_{-1}(\bullet)e^{-j\Delta KL}; \tag{2.48d}$$

[see Fig. 2.20(c)]. Note that all of the terms in Eqs. (2.47) and (2.48) are multiplied by $e^{-jk_0C(I_1+I_{-1})L}$.

The total intensities of the different Bragg and non-Bragg orders at the exit plane of the PR material can be defined as

$$(\text{PC})I_{3T} = |-jE_1J_1(\bullet)e^{-j\Delta KL} - E_{-1}e^{-j\phi}J_2(\bullet)e^{j\Delta KL}|^2, \tag{2.49a}$$

$$(\text{R})I_{1T} = |E_1J_0(\bullet) - jE_{-1}e^{-j\phi}J_1(\bullet)|^2, \tag{2.49b}$$

$$(\text{O})I_{-1T} = |jE_1J_{-1}(\bullet) + E_{-1}e^{-j\phi}J_0(\bullet)|^2, \tag{2.49c}$$

$$(\text{PE})I_{-3T} = |-E_1J_{-2}(\bullet)e^{j\Delta KL} + jE_{-1}e^{-j\phi}J_{-1}(\bullet)e^{-j\Delta KL}|^2, \tag{2.49d}$$

where the subscript T denotes the total intensities [see Fig. 2.20(d)]. After some algebra, Eq. (2.49) becomes

$$(\text{PC})I_{3T} = I_1J_1^2(\bullet) + I_{-1}J_2^2(\bullet) - 2\sqrt{I_1I_{-1}}J_1(\bullet)J_2(\bullet)\sin(\phi - \phi_0), \tag{2.50a}$$

$$(\text{R})I_{1T} = I_1J_0^2(\bullet) + I_{-1}J_1^2(\bullet) - 2\sqrt{I_1I_{-1}}J_0(\bullet)J_1(\bullet)\sin(\phi), \tag{2.50b}$$

$$(\text{O})I_{-1T} = I_1J_1^2(\bullet) + I_{-1}J_0^2(\bullet) + 2\sqrt{I_1I_{-1}}J_0(\bullet)J_1(\bullet)\sin(\phi), \tag{2.50c}$$

$$(\text{PE})I_{-3T} = I_1J_2^2(\bullet) + I_{-1}J_1^2(\bullet) + 2\sqrt{I_1I_{-1}}J_1(\bullet)J_2(\bullet)\sin(\phi + \phi_0), \tag{2.50d}$$

where $\phi_0 = 2\Delta KL$, $J_{-n}(z) = (-1)^nJ_n(z)$ is used. After some algebra, ϕ can be found from Eq. (2.50) to be

$$\tan\phi = \sin\phi_0 \left[\frac{J_2(k_02C\sqrt{I_1I_{-1}}L)}{J_0(k_02C\sqrt{I_1I_{-1}}L)} \right]$$

$$\times \left[\frac{(I_{1T}-I_{-1T})+(J_0^2(k_02C\sqrt{I_1I_{-1}}L)-J_1^2(k_02C\sqrt{I_1I_{-1}}L))(I_{-1}-I_1)}{(I_{3T}-I_{-3T})+(J_1^2(k_02C\sqrt{I_1I_{-1}}L)-J_2^2(k_02C\sqrt{I_1I_{-1}}L))(I_{-1}-I_1)} \right].$$

$$\tag{2.51}$$

Equation (2.51) is reminiscent of Eq. (2.40), which describes the phase of an object in terms of recorded intensities with different phases (i.e., $m\pi/2$) imparted to the reference beam. Therefore, Eq. (2.51) shows that it is feasible to obtain the phase information by monitoring the intensities of the various simultaneously generated diffracted orders that may have phases imparted to them by the material (in this case, through the phase mismatch between the Bragg and the non-Bragg orders during interaction in the material). In addition to the phase determination of an object using simultaneous read out from the Bragg and non-Bragg orders, it is also possible to determine the displacement or deformation of the object by examining these orders. The advantage of the phase-conjugated image of order (3) over the Bragg "image" of order (1) [as shown in Fig. 2.20(d)] is that the latter is a propagated version of the object and can result in the object's diffraction pattern, especially if the object size is small. Furthermore, the phase-conjugated image offers the opportunity to monitor different longitudinal planes in the object because these planes image at different phase-conjugate image planes. The advantage of detecting fringes in the phase conjugate is that it provides displacement information that is now superposed on the phase conjugate image rather than the Bragg "image" which is the Fresnel diffraction pattern of the object. This is particularly useful when the object feature sizes are small. In a similar way, it can be shown that the other non-Bragg diffracted order doubles the object phase and may yield other important information about the object, such as the solution of the sign ambiguity problem. Calculations similar to the heuristic determination of the diffracted intensities show that for a diffuse object where there is a displacement Δx, Δy, Δz, with z being the longitudinal coordinate, the fringes in the direction of the phase conjugate ($+3$) can give information about the object displacement, superposed on the real image of the object. Specifically, the intensity in the $+3$ order can be written, after some algebra, as

$$I = |\psi_{obs}|^2 \propto J_1^2 + aJ_1J_2 \cos\left[\frac{2k_0\Delta x}{\Delta z}x + \frac{2k_0\Delta y}{\Delta z}y + k_0\Delta x^2\left(\frac{1}{\Delta z}+\frac{1}{z_0}\right)\right.$$
$$\left. + k_0\Delta y^2\left(\frac{1}{\Delta z}+\frac{1}{z_0}\right) + \Delta\phi\right], \tag{2.52}$$

which implies that the fringe periods in x and y become

$$\Lambda_{x,y} = \frac{\pi}{k_0}\frac{\Delta z}{\Delta x, y}. \tag{2.53}$$

The optics setup is shown in Fig. 2.21.

Figure 2.22 shows an example of phase-shifting interferometry realized in one exposure using PTP. The results, which are similar to those obtained using PR LN, show imaging and interferometry [see Fig. 2.22(a)] from a diffused

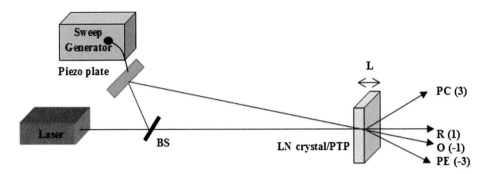

Figure 2.21 Scheme of the dynamic hologram recording in LN crystal/PTP (object O and reference R waves) with the generation of the first non-Bragg orders (+3, −3), phase conjugate (PC), reference (R), object (O), and phase-enhanced (PE, double the original phase) beam.[20,21]

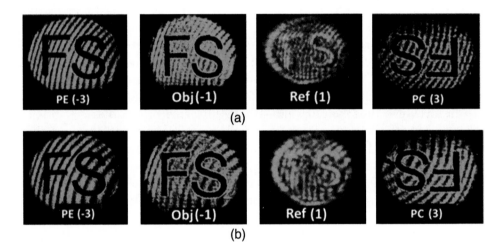

Figure 2.22 Imaging and interferometry in Bragg (1, −1) and in non-Bragg (+3, −3) diffraction orders: (a) initial state and (b) object after deformation (rotation around the vertical axis).

reflecting metal object, with the letters FS (initial state). Incidentally, note that after a small distortion of the object (i.e., rotation in the transverse plane), the interference pattern changes [Fig. 2.22(b)] in all diffracted orders. In all cases, the phase-conjugated +3 non-Bragg order is inverted, akin to what happens to a real image of an object.

References

1. T.-C. Poon and P. P. Banerjee, *Contemporary Optical Image Processing with MATLAB®*, Elsevier Science, Amsterdam (2001).
2. J. W. Goodman, *Introduction to Fourier Optics*, 3rd Ed., Roberts & Co., Englewood, CO (1996).

3. U. Schnars and W. Jueptner, *Digital Holography*, Springer, Berlin (2005).
4. T. Kreis, *Holographic Interferometry: Principles and Methods*, Akademie Verlag, Berlin (1996).
5. P. Hariharan, *Optical Holography*, Cambridge University Press, Cambridge, UK (1984).
6. P. Hariharan, *Optical Interferometry*, 2nd Ed., Academic Press, Amsterdam (2003).
7. C. M. Vest, *Holographic Interferometry*, John Wiley & Sons, New York (1979).
8. P. P. Banerjee, G. Nehmetallah, N. Kukhtarev, and S. C. Praharaj, "Determination of model airplane attitudes using dynamic holographic interferometry," *Appl. Opt.* **47**(21), 3877–3885 (2008).
9. B. L. Volodin, B. Kippelen, K. Meerholz, N. V. Kukhtarev, H. J. Caulfield, and N. Peyghambarian, "Non-Bragg orders in dynamic self-diffraction on thick phase gratings in a photorefractive polymer," *Opt. Lett.* **21**(7), 519–521 (1996).
10. A. Chirita, "Real-time scaling of micro-objects by multiplexed holographic recording on photo- thermo-plastic structure," *J. Mod. Opt.* **57**(10), 854–858 (2010).
11. T. Credelle and F. Spong, "Thermoplastic media for holographic recording," *RCA Rev.* **33**, 207–226 (Mar. 1972).
12. M. A. Golub, A. A. Friesem, and L. Eisen, "Bragg properties of efficient surface relief gratings in the resonance domain," *Opt. Comm.* **235**(4–6), 261–267 (2004).
13. M. Arevalillo Herráez, D. R. Burton, M. J. Lalor, and M. A. Gdeisat, "Fast two-dimensional phase-unwrapping algorithm based on sorting by reliability following a noncontinuous path," *Appl. Opt.* **41**(35), 7437–7444 (2002).
14. D. C. Ghiglia and L. A. Romero, "Robust two-dimensional weighted and unweighted phase unwrapping that uses fast transforms and iterative methods," *J. Opt. Soc. Am. A* **11**(1), 107–117 (1994).
15. R. M. Goldstein, H. A. Zebker, and C. L. Werner, "Satellite radar interferometry: two-dimensional phase unwrapping," *Radio Sci.* **23**(4), 713–720 (1988).
16. H. A. Zebker and Y. Lu, "Phase unwrapping algorithms for radar interferometry: residue-cut, least-squares, and synthesis algorithms," *J. Opt. Soc. Am. A* **15**(3), 586–597 (1998).
17. J. Bioucas-Dias and G. Valadão, "Phase unwrapping via graph cuts," *IEEE Trans. Image Processing* **16**(3), 698–709 (2007).
18. T. Kreis, "Digital holographic interference-phase measurement using the Fourier-transform method," *J. Opt. Soc. Am. A* **3**(6), 847–855 (1986).
19. R. J. Parker, "A quarter century of thermoplastic holography," *Int. Conf. Hologram Interferometry Speckle Metrol.*, K. Stetson and R. Pryputniewicz, eds., 217–224 (1990).

20. N. Kukhtarev, T. Kukhtareva, P. P. Banerjee, and G. Nehmetallah, "Holographic imaging and interferometry with non-Bragg diffraction orders in the volume gratings," *Topical Meeting in Digital Holography and Three-Dimensional Imaging*, Miami, FL (2012).

21. P. P. Banerjee, G. Nehmetallah, U. A. Abeywickrema, S. F. Lyuksyutov, and N. V. Kukhtarev, "Non-Bragg diffraction orders in lithium niobate and its application to one-shot phase-shifting holographic interferometry," *Proc. SPIE* **8644**, 864402 (2013) [doi: 10.1117/12.2005489].

Chapter 3

Fringe Deciphering Techniques Applied to Analog Holographic Interferometry

3.1 Introduction

Different types of interferometers can be used to produce a fringe pattern phase modulated by the physical quantity being measured. Several physical quantities can be measured with interferometric fringe techniques, such as strain and stress analysis, temperature deformation and gradient, surface deformation, and many others. The ultimate goal of fringe pattern analysis is to decipher the underlying phase profile that encodes information about the physical parameter being measured. This chapter reviews many techniques often used in fringe analysis that are also useful in holographic interferometry analysis. Interferograms can be divided into two general categories:

(a) those containing a spatial carrier in the interferometric pattern, typically introduced through a tilt in the reference wavefront; and
(b) those in which no spatial carrier exists, which will produce additional difficulties in automatically deciphering the interferograms.

This chapter starts by explaining the frequency-domain fringe deciphering techniques that assume a spatial carrier exists. In Section 3.3, the concept of fringe orientation and direction is applied to fringe deciphering. In Section 3.4, phase demodulation using the Hilbert transform is discussed in detail, including its relation to fringe orientation and direction. In Section 3.5, the concept of fringe skeletonization and normalization is applied to fringe processing; Section 3.6 introduces fringe contrast enhancement. Finally, a brief discussion of phase unwrapping for interferogram analysis is discussed in Section 3.7.

3.2 Interferogram Processing Using Frequency Techniques

3.2.1 Demodulating simulated fringes due to a tilt

This section simulates a typical interference pattern and deciphers it using the frequency technique. Consider the following test interferogram consisting of parallel interference fringes with an inclination angle of θ, whose intensity is given by

$$I(x,y) = a + b \sin[k_0(x \cos \theta + y \sin \theta)], \tag{3.1}$$

where a and b are constants. These fringes represent a carrier frequency or an impulse in the frequency domain. In an optical interferometer, the fringes represent a tilt between the reference and the object beam.

The MATLAB script "my_tilt.m," listed in Table 3.1, deciphers the fringes and produces a tilt. Figures 3.1(a) and 3.1(b) show the fringes and the deciphered fringe pattern. In this example, the information is the tilt, so the algorithm works by cropping only where the carrier is and performing an inverse Fourier transform. The general case in which the carrier must be eliminated is discussed in Section 3.2.2.

3.2.2 Demodulating fringes embedded with a carrier

The measured interferometric intensity distribution $I(x,y)$ can be written as

$$I(x,y) = a(x,y) + b(x,y) \cos[(k_{x_0}x + k_{y_0}y) + \phi(x,y)], \tag{3.2}$$

where k_{x_0,y_0} are the carrier spatial frequencies, $a(x,y)$ is the background variation, and $b(x,y)$ is related to the local contrast of the pattern. In other words, $a(x,y)$ carries the additive and $b(x,y)$ carries the multiplicative disturbances, respectively, and $\phi(x,y)$ is the interference phase to be computed from $I(x,y)$. Equation (3.2) can be written as [1,2]

$$\begin{aligned} I(x,y) = a(x,y) &+ b_c(x,y) \exp[j(k_{x_0}x + k_{y_0}y)] \\ &+ b_c^*(x,y) \exp[-j(k_{x_0}x + k_{y_0}y)], \end{aligned} \tag{3.3}$$

where $b_c(x,y) = (b(x,y)/2) \exp[j\phi(x,y)]$. The Fourier transform of Eq. (3.3) produces

$$\tilde{I}(k_x,k_y) = \tilde{a}(k_x,k_y) + \tilde{b}_c(k_x - k_{x_0}, k_y - k_{y_0}) + \tilde{b}_c^*(k_x + k_{x_0}, k_y + k_{y_0}), \tag{3.4}$$

where $\sim$ indicates the function in the Fourier domain. Assuming that the background intensity $a(x,y)$ is slowly varying compared to the fringe spacing, the amplitude spectrum $\tilde{I}(k_x,k_y)$ will be a trimodal function with $\tilde{a}(k_x,k_y)$ broadening the zero peak and $\tilde{b}_c$, $\tilde{b}_c^*$ placed symmetrically with respect to the

Table 3.1   MATLAB code "my_tilt.m" creates a fringe pattern [see Figs. 3.1(a) and (b)].

```
1   %%This section starts with a computer-generated fringe
2   %and
3   %tries to decipher the unwrapped phase
4   clc
5   close all
6   clear all
7   lambda=0.632;                            %In microns
8   %-------------Create Test Image-------------
9   pts=2^8;
10  x=linspace(0,pts/8-1,pts);
11  y=x;
12  [X0,Y0]=meshgrid(x,y);
13  theta=45*pi/180;
14  f0=1;
15  I=128+127*...
16  sin(2*pi*(X0*f0*cos(theta)+Y0*f0*sin(theta)));
17  figure
18  imagesc(I)
19  colormap(gray(256))
20  colorbar
21  title('Simulated fringe pattern')
22  %Crop to make it square
23  [rows,cols]=size(I);
24  if cols>rows
25  rect_crop=[floor(cols/2)-floor(rows/2) 1 rows-1 rows];
26  elseif cols<rows
27  rect_crop=[1 floor(rows/2)-floor(cols/2) cols cols-1];
28  else
29  rect_crop=[1 1 cols rows];
30  end
31  I=imcrop(I,rect_crop);
32  im(I)
33  axis xy
34  max(I(:))
35  min(I(:))
36  %Go to Fourier domain to select the region of interest
37  I1F=(fft2(fftshift(I)));
38  I1F_s=fftshift(I1F);
39  abs_I=abs(I1F_s).^2;
40  I1F_c=zeros(pts,pts);
41  %%
42  mesh(abs_I)
43  for m=1:1:1
44  im(abs_I)
45  axis xy
46  [Ro,Co]=size(I1F);
47  line([ceil(Co/2)+1 ceil(Co/2)+1],[0 ceil(Ro)])
48  line([0 ceil(Co)],[ceil(Ro/2)+1 ceil(Ro/2)+1])
49  rect1=[151-5 151-5 10 10];
50  [I1,rect]=imcrop(abs_I,rect1);
51  I1F_c(round(rect(2)):round(rect(2)+rect(4)),...
52  round(rect(1)):round(rect(1)+rect(3)))=...
53  I1F_s(round(rect(2)):round(rect(2)+rect(4)),...
54  round(rect(1)):round(rect(1)+rect(3)));
55  end
```

(continued)

Table 3.1 (*Continued*)

```
56   abs_I_c=abs(I1F_c).^2;
57   im(abs_I_c)
58   [Ro,Co]=size(abs_I_c);
59   line([ceil(Co/2)+1 ceil(Co/2)+1],[0 ceil(Ro)])
60   line([0 ceil(Co)],[ceil(Ro/2)+1 ceil(Ro/2)+1])
61   axis xy
62   %%
63   %Calculate the wrapped phase
64   I2=fftshift(ifft2(fftshift(I1F_c)));
65   [ro,co]=size(I2);
66   I3=I2(:);
67   ind=find(real(I3)>0);
68   I3_phase=zeros(1,length(I3))';
69   I3_phase(ind)=atan(imag(I3(ind))./real(I3(ind)));
70   ind=find(real(I3)<=0);
71   I3_phase(ind)=atan(imag(I3(ind))./...
72   real(I3(ind)))+pi*sign(imag(I3(ind))));
73   I2_phase=reshape(I3_phase,ro,co);
74   %I2_phase=atan2(imag(I2),real(I2));
75   close all
76   figure
77   imshow(I2_phase)
78   max(I2_phase(:))
79   min(I2_phase(:))
80   %%%---Unwrapping using the 2D_SRNCP algorithm:
81   %http://www.ljmu.ac.uk/GERI/90225.htm
82   %Call the 2D phase unwrapper from C language.
83   %To compile the C code: in MATLAB command window, type
84   %Miguel_2D_unwrapper.cpp. The file has to be in the same
85   %directory
86   %as the script to work.
87   WrappedPhase=I2_phase;
88   mex Miguel_2D_unwrapper.cpp
89   %The wrapped phase should have the single (float in C)
90   %data type
91   WrappedPhase = single(WrappedPhase);
92   UnwrappedPhase = Miguel_2D_unwrapper(WrappedPhase);
93   UnwrappedPhase=double(UnwrappedPhase);
94   h = fspecial('average',15);
95   eta1 = imfilter(UnwrappedPhase,h);
96   eta1=eta1(10:end-10,10:end-10);
97   figure;
98   surfl(eta1/(4*pi)*lambda);shading interp;
99   colormap(gray);
100  title('Unwrapped 3D Depth Map')
101  zlabel('Depth in microns')
```

origin. The next step is to eliminate the zero-frequency term and one of the sidebands $\tilde{b}_c$, $\tilde{b}_c^*$. The new spectrum is no longer symmetric, and the space-domain function is no longer real but complex. Therefore, Eq. (3.4) becomes

$$\tilde{I}'(k_x, k_y) = \tilde{b}_c(k_x - k_{x_0}, k_y - k_{y_0}), \qquad (3.5)$$

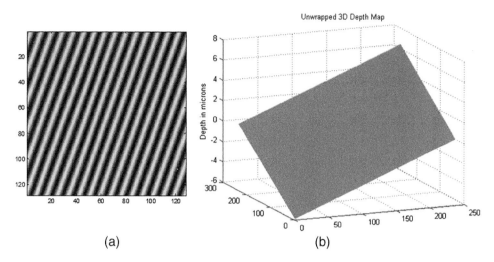

Figure 3.1   (a) Parallel interference fringes with an angle θ and (b) deciphered fringes showing relative tilt between two beams.

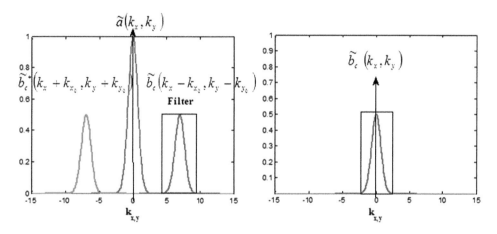

Figure 3.2   Schematic of the process.

which is the new filtered spectrum centered around the zero frequency. Then the inverse Fourier transform is performed on Eq. (3.5) to get

$$I'(x, y) = b_c(x, y) = \frac{1}{2} b(x, y) \exp[j\phi(x, y)]. \tag{3.6}$$

The following operation is performed to find the wrapped phase:

$$\phi(x, y) = \arctan\left\{ \frac{\mathrm{Im}[b_c(x, y)]}{\mathrm{Re}[b_c(x, y)]} \right\}. \tag{3.7}$$

Figure 3.2 illustrates the process. A second example, the MATLAB script "freq_decipher.m," which uses the frequency deciphering technique, is shown in Table 3.2. Figure 3.3(a) shows the initial fringe pattern, Fig. 3.3(b) shows

Table 3.2 MATLAB code "freq_decipher.m" uses the frequency technique to decipher the fringe pattern (see Fig. 3.3).

```
1    %%This program takes an image that has fringes riding
2    %on a carrier and tries to get rid of the carrier and
3    %unwrap the phase
4    close all
5    clear all
6    clc
7    lambda=0.632;                          %In microns
8    I=double(imread('Campsp3.tif'));
9    I=I(:,:,1);
10   im(I)
11   axis xy
12   I = padarray(I,[50 50],0,'both');
13   im(I)
14   axis xy
15   [rows,cols]=size(I);
16   if cols>rows
17   rect_crop=[floor(cols/2)-floor(rows/2) 1 rows-1 rows];
18   elseif cols<rows
19   rect_crop=[1 floor(rows/2)-floor(cols/2) cols cols-1];
20   else
21   rect_crop=[1 1 cols rows];
22   end
23   I=imcrop(I,rect_crop);
24   im(I)
25   axis xy
26   max(I(:))
27   min(I(:))
28   %Go to Fourier domain to select the region of interest
29   I1F=(fft2(fftshift(I)));
30   I1F_s=fftshift(I1F);
31   abs_I=abs(I1F_s).^2;
32   [ro,co]=size(I);
33   im(abs_I)
34   %%
35   clc
36   disp('Drag the circle and center it around the carrier')
37   disp('which is a white circle centered at 250, 350')
38   disp('then double click the left button of the mouse')
39   [Ro,Co]=size(I1F);
40   line([round(Co/2) round(Co/2)],[0 round(Ro)])
41   line([0 round(Co)],[round(Ro/2) round(Ro/2)])
42   h = imellipse(gca,[10,10,50,50]);
43   vertices = wait(h);
44   X=vertices(:,1);
45   Y=vertices(:,2);
46   I1F_s_selection=I1F_s(floor(min(Y)):...
47   floor(max(Y)),floor(min(X)):floor(max(X)));
48   im(abs(I1F_s_selection).^2)
49   %Use the Hamming window
50   if mod(size(I1F_s_selection,1),2)==0
51   I1F_s_selection=I1F_s_selection(1:end-1,1:end-1);
52   end
53   [A, XI, YI]=myhamming2D(size(I1F_s_selection,1))
54   I1F_c=A.*I1F_s_selection;
```

(*continued*)

Table 3.2 *(Continued)*

```
55  im(abs(I1F_c).^2)
56  % I1F_c=I1F_s_selection;
57  % calculate the wrapped phase
58  I2=fftshift(ifft2(fftshift(I1F_c)));
59  im(abs(I2))
60  [ro,co]=size(I2);
61  I3=I2(:);
62  ind=find(real(I3)>0);
63  I3_phase=zeros(1,length(I3))';
64  I3_phase(ind)=atan(imag(I3(ind))./real(I3(ind)));
65  ind=find(real(I3)<=0);
66  I3_phase(ind)=atan(imag(I3(ind))./real(I3(ind)))+ ...
67  pi*sign(imag(I3(ind)));
68  I2_phase=reshape(I3_phase,ro,co);
69  %Calculate the unwrpped phase on a certain line
70  figure
71  imshow(I2_phase)
72  max(I2_phase(:))
73  min(I2_phase(:))
74  %Uncomment if you like to select to unwrap along
75  %a certain line.
76  %h=improfile;
77  %figure
78  %subplot(2,1,1)
79  %plot(h)
80  %unwraph=unwrap(h);
81  %subplot(2,1,2)
82  %plot(unwraph)
83  %clear abs* h v* I I1* I2 I3* A C* R* X* Y* ans c* r*
84  %i* u*
85  %%%- - -Unwrapping using the 2D_SRNCP algorithm:
86  %http://www.ljmu.ac.uk/GERI/90225.htm
87  %Call the 2D phase unwrapper from C language.
88  %To compile the C code: in MATLAB command window, type
89  %Miguel_2D_unwrapper.cpp. The file has to be in the same
90  %directory as the script to work.
91  clc
92  disp('Choose a rectangular area')
93  disp('using the mouse to unwrap')
94  figure
95  imshow(I2_phase)
96  I2_phase=imcrop;
97  WrappedPhase=I2_phase;
98  mex Miguel_2D_unwrapper.cpp
99  %The wrapped phase should have the single (float in C)
100 %data type
101 WrappedPhase = single(WrappedPhase);
102 UnwrappedPhase = Miguel_2D_unwrapper(WrappedPhase);
103 UnwrappedPhase=double(UnwrappedPhase);
104 h = fspecial('average',15);
105 eta1 = imfilter(UnwrappedPhase,h);
106 figure;
107 surfl(eta1/(4*pi)*lambda);shading interp;
108 colormap(gray);
109 title('Unwrapped 3D Depth Map')
110 zlabel('Depth in microns')
```

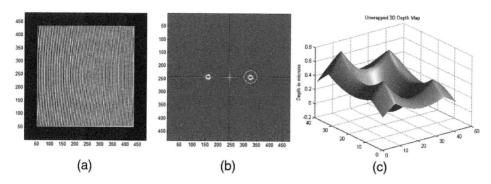

Figure 3.3 (a) The initial fringe pattern, (b) the frequency domain where the region of interest is inside the circle, and (c) the deciphered phase.

the frequency domain where the region of interest is inside a circle, and Fig. 3.3(c) shows the deciphered phase.

3.3 Interferogram Processing Using Fringe Orientation and Fringe Direction

Fringe orientation is often used for fringe processing.[3,4] Knowledge of the fringe orientation is useful in applications such as

(a) contoured window filtering,[5–7]
(b) filtering noise from electronic speckle pattern interferometry (ESPI) fringes,
(c) the contoured correlation method used to generate noise-free fringe patterns for ESPI,[8–10]
(d) corner detection and directional filtering,[11,12] and
(e) phase demodulation based on fringe orientation, where the phase information can be deciphered by computing the fringe orientation using the spiral-phase transform, as shown in Section 3.4.[13–15]

Orientation is related to the local features pertaining to spatial information of an interferogram. Structured and well-patterned features have a specific, well-defined orientation, while noisy regions, without any discernable structure, have no specific orientation.[16] Consequently, by performing the Fourier transform of a small region of a typical interferogram, the spectrum will be concentrated in a small spot oriented at the same angle as the local gradient of that specific region.[17] Thus, the fringe orientation is parallel to the interferogram gradient and is the local spatial-frequency vector orientation in the Fourier domain.[18,19] This section introduces some of the fringe-orientation computation techniques. A summary of the different methods is presented along with their corresponding MATLAB codes. At the end of the section, a comparison table outlines the advantages and

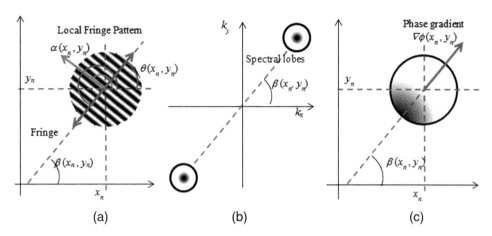

Figure 3.4 (a) Local fringe orientation angle θ, (b) spectral side lobes related to the local fringe pattern, and (c) the direction, defined as the phase gradient direction.

disadvantages of each method. Note that other powerful methods exist; this is not a comprehensive list of all possible techniques.

3.3.1 Definition of fringe orientation and fringe direction

Fringe directions can be visualized as a vector field perpendicular to the fringes at every localized region of the interferogram [see Fig. 3.4(a)]. Because it is assumed that there is no carrier frequency, the interferogram can be described as

$$I(x,y) = a(x,y) + b(x,y)\cos[\phi(x,y)], \qquad (3.8)$$

where $I(x,y)$ is the 2D intensity pattern, $a(x,y)$ is a low-frequency background offset, and $b(x,y)$ is a low-frequency fringe contrast modulation of the fringe pattern. The modulating phase information $\phi(x,y)$ is the unknown that must be solved for and is assumed to have higher frequency content. Because points of equal intensity have equal phase for a given fringe, the *fringe direction vector* at each point can be computed from the gradient as[16]

$$\vec{n}_\varphi = \vec{\nabla}\phi/|\vec{\nabla}\phi| = (k_x, k_y)/|\vec{\nabla}\phi|, \qquad (3.9)$$

where $\vec{\nabla}\phi = [(\partial\phi/\partial x), (\partial\phi/\partial y)] = (k_x, k_y)$ is a vector representing the interferogram's spatial frequencies [see Fig. 3.4(b)]. Note that for typical, locally linear monochromatic fringes $\phi(x,y) = k_x x + k_y y$, then $\vec{\nabla}\phi = (k_x, k_y)$. Therefore, the fringe direction vector $\vec{n}_\phi$ has a specific direction that is perpendicular to the fringes. Thus, the *fringe direction angle* $\beta_{2\pi}(x, y)$ can be defined as

$$\beta_{2\pi} = \arctan\left(\frac{\partial\phi/\partial y}{\partial\phi/\partial x}\right) = \arctan\left[\frac{k_y}{k_x}\right], \qquad (3.10)$$

where the 2π subscript in β indicates the period. The fringe direction vector and the fringe direction angle are related by

$$\vec{n}_\phi = (\cos\beta_{2\pi}, \sin\beta_{2\pi}) = \left(\frac{k_x}{\sqrt{k_x^2 + k_y^2}}, \frac{k_y}{\sqrt{k_x^2 + k_y^2}}\right). \qquad (3.11)$$

Because the modulating phase $\phi(x, y)$ is unknown and inside the cosine function [see Eq. (3.8)], the fringe direction vector cannot be computed directly, although the *fringe orientation vector* $\vec{n}_I$ (defined below) can be computed from the intensity of the interferogram. Because the intensity pattern in the interferogram represents the phase, Eq. (3.9) can be equivalently rewritten as

$$\vec{n}_I = \vec{\nabla}I/|\vec{\nabla}I| = (I_x, I_y)/|\vec{\nabla}I|, \qquad (3.12)$$

where

$$\vec{\nabla}I = (I_x, I_y) = \left(\frac{\partial I}{\partial x}, \frac{\partial I}{\partial y}\right)$$

$$= \frac{1}{2}[I(x-1, y) - I(x+1, y), I(x, y-1) - I(x, y+1)].$$

Applying Eq. (3.12) to Eq. (3.8), and assuming that $a(x, y)$ and $b(x, y)$ are smooth functions,

$$\vec{n}_I \approx -b\,\sin(\phi)\vec{\nabla}\phi/|\vec{\nabla}I| = -\text{sgn}[\sin(\phi)].\vec{n}_\phi, \qquad (3.13)$$

where the signum function sgn[•] indicates that the orientation vector $\vec{n}_I$ direction will flip when the sign of $\sin(\phi)$ changes. Similarly, the fringe orientation angle $\theta_\pi(x, y)$ can be defined as

$$\theta_\pi = \arctan[I_y/I_x], \qquad (3.14)$$

where the π subscript on θ indicates the period. The fringe orientation vector and the *fringe orientation angle* are thus related by

$$\vec{n}_I = (\cos\theta_\pi, \sin\theta_\pi) = \left(\frac{I_x}{\sqrt{I_x^2 + I_y^2}}, \frac{I_y}{\sqrt{I_x^2 + I_y^2}}\right). \qquad (3.15)$$

Note that if the smoothness assumption is not valid, then fringe normalization, either digitally or experimentally, must be performed to obtain valid results. (Fringe normalization is discussed in Section 3.5.) *Direction* applies to vectors, and, like the gradient in two dimensions, the *direction angle* $\beta_{2\pi}$ is uniquely defined in the range 0–360 deg (modulo 2π) [see Fig. 3.4(c)]. In contrast, the *orientation angle* θ_π is indistinguishable from that of a 180-deg rotated ridge (modulo π).[20]

3.3.2 Orientation computation methods

Many methods can be used to compute orientations. This section introduces various numerical techniques for orientation computation:

(a) gradient-based,
(b) plane-fit,
(c) spin-filter,
(d) Fourier transform, and
(e) accumulate-differences.

3.3.2.1 Gradient-based method

Gradient-based techniques have traditionally been used for fringe processing in interferograms.[10,16] The fringe direction vector $\vec{n}_\phi$ (approximately parallel to the phase gradient vector $\vec{\nabla}\phi$) is perpendicular to the *fringe tangential orientation* angle α [tangential to the fringes, as shown in Fig. 3.4(a)]. Thus, the inner product of these two vectors equals zero:

$$(\cos\alpha, \sin\alpha) \cdot \vec{\nabla}\phi(x,y) = 0, \qquad (3.16a)$$

where

$$\alpha(x,y) = \arctan\left[\frac{\partial\phi(x,y)/\partial y}{\partial\phi(x,y)/\partial x}\right] \pm \frac{\pi}{2}.$$

Equivalently,

$$(\cos\alpha, \sin\alpha) \cdot \vec{\nabla}I(x,y) = 0, \qquad (3.16b)$$

where

$$\alpha(x,y) = \arctan\left[\frac{\partial I(x,y)/\partial y}{\partial I(x,y)/\partial x}\right] \pm \frac{\pi}{2} = \theta_\pi(x,y) \pm \frac{\pi}{2}.$$

While an averaging strategy is an appropriate methodology to adopt, it cannot be directly applied because the *orientation angle* θ_π is indistinguishable from that of a 180-deg rotated ridge (modulo π), and averaging will result in a zero answer. To avoid that, the local orientation angle θ_π is doubled, which has two effects: the same-orientation angles θ_π (0 and π) will be transformed into the same-direction angles (0 and 2π), and the perpendicular-orientation angles (0 and $\pi/2$) will be transformed into the opposite-direction angles (0 and π). To avoid 2π-discontinuities, the averaging calculation is performed in the complex domain. Assume that the complex information can be written as[10]

$$c(x, y) = \cos[2\theta_\pi(x, y)] + j \sin[2\theta_\pi(x, y)]. \tag{3.17}$$

Performing the average of Eq. (3.17) produces

$$\bar{c} = \frac{\sum_{n=1}^{N} c(x_n, y_n)}{N} = \frac{1}{N}\sum_{n=1}^{N} \cos[2\theta_\pi(x_n, y_n)] + j\frac{1}{N}\sum_{n=1}^{N} \sin[2\theta_\pi(x_n, y_n)], \tag{3.18}$$

where N is the total number of pixels in the averaging window. Using Eq. (3.18), the orientation angle can be computed as

$$\begin{aligned}
\theta_\pi &= \frac{1}{2} \arctan\left[\frac{\sum_{n=1}^{N} \sin[2\theta_\pi(x_n, y_n)]}{\sum_{n=1}^{N} \cos[2\theta_\pi(x_n, y_n)]}\right] \\
&= \frac{1}{2} \arctan\left[\frac{\sum_{n=1}^{N} 2 \sin[\theta(x_n, y_n)] \cos[\theta_\pi(x_n, y_n)]}{\sum_{n=1}^{N} (\cos^2[\theta_\pi(x_n, y_n)] - \sin^2[\theta_\pi(x_n, y_n)])}\right]. \tag{3.19}
\end{aligned}$$

Substituting Eq. (3.15) into Eq. (3.19) yields

$$\theta_\pi = \frac{1}{2} \arctan\left[\frac{\sum_{n=1}^{N} 2I_x(x_n, y_n)I_y(x_n, y_n)}{\sum_{n=1}^{N} (I_y^2(x_n, y_n) - I_x^2(x_n, y_n))}\right], \tag{3.20}$$

where I_x and I_y can be easily obtained by operators such as Sobel or Prewitt, which are standard functions in MATLAB. The MATLAB script "Gradient_based_method.m," which uses the gradient-based method to obtain the fringe orientation, is shown in Table 3.3. Figure 3.5(a) shows simulated fringes, and Fig. 3.5(b) shows the orientation image computed by the gradient-based method.

3.3.2.2 Plane-fit method

This section discusses a technique based on a local-plane least-squares fit of pixels in a certain window of the interferogram.[5,6,21] Consider a window of size $2N + 1$ pixels; the local intensity at any pixel (x_n, y_n) of that window can be fitted as

$$I(x_n, y_n) = a + bx_n + cy_n, \tag{3.21}$$

where $(x_n, y_n) : n = -N, \ldots 0, \ldots, N$.

Table 3.3 MATLAB code "Gradient_based_method.m" uses the gradient-based method to obtain the fringe orientation (see Fig. 3.5).

```
1   %%Find the fringe orientation using the gradient sobel
2   load sfringe1
3   pts=size(I,1);
4   x=linspace(0,pts-1,pts);
5   y=linspace(0,pts-1,pts);
6   [X,Y] = meshgrid(x,y);
7   Ihp=I - mean(I(:));
8   If=Ihp;
9   figure
10  imagesc(If)
11  colormap (gray(256))
12  title('Inital fringe pattern')
13  colorbar
14  %%Sobel %Method 1: Apply gradient-based method
15   w=21;                              %Window size
16  pmin=floor(w/2)+1;
17  pmax=pts-floor(w/2)-1;             %pts is the number of points in I
18  H = fspecial('sobel');
19  theta=zeros(size(I,1));
20  for m=pmin:1:pmax
21  for n=pmin:1:pmax
22  window=If(m-floor(w/2):m-floor(w/2)+...
23  w-1,n-floor(w/2):n-floor(w/2)+w-1);
24  windowx = imfilter(window,H);
25  windowy = imfilter(window,transpose(H));
26  Num=sum(sum(2*windowx.*windowy));
27  Den=sum(sum(windowy.^2-windowx.^2));
28  theta(m,n)=0.5*atan2(Num,Den);
29  end
30  end
31  figure
32  imagesc(theta)
33  title('Orientation image')
34  colormap (gray(256))
35  colorbar
36  %%Method 2: Apply gradient-based method convolution
37  w=21;                              %Window size
38  pmin=floor(w/2)+1;
39  pmax=pts-floor(w/2)-1;             %pts is the number of points in I
40  H = fspecial('sobel');
41  theta2=zeros(size(I,1));
42  windowx = imfilter(If,H);
43  windowy = imfilter(If,transpose(H));
44  Num=conv2(2*windowx.*windowy,ones(w,w)/w^2,'same');
45  Den=conv2(windowy.^2-windowx.^2,ones(w,w)/w^2,'same');
46  theta2=0.5*atan2(Num,Den);
47  figure
48  imagesc(theta2)
49  title('Orientation image')
50  colormap (gray(256))
51  colorbar
```

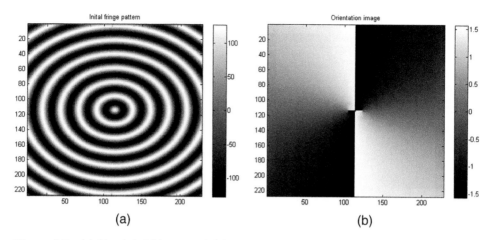

Figure 3.5 (a) Simulated fringes and (b) the orientation image computed by the gradient-based method.

Least-squares fitting can rewrite this problem as a system of linear equations:

$$
\begin{bmatrix}
\sum_{n=-N}^{N} 1 & \sum_{n=-N}^{N} x_n & \sum_{n=-N}^{N} y_n \\
\sum_{n=-N}^{N} x_n & \sum_{n=-N}^{N} x_n^2 & \sum_{n=-N}^{N} x_n y_n \\
\sum_{n=-N}^{N} y_n & \sum_{n=-N}^{N} x_n y_n & \sum_{n=-N}^{N} y_n^2
\end{bmatrix}
\begin{bmatrix} a \\ b \\ c \end{bmatrix}
=
\begin{bmatrix}
\sum_{n=-N}^{N} I(x_n, y_n) \\
\sum_{n=-N}^{N} x_n I(x_n, y_n) \\
\sum_{n=-N}^{N} y_n I(x_n, y_n)
\end{bmatrix}.
$$

$$(3.22)$$

Because the selected window is symmetric, then

$$
\sum_{n=-N}^{N} x_n, \ \sum_{n=-N}^{N} y_n, \ \sum_{n=-N}^{N} x_n y_n = 0, \quad \text{and} \quad \sum_{n=-N}^{N} x_n^2 = \sum_{n=-N}^{N} y_n^2.
$$

Based on this symmetry assumption,

$$
a = \frac{\sum_{n=-N}^{N} I(x_n, y_n)}{2N+1}, \quad b = \frac{\sum_{n=-N}^{N} x_n I(x_n, y_n)}{\sum_{n=-N}^{N} x_n^2}, \quad c = \frac{\sum_{n=-N}^{N} y_n I(x_n, y_n)}{\sum_{n=-N}^{N} y_n^2}.
$$

$$(3.23)$$

It can be shown that the fringe orientation angle is obtained by

$$
\theta_\pi = \arctan\left[\frac{\partial I(x,y)/\partial y}{\partial I(x,y)/\partial x}\right] = \arctan\left[\frac{c}{b}\right] = \arctan\left[\frac{\sum_{n=-N}^{N} y_n I(x_n, y_n)}{\sum_{n=-N}^{N} x_n I(x_n, y_n)}\right].
$$

$$(3.24)$$

To acheive more-robust results, a complex average strategy can be applied, as in the gradient-based method. The orientation is obtained by

$$
\begin{aligned}
\theta_\pi &= \frac{1}{2}\arctan\left[\frac{\sum_{n=-N}^{N}\left(2I_x(x_n,y_n)I_y(x_n,y_n)\right)}{\sum_{n=-N}^{N}\left(I_y^2(x_n,y_n)-I_x^2(x_n,y_n)\right)}\right] \\
&= \frac{1}{2}\arctan\left[\frac{\sum_{n=-N}^{N}(2bc)}{\sum_{n=-N}^{N}(b^2-c^2)}\right],
\end{aligned}
\tag{3.25}
$$

where

$$
I_x = c = \frac{\sum_{n=-N}^{N}y_n I(x_n,y_n)}{\sum_{n=-N}^{N}y_n^2}, \quad I_y = b = \frac{\sum_{n=-N}^{N}x_n I(x_n,y_n)}{\sum_{n=-N}^{N}x_n^2}.
$$

The MATLAB script "Plane_fit_method.m," which uses the plane-fit method to obtain the fringe orientation, is shown in Table 3.4. Figure 3.6(a) shows an interferogram, and Fig. 3.6(b) shows the orientation image computed by the plane-fit method.

3.3.2.3 Spin-filter method

Another technique to find the fringe orientation uses spin filters.[5,6,22,23] In the first step, the spin filters spin their directional filter arms to find the fringe tangential direction and then perform a median or average filter operation on the tangent line to filter out the random noise in that direction. The fringe directions are then computed through the recording of the fringe direction at every point of the interferogram, as shown in Fig. 3.7(a).

The noise is easily filtered due to the fact that the fringe frequency is close to zero along the tangential direction of the fringes. Therefore, a simple lowpass filter can filter out the high-frequency noise without any distortion to the signal near the zero frequency.

The spin filter is named as such because the filtering process around a certain point is performed using a directional filter line that spins around that particular point. There are two versions of this technique. One is called *two-arm*, which uses two symmetric filters on either side of the spinning center, and another is *one-arm*, where the current point is at the end of the directional filter line and the directional filter line spins around that end. The latter is often used when the fringes resemble a moiré pattern.[22]

The spin-filter method algorithm works as follows:

Step 1: A gradient filter line centered on a certain point is spun to find the direction that gives the minimum gradient, which will be the tangent direction to the fringe where this current point is located.

Step 2: Perform a median filter or average filter in the direction of this tangent. Consider a window of size $N \times N$ (e.g., 7×7) pixels centered around the current pixel to be processed in this window. Either eight

Table 3.4 MATLAB code "Plane_fit_method.m" uses the plane-fit method to obtain the fringe orientation (see Fig. 3.6).

```
1    %%Find the fringe orientation using the plane-fit
2    %method
3    load espiyang
4    pts=size(I,1);
5    x=linspace(0,pts-1,pts);
6    y=linspace(0,pts-1,pts);
7    [X,Y] = meshgrid(x,y);
8    Ihp=I - mean(I(:));
9    If=Ihp;
10   figure
11   imagesc(If)
12   title('Inital fringe pattern')
13   colormap (gray(256))
14   colorbar
15   %%Plane-fit method
16   %If = mat2gray(Ihp,[0 255])
17   %imshow(If)
18   %figure
19   %imshow(Ihp)
20   w=25; %window size
21   pmin=floor(w/2)+1;
22   pmax=pts-floor(w/2)-1;
23   xl=-(w-1)/2:1:(w-1)/2;
24   yl=xl;
25   for m=pmin:1:pmax
26   for n=pmin:1:pmax
27   Num=0;
28   Den=0;
29   window=If(m-floor(w/2):m-floor(w/2)+w-1,...
30   n-floor(w/2):n-floor(w/2)+w-1);
31   for i=1:1:w
32   Num=Num+sum(window(:,i)*yl(i));
33   Den=Den+sum(window(i,:)*xl(i));
34   end
35   theta(m,n)=atan(Num/Den)+pi/2;
36   end
37   end
38   figure
39   imagesc(theta)
40   title('Orientation image')
41   colormap (gray(256))
42   colorbar
```

(for the two-arm version) or 16 directions (for the one arm version) can be used as filters. Five of these directions are shown in Fig. 3.7(b). At the current pixel (i,j) and the kth direction, the average gray-level intensity can be defined as

$$M_{ij}^k = \frac{1}{N} \sum_{n=1}^{N} I_n^k, \tag{3.26}$$

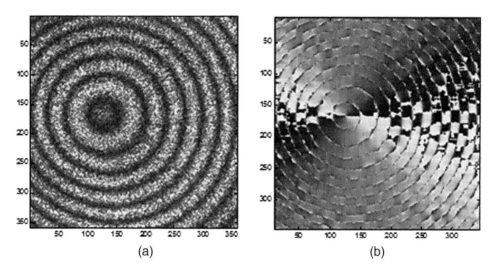

Figure 3.6 (a) Interferogram and (b) orientation image computed by the plane-fit method.

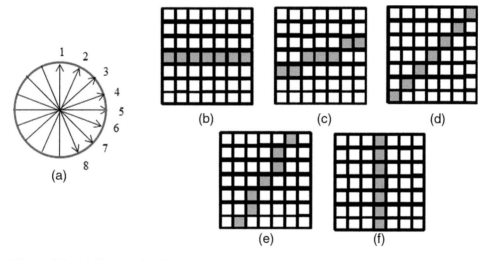

Figure 3.7 (a) Schematic of direction lines and (b-f) actual direction definition for the fringe orientation.[22]

where I_n^k is the gray-level intensity of the nth point in the kth direction.

Step 3: The sum of the absolute difference between the gray-level intensity of each pixel and the computed average in each kth direction is computed as

$$D_{ij}^k = \sum_{n=1}^{N} |I_n^k - M_{ij}^k|. \tag{3.27}$$

Therefore, D_{ij}^k represents the varying gradient of gray levels in the kth direction.

Step 4: The tangential orientation to be associated with the minimum value of D_{ij}^k is denoted as

$$k_{Tan} = dir[\min(D_{ij}^k)].   \qquad (3.28)$$

Step 5: Apply a 1D median or average filter on the tangent line. In the case of the median filter, the current point (i,j) will be replaced by the median value of the tangent line, thus filtering high-frequency noise. In the case of Gaussian noise, an average filter is used, and the mean value of the k_{Tan} line $M_{ij}^{k_{Tan}}$ is used to replace the current (i,j) pixel.[22]

Step 6: Repeat this process for every pixel in the interferogram.

The MATLAB script "Spin_filt_method.m" that uses the spin-filter method to obtain the fringe orientation is shown in Table 3.5. Figure 3.8(a) shows an interferogram, and Fig. 3.8(b) shows the fringe orientation map after median filter by a 7×7 window. The darkest gray level is along the direction labeled "5," and the brightest gray level is along the direction labeled "8" in Figure 3.7(a). The discontinuity in Fig. 3.8(b) is due to the discrete number of directions.

3.3.2.4 Fourier transform method

The Fourier transform method is based on the energy spectral density analysis of the Fourier transform of the interferogram. Performing the traditional Fourier transform and enhancing the interferogram image in the Fourier domain by root filtering can estimate the optical fringe orientation.[24] Let the interferogram grayscale intensity at a certain point (i,j) be described as $I(x_i, y_j)$, and consider a window of size $N \times N$ pixels around that specific point. Let the pixel position in the window be (k,l). The discrete Fourier transform of each window of the interferogram can be defined as

$$\tilde{I}(m,n) = \frac{1}{N^2} \sum_{k=0}^{N-1} \sum_{l=0}^{N-1} I(k,l)e^{-j\frac{2\pi}{N}(mk+nl)},   \qquad (3.29)$$

where (m,n) are the discrete spatial frequencies in the window, and

$$\tilde{I}(m,n) = \text{Re}\{\tilde{I}(m,n)\} + j\,\text{Im}\{\tilde{I}(m,n)\} = |\tilde{I}(m,n)|e^{j\phi(m,n)}.   \qquad (3.30)$$

The energy spectral density in the polar and rectangular coordinates can be defined as the square of the Fourier spectrum:[24]

$$\tilde{E}(r_m, \theta_n) = \tilde{E}(m,n) = |\tilde{I}(m,n)|^2,   \qquad (3.31)$$

Table 3.5 MATLAB code "Spin_filt_method.m" uses the spin-filter method to obtain the fringe orientation (see Fig. 3.8).

```
1   %%Find the fringe orientation using the spin-filter
2   %method
3   clear all;
4   close all;
5   clc;
6   load sfringe1
7   pts=size(I,1);
8   x=linspace(0,pts-1,pts);
9   y=linspace(0,pts-1,pts);
10  [X,Y] = meshgrid(x,y);
11  Ihp=I - mean(I(:));
12  If=Ihp;
13  im(If)
14  figure
15  imagesc(If)
16  title('Inital fringe pattern')
17  colormap (gray(256))
18  colorbar
19  %%Spin filter
20  %I=Inew;
21  wd=5;
22  window=zeros(8,wd);
23  for m=5:1:size(I,1)-5
24  for n=5:1:size(I,2)-5
25  window(1,:)=I(m-floor(wd/2):m+floor(wd/2),n);
26  O(1)=mean(window(1,:));
27  window(5,:)=I(m,n-floor(wd/2):n+floor(wd/2));
28  O(5)=mean(window(5,:));
29  window(7,:)=[I(m+2,n-2),I(m+1,n-1),I(m,n),...
30  I(m-1,n+1),I(m-2,n+2)];
31  O(7)=mean(window(7,:));
32  window(8,:)=[I(m+1,n-2),I(m+1,n-1),I(m,n),...
33  I(m-1,n+1),I(m-1,n+2)];
34  O(8)=mean(window(8,:));
35  window(6,:)=[I(m+2,n-1),I(m+1,n-1),I(m,n),...
36  I(m-1,n+1),I(m-2,n+1)];
37  O(6)=mean(window(6,:));
38  window(3,:)=[I(m-2,n-2),I(m-1,n-1),I(m,n),...
39  I(m+1,n+1),I(m+2,n+2)];
40  O(3)=mean(window(3,:));
41  window(2,:)=[I(m-1,n-2),I(m-1,n-1),I(m,n),...
42  I(m+1,n+1),I(m+1,n+2)];
43  O(2)=mean(window(2,:));
44  window(4,:)=[I(m-2,n-1),I(m-1,n-1),I(m,n),...
45  I(m+1,n+1),I(m+2,n+1)];
46  O(4)=mean(window(4,:));
47  for xx=1:1:8
48  D(xx)=sum(abs(window(xx,:)-O(xx)));
49  end
50  kk=find(D==min(D));
51  kk=kk(1);
52  checkabs=abs(window(kk,:)-O(kk));
53  mm=find(checkabs==max(checkabs));
```

(continued)

Table 3.5 (*Continued*)

```
54  Inew(m,n)=(sum(window(kk,:))-window(kk,mm(1)))/(wd);
55  mapdirec(m,n)=kk(1);
56  switch kk(1)
57  case 1
58  rr=5;
59  case 2
60  rr=6;
61  case 3
62  rr=7;
63  case 4
64  rr=8;
65  case 5
66  rr=1;
67  case 6
68  rr=2;
69  case 7
70  rr=3;
71  case 8
72  rr=4;
73  end
74  derivative= sum (window(rr,5)-window(rr,1)...
75  +window(rr,4)-window(rr,2));
76  if sign(derivative)>0
77  SG(m,n)=1;
78  else SG(m,n)=0;
79  end
80  end
81  end
82  figure
83  imagesc(mapdirec)
84  title('Fringe orientation map after median filter')
85  colormap (gray(256))
86  colorbar
87  figure
88  imagesc(SG)
89  title('Derivative-sign binary-fringe image')
90  colormap (gray(256))
91  colorbar
```

where (r_m, θ_n) are the polar coordinates. It is worth noting that the angular distribution of the energy spectral density is related to the direction of the fringes in that window.[25,26] The probability of energy spectral density of a certain location (r_m, θ_n) can be written as[24]

$$p(r_m, \theta_n) = p(m,n) = \frac{\tilde{E}(m,n)}{\tilde{E}_{Total}}, \quad (3.32)$$

where

$$\tilde{E}_{Total} = \sum_{m=1}^{N-1}\sum_{n=1}^{N-1} \tilde{E}(r_m, \theta_n) = \sum_{m=1}^{N-1}\sum_{n=1}^{N-1} \tilde{E}(m,n).$$

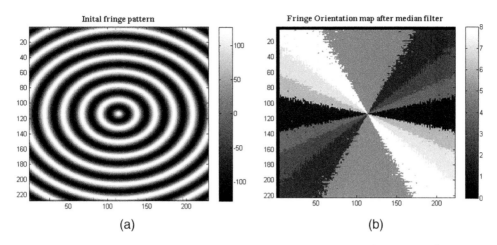

Figure 3.8 (a) Initial fringe pattern and (b) fringe orientation map after median filter by a 7 × 7 window. The darkest gray level is along the direction labeled "5," and the brightest gray level is along the direction labeled "8" in Fig. 3.7(a).

On the other hand, the angular probability of the energy spectral density at a certain angle θ_n can be defined as

$$p(\theta_n) = \sum_{m=1}^{N-1} p(r_m, \theta_n).$$
(3.33)

It is assumed that the orientation θ_n is a random variable that has the probability density function $p(\theta_n)$.[24]

Vector averaging can show that the orientation at the current pixel (i,j) is given by

$$\Theta(i,j) = \frac{1}{2}\arctan\left(\frac{\sum_n p(\theta_n)\sin(2\theta_{m,n})}{\sum_n p(\theta_n)\cos(2\theta_{m,n})}\right) = \frac{1}{2}\arctan\left(\frac{\sum_m\sum_n \tilde{E}(m,n)\sin(2\theta_{m,n})}{\sum_m\sum_n \tilde{E}(m,n)\cos(2\theta_{m,n})}\right),$$
(3.34)

where

$$\theta_{m,n} = \arctan\left(\frac{n}{m}\right).$$
(3.35)

The terms $\sin(2\theta_{m,n})$ and $\cos(2\theta_{m,n})$ are used to resolve the orientation ambiguity between orientations ± 180 deg. The main steps of the algorithm are implemented as follows:[24]

1. **Normalization:** The normalization step reduces noise. The initial interferogram with a mean μ and variance σ^2 is normalized to

have a specific mean μ_N and variance σ_N^2 according to the following formula:

$$I_N(x,y) = \begin{cases} \mu_N + \left(\frac{\sigma_N^2[I(x,y)-\mu]}{\sigma^2}\right)^{1/2}, & \text{if } I(x,y) > \mu, \\ \mu_N - \left(\frac{\sigma_N^2[I(x,y)-\mu]}{\sigma^2}\right)^{1/2}, & \text{otherwise.} \end{cases} \qquad (3.36)$$

2. **Fourier transform:** Perform a local Fourier transform on each window of size $N \times N$ pixels around the current point (i,j) to obtain $\tilde{I}(m,n)$.

3. **Image enhancement:** Perform image enhancement in the Fourier domain using root filtering, as in the following equation:[27]

$$\tilde{I}_{Enh}(m,n) = \tilde{I}(m,n)|\tilde{I}(m,n)|^p, \qquad (3.37)$$

where p is a constant (e.g., 1).

4. **Orientation calculation:** For each point of the window, use Eq. (3.35) and compute $\theta_{m,n}$.

5. **Compute the enhanced energy density:** For each pixel of the window, compute $\tilde{E}_{Enh}(m,n) = |\tilde{I}_{Enh}(m,n)|^2$.

6. **Compute the fringe orientation of the current point (i,j):** Use Eq. (3.34) to estimate $\Theta(i,j)$ for the current pixel of the interferogram.

7. Repeat steps 2 through 6 for all of the pixels of the interferogram.

8. **Lowpass filter** Perform lowpass filtering of the orientation angle $\Theta(i,j)$ to cancel speckle noise by converting the orientation image to a continuous vector field using the following equations:

$$\Phi'_x(i,j) = \sum_{k=-\frac{w-1}{2}}^{\frac{w-1}{2}} \sum_{l=-\frac{w-1}{2}}^{\frac{w-1}{2}} h(k,l)\Phi_x(i+k,j+l), \qquad (3.38a)$$

$$\Phi'_y(i,j) = \sum_{k=-\frac{w-1}{2}}^{\frac{w-1}{2}} \sum_{l=-\frac{w-1}{2}}^{\frac{w-1}{2}} h(k,l)\Phi_y(i+k,j+l), \qquad (3.38b)$$

where $h(k,l)$ is a 2D rotationally symmetric Gaussian lowpass filter of size $w \times w$, and

$$\Phi_x(i,j) = \cos[2\Theta(i,j)], \quad \Phi_y(i,j) = \sin[2\Theta(i,j)].$$

The smoothed orientation can be found to be

$$\Theta_{smooth}(i,j) = \frac{1}{2}\arctan\left[\frac{\Phi'_y(i,j)}{\Phi'_x(i,j)}\right]. \qquad (3.39)$$

Table 3.6 MATLAB code "FT_Orient_method.m" uses the Fourier transform method to obtain the fringe orientation (see Fig. 3.9).

```
1   %%Find the fringe orientation using the Fourier
2   %transform orientation method
3   clear all;close all;clc;
4   load espi2;
5   pts=size(I,1);
6   x=linspace(0,pts-1,pts);
7   y=linspace(0,pts-1,pts);
8   [X,Y] = meshgrid(x,y);
9   Ihp=I - mean(I(:));
10  If=Ihp;
11  figure
12  imagesc(If); colormap (gray(256))
13  title('Inital fringe pattern');colorbar
14  %%"Regular Fourier Transform," Tang, Applied Optics,
15  %Vol. 49, p 554
16  w=31;                           %Window size
17  pmin=floor(w/2)+1;
18  pmax=pts-floor(w/2)-1;
19  xl=1:1:w; yl=xl;
20  for i=1:1:w
21  th(:,i)=atan(xl/yl(i));
22  end
23  for m=pmin:1:pmax
24  for n=pmin:1:pmax
25  window=If(m-floor(w/2):m-floor(w/2)+w-1,...
26  n-floor(w/2):n-floor(w/2)+w-1);
27  fwindow=fft2(window);
28  fwindowe=fwindow.*abs(fwindow).^1;        %Root filter
29  Ewindow=abs(fwindowe).^2;
30  num=sum(sum(Ewindow.*sin(2.*th)));
31  dem=sum(sum(Ewindow.*cos(2.*th)));
32  theta(m,n)=0.5*atan(num/dem);
33  end
34  end
35  figure
36  imagesc(theta)
37  title('Orientation image')
38  colormap (gray(256));colorbar
39  %Lowpass the result
40  H = fspecial('gaussian');       %Default size is 3*3
41  thetaf=imfilter(theta,H);
42  figure
43  imagesc(thetaf);title('Orientation image')
44  colormap (gray(256));colorbar
```

The MATLAB script "FT_Orient_method.m," which uses the Fourier transform method to obtain the fringe orientation is shown in Table 3.6. Figure 3.9(a) shows an interferogram, and Fig. 3.9(b) shows the orientation image computed by the Fourier transform method.

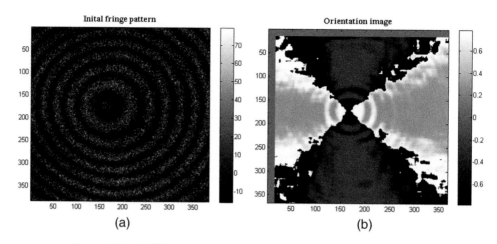

Figure 3.9 (a) Fringe pattern with noise, and (b) an orientation map.

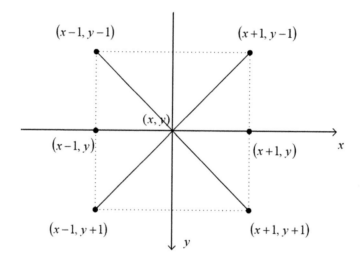

Figure 3.10 Neighbors and corners of point (i,j).[21]

3.3.2.5 Accumulate-differences method

The directional differences generally have a minimum value along the tangent direction of the fringe and a maximum value along the normal direction. In the accumulate-differences method, the difference along a certain direction is specified in an alternate way. This technique accumulates differences along four directions (i.e., 0, 45, 90, and 135 deg) and then computes the local orientation according to the difference. If the minimum directional difference is found, then the fringe direction can be obtained.

Consider a current point (i,j), as shown in Fig. 3.10, where the four differences can be found using[21]

$$d_0(i,j) = |I(i-1,j) - I(i+1,j)| \times \sqrt{2}, \qquad (3.40a)$$

$$d_{45}(i,j) = |I(i-1,j+1) - I(i+1,j-1)|, \qquad (3.40b)$$

$$d_{90}(i,j) = |I(i,j-1) - I(i,j+1)| \times \sqrt{2}, \qquad (3.40c)$$

$$d_{135}(i,j) = |I(i-1,j-1) - I(k+1,j+1)|, \qquad (3.40d)$$

where $I(i,j)$ is the intensity at the point (i,j). The square root in the above equation is due to the fact that the corners are farther from the center point by that amount.

To reduce the noise effect, an accumulating strategy is employed in a certain window. This is done by adding up all of the differences between neighboring points in the window along a certain direction, and the sum that produces the smallest result will be along the local fringe direction. Therefore, by calculating the sums along all of the orientations and finding the smallest one, one can obtain the fringe orientation. In a certain window of size $w \times w$, the four sums of the differences along the four directions are calculated as follows:

$$D_{angle}(i,j) = \sum_{(i,j) \in w \times w} d_{angle}(i,j), \quad (angle = 0°, 45, °90°, 135°). \qquad (3.41)$$

In the accumulate-difference method, the orientation $\theta(i,j)$ at point (i,j) can be estimated by[21]

$$\theta(i,j) = \frac{1}{2} \arctan\left(\frac{D_{0°} - D_{90°}}{D_{45°} - D_{135°}}\right) + \frac{\pi}{2}. \qquad (3.42)$$

The MATLAB script "Acc_Diff_method.m," which uses the accumulate-differences method to obtain the fringe orientation, is shown in Table 3.7. Figure 3.11(a) shows the initial interferogram, and Fig. 3.11(b) shows the orientation image computed by the accumulate-difference method.

3.3.2.6 Comparison of the different methods

All of the methods mentioned earlier have advantages and disadvantages, listed in Table 3.8. These techniques produce more or less similar results (sometimes rotated by 90 deg, such as Figs. 3.5 and 3.11), depending on the number of orientations (compare Figs. 3.5 and 3.8, which have only eight orientations) and on how good the approximation is (compare Figs 3.6 and 3.9).

3.3.3 Phase unwrapping and fringe direction computation using regularized phase tracking

This section discusses phase-unwrapping and fringe-direction techniques based on a regularized phase-tracking (RPT) system.[29–32] In terms of the SNR in the estimated phase, the RPT method is superior to other phase-unwrapping techniques, such as Fourier,[1,2] or phase-shifting interferometry (PSI)

Table 3.7 MATLAB code "Acc_Diff_method.m" uses the accumulate-difference method to obtain the fringe orientation (see Fig. 3.11).

```
1   %%Find the fringe orientation using the accumulate-
2   %difference method
3   clear all;close all;clc;
4   load sfringe1;
5   pts=size(I,1);
6   x=linspace(0,pts-1,pts);  y=linspace(0,pts-1,pts);
7   [X,Y] = meshgrid(x,y);
8   Ihp=I - mean(I(:));
9   If=Ihp;
10  figure
11  imagesc(If)
12  colormap (gray(256));title('Inital fringe pattern')
13  colorbar
14  %%
15  wa=27;                                        %Window size
16  w=wa+2;
17  pmin=floor(w/2)+1; pmax=pts-floor(w/2)-1;
18  for m=pmin:1:pmax
19  for n=pmin:1:pmax
20  window=If(m-floor(w/2):m-floor(w/2)+w-1,...
21  n-floor(w/2):n-floor(w/2)+w-1);
22  floor(w/2)+w-1);
23  D0=0;D45=0;D90=0;D135=0;
24  for x=2:1:wa
25  for y=2:1:wa
26  D0= D0+abs(window(x-1,y)-window(x+1,y)*sqrt(2));
27  D45=D45+abs(window(x-1,y+1)-window(x+1,y-1));
28  D90=D90+abs(window(x,y-1)-window(x,y+1)*sqrt(2));
29  D135=D135+abs(window(x-1,y-1)-window(x+1,y+1));
30  end
31  end
32  num=D0-D90;
33  dem=D45-D135;
34  theta(m,n)=0.5*atan2(dem,num);
35  end
36  end
37  theta=mod(theta+pi/2,pi);
38  figure
39  imagesc(theta);title('Orientation image')
40  colormap (gray(256));colorbar
```

techniques. This method is superior because it acts like a narrow-bandpass filter tracking a wideband fringe pattern signal.[29]

A. Phase unwrapping based on regularized phase tracking

The unwrapping method discussed here is a generalization of the phase-locked loop (PLL) technique.[33,34] Phase unwrapping is achieved in two steps. First, two phase-shifted fringe patterns (the sine and the cosine) are obtained from the demodulated wrapped phase, and then the RPT technique is used to demodulate the two fringe patterns.[29]

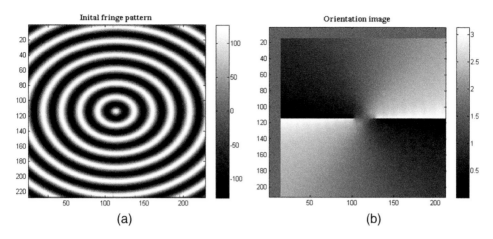

Figure 3.11 (a) Fringe pattern with noise, and (b) an orientation map.

Table 3.8 Comparison of the different orientation techniques.

Method	Advantages	Disadvantages
Gradient based	Efficient	Low accuracy in the presence of speckle noise. Failure in the zero gradient regions.
Plane fit	Efficient in high noise	Limited by the size of the calculating window. Failure in the zero gradient regions.
Spin filter	Filters random noise efficiently. No blurring effect or phase distortion.	Some problems with moiré patterns (especially the two-arm version)
Regular Fourier transform	Computes orientation even with very-low-quality fringes due to low and high fringe density, high noise, and low contrast	Time consuming
Accumulate difference	Works well with noise	Needs filter preprocessing
Spiral-phase 2D energy operator	Works well for fringes with strong curvature	Complex algorithm[28]

Similar to Eq. (3.8), the interference pattern can be described as

$$I(x, y) = a(x, y) + b(x, y) \cos[\phi_W(x, y)], \qquad (3.43)$$

where the relationship between the wrapped $\phi_W(x, y)$ and unwrapped phase $\phi(x, y)$ can be written as

$$\phi(x, y) = \phi_W(x, y) + 2\pi k(x, y), \qquad (3.44)$$

and k is an integer. The first step is to obtain two phase-shifted fringes from the observed wrapped phase $\phi_W(x, y)$:[29]

$$I_C(x, y) = \cos[\phi_W(x, y)], \qquad (3.45a)$$

$$I_S(x, y) = \sin[\phi_W(x, y)], \qquad (3.45b)$$

The second step is to demodulate these two phase-shifted fringe patterns using the RPT technique. In fringe-analysis phase-detection problems, regularization finds an energy or cost function that at least uses two terms that act as constraints for the estimated unwrapped phase, which will minimize the cost function with respect to (ϕ, k_x, k_y). These terms are often related to (a) the fidelity between the estimated unwrapped phase and the observed wrapped phase, and (b) the smoothness of the modulated phase. The RPT cost function at each point (x, y) can be written as[29,30]

$$U_{(x,y)}(\phi, k_x, k_y) =$$

$$\sum_{(\xi, \eta) \in (N_{(x,y)} \cap L)} \{|I_c(\xi, \eta) - \cos[p(x, y, \xi, \eta)]|^2 + |I_S(\xi, \eta) - \sin[p(x, y, \xi, \eta)]|^2$$

$$+ \mu |\phi(\xi, \eta) - p(x, y, \xi, \eta)|^2 m(\xi, \eta)\}, \qquad (3.46a)$$

with

$$p(x, y, \xi, \eta) = \phi(x, y) + k_x(x, y)(x - \xi) + k_y(x, y)(y - \eta), \qquad (3.46b)$$

where L is a 2D matrix with fringe data; $N_{(x,y)}$ is a neighborhood around the current point (x, y); $k_{x,y}(x, y)$ are the estimated local frequencies along the x and y directions, respectively [fringe patterns are assumed to be locally and spatially monochromatic, such that $(\partial \phi / \partial x, \partial \phi / \partial y) = (k_x, k_y)$]; μ is the regularizing parameter that controls the smoothness of the unwrapped phase; and the binary indicator function is given by

$$m(\xi, \eta) = \begin{cases} 1, & \text{if } (x, y) \text{ is unwrapped} \\ 0, & \text{otherwise.} \end{cases} \qquad (3.46c)$$

The first two terms in Eq. (3.46a) correspond to the fidelity constraint (a) in the RPT method, where the observed two phase-shifted fringes $I_{C,S}(x, y)$ are modeled as sinusoidal functions modulated by a plane $\cos[p(x, y, \xi, \eta)]$ or $\sin[p(x, y, \xi, \eta)]$ in phase space. The amplitude of these sinusoidal functions must be kept close to $I_{C,S}(x, y)$ in a least-squares sense within the neighborhood $N_{(x,y)}$. The third term is the regularization term, where the assumption of smoothness and continuity of (b) is enforced. In other words, the unwrapped-phase $\phi(x, y)$ must be kept close to the locally adaptive phase plane $p(x, y, \xi, \eta)$ in the least-squares sense within the neighborhood $N_{(x,y)}$. The steps needed for this algorithm are as follows:

1. At a chosen seed point (x_0, y_0) in L, set $m(x_0, y_0) = 0$. The cost function $U_{(x_0, y_0)}(\phi, k_x, k_y)$ is then minimized with respect to $(\phi(x_0, y_0), k_x(x_0, y_0), k_y(x_0, y_0))$, then mark $m(x_0, y_0) = 1$.
2. Choose another pixel (x, y).
3. If $m(x, y) = 1$, then go back to step (2); otherwise, test if $m(x_i, y_j) = 1$ for any adjacent pixel (x_i, y_j). If no adjacent pixel has been unwrapped, then

go back to step (2); otherwise, take $(\phi(x_i, y_j), k_x(x_i, y_j), k_y(x_i, y_j))$ as the initial conditions to minimize $U_{(x,y)}(\phi, k_x, k_y)$ using the following gradient descent formulation:

$$\phi^{p+1}(x,y) = \phi^p(x,y) - \alpha \frac{\partial U_{(x,y)}(\phi, k_x, k_y)}{\partial \phi(x,y)}, \qquad (3.47a)$$

$$k_x^{p+1}(x,y) = k_x^p(x,y) - \alpha \frac{\partial U_{(x,y)}(\phi, k_x, k_y)}{\partial k_x(x,y)}, \qquad (3.47b)$$

$$k_y^{p+1}(x,y) = k_y^p(x,y) - \alpha \frac{\partial U_{(x,y)}(\phi, k_x, k_y)}{\partial k_y(x,y)}, \qquad (3.47c)$$

where α is the step size, and p is the iteration number.
4. Set $m(x,y) = 1$, and go back to step (2).

B. Fringe direction ($\beta_{2\pi}$) estimation through phase unwrapping of the fringe orientation angle θ_π

To estimate the fringe direction $\beta_{2\pi}$ (0 deg, 360 deg) from the fringe orientation θ_π (0 deg, 180 deg), the RPT phase-unwrapping method discussed in part A can be used [30]. The relation between the orientation angle and the direction angle is:

$$\theta_\pi = \beta_{2\pi} + k\pi, \qquad (3.48)$$

where k denotes an integer such that $0 \leq \theta_\pi \leq \pi$. Equation (3.48) can be written as

$$W(2\theta_\pi) = W(2\beta_{2\pi} + 2k\pi) = W(2\beta_{2\pi}), \qquad (3.49)$$

where W is the wrapping operator defined as $W(\phi) = \phi + 2k\pi$, such that $-\pi < W(\phi) < \pi$. Equation (3.49) suggests that the wrapped version of $2\theta_\pi$ and that of $2\beta_{2\pi}$ are the same, and thus it is possible to obtain the direction angle $2\beta_{2\pi}$ by unwrapping $W(2\theta_\pi)$ and dividing it by two. This is not a trivial matter due to both the discontinuity of $2\beta_{2\pi}$ and the presence of noise.[30]

Therefore, a modified version of the RPT phase-unwrapping algorithm can be used for this purpose. Denote the phase map to be unwrapped as $W(2\theta_\pi)$, and define the following two quadrature patterns:

$$I_C = \cos[W(2\theta_\pi)] = \cos[2\beta_{2\pi}], \qquad (3.50a)$$

$$I_S = \sin[W(2\theta_\pi)] = \sin[2\beta_{2\pi}]. \qquad (3.50b)$$

This version is similar to the RPT method employed in part A; however, in this case, the minimization of the cost function will be with respect to $(2\beta_{2\pi}(x,y), 2\partial\beta_{2\pi}(x,y)/\partial x, 2\partial\beta_{2\pi}(x,y)/\partial y)$, and the cost function of Eq. (3.46) will be modified to be[30]

$$U_{(x,y)}(2\beta_{2\pi}, 2\partial\beta_{2\pi}/\partial x, 2\partial\beta_{2\pi}/\partial y) =$$
$$\sum_{(\xi,\eta)\in N_{(x,y)}\cap L} \{|I_c(\xi,\eta) - \cos[p(x,y,\xi,\eta)]|^2 + |I_S(\xi,\eta) - \sin[p(x,y,\xi,\eta)]|^2$$
$$+ \mu |W_{4\pi}[2\beta_{2\pi}(\xi,\eta) - p(x,y,\xi,\eta)]|^2 m(\xi,\eta)\},$$

$$(3.51a)$$

where

$$p(x,y,\xi,\eta) = 2\beta_{2\pi}(x,y) + \frac{2\partial\beta_{2\pi}(x,y)}{\partial x}(x-\xi) + \frac{2\partial\beta_{2\pi}(x,y)}{\partial y}(y-\eta), \quad (3.51b)$$

and $W_{4\pi}$ denotes the modulo 4π operation $W_{4\pi}(\phi) = \phi + 4k\pi$, such that $-2\pi < W_{4\pi}(\phi) < 2\pi$. In Eq. (3.51) the regularization uses the 4π wrapping operator $W_{4\pi}$ due to the 4π continuity feature of the $2\beta_{2\pi}(x,y)$ function instead of the regular difference seen in Eq. (3.46). One note about this technique is that the scanning strategy is very crucial. Regions that contain critical orientation points, such as saddle points, fringe centers, and flat phases, are to be encircled and processed last, and typical quality maps used to guide the minimization of the cost function can be based on the magnitude of the fringe pattern gradient $|\nabla I|$.[16,30]

The MATLAB script "RPT_method.m," which uses the regularized phase-tracking method to obtain the fringe direction, is shown in Table 3.9. Figure 3.12(a) shows an interferogram, Fig. 3.12(b) shows the orientation computed by the accumulate-differences method, and Fig. 3.12(c) shows the direction map computed by the RPT method.

3.4 Phase Demodulation Using the Hilbert Transform Technique

Automatic demodulation of a single interferogram containing closed fringes is complicated. The first fully automatic technique is the RPT, discussed in Section 3.3.3.[29,30] A 2D generalization of the Hilbert transform as a different approach to the problem was recently proposed;[13,14] the method is known as spiral-phase or vortex demodulation, and it effectively generalizes the Hilbert transform from one dimension to two dimensions.

A. Background for the 1D Hilbert transform

The Hilbert transform $\mathcal{H}$ in 1D is an important tool in communication and signal processing.[35] Note that this section adopts different definitions of the

Table 3.9 MATLAB code "RPT_method.m" uses the RPT method to obtain the fringe direction (see Fig. 3.12).

```
1   %%This script is adapted from the code kindly obtained
2   %from Dr. J. Antonio Quiroga, Departamento de Optica
3   %Facultad de CC Fisicas,
4   %Universidad Complutense de Madrid,
5   %Madrid 28040
6   %http://www.ucm.es/info/optica/
7   %Reference: "Modulo 2pi fringe orientation angle
8   %estimation by phase unwrapping with a regularized
9   %phase tracking algorithm" JOSA A (2002).
10  %%
11  clc;
12  clear all;
13  close all;
14  %%
15  g=mat2gray(imread('miract_crop.jpg'));
16  [NR, NC]=size(g);
17  [x,y]=meshgrid(1:NC, 1:NR);
18  x=x-0.5*NC; y=y-0.5*NR;
19  R=2:20:NR; C=2:20:NC;
20  N=35;
21  %%Estimate orientation using the difference technique
22  MinusOneC=[2:NC NC];
23  PlusOneC=[1 1:NC-1];
24  MinusOneR=[2:NR NR];
25  PlusOneR=[1 1:NR-1];
26  d0=sqrt(2)*abs(g(MinusOneR,:)-g(PlusOneR,:));
27  d45=abs(g(MinusOneR,PlusOneC)-g(PlusOneR,MinusOneC));
28  d90=sqrt(2)*abs(g(:,MinusOneC)-g(:,PlusOneC));
29  d135=abs(g(MinusOneR,MinusOneC)-g(PlusOneR,PlusOneC));
30  D0=conv2(d0, ones(N,N)/N^2, 'same');
31  D45=conv2(d45, ones(N,N)/N^2, 'same');
32  D90=conv2(d90, ones(N,N)/N^2, 'same');
33  D135=conv2(d135, ones(N,N)/N^2, 'same');
34  b=0.5*(D0-D90);
35  c=-0.5*(D45-D135);
36  Or=0.5*atan2(c,b);
37  orn = mod(Or+pi/2,pi);
38  ornMod=mat2gray(abs(c+1i*b));
39  im(orn)
40  im(ornMod)
41  %%Calculation of the direction
42  clear b;
43  t=5;
44  mu=1;
45  m=mat2gray(imread('miract_cropMask.tif'));
46  theta=orn;
47  q=ornMod;
48  r0=[];
49  n=size(theta);
50  px=ones(n);py=ones(n);q=abs(q).*m;
51  s=zeros(n);beta=zeros(n);
52  dx=cos(theta).*m;dy=sin(theta).*m;
53  na=10;maxi=0;
```

(continued)

Table 3.9 *(Continued)*

```
54  q=round(q./max(max(q))*(na-1))+1;
55  for k=1:na
56  [ry,rx]=find(q==k);
57  if maxi<length(ry) maxi=length(ry);end
58  end
59  hy=zeros(na,maxi);hx=zeros(na,maxi);
60  front=zeros(1,na);final=zeros(1,na);
61  cont=0;ind=1;
62  if isempty(r0)
63  [yy,xx]=find(q==(max(q(:))));
64  y=yy(1);
65  x=xx(1);
66  else
67  x=r0(1);
68  y=r0(2);
69  end
70  px(y,x)=-dy(y,x);py(y,x)=dx(y,x);
71  beta(y,x)=atan2(dy(y,x),dx(y,x));
72  s(y,x)=1;
73  puntos_total=sum(sum(m));
74  handle_bar = waitbar(0,' Please wait...');
75  while ind>0
76  xx=[x-1;x-1;x-1;x;x;x+1;x+1;x+1];
77  yy=[y-1;y;y+1;y-1;y+1;y-1;y;y+1];
78  for k=1:8                        %%Cost function as in Eq (3.51)
79  if s(yy(k),xx(k))==0 & m(yy(k),xx(k))>0 & ...
80  xx(k)>t & xx(k)<n(2)-t+1 & ...
81  yy(k)>t & yy(k)<n(1)-t+1
82  xt=xx(k);yt=yy(k);
83  dx2=dx(yt-t:yt+t,xt-t:xt+t);
84  dy2=dy(yt-t:yt+t,xt-t:xt+t);
85  s2=s(yt-t:yt+t,xt-t:xt+t);
86  m2=m(yt-t:yt+t,xt-t:xt+t);
87  px2=px(yt-t:yt+t,xt-t:xt+t);
88  py2=py(yt-t:yt+t,xt-t:xt+t);
89  G(1,1)=sum(sum(dx2.^2.*m2))+mu*sum(sum(s2.*m2));
90  G(1,2)=sum(sum(dy2.*dx2.*m2));
91  b(1)=mu*sum(sum(px2.*s2.*m2));
92  G(2,2)=sum(sum(dy2.^2.*m2))+mu*sum(sum(s2.*m2));
93  b(2)=mu*sum(sum(py2.*s2.*m2));
94  G(2,1)=G(1,2);
95  R=inv(G)*b';
96  px(yt,xt)=R(1);py(yt,xt)=R(2);
97  beta(yt,xt)=atan2(-px(yt,xt),py(yt,xt));
98  s(yt,xt)=1;h=q(yt,xt);
99  if final(h)==maxi final(h)=1;
100 else final(h)=final(h)+1;end
101 hx(h,final(h))=xt;hy(h,final(h))=yt;
102 if front(h)==0 front(h)=1;end
103 cont=cont+1;
104 end
105 end
106 k=na;ind=0;
107 while ind==0 && k>0
```

(continued)

Table 3.9 *(Continued)*

```
108  ind=front(k);
109  if ind>0
110  x=hx(k,front(k));
111  y=hy(k,front(k));
112  if front(k)==final(k)
113  front(k)=0;final(k)=0;
114  else
115  if front(k)==maxi front(k)=1;
116  else front(k)=front(k)+1;end
117  end
118  end
119  k=k-1;
120  end
121  if mod(cont, 500)==0
122  waitbar(cont/puntos_total)
123  imagesc(beta); figure(gcf);
124  drawnow;
125  end
126  end
127  close(handle_bar)
128  beta=beta+pi;
129  px=-cos(beta);
130  py=sin(beta);
```

Hilbert transform and the Fourier transform according to Refs. 13, 14, and 35, which are opposite that of Chapter 2, namely:

$$\hat{I}(x) = \mathcal{H}\{I(x)\} = \frac{1}{\pi} p.v. \int_{-\infty}^{\infty} \frac{I(x')}{x - x'} dx', \qquad (3.52a)$$

$$I(x) = \mathcal{H}^{-1}\{\hat{I}(x)\} = -\frac{1}{\pi} p.v. \int_{-\infty}^{\infty} \frac{\hat{I}(x')}{x' - x} dx'. \qquad (3.52b)$$

where *p.v.* stands for the Cauchy principal value, and $\wedge$ indicates the Hilbert domain. The 1D Fourier transform pair is also redefined as

$$\tilde{I}(f_x) = \mathfrak{F}\{I(x)\} = \int_{-\infty}^{\infty} I(x) \exp(-j2\pi f_x x) dx, \qquad (3.53a)$$

$$I(x) = \mathfrak{F}^{-1}\{\tilde{I}(f_x)\} = \int_{-\infty}^{\infty} \tilde{I}(f_x) \exp(j2\pi f_x x) df_x. \qquad (3.53b)$$

where $\sim$ indicates the Fourier domain $k_x = 2\pi f_x$. One important property of the Hilbert transform is its ability to transform a cosine function into a sine function and vice versa:

$$\mathcal{H}\{\cos(k_0 x)\} = -\sin(k_0 x), \qquad (3.54a)$$

$$\mathcal{H}\{\sin(k_0 x)\} = \cos(k_0 x). \qquad (3.54b)$$

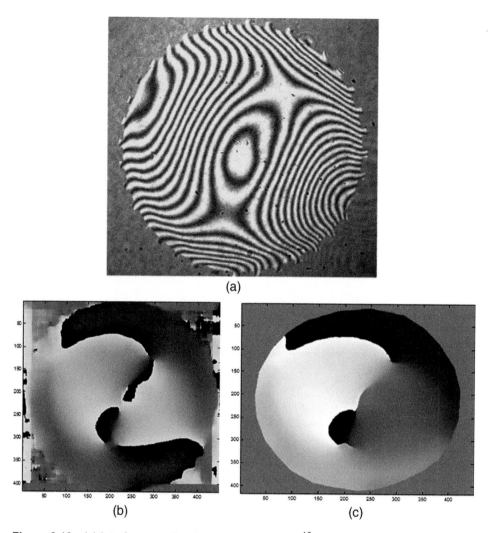
(a)

(b)   (c)

Figure 3.12 (a) Interferogram [reprinted from Kaufmann[16] with permission], (b) orientation computed by the accumulate-differences method, and (c) the direction map computed by the RPT method.

The 1D complex analytic function can thus be defined as

$$p(x) = I(x) - j\hat{I}(x) = |b(x)|e^{j\phi(x)}. \tag{3.55}$$

According to Section 2.5, the Fourier transform of the Hilbert transform of $I(x)$ can be given by

$$\Im\{\mathcal{H}\{I(x)\}\} = \Im\{\hat{I}(x)\} = j\,\mathrm{sgn}(f_x) \cdot \tilde{I}(f_x), \tag{3.56}$$

where $\mathrm{sgn}(\bullet)$ is the signum function. Note that extending the signum function to 2D is not a straightforward task (as explained the following subsection).

B. 2D quadrature function and the vortex transform

The 2D Fourier transform pair is defined as

$$\tilde{I}(f_x, f_y) = \Im\{I(x,y)\} = \int_{-\infty}^{\infty} \int_{-\infty}^{\infty} I(x,y) \exp[-j2\pi(f_x x + f_y y)]dxdy, \quad (3.57a)$$

$$I(x,y) = \Im^{-1}\{\tilde{I}(f_x, f_y)\} = \int_{-\infty}^{\infty} \int_{-\infty}^{\infty} \tilde{I}(f_x, f_y) \exp[j2\pi(f_x x + f_y y)]df_x df_y, \quad (3.57b)$$

where $(f_x, f_y) = (1/2\pi)(k_x, k_y)$ are the spatial frequencies with a m^{-1} unit, and the polar coordinates (r, α) are defined as $(f_x, f_y) = (f_0 \cos\alpha, f_0 \sin\alpha)$.

A 2D signum function $\tilde{S}(f_x, f_y)$, defined as a pure spiral-phase operator in the spatial frequency space (f_x, f_y), can be written as[13,14]

$$\tilde{S}(f_x, f_y) = \frac{f_x + jf_y}{\sqrt{f_x^2 + f_y^2}} = \exp[j\alpha(f_x, f_y)], \quad (3.58)$$

The spectral polar angle $\alpha(f_x, f_y) = \arctan[f_y/f_x]$ is shown in Fig. 3.13. Note that any section through the origin is a signum function. The MATLAB script "myspiral.m," which computes $\alpha(f_x, f_y)$ from Eq. (3.58), is shown in Table 3.10. Figure 3.13 shows the spiral-phase signum function exponent $\alpha(f_x, f_y)$.

Consider a general fringe pattern intensity function $I(x,y)$ of the form shown in Eq. (3.8). The objective of fringe pattern analysis is to extract both the amplitude and phase modulation terms $b(x,y)$ and $\phi(x,y)$, respectively. The following algorithm explains the steps for phase demodulation:

Step 1: Remove the offset pattern ("DC" term):

$$g(x,y) = I(x,y) - a(x,y) = b(x,y) \cos[\phi(x,y)]. \quad (3.59)$$

There are several techniques to remove the DC term. One of them is lowpass filtering, which is the simplest but not the best technique. Adaptive filtering can provide better results. Note that removing this DC term is crucial to the success of this method. The quadrature function (or the Hilbert transform) of Eq. (3.59) can be written as

$$\hat{g}(x,y) = \mathcal{H}\{g(x,y)\} = -b(x,y) \sin[\phi(x,y)], \quad (3.60)$$

and the 2D complex analytic interferogram can be written as

$$p(x,y) = g(x,y) - j\hat{g}(x,y). \quad (3.61)$$

Step 2: Perform the spiral-phase quadrature transformation through the multiplication of the Fourier transform of $g(x,y)$ with the spiral-phase

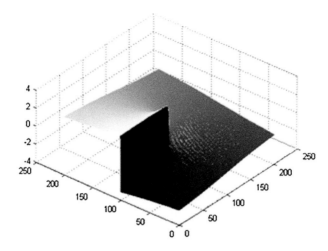

Figure 3.13   Spiral-phase signum function exponent $\alpha(f_x, f_y)$.

Table 3.10   MATLAB code "myspiral.m" (see Fig. 3.13).

```
1   clc
2   close all
3   clear all
4   load larkin_data
5   Fs=2^18;
6   N=size(Ihp,1);
7   e1 = 2*pi*Fs/2*linspace(-1,1,N)';
8   e2=e1;
9   [E1,E2]=meshgrid(e1,e2);
10   S=(E1+i*E2)./(sqrt(E1.^2+E2.^2));
11  im((angle(S)))
12  axis xy
13  phi=((angle(S)));
14  S2=exp(i.*phi);
15  mesh(phi)
```

operator $\tilde{S}(f_x, f_y)$ and then transforming back to the space domain, as shown in the following equation:

$$\begin{aligned}
Q\{g(x,y)\} &= \Im^{-1}\{\exp[j\alpha(f_x,f_y)] \cdot \Im\{g(x,y)\}\} \\
&\cong j\exp[j\beta_{2\pi}(x,y)] \cdot b(x,y)\sin[\phi(x,y)] \\
&= -j\exp[j\beta_{2\pi}(x,y)]\hat{g}(x,y),
\end{aligned} \quad (3.62)$$

where $Q\{\bullet\}$ denotes the quadrature transform operator. Note that the cosine term is converted to a sine after application of the spiral-phase operator. A directional-phase multiplier has also appeared, and the demodulation problem has become one of estimating the direction map for the entire image. Note that Eq. (3.62) can be written in the space domain as a convolution:

$$Q\{g(x,y)\} = g(x,y) * s(x,y), \tag{3.63}$$

where

$$s(x,y) = \frac{j(x+jy)}{2\pi(x^2+y^2)^{3/2}} = j\frac{e^{j\theta}}{2\pi r^2},$$

and $x = r \cos \theta$ and $y = r \sin \theta$ are the spatial polar coordinates.

Step 3: Compute the orientation map, as discussed in Section 3.3.2 and shown in Fig. 3.4.

Step 4: Unwrap the orientation map to obtain the direction map $\beta_{2\pi}$ as discussed in Section 3.3.3 and shown in Fig. 3.4.

Step 5: Use the direction map to obtain the vortex transform, as in the following formula:

$$
\begin{aligned}
V\{g(x,y)\} &= -j \exp[-j\beta_{2\pi}(x,y)] \cdot Q\{g(x,y)\} \\
&= -\hat{g}(x,y) \\
&= b(x,y) \sin[\phi(x,y)].
\end{aligned}
\tag{3.64}
$$

Step 6: By combining the result of Eq. (3.64) with the original offset-removed interferogram $g(x,y)$, the 2D complex amplitude interferogram can be written as

$$
\begin{aligned}
p(x,y) &= g(x,y) - j\hat{g}(x,y) \\
&= b(x,y) \cos[\phi(x,y)] + jV\{g(x,y)\}, \\
&= b(x,y) \exp[i\phi(x,y)],
\end{aligned}
\tag{3.65}
$$

and the raw modulating phase map $\phi(x,y)$ can be obtained by

$$\phi(x,y) = \arctan\left\{\frac{\mathrm{Im}[p(x,y)]}{\mathrm{Re}[p(x,y)]}\right\}. \tag{3.66}$$

Finally, it is worth proving a particular case of Eq. (3.62), in which a monochromatic fringe pattern is assumed. Equation (3.59) can be written as

$$g_0(x,y) = b_0 \cos[2\pi(f_{x_0}x + f_{y_0}y)]. \tag{3.67}$$

The Fourier transform of Eq. (3.67) can be written as

$$\tilde{G}_0(f_x,f_y) = \Im\{g_0(x,y)\} = \frac{b_0}{2}[\delta(f_x - f_{x_0}, f_y - f_{y_0}) + \delta(f_x + f_{x_0}, f_y + f_{y_0})]. \tag{3.68}$$

From Eq. (3.10), $\beta_{0(2\pi)} = \arctan[f_{y_0}/f_{x_0}] = \alpha(f_{x_0},f_{y_0})$, and multiplying the spiral-phase factor $\tilde{S}(f_x,f_y)$ with $\tilde{G}_0(f_x,f_y)$ produces the following:

$$\tilde{S}(f_x,f_y) \cdot \tilde{G}_0(f_x,f_y) = S(f_x,f_y) \cdot \tilde{g}_0(f_x,f_y)$$

$$= \frac{b_0}{2}\{\tilde{S}(f_{x_0},f_{y_0})\delta(f_x - f_{x_0},f_y - f_{y_0}) - \tilde{S}(f_{x_0},f_{y_0})\delta(f_x + f_{x_0},f_y + f_{y_0})\}$$

$$= \frac{b_0}{2}e^{j\beta_{0(2\pi)}}[\delta(f_x - f_{x_0},f_y - f_{y_0}) - \delta(f_x + f_{x_0},f_y + f_{y_0})]. \tag{3.69}$$

The inverse Fourier transform of Eq. (3.69) provides the spiral-phase quadrature transformation:

$$Q\{g_0(x,y)\} = \mathfrak{S}^{-1}\{e^{j\beta_{0(2\pi)}} \cdot \mathfrak{S}\{g_0(x,y)\}\} = je^{j\beta_{0(2\pi)}}b_0 \sin[2\pi(f_{x_0}x + f_{y_0}y)], \tag{3.70}$$

which is a particular case of Eq. (3.62). Although this proof is performed for a monochromatic interferogram, it can be generalized to a single-image, closed-fringe interferogram with a nonmonotonic phase.

The MATLAB script "larkin.m," which uses the vortex technique to obtain the 2D complex amplitude, is shown in Table 3.11. This script has an input "larkin_data.mat" file that contains the orientation map obtained from any of the previous techniques. Figure 3.14(a) shows the amplitude, 3.14(b) shows the wrapped phase, and 3.14(c) shows the unwrapped phase of the 2D complex amplitude interferogram. The MATLAB code "larkin_expanded.m" (not shown in this section; it can be found in the misc directory of Chapter 3 programs on the CD-ROM) shows the entire vortex technique starting from the fringe pattern rather than using the orientation map as an input.

3.5 Fringe Skeletonization and Normalization

Several techniques have been developed to locate fringe extremes, such as guidance of extreme map,[36] intensity-based analysis,[37] skeletonization based on the gradient vector field (GVF),[38] line tracking, threshold comparison, and adaptive binarization.[39,40] The local extremes correspond to the maxima and minima of the cosine function defined in Eq. (3.8). Locating fringe extremes is an important step in many techniques used for phase demodulation from a fringe pattern.

Before attempting to extract the fringe skeletons for a highly noisy fringe pattern, it is recommended to improve the SNR through adaptive filtering. Adaptive filtering can remove Gaussian noise while preserving the local features of the fringes by preserving the contrast. One such filter uses the weighted functions of the gradient;[36] this technique uses an $N \times N$ window. Figure 3.15(a) shows a 3×3 window that contains the sampling points. Point p_4 is at the center of the window, and the directions of the used axes are indicated in Fig. 3.15(b). In the adaptive weighted filtering technique,

Table 3.11 MATLAB code "larkin.m.m" uses the vortex method to obtain the unwrapped phase (see Fig. 3.14).

```
1    %%fft on input with DC removed
2    clc
3    close all
4    clear all
5    load larkin_data
6    I1F=(fft2(fftshift(Ihp)));
7    I1F_s=fftshift(I1F);
8    I1F_s_a=abs(I1F_s).^2;
9    im(I1F_s_a);
10   title('magnitude')
11   im(angle(I1F_s))
12   title('phase')
13   %%
14   w=25;
15   I1FS=I1F_s.*S;
16   I1S=fftshift(ifft2(fftshift(I1FS)));
17   im(real(I1S))
18   title({'real after multiplying by Spiral',
19   'phase and inverse fourier'})
20   im(imag(I1S))
21   title({'imaginary after multiplying by Spiral',
22   'phase and inverse fourier'})
23   %
24   %Crop I1S to the size of the orientation
25   I1S=I1S(floor(w/2)+1:size(theta,1)-floor(w/2)-1,...
26   floor(w/2)+1:size(theta,1)-floor(w/2)-1);
27   Ifinal=I1S.*orientation;
28   im(real(Ifinal))
29   title ('Real')
30   im(imag(Ifinal))
31   title('Imaginary')
32   %Crop original image to Ifinal size
33   Iorig=Ihp(floor(w/2)+1:size(theta,1)-floor(w/2)-1,...
34   floor(w/2)+1:size(theta,1)-floor(w/2)-1);
35   close all
36   p=Iorig+(Ifinal);           %p=Iorig+i*real(Ifinal);
37   pfinal=angle(p);
38   figure
39   imagesc(pfinal)
40   title('Phase')
41   colormap(gray(256))
42   figure
43   imagesc(abs(p))
44   title('magnitude')
45   colormap(gray(256))
46   %%
47   %%%---Unwrapping using the 2D_SRNCP algorithm:
48   %http://www.ljmu.ac.uk/GERI/90225.htm
49   %Call the 2D phase unwrapper from C language.
50   %To compile the C code: in MATLAB command window, type
51   %Miguel_2D_unwrapper.cpp. The file has to be in the same
52   %directory
53   %as the script to work.
```

(continued)

Table 3.11 (*Continued*)

```
54  WrappedPhase=pfinal;
55  mex Miguel_2D_unwrapper.cpp
56  %The wrapped phase should have the single (float in C)
57  %data type
58  WrappedPhase = single(WrappedPhase);
59  UnwrappedPhase = Miguel_2D_unwrapper(WrappedPhase);
60  UnwrappedPhase=double(UnwrappedPhase);
61  figure;
62  surfl(UnwrappedPhase);
63  shading interp; colormap(gray);
64  title('Unwrapped 3D Depth Map');
65  zlabel('Depth in radians')
```

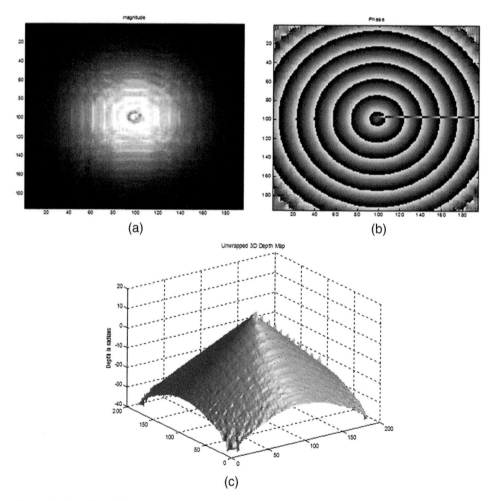

(a)   (b)

(c)

Figure 3.14 The (a) amplitude, (b) wrapped phase, and (c) unwrapped phase of the 2D complex amplitude interferogram.

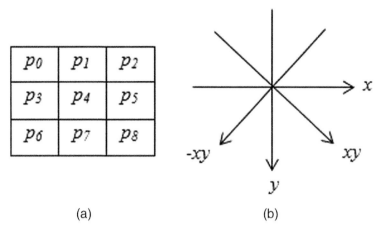

Figure 3.15   (a) 3 × 3 mask window and (b) the direction of axes.[36]

the intensity gradient ∇I for each pixel is computed using the following equation:

$$\nabla I(p_k) = |I(p_k) - I(p_4)|, \ k = 0, 1, \ldots, 8. \tag{3.71}$$

The adaptive gradient-weighted filter can be obtained as

$$H_{Filter}(p_4) = \frac{\sum_{k=0}^{8} e^{\nabla I(p_k)} I(p_k)}{\sum_{k=0}^{8} e^{\nabla I(p_k)}}, \tag{3.72}$$

where $e^{\nabla I(p_k)}$ is the weighting function between p_4 and p_k. This filter is traditionally followed by a 3 × 3 window median filter to cancel salt-and-pepper noise. This sequence of filters can be employed several times to improve the quality of the fringes.

To detect an extreme value, the following scheme is employed:[36]

In the x direction,

$$p_4 > p_3, \quad p_4 > p_5, \tag{3.73a}$$

$$p_4 < p_3, \quad p_4 < p_5, \tag{3.73b}$$

In the y direction,

$$p_4 > p_1, \quad p_4 > p_7, \tag{3.74a}$$

$$p_4 < p_1, \quad p_4 < p_7. \tag{3.74b}$$

In the xy direction,

$$p_4 > p_0, \quad p_4 > p_8, \tag{3.75a}$$

$$p_4 < p_0, \quad p_4 < p_8. \tag{3.75b}$$

In the $-xy$ direction,

$$p_4 > p_2, \quad p_4 > p_6, \tag{3.76a}$$

$$p_4 < p_2, \quad p_4 < p_6. \tag{3.76b}$$

If conditions (3.73a) and (3.74a) or (3.75a) and (3.76a) are satisfied, then pixel p_4 is counted as a peak. If conditions (3.73b) and (3.74b) or (3.75b) and (3.76b) are satisfied, then pixel p_4 is counted as a trough.

Because the points of the extreme map obtained in the previous step do not form continuous lines, the second step connects the peaks of a specific fringe, as well as the troughs. In an extreme map, 1 represents a maximum point, -1 represents a minimum point, and 0 represents an intermediate point. The following algorithm is used for this purpose.[36]

A. Small discontinuity

If the discontinuity in a specific fringe extreme line is less than 3 pixels, then a 3×3 or 5×5 mask window can be used, as shown in Fig. 3.15(a). If one of the conditions in Eqs. (3.77a)–(3.77c) is satisfied, then the middle point of the window p_4 is a point of discontinuity and is assigned the value 1 (for a peak) or -1 (for a trough):

$$p_k p_{8-k} = 1 \quad \text{or} \quad p_k p_{k+5} = 1, \quad k = 0, 1, 2, 3, \tag{3.77a}$$

$$p_k p_{k+7} = 1, \quad k = 0, 1, 2, 3, \tag{3.77b}$$

$$p_2 p_3 = 1 \quad \text{or} \quad p_5 p_6 = 1, \tag{3.77c}$$

B. Large discontinuity

If the discontinuity in a specific fringe extreme line is more than 3 pixels, then the methodology is as follows:

Step 1: Determine the line direction.
Step 2: Search in a certain region (a typical search is performed in 8 directions of 45-deg increments).
Step 3: Connect the broken lines.

Figure 3.16 shows three types of mask windows used to determine the discontinuity in the fringe direction. First, the 5×3 window shown in Fig. 3.16(a) is used, starting from left to right at point p_0. The fringe direction will be along the x direction if

$$(p_k \text{ or } p_{k+5} \text{ or } q_{k+10}) = 1, \ p_4 + p_9 + p_{14} = 0, \ \text{for } k = 0, 1, 2, 3. \tag{3.78a}$$

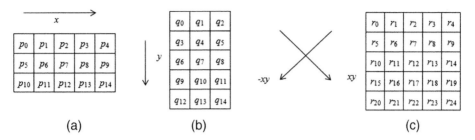

Figure 3.16 Mask windows for line connections in the (a) x, (b) y, and (c) xy directions, respectively.[36]

Second, the 3×5 window shown in Fig. 3.16(b) is used, starting from top to bottom at point q_0. The fringe direction will be along the y direction if

$$(q_k \text{ or } q_{k+1} \text{ or } q_{k+2}) = 1, \; q_{12} + q_{13} + q_{14} = 0, \quad \text{for } k = 0, 3, 6, 9. \quad (3.78b)$$

Third, the 5×5 window shown in Fig. 3.16(c) is used, starting from point r_0 for a search in the xy direction and r_4 for a search in the $-xy$ direction. The fringe direction will be along the xy direction if

$$r_0 r_6 r_{12} r_{18} = 1, \quad r_k = 0, \quad \text{for} \quad k \neq 0, 6, 12, 18$$

or along the $-xy$ direction if

$$r_4 r_8 r_{12} r_{16} = 1, \quad r_k = 0, \quad \text{for} \quad k \neq 4, 8, 12, 16.$$

The algorithm mentioned here has a very useful feature that detects and deletes broken lines that are in a wrong direction.

The final step normalizes the fringe pattern. In order to perform normalization, the background should be suppressed and the modulation should be normalized. The grayscale intensity values of pixels between the two nearest extremes are converted to the range -1 to 1 using the following contrast-stretching transformation:[36]

$$I'(k) = \frac{2[I(k) - \min_{s \in S} I(k)]}{\max_{s \in S} I(s) - \min_{s \in S} I(s)} - 1, \quad (3.79)$$

where S is a set of points between the two nearest extremes, and pixel s belongs to S. The set of points S lies on a straight line that is the shortest distance between the two points located at each of the two nearest extreme curves.

The MATLAB script "FringeSkeleton.m," which uses the guidance-of-extreme map method for discontinuity filling, is shown in Table 3.12. Figure 3.17(a) shows the initial interferogram, Fig. 3.17(b) shows the skeleton extraction, and Fig. 3.17(c) shows a small-discontinuity filled fringe skeleton.

Table 3.12 MATLAB code "FringeSkeleton.m" uses the guidance-of-extreme map method to obtain the fringe skeletons and discontinuity filling of an interference pattern (see Fig. 3.17).

```
1   %Fringe skeleton
2   clc;clear all
3   pts=2^8;
4   x=linspace(0,pts-1,pts); y=x;
5   [X0,Y0]=meshgrid(x,y);
6   phi=((X0-2^7).^2+(Y0-2^7).^2)/400;
7   If =exp((-(X0-2^7).^2-(Y0-2^7).^2)/5000)...
8   .*(0.5+0.5.*cos(phi));
9   max(If(:))
10  min(If(:))
11  figure
12  imagesc(If);colormap(gray(256));
13  title('Original image');
14  %%C.J. Tay: skeleton extraction
15  wx=3;                        %Window size
16  wy=3;
17  pmin=floor(wx/2)+1;
18  pmax=pts-floor(wx/2)-1;      %pts = the number of points in I
19  Inorm=zeros(size(If,1));
20  for m=pmin:1:pmax
21  for n=pmin:1:pmax
22  window=If(m-floor(wx/2):m-floor(wx/2)+wx-1,...
23  n-floor(wy/2): n-floor(wy/2)+wy-1);
24  p0=window(1,1); p1=window(1,2); p2=window(1,3);
25  p3=window(2,1); p4=window(2,2); p5=window(2,3);
26  p6=window(3,1); p7=window(3,2);p8=window(3,3);
27  if (p4>p3) && (p4>p5)&&(p4>p1) &&(p4>p7)
28  Inorm(m,n)=1;
29  elseif (p4<p3) && (p4<p5)&&(p4<p1)&&(p4<p7)
30  Inorm(m,n)=-1;
31  elseif (p4>p0)&&(p4>p8)&&(p4>p2)&&(p4>p6)
32  Inorm(m,n)=1;
33  elseif (p4<p0)&&(p4<p8)&&(p4<p2)&&(p4<p6)
34  Inorm(m,n)=-1;
35  end
36  end
37  end
38  im(Inorm)
39  title('Processed image')
40  %%Discontinuity filling    %%Small discontinuity
41  wx=3;                        %Window size
42  wy=3;
43  pmin=floor(wx/2)+1;
44  pmax=pts-floor(wx/2)-1;      %pts = the number of points in I
45  Idisc=Inorm;
46  for m=pmin:1:pmax
47  for n=pmin:1:pmax
48  window=Inorm(m-floor(wx/2):m-floor(wx/2)+wx-1,...
49  n-floor(wy/2):n-floor(wy/2)+wy-1);
50  p0=window(1,1); p1=window(1,2); p2=window(1,3);
51  p3=window(2,1); p4=window(2,2); p5=window(2,3);
52  p6=window(3,1); p7=window(3,2); p8=window(3,3);
```

(continued)

Table 3.12 *(Continued)*

```
53  if (p2*p3)==1
54  Idisc(m,n)=p2;
55  end
56  if (p5*p6==1)
57  Idisc(m,n)=p5;
58  end
59  if (p0*p8==1|| p0*p5==1)&&(p1*p7==1|| p1*p6==1)...
60  &&(p2*p6==1|| p2*p7==1)&&(p3*p5==1 ||p3*p8==1)
61  Idisc(m,n)=p0
62  end
63  if (p0*p7)==1 || (p2*p7)==1
64  Idisc(m,n)=p7;
65  end
66  if (p1*p6)==1 || (p1*p8)==1
67  Idisc(m,n)=p1;
68  end
69  if (p0*p5)==1
70  Idisc(m,n)=p0;
71  end
72  end
73  end
74  im(Idisc);title('discontinuity filling')
```

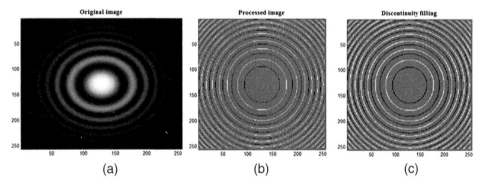

Figure 3.17 (a) Initial fringe pattern, (b) skeleton extraction, and (c) the result after applying the small-discontinuity filling algorithm.

3.6 Contrast Enhancement of Fringe Patterns

As mentioned in the previous section, contrast enhancement and extremum extraction of interference fringes are two important steps in many of the algorithms used for phase extraction from interferograms. The purpose of contrast enhancement is to obtain a uniform brightness and high contrast (near 1) over the entire image from an input-captured fringe pattern with low contrast due to different reflectivity distribution, nonlinearity of the CCD device, and nonuniform illumination.[41]

Several techniques for contrast enhancement have been developed. A typical method of contrast enhancement is based on histogram equalization, which stretches specific grayscale regions of an interferogram using the histogram cumulative-distribution function.[42–44] Another approach uses companding (compression and decompression) techniques, which transforms the grayscale values with logarithmic or exponential functions.[44,45] This section discusses a simple algorithm that can be used for contrast enhancement, as well as extremum extraction.

Starting from Eq. (3.8), the local contrast of the fringes is defined as[41]

$$V(x,y) = b(x,y)/a(x,y) < 1. \tag{3.80}$$

The local contrast $V(x,y)$ is variable depending on location, which makes fringe processing a difficult task. Equation (3.8) can be written as

$$\cos[\phi(x,y)] = \frac{I(x,y) - a(x,y)}{b(x,y)}. \tag{3.81}$$

Note that for a window size comparable to the local period of $\cos[\phi(x,y)]$ and centered around a point (x,y) [and if $a(x,y)$ and $b(x,y)$ are slowly varying functions with respect to $\phi(x,y)$], the local maximum and local minimum of $I(x,y)$ can be approximated as

$$I_{\max}(x,y) = a(x,y) + b(x,y), \tag{3.82a}$$

$$I_{\min}(x,y) = a(x,y) - b(x,y), \tag{3.82b}$$

respectively, and the local average intensity can be written as

$$\langle I(x,y)\rangle = \frac{I_{\max}(x,y) + I_{\min}(x,y)}{2} = a(x,y). \tag{3.82c}$$

Substituting Eqs. (3.82a)–(3.82c) into Eq. (3.81) produces the following equation:

$$\cos[\phi(x,y)] = 2\frac{I(x,y) - \langle I(x,y)\rangle}{I_{\max}(x,y) - I_{\min}(x,y)}. \tag{3.83}$$

Thus, the normalized contrast enhanced image that will ensure $V(x,y) = 1$ can be written as

$$I_{Enh}(x,y) = \frac{1}{2}\{1 + \cos[\phi(x,y)]\} = \frac{1}{2} + \frac{I(x,y) - \langle I(x,y)\rangle}{I_{\max}(x,y) - I_{\min}(x,y)}. \tag{3.84}$$

The MATLAB script "contrast_enhancement.m," which uses a simple method to enhance the contrast of the fringe pattern, is shown in Table 3.13. Figure 3.18(a) shows the original fringe pattern, and Fig. 3.18(b) shows a profile of the fringes on a diagonal slice of Fig. 3.18(a). Figures 3.18(c) and (d)

Table 3.13 MATLAB code "contrast_enhancement.m" uses a simple technique to enhance the contrast of the fringe pattern (see Fig. 3.18).

```
1    %%Generate test image
2    clc
3    clear all
4    pts=2^8;
5    x=linspace(0,pts-1,pts);
6    y=x;
7    [X0,Y0]=meshgrid(x,y);
8    phi=((X0-2^7).^2+(Y0-2^7).^2)/400;
9    I=exp((-(X0-2^7).^2-(Y0-2^7).^2)/5000).* ...
10   (0.5+0.5.*cos(phi));
11   max(I(:));
12   min(I(:));
13   figure
14   imagesc(I);
15   colormap(gray(256));
16   title('Original image');
17   display('Use the mouse to select a slice')
18   disp('profile of the fringes')
19   c=improfile;
20   figure
21   plot(c)
22   %%Fixed window cai
23   wx=7                        %Window size
24   wy=7;
25   pmin=floor(wx/2)+1;
26   pmax=pts-floor(wx/2)-1;     %pts = the number of points in I
27   Inorm=zeros(size(I,1));
28   for m=pmin:1:pmax
29   for n=pmin:1:pmax
30   window=I(m-floor(wx/2):m-floor(wx/2)+...
31   wx-1,n-floor(wy/2):n-floor(wy/2)+wy-1);
32   meanI=mean(mean(window));
33   Imax=max(max(window));
34   Imin=min(min(window));
35   Inorm(m,n)=0.5+(I(m,n)-meanI)/(Imax-Imin);
36   end
37   end
38   figure
39   imagesc(Inorm);
40   colormap(gray(256));
41   title('Processed image');
42   clc
43   display('Use the mouse to select a slice')
44   display('profile of the processed fringes')
45   c=improfile;
46   figure
47   plot(c)
48   %Inormf=imlin2(Inorm,-1,1);
49   %min(Inormf(:));
50   %max(Inormf(:));
51   %figure
52   %imagesc(Inormf);
53   %colormap(gray(256));
54   %clc
55   %display('Use the mouse to select a slice profile
56   %of the processed fringes')
57   %improfile
```

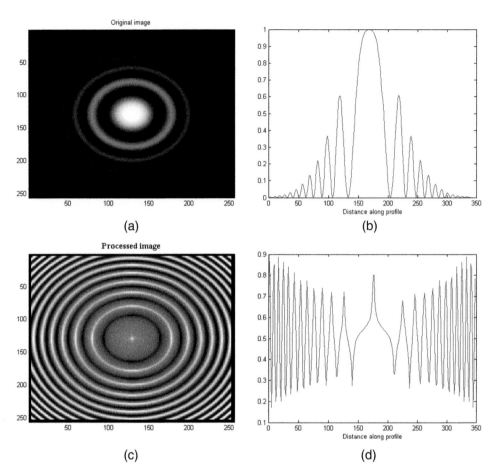

Figure 3.18 (a) Original fringe pattern, and (b) a diagonal slice profile of the fringes of (a). (c) Processed fringes and (d) diagonal slice profile after applying the contrast enhancement method.

are the processed fringes and diagonal slice profile, respectively, after applying the contrast-enhancement method.

3.7 Phase Unwrapping: Interferogram Analysis

The intensity in an interference pattern can generally be represented by Eq. (3.8). This formulation assumes that the background offset $a(x, y)$ and the amplitude contrast $b(x, y)$ are smooth real functions. Note that Eq. (3.8) can also be used to model a fingerprint image.[46] All of the techniques to obtain the phase $\phi(x, y)$ result in the following equation:

$$\phi(x, y) = \arctan\left(\frac{A(x, y)}{B(x, y)}\right), \tag{3.85}$$

where A and B are functions of the recorded intensity of the interference pattern. Because the arctan function is multivalued, the phase must be

Figure 3.19   Sequential line scanning.[47]

unwrapped. Section 2.4 discussed some of the phase-unwrapping techniques; this section briefly classifies these techniques for completeness.

As mentioned in Section 2.4, a fundamental principle of phase unwrapping is to integrate the wrapped phase $\phi(x, y)$ along a certain path in the image. At each pixel the phase gradient is computed through a differentiation process:[47]

$$\Delta\phi_k = \phi_k - \phi_{k-1}. \tag{3.86}$$

where ϕ_k is the kth pixel. If the absolute value of the difference $|\Delta\phi_k| > \pi$, then a fringe edge is assumed and corrected through the addition or subtraction of 2π if $\Delta\phi_k$, ($\Delta\phi_k(>0$ or <0), respectively.

One class of techniques used to correct for missed 2π phase jumps suggests that the phase difference (calculated through adding the phase differences through a certain path) for any two points on the interferogram should be independent of the path chosen, assuming no discontinuity in that path. Therefore, phase-unwrapping techniques are divided into two main classes: (a) path dependent and (b) path independent.

3.7.1 Path-dependent techniques

Path-dependent techniques are applied to high-quality interferograms. One of the simplest scanning methods is the raster scan, shown in Fig. 3.19, where consecutive lines are scanned in opposite directions. However, in the presence of noise, more elaborate schemes are necessary.[48] These elaborate schemes concentrate on unwrapping regions with low noise first, then the high noise regions. One of these techniques determines low-noise regions by locating the small phase gradients; these are the regions that are unwrapped before the high-gradient regions.[49] Other techniques determine low-noise regions through high contrast or visibility,[50] or through segmentation into regions with no phase ambiguities.[51]

3.7.2 Path-independent techniques

Section 2.4 discussed in detail a basic example of a path-independent, 2D phase-unwrapping technique using the fast discrete cosine transform (DCT) and iterative techniques.[52] Another path-independent technique based on the cellular automata method for phase unwrapping works as follows:[53] Consider a 3×3 mask window. Let the central pixel of that window be labeled p_4, similar to Fig. 3.15(a). The first step computes the phase difference $|\Delta\phi_{k4}| = |\phi_k - \phi_4|$, $k = 1, 3, 5, 7$ between this central point p_4 and the four nearest neighbors in the horizontal and vertical direction. The second step is the decision step involving three scenarios:

(a) If any one of the $|\Delta\phi_{k4}| > \pi$, a 2π is added to or subtracted from p_4 if the majority of the four differences are positive or negative, respectively;

(b) In the case of a tie, a random choice will be made to add or subtract 2π; and

(c) If all of the $|\Delta\phi_{k4}| < \pi$, then p_4 remains unchanged.

Chapter 2 discusses several phase-unwrapping algorithms and their corresponding code.

References

1. M. Takeda, H. Ina, and S. Kobayashi, "Fourier-transform method of fringe-pattern analysis for computer-based topography and interferometry," *J. Opt. Soc. Am.* **72**(1), 156–160 (1982).

2. S. De Nicola and P. Ferraro, "A two-dimensional fast Fourier transform method for measuring the inclination angle of parallel fringe patterns," *Opt. Laser Technol.* **30**(3/4), 167–173 (1998).

3. P. Vizcaya and L. Gerhardt, "A nonlinear orientation model for global description of fingerprints," *Pattern Recognition* **29**(7), 1221–1231 (1996).

4. P. Perona, "Orientation diffusion," *IEEE Trans. Image Process.* **7**(3), 457–467 (1998).

5. Q. Yu, X. Sun, and X. Liu, "Spin filtering with curve windows for Interferometric fringe patterns," *Appl. Opt.* **41**(14), 2650–2654 (2002).

6. Q. Yu, X. Sun, and X. Liu, "Removing speckle noise and extracting the skeletons from a single speckle fringe pattern by spin filtering with curved-surface windows," *Opt. Eng.* **42**(1), 68–74 (2003) [doi: 10.1117/1.1522726].

7. Q. Yu, S. Fu, X. Yang, X. Sun, and X. Liu, "Extraction of phase field from a single contoured correlation fringe pattern of ESPI," *Opt. Express* **12**(1), 75–83 (2004).

8. Q. Yu, S. Fu, X. Liu, X. Yang, and X. Sun, "Single-phase-step method with contoured correlation fringe patterns for ESPI," *Opt. Express* **12**(20), 4980–4985 (2004).

9. Q. Yu, X. Yang, and S. Fu, "Two improved algorithms with which to obtain contoured windows for fringe patterns generated by electronic speckle-pattern interferometry," *Appl. Opt.* **44**(33), 7050–7054 (2005).

10. X. Yang, Q. Yu, and S. Fu, "A combined method for obtaining fringe orientations of EPSI," *Opt. Comm.* **273**(1), 60–66 (2007).

11. C. Harris and M. Stephens, "A combined corner and edge detector," *Proc. 4th Alvey Vision Conf.*, 147–151 (1988).

12. W. T. Freeman and E. H. Adelson, "The design and use of steerable filters," *IEEE Trans. Pattern Anal.* **13**(9), 891–906 (1991).

13. K. G. Larkin, "Natural demodulation of two-dimensional fringe patterns I. General background of the spiral phase quadrature transform," *J. Opt. Soc. Am. A* **18**(8), 1862–1870 (2001).

14. K. G. Larkin, "Natural demodulation of two-dimensional fringe patterns II. Stationary phase analysis of the spiral phase quadrature transform," *J. Opt. Soc. Am. A* **18**(8), 1871–1881 (2001).

15. M. Servín, J. A. Quiroga, and J. L. Marroquín, "General N-dimensional quadrature transform and its application to Interferogram demodulation," *Opt. Soc. Am. J.* **20**(5), 925–934 (2003).

16. G. H. Kaufmann, *Advances in Speckle Metrology and Related Techniques*, Wiley-VCH, Weinheim, Germany (2011).

17. G. H. Granlund and H. Knutsson, *Signal Processing for Computer Vision*, Kluwer Academic Publishers, Boston (1995).

18. M. Servin, J. L. Marroquin, and F. J. Cuevas, "Fringe-follower regularized phase tracker for demodulation of closed fringe interferograms," *J. Opt. Soc. Am. A* **18**(3), 689–695 (2001).

19. J. L. Marroquin, R. Rodriguez-Vera, and M. Servin, "Local phase from local orientation by solution of a sequence of linear systems," *J. Opt. Soc. Am. A* **15**(6), 1536–1544 (1998).

20. B. Jähne, *Practical Handbook on Image Processing for Scientific Applications*, CRC Press, Boca Raton, FL (1997).

21. X. Yang, Q. Yu, and S. Fu, "An algorithm for estimating both fringe orientation and fringe density," *Opt. Comm.* **274**(2), 286–292 (2007).

22. Q. Yu, X. Liu, and K. Andresen, "New spin filters for interferometric fringe patterns and grating patterns," *Appl. Opt.* **33**(17), 3705–3711 (1994).

23. Q. Yu and K. Anderson, "Fringe orientation maps and fringe skeleton extraction by the two dimensional derivative sing binary fringe method," *Appl. Opt.* **33**(29), 6873–6878 (1994).

24. C. Tang, Z. Wang, L. Wang, J. Wu, T. Gao, and S. Yan, "Estimation of fringe orientation for optical fringe patterns with poor quality based on Fourier transform," *Appl. Opt.* **49**(4), 554–561 (2010).

25. S. Chikkerur, A. N. Cartwright, and V. Govindaraju, "Fingerprint enhancement using STFT analysis," *Pattern Recognition* **40**(1), 198–211 (2007).

26. M. F. Augusteijn, L. E. Clemens, and K. A. Shaw, "Performance evaluation of texture measures for ground cover identification in satellite images by means of a neural network classifier," *IEEE Trans. Geosci. Remote Sensing* **33**(3), 616–626 (1995).

27. A. K. Jain, *Fundamentals of Digital Image Processing*, Prentice Hall, Englewood Cliffs, NJ (1989).

28. K. G. Larkin, "Uniform estimation of orientation using local and nonlocal 2D energy operators," *Opt. Exp.* **13**(20), 8097–8121 (2005).

29. M. Servin, F. J. Cuevas, D. Malacara, and J. L. Marroquin, "Phase unwrapping through demodulation by use of the regularized phase-tracking technique," *Appl. Opt.* **38**(10), 1934–1941 (1999).

30. J. A. Quiroga, M. Servin, and F. Cuevas, "Modulo 2π fringe orientation angle estimation by phase unwrapping with a regularized phase tracking algorithm," *J. Opt. Soc. Am.* **19**(8), 1524–1531 (2002).

31. M. Servin, J. L. Marroquin, and J. A. Quiroga, "Regularized quadrature and phase tracking from a single closed-fringe interferogram," *J. Opt. Soc. Am. A* **21**(3), 411–419 (2004).

32. M. Servin, J. L. Marroquin, and F. J. Cuevas, "Demodulation of a single interferogram by use of a two-dimensional regularized phase-tracking technique," *Appl. Opt.* **360**(19) 4540–4548 (1997).

33. M. Servin, D. Malacara, and F. J. Cuevas, "Direct phase detection of modulated Ronchi rulings using a phase locked loop," *Opt. Eng.* **33**(4), 1193–1199 (1994) [doi: 10.1117/12.163111].

34. M. Servin and R. Rodriguez-Vera, "Two dimensional phase locked loop demodulation of carrier frequency interferograms," *J. Mod. Opt.* **40**(11), 2087–2094 (1993).

35. R. N. Bracewell, *The Fourier Transform and Its Applications*, 3rd Ed., McGraw-Hill, Boston (2000).

36. C. Quan, C. Tay, F. Yang, and X. He, "Phase extraction from a single fringe pattern based on guidance of an extreme map," *Appl. Opt.* **44**(23), 4814–4821 (2005).

37. T. Yatagai, "Intensity Based Analysis Methods," Chapter 3 in *Interferogram Analysis: Digital Fringe Pattern Measurement Techniques*, D. W. Robinson and G. T. Reid, eds., Institute of Physics, Bristol, UK (1993).

38. Y.-H. Li, X.-J. Chen, S.-L. Qu, and Z.-Y. Luo, "Algorithm for skeletonization of gray-scale optical fringe patterns with high density," *Opt. Eng.* **50**(8), 0870003 (2011) [doi: 10.1117/1.3607411].

39. G. T. Reid, "Image processing techniques for fringe pattern analysis," *Proc. SPIE* **945**, 468–477 (1988) [doi: 10.1117/12.947624].

40. H. A. Vrooman and A. Mass, "Interferogram analysis using image processing techniques," *Proc. SPIE* **1121**, 655–659 (1989) [doi: 10.1117/12.961340].
41. L. Z. Cai, Q. Liu, and X. L. Yang, "A simple method of contrast enhancement and extremum extraction for interference fringes," *Opt. Laser Technol.* **35**, 295–302 (2003).
42. W. K. Pratt, *Digital Image Processing*, 2nd Ed., John Wiley & Sons, New York (1991).
43. A. Rosenfeld and A. C. Kak, *Digital Picture Processing*, 2nd Ed., Academic Press, New York (1982).
44. W. Frei, "Image enhancement by histogram hyperbolization," *Comput. Graphics Image Process.* **6**(3), 286–94 (1977).
45. E. L. Hall, *Computer Image Processing and Recognition*, Academic Press, New York (1979).
46. K. G. Larkin and P. A. Fletcher, "A coherent framework for fingerprint analysis: are fingerprints holograms?" *Opt. Exp.* **15**(14), 8667–8677 (2007).
47. K. J. Gåsvik, *Optical Metrology*, 3rd ed., John Wiley & Sons, West Sussex, UK (2002).
48. D. Ghiglia and M. Pritt, *Two-dimensional Phase Unwrapping: Theory, Algorithms, and Software*, John Wiley & Sons, New York (1998).
49. J. Schöner, A. Ettemeyer, U. Neupert, H. Rottenkolber, C. Winter, and P. Obermeier, "New approaches in interpreting holographic images," *Opt. Lasers Eng.* **14**(4), 283–291 (1991).
50. D. P. Towers, T. R. Judge, and P. J. Bryanston-Cross, "Automatic interferogram analysis techniques applied to quasi-heterodyne holography and ESPI," *Opt. Lasers Eng.* **14**(4), 239–282 (1991).
51. O. Y. Kwon, D. M. Shough, and R. A. Williams, "Stroboscopic phase-shifting interferometry," *Opt. Lett.* **12**(11), 855–857 (1987).
52. D. C. Ghiglia and L. A. Romero, "Robust two-dimensional weighted and unweighted phase unwrapping that uses fast transforms and iterative methods," *J. Opt. Soc. Am. A* **11**(1), 107–117 (1994).
53. D. C. Ghiglia, G. A. Mastin, and L. A. Romero, "Cellular-automata method for phase unwrapping," *J. Opt. Soc. Am. A* **4**(1), 267–80 (1987).

Chapter 4
Digital Holography and Digital Holographic Microscopy

4.1 Basics of Digital Holography

Whereas conventional analog holography (AH) entails physical re-illumination of the hologram of the object with a reading beam and finding the 3D real or virtual image, digital holography (DH) is a numerical procedure that simulates Fresnel diffraction of light from the re-illuminated hologram on a computer and numerically determines the images, which can be displayed on a computer screen.

Digital holography, like AH, records light scattered from an object along with a reference wave, but unlike AH, the light is recorded directly on a CCD camera, which is the recording device. Reconstruction of the hologram is performed by computational tools that simulate the propagation of light through the hologram and its subsequent diffraction to finally yield the complex optical fields that reconstitute or reconstruct the image.[1-4]

The basic concept of DH is shown in Fig. 4.1. Other geometries exist, but the same principle generally holds.[5] A plane reference wave and the wave (reflected or scattered) from the object are set to interfere at the surface of a CCD camera. The resulting hologram, which is the intensity pattern of the interference between the complex scattered field from the object and the reference, is electronically recorded and stored. The object can, in general, be a 3D diffuse or specular reflecting surface located at a distance d from the CCD.

The diffraction of light waves from the recorded hologram amplitude transmission $h(x,y)$ [which is proportional to the intensity I, as in Eq. (2.10)] illuminated by $E_R^*(x,y)$ is described by the Fresnel–Kirchhoff (FK) or Rayleigh–Sommerfeld (RS) integral described in Eqs. (2.5) and (2.7).[1] Following the standard notation in DH,[5] this diffracted field at a distance $z = d$ from the hologram can be expressed as

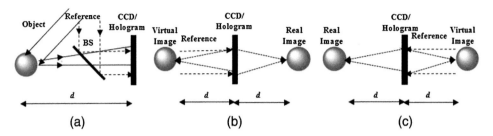

Figure 4.1 Digital holography: (a) optoelectronic recording, (b) electronic reconstruction with E_R, and (c) electronic reconstruction with E_R^*. The beamsplitter is marked as BS.

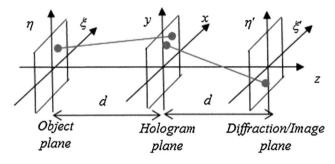

Figure 4.2 Coordinate system for DH reconstruction.

$$\Gamma(\xi,\eta) = \int\limits_{-\infty}^{\infty}\int\limits_{-\infty}^{\infty} h(x,y)E_R^*(x,y)g_{PSF}(x-\xi,y-\eta)dxdy, \qquad (4.1a)$$

$$g_{PSF} = j\frac{e^{-jk_0\sqrt{(x-\xi)^2+(y-\eta)^2+d^2}}}{\lambda\sqrt{(x-\xi)^2+(y-\eta)^2+d^2}}, \qquad (4.1b)$$

where $E_R^*(x,y)$ is the conjugate of the reference beam used to digitally reconstruct the hologram. Equation (4.1) is the basis for numerical reconstruction. Because the reconstructed field $\Gamma(\xi,\eta;d)$ is a complex quantity, both the intensity and the phase can be calculated. Pertinent distances/coordinates are shown in Fig. 4.2.

4.2 Digital Holography Reconstruction Algorithms

Several numerical reconstruction algorithms have been developed for digital holography, although the most common are the discrete Fresnel transform, the convolution approach, and reconstruction by angular spectrum.

4.2.1 Numerical reconstruction by the discrete Fresnel transformation

Under the paraxial approximation, i.e., $d^3 \gg (2\pi/\lambda)[(\xi - x)^2 + (\eta - y)^2]$, Eq. (4.1) can be approximated by the Fresnel transformation:[5]

$$\Gamma(\xi,\eta) = j\frac{1}{\lambda d} \exp\left(-j\frac{2\pi d}{\lambda}\right) \exp\left[-j\frac{\pi}{\lambda d}(\xi^2 + \eta^2)\right]$$

$$\times \int_{-\infty}^{\infty} \int_{-\infty}^{\infty} h(x,y)E_R^*(x,y) \exp\left[-j\frac{\pi}{\lambda d}(x^2 + y^2)\right]$$

$$\times \exp\left[j\frac{2\pi}{\lambda d}(x\xi + y\eta)\right] dxdy$$

$$\equiv \hat{z}(\xi,\eta)\Im_{x,y}[hE_R^*w]|_{k_x=2\pi\xi/\lambda d, k_y=2\pi\eta/\lambda d} \tag{4.2}$$

where $\Im_{x,y}[\bullet]$ is the Fourier transform operator. The intensity is calculated by squaring the optical field, i.e., $I(\xi,\eta) = |\Gamma(\xi,\eta)|^2$, and the phase is calculated using $\phi(\xi,\eta) = \arctan(\text{Im}[\Gamma(\xi,\eta)]/\text{Re}[\Gamma(\xi,\eta)])$. If x, y are discretized on a rectangular raster of $N_x \times N_y$ points (corresponding to the number of pixels in the CCD camera in the x and y dimensions, respectively) with step sizes Δx, Δy, which are the pixel-to-pixel distances on the CCD in the x and y directions, respectively, then Eq. (4.1) can be rewritten in discretized form as[6]

$$\Gamma(m,n) = \hat{z}(m,n) \times \sum_{k=0}^{N_x-1} \sum_{l=0}^{N_y-1} E_R^*(k,l)h(k,l)w(k,l) \exp\left[j2\pi\left(\frac{km}{N_x} + \frac{ln}{N_y}\right)\right],$$

$$\tag{4.3}$$

$$\hat{z}(m,n) = \frac{j}{\lambda d} \exp\left(-j\frac{2\pi d}{\lambda}\right) \exp\left[-j\lambda d\left(\frac{m^2}{N_x^2 \Delta x^2} + \frac{n^2}{N_y^2 \Delta y^2}\right)\right], \tag{4.4a}$$

$$w(k,l) = \exp\left[-j\frac{\pi}{\lambda d}(k^2 \Delta x^2 + l^2 \Delta y^2)\right], \tag{4.4b}$$

where $m = 0,1,\ldots,N_x - 1$; $n = 0,1,\ldots,N_y - 1$, and

$$N_x = \frac{\lambda d}{\Delta\xi\Delta x} = \frac{2X_{\max}}{\Delta x}, N_y = \frac{\lambda d}{\Delta\eta\Delta y} = \frac{2Y_{\max}}{\Delta y}, \tag{4.5}$$

where $\Delta\xi$ and $\Delta\eta$ represent the step sizes in ξ, η coordinates, respectively. The maximum object size that can be imaged is $X_{\max}$, $Y_{\max}$, which can be found from Eq. (4.5) if the pixel spacing Δx, Δy and the number of pixels N_x, N_y are known. Equation (4.5) is important in determining the final resolution $\Delta\xi$, $\Delta\eta$ of the reconstructed image. For an Ar laser with wavelength $\lambda = 0.514$ μm, a typical distance of $d = 0.5$ m from the model object, a $N_x \times N_y = 512 \times 512$

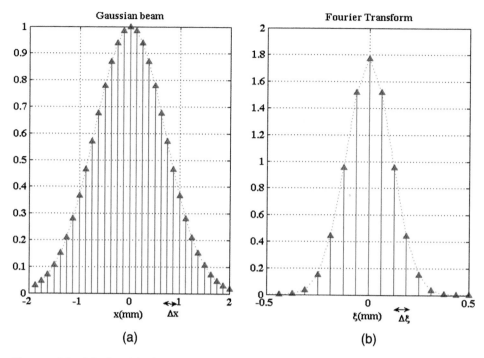

Figure 4.3 (a) Spatial domain of a certain spatial signal, (b) frequency domain representation.

CCD camera, and a 10-μm pixel size, the image resolution in the ξ, η coordinates are given by

$$\Delta\xi = \frac{\lambda d}{N_x \Delta x}, \Delta\eta = \frac{\lambda d}{N_y \Delta y} \qquad (4.6)$$

and found to be ~50 μm. Figure 4.3(a) shows a typical spatial-domain signal, and Fig. 4.3(b) shows its frequency-domain representation. To prove Eq. (4.6), the Nyquist criterion is used, which states that the sampling frequency should be at least twice that of the maximum frequency of the signal:

$$\frac{1}{\Delta x} = 2f_{max} = N\Delta f_x. \qquad (4.7)$$

However, from Eq. (4.2),

$$k_x = 2\pi f_x = \frac{2\pi\xi}{\lambda d}, \quad \text{or} \quad f_x = \frac{\xi}{\lambda d}.$$

Differentiating the previous result

$$\Delta f_x = \frac{\Delta\xi}{\lambda d} = \frac{1}{N_x \Delta x}.$$

produces $\Delta\xi = (\lambda d)/(N_x\Delta x)$. The image resolution given by Eq. (4.6) is generally regarded to be "naturally scaled," such that the value of $\Delta\xi$ is automatically equal to the physical resolution limit imposed by the CCD-sampled signal bandwidth.[5]

Thus, the major steps in the hologram-processing algorithm using the Fresnel transformation are as follows:

1. Compute the complex field using the relation performed using numerical FFT techniques.
2. Find image intensity and phase using the relations $I(\xi,\eta) = |\Gamma(\xi,\eta)|^2$ and $\phi(\xi,\eta) = \arctan\left(\frac{\mathrm{Im}[\Gamma(\xi,\eta)]}{\mathrm{Re}[\Gamma(\xi,\eta)]}\right)$, respectively.

4.2.2 Numerical reconstruction by the convolution approach

Following Eqs. (2.5) and (2.7), and using the notation in the previous subsection,

$$\Gamma(\xi,\eta) = (hE_R^*) * g_{PSF}, \quad g_{PSF}(\xi,\eta) = \frac{j}{\lambda}\frac{\exp\left(-jk_0\sqrt{d^2+\xi^2+\eta^2}\right)}{\sqrt{d^2+\xi^2+\eta^2}}, \quad (4.8)$$

where * denotes convolution, so that

$$\Gamma(\xi,\eta) = \mathfrak{I}_{x,y}^{-1}\{\mathfrak{I}_{x,y}(h \cdot E_R^*) \cdot \mathfrak{I}_{x,y}(g_{PSF})\} \equiv \mathfrak{I}_{x,y}^{-1}\{\mathfrak{I}_{x,y}(h \cdot E_R^*) \cdot (\tilde{G}_{PSF})\}. \quad (4.9)$$

In discretized form,

$$g_{PSF}(k,l) = \frac{j}{\lambda}\frac{\exp\left[-j\frac{2\pi}{\lambda}\sqrt{d^2+\left(k-\frac{N}{2}\right)^2\Delta x^2+\left(l-\frac{N}{2}\right)^2\Delta y^2}\right]}{\sqrt{d^2+\left(k-\frac{N}{2}\right)^2\Delta x^2+\left(l-\frac{N}{2}\right)^2\Delta y^2}}, \quad (4.10)$$

which has a Fourier transform

$$\tilde{G}_{PSF}(m,n) = \exp\left[-j\frac{2\pi}{\lambda}d\sqrt{1-\frac{\lambda^2\left(n+\frac{N^2\Delta x^2}{2d\lambda}\right)^2}{N^2\Delta x^2}-\frac{\lambda^2\left(m+\frac{N^2\Delta y^2}{2d\lambda}\right)^2}{N^2\Delta y^2}}\right]. \quad (4.11)$$

Note that the pixel sizes of the images reconstructed by the convolution approach are equal to that of the hologram, namely, $\Delta\xi = \Delta x$, $\Delta\eta = \Delta y$. The physical image resolution remains according to Eq. (4.5) and is ultimately governed by physical diffraction.[5,7]

4.2.3 Numerical reconstruction by the angular spectrum approach

The scalar diffraction theory closely resembles the theory of linear, invariant systems. If the complex field distribution of a monochromatic wave is analyzed in the Fourier space across any plane, the various spatial Fourier components can be considered as plane waves traveling in different directions away from that plane. The field amplitude at any other point can be calculated by adding the weighted contributions of these plane waves, taking into account the phase shifts they have undergone during propagation.[1] The angular plane-wave spectrum was formally defined in Eq. (2.3), and its propagation is shown in Eq. (2.4). Similar to the convolution approach earlier, the angular spectrum approach is based on directly applying the angular spectrum propagation of the field in the hologram plane. Accordingly, the angular spectrum of the field hE_R^* at the hologram plane is defined as[1]

$$\tilde{E}_h(k_\xi,k_\eta) = \Im_{x,y}(h \cdot E_R^*) = \frac{1}{4\pi^2} \int_{-\infty}^{\infty} \int_{-\infty}^{\infty} (h \cdot E_R^*) \, \exp[j(k_\xi\xi + k_\eta\eta)]d\xi d\eta,$$

(4.12)

where k_ξ, k_η are the spatial frequency variables corresponding to ξ, η. After propagating a distance z, each plane wave component of the angular spectrum acquires an additional phase factor $\exp\{-jk_zz\}$, where

$$k_z = \sqrt{k_0^2 - k_\xi^2 - k_\eta^2}.$$

(4.13)

Therefore, the reconstructed field at a distance $z = d$ becomes

$$\Gamma(\xi,\eta) = \frac{1}{4\pi^2} \int_{-\infty}^{\infty} \int_{-\infty}^{\infty} \tilde{E}_h(k_\xi,k_\eta) \, \exp\left[-jd\sqrt{k_0^2 - k_\xi^2 - k_\eta^2}\right]$$
$$\times \exp[-j(k_\xi\xi + k_\eta\eta)]dk_\xi dk_\eta,$$

(4.14)

which is similar to Eq. (4.9). Table 4.1 lists the advantages and disadvantages of the different reconstruction techniques discussed in this section.

4.3 DC Suppression during Reconstruction

One issue involved with inline holography is the suppression of the DC term. This is often required because the term is superposed on the reconstructed image. However, because the reconstruction is digital, this can be rather easily achieved, and one of the following two techniques is usually adopted:

A. Average intensity subtraction

The average intensity of the pixels of the hologram matrix is I_μ.[8] This average intensity is subtracted from the hologram intensity I to produce $I_s = I - I_\mu$, thereby conveniently discarding the DC term. A typical reconstructed hologram before and after DC suppression is shown in Figs. 4.4(a) and 4.4(b), respectively. A similar effect is achieved if, rather than subtracting the mean hologram

Table 4.1 Advantages and disadvantages of several digital holography reconstruction techniques.

Technique	Advantages	Disadvantages
Fresnel	• Fast (uses one FFT) • Used primarily for long distances (short distances possible with hologram upsampling prior to reconstruction) • May be used for larger objects • Image resolution can be arbitrarily scaled by applying zero padding or upsampling to the hologram	• Image pixel size depends on reconstruction distance and wavelength • Poor depth resolution for isolating adjacent hologram planes along the propagation axis (compared to newer methods, e.g., compressive sensing) • Not useful for inline holograms of scattering particles that must be evaluated at different depths
Convolution	• Limited numerical image magnification is possible during reconstruction • Image pixel size does not depend on distance and wavelength, and it is equal to the hologram pixel size (physical resolution is still governed by diffraction limit) • Useful in inline holograms of scattering particles that have to be evaluated on different depths • Numerical image magnification does not improve the object "resolution"	• Slower (uses at least two FFTs) • Used for small objects • Used for short distances
Angular spectrum	• Image pixel size is typically equal to the hologram pixel size (physical resolution is still governed by the diffraction limit) • May be used for very short distances where the Fresnel technique fails (no minimum distance required between the object and CCD)	• Typically used for inline holograms • Slower (uses at least two FFTs) • Used for smaller objects that do not exceed the lateral extent of the CCD for inline scenarios • Zero-padding techniques do not alter the resolution

intensity, the illumination/reference beam profile (recorded separately, without the object present) is subtracted pixel-wise from the hologram prior to reconstruction.

B. Spatial separation by tilted reference

If the reference wave in Eq. (4.3) is tilted, then E_R can be replaced by $a \exp(-j2\pi x \sin(\theta)/\lambda)$. This replacement spatially shifts the transverse location of the image by a distance of $2d \sin \theta$, which allows for discrimination of the image from the DC term. However, it has a drawback that is imposed by a maximum spatial-frequency constraint or, equivalently, the dimensions of the CCD pixels. The maximum relative angle between the plane wave components from the object and that from the reference (as shown in Fig. 4.1) should not exceed a critical value, determined by the maximum resolution of the CCD camera. Consider the interference between

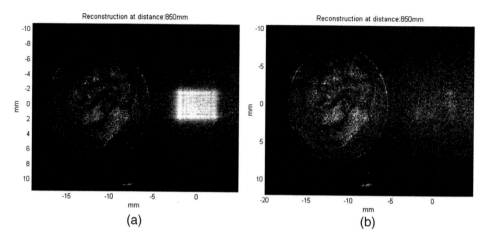

Figure 4.4 Typical reconstruction of a hologram of a coin object (a) before DC suppression and (b) after DC suppression.

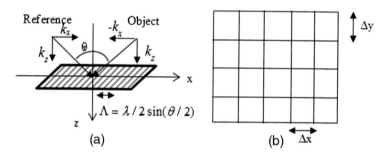

Figure 4.5 (a) Illustration of the maximum angle limit between the reference and object beam. (b) CCD pixel sizes.

the two waves, as shown in Fig. 4.5(a). The interference pattern can be written as

$$I \propto |\exp(-j(k_x x + k_z z)) + \exp(-j(-k_x x + k_z z))|^2 = 4\cos^2(k_x x), k_x$$
$$= k_0 \sin(\theta/2).$$

Therefore, the period of the grating can be written as

$$\Lambda = \frac{\pi}{k_0 \sin(\theta/2)} = \frac{\lambda}{2 \sin(\theta/2)}.$$

Note that the maximum angle θ_{max} between two waves can be found to be[5]

$$f_{max} = \frac{1}{\Lambda} = \frac{2}{\lambda} \sin(\theta_{max}/2) = \frac{1}{2 \times max[\Delta x, \Delta y]}.$$

Thus, $\theta_{max} \leq \lambda/(2 \times max[\Delta x, \Delta y])$.[2,5] For example, given a wavelength $\lambda = 0.5$ μm and a $\Delta x = 10$ μm pixel size, $\theta_{max} \approx \lambda f_{max} = \lambda/(2\Delta x) = 0.05$ rad $= 1.4$ deg.[9]

It should be noted that spatial separation via tilted reference is typically combined with suppression of the DC term, which serves to increase the overall (apparent) object contrast of the digitally reconstructed image.

4.4 Digital Holography Example

A reflection-type Fresnel DH setup based on the Mach–Zehnder interferometer is shown in Fig. 4.6(a). Light from an Ar laser @ 514 nm is collimated and divided into two parts with a beamsplitter. One of the beams forms the reference, and the other is reflected off the object; both beams then interfere on a CCD camera to form a Fresnel hologram. Figure 4.6(b) shows an example laboratory arrangement using fiber-coupled lasers.[10,11]

Three different targets are shown in Figs. 4.7(a)–(c), and the recorded holograms of those objects are shown in Figs. 4.7(d)–(f), respectively. The Fresnel algorithm described earlier has been used to reconstruct the different holograms. The intensities of the reconstructed holograms are shown in Figs 4.7(g)–(i); they demonstrate a marked similarity with the targets in Figs. 4.7(a)–(c), as expected. Note the presence of speckle or coherent noise,

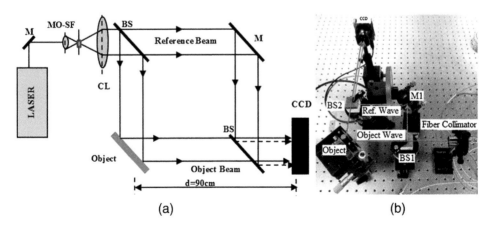

(a) (b)

Figure 4.6 (a) Schematic of the reflection-type Fresnel DH setup, and (b) a tabletop setup of the Mach–Zehnder configuration. The angle of the mirror determines the nature of the recorded hologram, either inline ($\theta = 0$) or off-axis ($\theta \neq 0$). Labeled parts: microscope objective-spatial filter (MO-SF), beamsplitter (BS), mirror (M), collimating lens (CL), and the distance between the object and CCD (d).

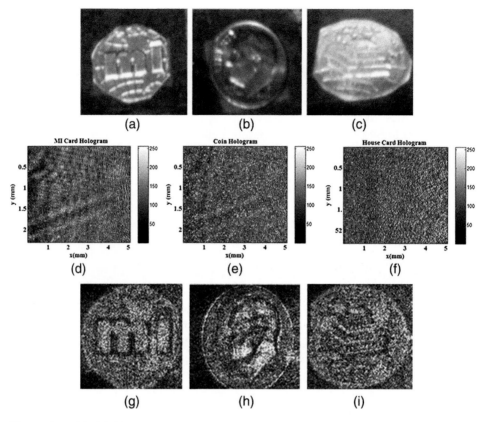

Figure 4.7 (a)–(c) Objects examined, (d)–(f) recorded Fresnel holograms of objects, and (g)–(i) intensity distribution of the reconstructed objects. The resolution of the dime image is $\Delta\xi = 92.5$ μm at a distance of $d = 90$ cm; $\lambda = 514$ nm; $N_x\Delta x = 5$ mm; and the size of the dime is found to be 194 pixels, or 17.91 mm.

which is characteristic of the coherent illumination of the objects. If the 3D profile of an object is desired, the phase information should be converted to depth information (as will be shown in several examples later in this book). Phase maps of reconstructed individual holograms contain spurious phases from aberrations, reference intensity and phase profiles, optical and electronic noise, dust, etc., and they will also contain high-frequency fringes resulting from large variations of the object depth (compared to the wavelength), as is the case for the objects in Fig. 4.7.

It is sometimes more useful to process the relative phase or depth information, e.g., assess small deformations using single-wavelength holographic interferometry, or to determine the surface profile using multiwavelength holography (discussed in Chapter 7). Only if the object phase is on the order of a few radians (between 0 and 2π without wrapping), it is possible to recover the exact phase or, alternatively, the depth information, as may be the case in digital holographic microscopy (DHM). Consider an example that

Table 4.2 MATLAB code "fresnel_reconstruction_coin.m" for the Fresnel reconstruction of a coin object.

```
1    %%Reading holograms and subtracting DC term
2    clc
3    clear all;
4    %Input hologram
5    I1=double(imread('coin.bmp'));
6    %I1=double(rgb2gray(I1));
7    [Ny,Nx]=size(I1);
8    minN=min(Ny,Nx);
9    %Crop to have rows equal to columns
10   I1=I1(1:minN,1:minN);
11   [Ny,Nx]=size(I1);
12   %----Subtract DC from hologram
13   Im1=1/(Nx*Ny)*sum(sum(I1));
14   I1=I1-Im1;
15   imagesc(I1)
16   %%-Reconstruction using the discrete Fresnel transform
17   lambda0=0.514*10^-3;                    %Wavelength in mm. Change
18                                           %depends on laser used.
19   k0=2*pi/lambda0;
20   delx=9.8*10^-3;                         %Pixel spacing in the x and y
21                                           %direction in mm of the CCD
22   dely=9.8*10^-3;                      %Change depends on CCD camera used
23   nx=[-Nx/2:1:Nx/2-1];                    %Create array of points
24   ny=[-Ny/2:1:Ny/2-1]';
25   X=nx*delx;
26   Y=ny*dely;
27   [XX,YY]=meshgrid(X,Y);                  %Create a mesh of spatial
28                                           %coordinates
29   d=[700:20:950];                         %Distance from object to CCD
30                                        %in mm: change depends on setup.
31   %The loop is just to show the reconstruction at
32   %different distances: the best is at 850 mm.
33   for m=1:1:length(d)
34   resolution_mm=lambda0*d(m)/(Nx*delx);
35   w=exp(i*pi/(lambda0*d(m))*(XX.^2+YY.^2)); %See Eq. (4.4b)
36   Rec_image=fftshift(ifft2(I1.*w));       %See Eq. (4.3)
37   Mag_Rec_image=abs(Rec_image);
38   colormap(gray(256))
39   imagesc(nx*resolution_mm,ny*resolution_mm,Mag_Rec_image)
40   title('Reconstructed Hologram')
41   xlabel('mm')
42   ylabel('mm')
43   axis([-(Nx/2)*resolution_mm (Nx/2)*resolution_mm...
44   -(Ny/2-1)*resolution_mm (Ny/2-1)*resolution_mm])
45   title(strcat('Reconstruction at distance:',...
46   num2str(d(m)),' mm'))
47   pause(0.5)
48   end
```

uses the Fresnel reconstruction technique; the MATLAB script is provided in Table 4.2.

As a second example, the MATLAB script in Table 4.3 uses several convolution techniques. The theory behind all of these techniques can be

Table 4.3 MATLAB code "convolution_reconstruction_coin.m" for reconstructing a coin object using convolution techniques.

```
1    %%Digital hologram reconstruction using multiple
2    %techniques
3    clc
4    close all;
5    clear all;
6    %Input hologram
7    I1=imread('coin.bmp');
8    IH1=double(I1(:,:,1));
9    [Ny,Nx]=size(IH1);
10   minN=min(Ny,Nx);
11   %Crop to have rows equal to columns
12   IH1=IH1(1:minN,1:minN);
13   [Ny,Nx]=size(IH1);
14   %----Subtract DC from hologram
15   Im1=1/(Nx*Ny)*sum(sum(IH1));
16   IH1=IH1-Im1;
17   colormap(gray(256))
18   imagesc(IH1);
19   lambda0=0.514*10^-3;   %0.6328*10^-3;                 %Wavelength in mm
20   k0=2*pi/lambda0;
21   delx=9.8*10^-3;                          %Pixel spacing in the x direction in mm
22   dely=9.8*10^-3;                          %Pixel spacing in the y direction in mm
23   xmax=Nx*delx/2;
24   ymax=Ny*dely/2;
25   d=850;                                   %Distance from object to CCD in mm
26   resolution_mm=lambda0*d/(Nx*delx)              %Actual resolution of
27                                                  %the reconstructed image.
28   %%Using convolution method with padding.
29   %This method uses the padding technique for
30   %reconstruction.
31   N=2^11;                                  %Size of padded hologram.
32   %Vary S1 and S2 in order to center the reconstructed
33   %hologram in the center of figure
34   S1=-N/2                          %Shift in x depends on the angle of reference
35   S2=0;                            %Shift in y depends on the angle of reference
36   b=zeros(N);
37   [rows,cols]=size(IH1);
38   %Zero padding. b is the padded hologram.
39   b(round(N/2-rows/2+1):round(N/2+rows/2),...
40   round(N/2-cols/2+1):round(N/2+cols/2))=IH1;
41   nx=[-N/2:1:N/2-1]-S1;
42   ny=([-N/2:1:N/2-1]-S2)';
43   X = nx*delx;
44   Y = ny*dely;
45   [XX,YY]=meshgrid(X,Y);
46   X2 = nx/(Nx*delx);
47   Y2 = ny/(Ny*dely);
48   [XX2,YY2]=meshgrid(X2,Y2);
49   for m=1:length(d)
50   num=exp(i*2*pi/lambda0*(d(m)^2+XX.^2+YY.^2).^0.5);
51   den=(d(m)^2+XX.^2+YY.^2).^0.5;
52   g=-i/lambda0*num./den;                          %See Eq. (4.10)
53   Rec_image4=fftshift(fft2(fft2(b).*fft2(g)));            %See Eq.
54                                                          %(4.9)
```

(continued)

Table 4.3 (*Continued*)

```
55  Mag_Rec_image=abs(Rec_image4);
56  imagesc(Mag_Rec_image)
57  colormap gray;
58  end
59  %%Using convolution method with magnification:
60  %Method 1, See Ref. 5: U. Schnars and W. Juptner,
61  %Digital Holography, 53-54, Springer, Berlin (2005).
62  nx=[-Nx/2:1:Nx/2-1];
63  ny=[-Ny/2:1:Ny/2-1]';
64  X=nx*delx;
65  Y=ny*dely;
66  [XX,YY]=meshgrid(X,Y);
67  X2=nx/(Nx*delx);
68  Y2=ny/(Ny*dely);
69  [XX2,YY2]=meshgrid(X2,Y2);
70  for mag=8
71  gamma=1/mag;
72  dp=d*gamma;
73  f=(1/d+1/dp)^-1;   % See Eq. 3.36 in Ref. 5
74  L=exp(i*pi/(lambda0*f)*(XX.^2+YY.^2));               %See Eq. (3.37)
75                                                       %in Ref. 5
76  P=exp(i*pi*lambda0*d^2/f*(XX2.^2+YY2.^2));              %See Eq.
77                                                       %(3.7) in Ref. 5
78  num=exp(-i*2*pi/lambda0*(dp^2+XX.^2+YY.^2).^0.5);
79  den=(dp^2+XX.^2+YY.^2).^0.5;
80  g=i/lambda0*num./den;                       %See Eq. (3.28) in Ref. 5.
81  %See Eq. (3.32) in Ref. 5.
82  Rec_image=fftshift(P.*ifft2(fft2(IH1.*L).*fft2(g)));
83  Mag_Rec_image=abs(Rec_image);
84  figure
85  imagesc(abs(Rec_image));
86  colormap gray;
87  end
88  %%Using convolution method with magnification:
89  %Method 2, See Ref. 5: U. Schnars and W. Juptner,
90  %Digital Holography, 53-54, Springer, Berlin (2005).
91  nx=[0:1:Nx-1];
92  ny=[0:1:Ny-1]';
93  X=nx*delx;
94  Y=ny*dely;
95  [XX,YY]=meshgrid(X,Y);
96  mag=[9.8];
97  for mm=1:1:length(mag)
98  gamma=1/mag(mm);
99  dp=d*gamma;
100 f=(1/d+1/dp)^-1; % See Eq. 3.36 in ref[5]
101 L=exp(i*pi/(lambda0*f)*(XX.^2+YY.^2));                  %See Eq.
102                                                      %(3.37) in Ref. 5
103 for m=0:1:Ny-1
104 for n=0:1:Nx-1
105 P(m+1,n+1)=exp(i*pi*lambda0*d^2/f*((m-Ny/2-1)^2/...
106 (Ny^2*dely^2)+(n-Nx/2-1)^2/...
107 (Nx^2*delx^2)));% See Eq. 3.7 in ref[5]
108 end
109 end
110 for l=0:1:Ny-1
```

(*continued*)

Table 4.3   (*Continued*)

```
111  for k=0:1:Nx-1
112  num=exp(-i*2*pi/lambda0*(dp^2+(l-Ny/2)^2*...
113  dely^2+(k-Nx/2)^2*delx^2)^0.5);
114  den=(dp^2+(l-Ny/2)^2*dely^2+(k-Nx/2)^2*delx^2)^0.5;
115  g(l+1,k+1)=i/lambda0*num/den;
116  end
117  end
118  Rec_image4=P.*ifft2(fft2(IH1.*L).*fft2((g)));      %See
119                                        %Eq. (3.32) in Ref. 5
120  Mag_Rec_image4=abs(Rec_image4);
121  colormap(gray(256))
122  %logim(Mag_Rec_image4,1.5)
123  imagesc(Mag_Rec_image4);
124  title(strcat('Reconstruction at magnification:',...
125  num2str(mag(mm))))
126  pause(0.5)
127  end
128  %%Using convolution method with magnification:
129  %Method 3
130  mag=[ 8];
131  for mm=1:1:length(mag)
132  gamma=1/mag(mm);
133  dp=d*gamma;
134  f=(1/d+1/dp)^-1;
135  nx =[ 0:1:Nx-1];
136  ny =[ 0:1:Ny-1]';
137  X = nx*delx;
138  Y = ny*dely;
139  [ XX, YY]=meshgrid(X,Y);
140  L=exp(i*pi/(lambda0*f)*(XX.^2+YY.^2));
141  for m=0:1:Ny-1
142  for n=0:1:Nx-1
143  P(m+1,n+1)=exp(i*pi*lambda0*d^2/f*((m)^2/...
144  (Ny^2*dely^2)+(n)^2/(Nx^2*delx^2)));
145  end
146  end
147  for m=0:1:Ny-1
148  for n=0:1:Nx-1
149  a=(lambda0/(Nx*delx))^2*((n)+Nx^2*...
150  delx^2/(2*dp*lambda0))^2;
151  b=(lambda0/(Ny*dely))^2*((m)+Ny^2*...
152  dely^2/(2*dp*lambda0))^2;
153  G(m+1,n+1)=exp(-i*2*pi*dp/lambda0*(1-a-b)^0.5);     %See
154                                   %Eq. (4.11), or Eq. (3.30) in Ref. 5
155  end
156  end
157  Rec_image5=P.*ifft2(fft2((IH1.*L)).*(G));      %See Eq.
158  %(4.9), or Eq. (3.32) in Ref. 5
159  Mag_Rec_image5=abs(Rec_image5);
160  colormap(gray(256))
161  %logim(Mag_Rec_image5,1.2)
162  imagesc(Mag_Rec_image5);
163  title(strcat('Reconstruction at magnification:',...
164  num2str(mag(mm))))
165  pause(0.5)
166  end
```

Table 4.4 MATLAB code "AngularSpectrum_reconstruction.m" to reconstruct a thin filament object using the angular spectrum technique.

```
1    %The angular spectrum method, as implemented here,
2    %reconstructs image
3    %pixels that are equal in size to the CCD pixels
4    clc
5    clear all
6    load Filament_Example              %Load hologram
7    d=[ 0.0001:0.0001:0.005];          %reconstruction_distance in
8                                       %meters: d = 0.0025;
9    w = 632.8e-9;                      %Wavelength in meters
10   dx = 6.7e-6;                       %Pixel size in meters
11   figure(1)
12   imagesc(h);
13   colormap gray
14   title ('Native Hologram')
15   axis square
16   A=size(h);
17   %If the image is not square, crop to be square along
18   %the smallest dimension
19   if A(1,1)<A(1,2)
20   %Crop the x axis of the image to match the y axis
21   %crops symmetrically about the center
22   h = h(:,round(A(1,2)/2+1-A(1,1)/2):...
23   round(A(1,2)/2+A(1,1)/2));
24   end
25   if A(1,1)>A(1,2)
26   %Crop the y axis of the image to match the x axis
27   h = h';                            %Transpose
28   C = size(h); %This is the line that fixes this part.
29   %After transposing, the sizes didn' t match anymore.
30   h = h(:,round(C(1,2)/2+1-C(1,1)/2):...
31   round(C(1,2)/2+C(1,1)/2));   %Crop
32   h = h';                            %Transpose back
33   end
34   %Use double precision to allow for complex numbers
35   h = double(h);
36   Image_Pixel_Size = dx
37   n = length(h);                     %Size of hologram matrix nxn
38   h = double(h)-mean(mean(h));         %Must be class double for
39                                        %imaginary numbers.
40   %%%%%%Angular spectrum method
41   k0=2*pi/w;
42   k =(-n/2:1:n/2-1)*dx;              %Array same dimensions as hologram
43   l =(-n/2:1:n/2-1)*dx;
44   [ XX,YY] = meshgrid(k,l);
45   step = k(2)-k(1);                  %Step size
46   k_max = 2*pi/step;                 %Maximum k vector
47   k_axis = linspace(0,k_max,n)-k_max/2; %Confine
48                                      %reconstruction to k<k_max
49   [ Kx Ky] =meshgrid(k_axis,k_axis);
50   for m=1:1:length(d)
51   E=exp(-1i*sqrt(k0^2-Kx.^2-Ky.^2)*d(m)-1i*k0*d(m));
52   %Angular spectrum
53   Hf=fftshift(fft2(sqrt(h)));
```

(continued)

Table 4.4 *(Continued)*

```
54  [Hr]=ifft2((Hf.*E));
55  %figure(2)
56  imagesc(abs(Hr).^2)
57  colormap gray
58  axis square
59  title(strcat('Angular Spectrum Reconstruction at ', ...
60  'distance:', num2str(d(m)*1000),' mm'))
61  pause(0.5)
62  end
```

found in Section 4.2.2 or in detail in Schnars and Juptner.[5] The third example, shown in Table 4.4, uses the angular spectrum technique to reconstruct the hologram of a tungsten lightbulb filament.

4.5 Digital Holograms of Large Objects

In order to perform Fresnel holograms and their reconstruction for large objects using a CCD, the maximum spatial frequency of the holographic microstructure should be adapted to the spatial resolution of the detector array. The maximum spatial frequency is determined by the angle between the interfering waves, as shown in Section 4.3, which is found to be on the order of a few degrees. This limits the size of the objects that can be recorded holographically. For larger objects to be recorded, a great distance between the object and CCD target is required.[9] However, if the dimensions of the object are reduced optically (e.g., by using a divergent lens), then larger objects with larger dimensions can be recorded with shorter distances, and thus enough light falls on the CCD array. Therefore, using a negative lens with focal length f in the setup, as shown in Fig. 4.8, the new reconstruction distance d' must be replaced by the distance of the virtual image to the CCD and can be computed as[9]

$$d' = |d_i| + z. \qquad (4.15)$$

where d_i is the distance of the virtual image.

It can be shown that the magnified pixel size $\Delta\xi_{mag}$ in the image scales according to

$$\Delta\xi_{mag} = \frac{\Delta\xi}{M} = \frac{\lambda d'}{N \cdot dx \cdot M}, \qquad (4.16)$$

which is simply the magnification predicted by geometric imaging. This is intuitively understood by realizing that the holographic recording is now simply a recording of the geometrically magnified/demagnified virtual image located at the new distance d'. Thus, the pixel resolution is automatically scaled accordingly. Because the object is demagnified by the lens, the reconstructed image will also become smaller, corresponding to larger values of $\Delta\xi$ per pixel covering the lateral extent of the object.

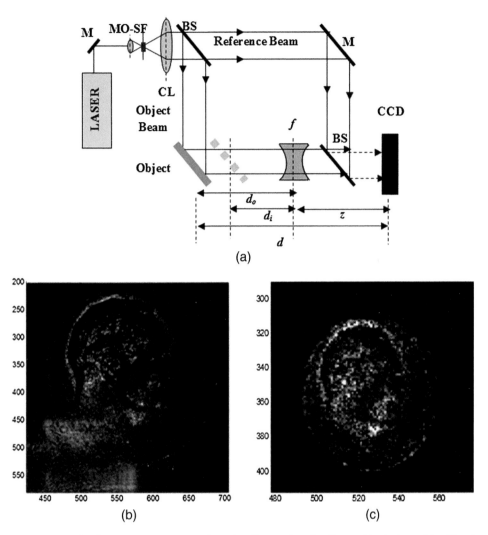

(a)

(b)   (c)

Figure 4.8 (a) Setup and reconstruction of a dime using the Fresnel technique (b) without and (c) with a lens. Feature size in the reconstructed hologram is 51.6 μm/pixel without demagnification, and 190.2 μm/pixel with demagnification, for a CCD camera pixel size of 6.7 μm, $\lambda = 633$ nm, $f = -50$ mm, $d = 56$ cm, $d' \approx 42$ cm, $d_i \approx 4$ cm, $d_o \approx 19$ cm, and $M \approx 0.2$.[9]

4.6 Digital Holographic Microscopy

Section 4.4 provided examples of the digital reconstruction of holograms to determine the intensities of various objects and reasoned why it is difficult to obtain the phase or depth information of the objects. This section describes a procedure to derive the depth information of a 3D object from the reconstructed phase, which is commonly desired in DHM. DHM is usually applied to determine 3D shapes of small objects, with height excursions on the order of microns (or phase excursions on the order of a few radians). Because small objects are involved, a microscope objective (MO) is often used to zoom

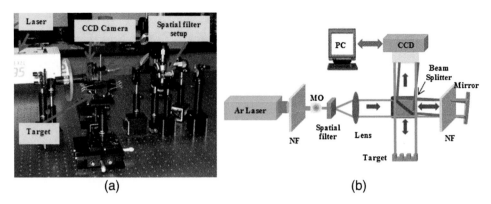

Figure 4.9 (a) Lab setup and (b) schematic of the reflection-type Fresnel DHM setup.[11,12]

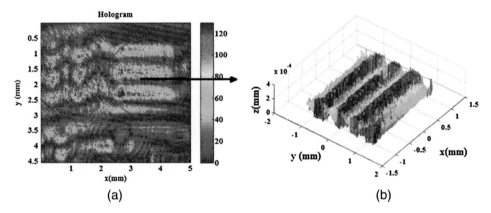

Figure 4.10 (a) DH of a part of the USAF 1951 resolution target, and (b) 3D perspective of the reconstructed height distribution (pixel size is 10 μm).[11]

onto a small area of the object to enhance the transverse resolution. Off-axis holograms recorded with a magnified image of microscopic objects can be numerically reconstructed in amplitude and phase using the Fresnel approximation. For phase-contrast imaging, the reconstruction method involves the computation of a digital replica of the reference wave. A digital method to correct the phase aberrations is presented, with a detailed description of the reconstruction procedure showing that the transverse resolution is equal to the diffraction limit of the imaging system.[12,13]

Figure 4.9 shows a generic off-axis DH setup. The height distribution on the sample surface is simply proportional to the reconstructed phase distribution $\phi(\xi,\eta) = \arctan\{\text{Im}[\Gamma(\xi,\eta)]/\text{Re}[\Gamma(\xi,\eta)]\}$ through[12]

$$h_z(\xi,\eta) = \left(\frac{\lambda}{4\pi}\right)\phi(\xi,\eta). \tag{4.17}$$

Figure 4.10(a) shows the DH of a part of an object (USAF 1951 resolution target, MIL-STD-150A), and Fig. 4.10(b) shows the 3D perspective

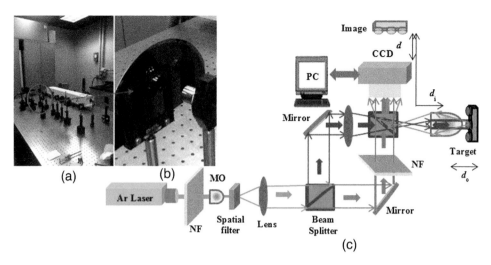

Figure 4.11 (a) Lab setup, (b) close-up of the silicon wafer sample with photoresist spherical bumps, and (c) schematic of the holographic microscope for reflection imaging.[11–14]

of the reconstructed height distribution, which matches the documented height for our sample.

As stated earlier, DHM introduces a MO to increase the spatial resolution of the previous example, which is limited to $\Delta\xi = \lambda d/N_x\Delta x$, $\Delta\eta = \lambda d/N_y\Delta y$ [see Eq. (4.5)]. The transverse resolution can be enhanced to be approximately equal to the diffraction limit $0.61\lambda/NA$ of the MO, where NA is the numerical aperture of the MO.

For an Ar ion laser and a microscope objective (MO) of 0.25, the resolution is now approximately 1.2 μm, as compared to ~50 μm if no MO were used. Figure 4.11(a) shows a typical lab setup, Fig. 4.11(b) shows a close-up of the silicon wafer sample with spherical bumps of deposited photoresist, and Fig. 4.11(c) shows the schematic of the holographic microscope for reflection imaging.[11] Figure 4.12(a) shows a schematic side view of the sample, Fig. 4.12(b) shows the hologram, and Fig. 4.12(c) shows the 3D profile of the deposited photoresist. The complete reconstruction algorithm is governed by the following equation:[11–14]

$$\Gamma(m,n) = \underbrace{Ae^{-j\left[\frac{\pi}{\lambda D}(m^2\Delta\xi^2 + n^2\Delta\eta^2)\right]}}_{\text{Phase mask}} \widehat{z}(m,n)$$

$$\times \Im_{x,y}\left\{\underbrace{A_R e^{-j\frac{2\pi}{\lambda}(k_x k\Delta x + k_y l\Delta y)}}_{E_{Re}^*}h(k,l)w(k,l)\right\}_{m,n} \qquad (4.18)$$

where $1/D = (1/d_i)[1 + (d_o/d_i)]$. Figure 4.13(a) shows an integrated holographic microscope that can be used to characterize microlens arrays, e.g., that shown in Fig. 4.13(b) using DHM.

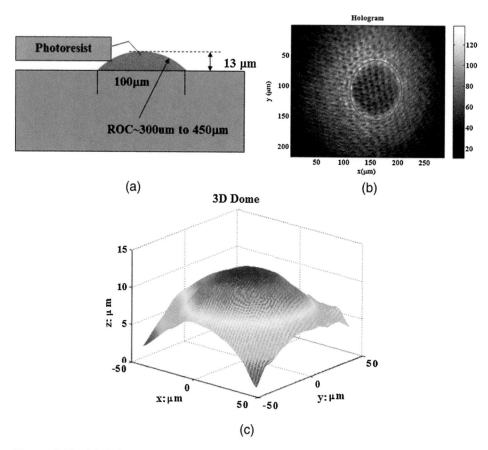

Figure 4.12 (a) Schematic of the test sample, (b) DH of the silicon wafer, and (c) 3D perspective of the reconstructed height distribution.[11]

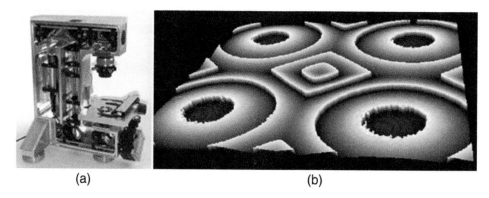

Figure 4.13 (a) Integrated DHM instrument (image © Lyncée Tec.), (b) square quartz microlens array.[14]

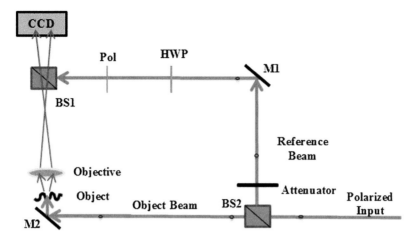

Figure 4.14 Transmissive holographic microscopy setup. BS: beamsplitter; M: mirror; Pol: polarizer; and HWP: half-wave plate.

4.7 Digital Holographic Microscopy Example

The setup for this example is shown in Fig. 4.14; it is similar to that of Fig. 4.11(c) but in transmission mode. The target is a USAF 1951 resolution chart, and its resolution is documented as

$$R_{[\text{lp/mm}]} = 2^{\left[G + \frac{(E-1)}{6}\right]}, \tag{4.19}$$

where R is the resolution in line pair per millimeter, G is the group number, and E is the element number (see Fig. 4.15).

For example, in group 4, element 2 has a resolution of 18 lp/mm; furthermore, 1 lp = 15 pixels, and 1 pixel ≈ 4.1 μm. The Rayleigh limit ≈ 1.5 μm. The laser used is a HeNe @ 633 nm, and the focal length of the lens used is $f = 50.2$ mm. The setup parameters are as follows: $d_o = 0.0524$ m, $d_i = -1.195$ m, $d' = 1.02$ m, and the magnification is $M \approx 22.8$. The MATLAB code is provided in Table 4.5; the name of the file is "AF_1951_Microscopy.m." This script uses the "myFresnel.m" function, which can be found in the same Chapter 4 directory on the CD. It should be noted that, in practice, it is very difficult to obtain such precise parameter measurements in the laboratory. Approximate measurements are typically made in the laboratory and then slightly varied during numerical reconstruction to yield the "best focus" image. Such a process was followed to obtain the parameters listed here.

4.8 Optimization of the Fresnel Transform

The image resolution of any Fresnel transform reconstruction is limited, as previously noted, by the Nyquist sampling criterion, given by Eqs. (4.6) and (4.7). However, it is possible to alter these parameters during reconstruction

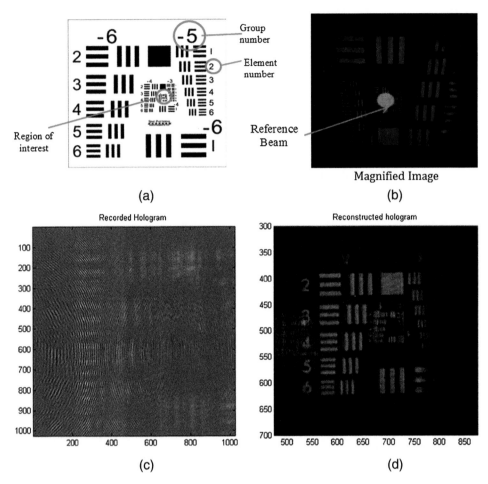

(a)   (b)

(c)   (d)

Figure 4.15 (a) Schematic of the USAF resolution target, (b) a magnified region of interest, (c) recorded hologram, and (d) reconstructed hologram using DHM principles.

to yield maximum performance. This is possible because the Fresnel transform is implemented numerically, such that the various sampling parameters N, Δx, and $\Delta \xi$ can be altered to a degree unavailable in AH. It should be noted that, although numerical values such as $\Delta \xi$ can be made arbitrarily small using numerical methods, in all cases the limiting physical resolution of the reconstructed image is dictated by diffraction of the object wave, which, in turn, is limited by the angular frequencies physically captured by the CCD and/or the Rayleigh criterion in the case of DHM.[1,5]

It is well known that the usefulness of the Fresnel transform is generally limited to the mid-to-far field, where d is on the order of or greater than the Rayleigh range of the object Z_R. A geometrical argument to determine the

Table 4.5 MATLAB code "AF_1951_Microscopy.m" for the Fresnel reconstruction of the AF_1951 object.

```
1   %Reconstruct the USAF 1951 resolution target,
2   %group 4, element 2 via DHM
3   clc;clear all
4   load Saved_Raw_holo2.mat
5   format compact
6   h = hraw1;                       %Reassign this variable
7   dx =6.7e-6;                      %CCD pixel size
8   N = 1024;                        %CCD array size
9   lambda = 632.8e-9;               %HeNe red
10  %Display the recorded hologram
11  figure(1)
12  imagesc(h);colormap(gray);axis square
13  title('Recorded Hologram' )
14  %Physical setup parameters
15  d = 0.231;    %Distance from object to CCD (not used here)
16  do = 0.0524;                     %Lens-to-object distance (must
17                                   %be precisely measured)
18  f = 0.0502;                      %Fixed, manufacturer spec
19  di = 1/(1/do-1/f);               %Image distance from lens
20  z = 0.175;                       %Distance from lens to CCD
21  dp = abs(di)-z                   %d prime, reconstruction
22                                   %distance from CCD to image plane
23  M=di/do                          %Geometrically calculated M
24  %Reconstruct the hologram using microscopy parameters
25  [ C0]=myFresnel(h,dp,lambda,dx,false);
26  figure(2)
27  %Geometric image is upside down, must be rotated.
28  %Taking the square root of C0 increases the apparent
29  %image contrast.
30  imagesc(rot90(abs(C0).^.5,2))
31  axis([ 475 875 300 700] )        %Location of interest within
32                                   %reconstruction
33  colormap(gray);axis square
34  title('Reconstructed hologram' )
35  Mag_Feature_size=lambda*dp/(dx*N* abs(M))     %With
36                                                %microscopy
```

minimum value of d based on the maximum angular frequency recorded by inline geometry is also given by Schnars and Jueptner,[5] which is

$$d_{\min} \approx \frac{x_{\max}}{\theta_{\max}} = \sqrt{2}\frac{\Delta x}{\lambda}(L_{Obj} + N\Delta x), \qquad (4.20)$$

where $x_{\max}$ is the maximum path length from the farthest extent of the object of size L_{Obj} to the farthest extent of the CCD array, and $\theta_{\max}$ is the maximum diffraction angle captured by the CCD array. However, both of these criteria are only heuristics. The actual limitation on d is given more rigorously by the extent of the object-field bandwidth that can be effectively captured by the CCD array under the Whittaker–Shannon sampling theorem. For Fresnel holograms, Goodman has shown the captured bandwidth of the object field B_x to be

$$B_x = \frac{L_\xi + L_x}{2\lambda d}, \tag{4.21}$$

where L_ξ and L_x are the total array lengths in the ξ and x directions, such that

$$L_\xi = N_\xi \cdot \Delta\xi \quad \text{and} \quad L_x = N_x \cdot \Delta x, \tag{4.22}$$

where N_ξ and N_x are the number of samples in the ξ and x directions, respectively, and they are necessarily equal by the properties of the discrete Fourier transform.[1] The minimum sampling interval for a given bandwidth dictated by the Whittaker–Shannon sampling theorem is

$$\Delta x = \frac{1}{2B_x}, \tag{4.23}$$

such that the total number of required samples is given by Goodman[1] to be

$$N_x = \frac{L_x}{\Delta x} = \frac{L_x(L_x + L_\xi)}{\lambda d} = \frac{L_x^2}{\lambda d} + \frac{L_x L_\xi}{\lambda d}. \tag{4.24}$$

Although this analysis concerns only the ξ and x directions, an equivalent analysis may be performed on the η and y dimensions.

Note that if the value of N_x is increased while L_ξ and L_x are kept constant, the value of d may be reduced while still satisfying the sampling theorem. Such is the case if the hologram matrix is upsampled via bicubic interpolation. In this case, N_x is increased by a scaling factor ς while Δx is reduced by the same factor, such that L_ξ and L_x remain constant:

$$L_\xi = \varsigma \cdot N_\xi \cdot \frac{\Delta\xi}{\varsigma}, \quad \text{and} \quad L_x = \varsigma \cdot N_x \cdot \frac{\Delta x}{\varsigma}. \tag{4.25}$$

The numerical effect of increasing N is that it increases the sample size available for the DFT operation, thus allowing the Fresnel transform to be accurately calculated at the reduced distance. The numerical resolution of the new reconstruction (based on the upsampled hologram) is still given by the familiar equation

$$\Delta\xi = \lambda d / L_x, \tag{4.26}$$

in which L_x remains constant. Therefore, if N_x is increased in this manner, d may then be reduced by the same factor, and the Fresnel transform may be calculated at a reduced distance. In the absence of computational limitations, it is possible to decrease d to such an extent that there is effectively no lower distance limit, allowing holograms to be recorded and reconstructed at any distance, including $d \approx 0$. This relationship has been experimentally verified by recording inline holograms of a tungsten filament (300-μm coil diameter) at various distances, then performing Fresnel reconstructions both with and

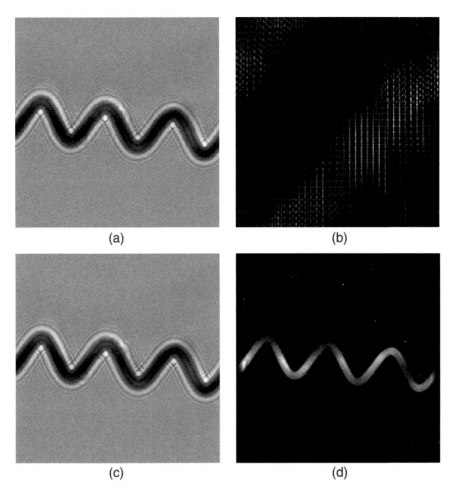

Figure 4.16 (a) Recorded inline hologram of a tungsten filament at $d = 2.5$ mm, with native size of 200×200 pixels, (b) the failed Fresnel reconstruction at $d = 2.5$ mm using the native CCD resolution, (c) the upscaled hologram, with upscaling factor $\varsigma = 6$, (d) the Fresnel reconstruction at $d = 2.5$ mm using the upscaled hologram, with numerical resolution of $\Delta \zeta = 1.17$ μm.

without bicubic upsampling of N. Figures 4.16(a)–(d) compare the Fresnel reconstruction of unscaled and upsampled ($\varsigma = 6$) holograms recorded at $d = 2.5$ mm, with $\lambda = 632.8$ nm. A Lumenera® camera consisting of a 1024×1024 pixel array is used, with a pixel size of $\Delta x = 6.7$ μm. The original hologram size is cropped to 200×200 pixels before upsampling to 1200×1200 pixels. The reconstructed image is also 1200×1200 pixels, with a numerical resolution of $\Delta \zeta = 1.17$ μm.

The reduction in the reconstruction distance to $d = 2.5$ mm is rather dramatic compared to the Rayleigh range of this object, which is $Z_R \approx 11$ cm (assuming that the feature size equals the half-width of the filament), or the geometrical argument of Eq. (4.20) that yields $d_{\min} \approx 10.5$ cm. Indeed, the Fresnel transform begins to adequately reconstruct this object when recorded

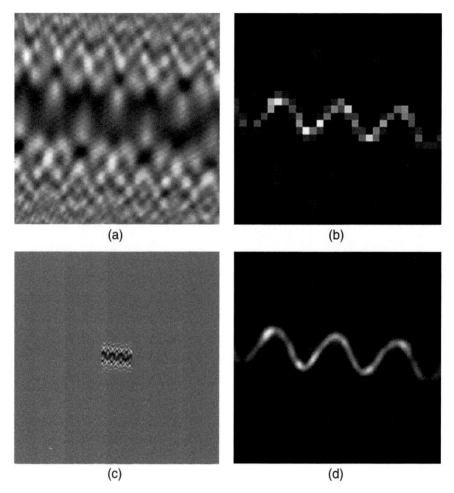

(a)   (b)

(c)   (d)

Figure 4.17 (a) Recorded hologram at $d = 10$ cm, with a native (cropped) size of 200×200 pixels; (b) the Fresnel reconstruction at $d = 10$ cm using the native 200×200 array size, with a native resolution of $\Delta\xi = 47$ μm; (c) the zero-padded hologram, with 600 zero indices added to each border; and (d) the Fresnel reconstruction at $d = 10$ cm using the zero-padded hologram, with a numerical resolution of $\Delta\xi = 6.74$ μm.

at a distance greater than about $d = 10$ cm, albeit rather poorly, with a corresponding resolution of $\Delta\xi = 47$ μm [see Fig. 4.17(b)]. It has been experimentally verified that with a scaling factor of $\varsigma=15$ the reconstruction distance can be reduced to $d \approx 500$ μm, which places the object directly on the CCD cover glass.

It is also possible to scale the value of N while keeping Δx constant, such that L_ξ and L_x do not remain constant. This is accomplished by zero padding the hologram prior to reconstruction. The resolution of the resulting reconstruction is still governed by Eq. (4.6); however, the value of N is that of the zero-padded hologram. As N increases, the value of $\Delta\xi$ decreases accordingly. Equation (4.6) is generally regarded as a "natural scaling" algorithm, such that the value of $\Delta\xi$

is automatically equal to the physical resolution limit of the CCD-sampled bandwidth.[5] Therefore, the "apparent" reconstructed image size appears to increase proportionally as $\Delta\xi$ decreases, such that the physical size of the object (as measured by $\Delta\xi$/pixel) remains constant.

This method of resolution scaling has two significant advantages. First, it can dramatically enhance the appearance of image reconstructions with a relatively poor native resolution. This can be seen in Figs. 4.17(a)–(d), in which the previous example of a 300-μm diameter tungsten filament is re-examined at $d = 10$ cm, near the limit of native Fresnel reconstruction, with $\Delta\xi = 47$ μm. However, after zero padding the perimeter of the hologram by 600 indices per side, the reconstructed resolution is $\Delta\xi = 6.74$ μm. It should be noted that because $d \sim Z_R$, the Fresnel reconstruction is on the edge of what could be called a "good" reconstruction.

The second advantage of zero padding the hologram is that it allows the reconstructed resolution of two holograms to be made equal when recorded with different parameters N, λ, or Δx. This trait is particularly useful when performing MWDH (discussed in detail in Chapter 5), in which two holograms are recorded at separate wavelengths λ_1 and λ_2. To effectively subtract the phases of two holograms pixel by pixel, the pixel sizes of both holograms must be equal, such that

$$\Delta\xi_1 = \frac{\lambda_1 d}{N_1 \Delta x} = \frac{\lambda_2 d}{N_2 \Delta x} = \Delta\xi_2, \qquad (4.27)$$

where the subscript 1 and 2 denote the hologram recordings made with either λ_1 or λ_2, respectively. If it is assumed that $\lambda_1 > \lambda_2$, then the λ_1 hologram (hologram #1) must be padded to reduce its resolution to equal that of hologram #2. The ratio of the initial resolutions is simply λ_1/λ_2, such that

$$N_1 = \frac{\lambda_1}{\lambda_2} \cdot N, \qquad (4.28)$$

where N is the original size of either hologram array (i.e., without padding). Therefore, the amount of zero padding that must be applied to each side of hologram #1 prior to reconstruction is given by

$$\text{pad size} = \text{round}\left[\frac{N}{2}\left(\frac{\lambda_1}{\lambda_2} - 1\right)\right], \qquad (4.29)$$

where the rounding function has been introduced to ensure an integer number of padded indices. Reconstructing the padded hologram #1 will result in a resolution equal to that of hologram #2 (which is reconstructed without prior padding). However, at this point, the total size of hologram #1 is N_1, although the size of hologram #2 is still N. To simplify the pixel-by-pixel subtraction computation, the size of hologram #2 may be increased to equal that of N_1 simply by padding hologram #2 post-reconstruction, which does not alter the value of $\Delta\xi_2$.

It may be noted that rounding the pad size to the nearest integer value potentially introduces quantization error, although it can be shown that this error is negligible. The maximum rounding error introduced by the pad size is one-half of a pixel, which is small compared to the typical CCD array size, where $N \sim 1000$. Therefore, the error in $\Delta\xi$ can be approximated by a Taylor series

$$\Delta\xi(N \pm 1/2) \approx \Delta\xi \pm \frac{\partial\Delta\xi}{\partial N} \cdot \frac{1}{2} + \dots. \tag{4.30a}$$

Applying Eq. (4.27) to Eq. (4.30a) produces

$$\Delta\xi(N \pm 1/2) \approx \Delta\xi \pm \frac{\Delta\xi}{2N}, \tag{4.30b}$$

where the expected error $\pm\Delta\xi/2\,N$ is negligibly small. Alternatively stated, the total quantization error using the zero-padding method will not exceed a *total* of one-half of a pixel over the full extent of the hologram.

Additionally, when the zero-padding technique is applied to holographic microscopy, the physical magnification factor M remains unchanged. This is again due to the "natural scaling" trait of Eq. (4.6), which is intuitively understood by realizing that padding is strictly a numerical effect and cannot increase the physical magnification of the recording configuration. Therefore, under both scaling scenarios (bicubic resampling and zero padding), the reconstructed resolution under DHM is still given by Eq. (4.16).

4.9 General Functions for Digital Holography Using MATLAB

The primary function used to reconstruct many of the examples in this text is "myFresnel.m," which is based on the Fresnel transform. This function, as written, includes a significant degree of additional functionality designed to numerically optimize the Fresenl transform for operation under a wide range of recording and reconstruction configurations. It should be noted that all input parameters should be in SI units. Table 4.6 shows the Fresnel reconstruction function.

Required input parameters for myFresnel.m

- Hologram: The recorded hologram. This function automatically subtracts the *dc* term from any hologram input, and it computes the size $N \times N$ of the hologram array. If the input hologram is not square, the function will automatically crop the hologram to be square, centered on the original hologram center. This is convenient when using CCD arrays that are not square.
- Reconstruction_distance: The distance d or d' from the CCD to the desired reconstruction plane (in meters).
- Wavelength: The illumination wavelength (in meters).
- Pixel_size: The physical size Δx of the CCD pixels (in meters).

Table 4.6 MATLAB code "myFresnel.m" for the Fresnel reconstruction method.

```
1  function[Hr] = ...
2  myFresnel(hologram,reconstruction_distance,...
3  wavelength,pixel_size,in_line,phase_mask,...
4  scale_factor,pad_size)
5  %%This function reconstructs a hologram using a Fresnel
6  %transform
7  %%and returns the reconstructed complex image matrix.
8  %%reconstruction_distance in meters,
9  %%wavelength in meters, and
10 %%pixel size in meters (pixels are assumed to be
11 %square).
12 %%If in_line is set to 1, the hologram will rescale
13 %with distance about the zero order (useful for
14 %inline holograms), defaults to 0.
15 %%NOTE: reconstruction_dist must be positive for
16 %in_line %scaling to work.
17 %%phase_mask should be the same size as the hologram.
18 %%If either one is not square, they will be
19 %cropped to square.
20 %If a scalar value is entered for phase_mask,
21 %%a constant array of that value is used (i.e.,
22 %uniform phase, plane wave).
23 %%scale_factor will change the size of the original
24 %hologram.
25 %%Increasing the scale factor will dramatically
26 %improve the reconstruction
27 %%results when in the very near field (without
28 %extra padding).
29 %%scale_factor defaults to 1.
30 %%Reducing the scale factor too low (<1/2 or so)
31 %will begin vignetting the
32 %%image significantly, losing the higher spatial
33 %frequency info due to resampling losses.
34 %%For very large CCD arrays, scale the image down.
35 %%For very-near-field holograms, scale the image up.
36 %%%%%Begin function
37 A = size(hologram);
38 if nargin < 8
39 pad_size=0;                        %Default to zero padding
40 end
41 if nargin < 7
42 scale_factor=1;                    %Default to original size
43 end
44 if nargin < 6
45 phase_mask=1;                      %Default to uniform phase
46                                    %(const, plane wave)
47 end
48 if nargin < 5
49 in_line=0;              %Default to off-axis-style hologram
50 end
51 if nargin < 4
52 error('Not enough input arguments')
53 end
54 if length(phase_mask) == 1
```

(continued)

Table 4.6 (*Continued*)

```
55  phase_mask = ones(A).*phase_mask;
56  end
57  B = phase_mask;
58  H = hologram;
59  d = reconstruction_distance;
60  w = wavelength;
61  dx = pixel_size;
62  %If the image is not square, crop to be square along
63  %the smallest dimension.
64  %This cropping is done manually (i.e., without the
65  %imcrop function) and should be fairly robust.
66  if A(1,1)<A(1,2)
67  %Crop the x axis of the image to match the y axis
68  %crops symmetrically about the center
69  H = H(:,round(A(1,2)/2+1-A(1,1)/2):...
70  round(A(1,2)/2+A(1,1)/2));
71  B = B(:,round(A(1,2)/2+1-A(1,1)/2):...
72  round(A(1,2)/2+A(1,1)/2));
73  end
74  if A(1,1)>A(1,2)
75  %Crop the y axis of the image to match the x axis
76  H = H';                           %Transpose
77  B = B';
78  C = size(H);%this is the line that fixes this part
79  %after transposing, the sizes didn't match anymore
80  H = H(:,round(C(1,2)/2+1-C(1,1)/2):...
81  round(C(1,2)/2+C(1,1)/2));        %Crop
82  B = B(:,round(C(1,2)/2+1-C(1,1)/2):...
83  round(C(1,2)/2+C(1,1)/2));        %Crop
84 H = H';                           %Transpose back
85  B = B';
86  end
87  %Use double precision to allow for complex numbers
88  H = double(H);
89  B = double(B);
90  %If the image is too big to compute efficiently,
91  %scale it down.
92  %To scale above 1, the phase mask can cause problems
93  %because the phase
94  %does not scale well with bicubic resampling. An
95  %appropriate phase mask
96  %should be generated external to this function.
97  if scale_factor ~= 1
98  H = imresize(H, scale_factor,'bicubic');
99  if length(B(:,1)) > 1             %Only rescale profile
100                                    %if it is not a scalar
101 B = imresize(B, scale_factor,'bicubic');
102 end
103 dx=dx/scale_factor;
104 end
105 n = length(H);                    %Size of hologram matrix nxn
106 H = double(H)-mean(mean(H));         %Must be class double
                                         %for imaginary numbers
107 if pad_size > 0                   %Only pad array AFTER mean
```

(*continued*)

Table 4.6 *(Continued)*

```
108                                          %subtraction
109  nr = length(H);                         %Save the original size
110  H = padarray(H,[ pad_size pad_size] );  %Pad the array
111  n = length(H)                           %Reset n after padding
112  dx = ((nr/(n-pad_size*2))*pixel_size);        %Account for
113                                                 %pad in scale
114  dx=dx/scale_factor;
115  if length(B(:,1)) > 2
116  %fprintf('Cannot pad with beam profile input. /n
117  %Assuming plane wave. /n' );
118  B = 1;
119  end
120  end
121  dy = dx;                                 %Assumes square CCD pixels -->
122  %Modify as needed for rectangle pixels.
123  Hr = complex(zeros(n));                  %Reconstructed H
124  E = complex(zeros(n));                   %Exponential term.
125  %Verified correct feature size (i.e., reconstructed
126  %pixel sizes)
127  feature_size = w*d/(length(H)*dx)
128  k = -n/2:1:n/2-1;                        %Array same dimensions as hologram
129  l = -n/2:1:n/2-1;
130  [ XX,YY] =meshgrid(k,l);
131  %Calculate the Fresnel transform
132  E(k+n/2+1,l+n/2+1) = B.* exp((-i*pi/(w*d)).*...
133  ((XX.*dx).^2 + (YY.*dy).^2));
134  %Reconstruction becomes complex valued
135  Hr = (fftshift(fft2(H.*E)));
136  %If padded...
137  if pad_size >0                           %Cut the initial padding out
138  Hr = Hr(pad_size:nr+pad_size, pad_size:nr+pad_size);
139  end
140  %Rescaling for INLINE HOLOGRAMS ONLY:
141  %scale by CCD size/object feature size = # of pixels
142  %to keep
143  %rescales based on the zeroth-order size only
144  if in_line == 1
145  N=min(A); %Smallest dimension of original hologram
146  obj_f = w*d/(N*dx);
147  P = round(N*dx/obj_f);                   %Should be size of center
148                                           %region.
149  %If P is odd, make it even.
150  if (mod(P,2) == 1)                       %If first dimension has odd
151                                           %number of rows
152  P = P+1;
153  end
154  %End rescaling of fresnel transform
155  if (P<N)
156  [ Hr] = Hr(round(N/2+1-P/2:N/2+P/2),...
157  round(N/2+1-P/2:N/2+P/2));
158  end
159  else if in_line == 0
160  [ Hr] =Hr;
161  end
162  end                                      %End function
```

Optional input parameters for myFresnel.m

- In_line: Set to "true" or "1" for inline, Gabor-style holograms. Set to "false" or "0" for off-axis or Leith–Upatnieks holograms. If in_line is set to "true," the Fresnel transform will be computed as usual, but the MATLAB display figure will be automatically cropped about the zero order for convenient viewing. The function defaults to the off-axis configuration.
- Phase_mask: Any real or complex 2D bitmap array can be assigned as a phase mask during reconstruction. This Fresnel transform will be multiplied by this phase mask during reconstruction. The function defaults to a uniform, real plane wave with zero additional phase, which is equivalent to multiplying the Fresnel transform by a value of "phase_mask = 1." It should be noted that a phase_mask input will not neccesarily scale properly with "scale_factor" or "pad_size" inputs, which should be considered when constructing the phase mask. Purely real phase masks should scale properly, whereas complex-valued masks will not.
- Scale_factor: The scale factor performs bicubic resampling of the input hologram prior to reconstruction, such that the new size of the hologram is equal to the old size multiplied by the scale factor. For example, scale_factor = 2 will double the size of the hologram, whereas scale_factor = 0.5 will halve the size of the hologram. The default value is "scale_factor = 1." The new equivelant pixel size Δx will be automatically computed. The only limit imposed on the scale factor will be determined by the computer being used; very large scale factors can overrun the computer's memory limit. Scale factors between 0 and 1 are useful to reduce the size of holograms to avoid memory overruns for some applications, such as tomography, whereas large scale factors allow the Fresnel transform to be adequately reconstructed in the near field.
- Pad_size: This parameter governs the number of indices that are zero padded around the perimeter of the input hologram prior to reconstruction. Pad_size = 10 will add 10 zero indices to the top, bottom, left, and right sides of the hologram. Zero padding allows the resolution $\Delta\xi$ of the Fresnel transform to be numerically altered, which is very useful for multiwavelength applications. Any padding added here will be automatically cropped out of the final reconstruction. For any pad size, the new value of $\Delta\xi_{padded}$ will be automatically computed by the function and printed in the MATLAB window.

Output parameters for myFresnel.m

- This function returns the complex valued hologram reconstruction performed via the Fresnel transform. The pixel size $\Delta\xi$ will also print to the screen, labeled as the image "feature size." Note that this "feature size" value will only be correct for nonmicroscopy applications. Although this function works very well for DHM applications (i.e., reconstruction at d' rather than d), the function does not automatically consider any information regarding magnification. Therefore, the pixel size under magnification should be computed separately by the user.

- As described in prior chapters, hologram reconstruction can also be performed via numerical convolution using the impulse response of propagation. Table 4.7 describes a hologram reconstruction using the convolution method "myConvolution.m." This function generally requires the same inputs as "myFresnel.m," although there are some unique differences when performing reconstruction by convolution, i.e., the convolution process allows the reconstruction to be numerically (not physically) magnified, as well as shifted laterally. Therefore, the new input parameters for "myConvolution.m" are as follows:

Optional input parameters for myConvolution.m

- Magnification: The numerical magnification applied during recon-struction via convolution. If this field is left blank or set to "0," then this function will automatically default to the "best" magnification based on the natural scaling algorithm governing the pixel size $\Delta\xi$. Note that any magnification, in general, will not produce a meaning-ful reconstruction. If the user enters any nondefault magnification, the function will automatically suggest (in the MATLAB output window) several alternative magnifications that should perform relatively well.
- Horiz_shift: This shifts the reconstructed image horizontally an equal number of pixels, either positive or negative.
- Vert_shift: Same as horiz_shift, but it shifts the image vertically.

It should be noted that this function contains the ability to compute the convolution both via either the numerical or analytic Fourier transform of the impulse response, although all code for the latter is commented out. The function, as written in Table 4.7, defaults to the numerical Fourier transform method. The user may alter this, if desired, by selectively commenting and uncommenting the code as needed. It should also be noted that this function does not internally support zero padding the original hologram, although there is no reason it cannot be added by the user.

The examples provided in Table 4.8 use the file "Reconstruction_ Examples.m" to illustrate the use of the myFresnel.m and myCon-volution.m functions. The example code and functions are found in the Chapter 4 directory on the accompanying CD and are used to produce Figs. 4.18(a)–(f).

The angular spectrum (AS) method is also sometimes used for hologram reconstruction. The primary advantage of the AS method is that it remains

Table 4.7 MATLAB code "myConvolution.m" for hologram reconstruction using the convolution method.

```
1    function[ Hr2] = myConvolution(hologram,...
2    reconstruction_distance,wavelength,pixel_size,...
3    magnification, in_line, horiz_shift, vert_shift,...
4    phase_mask,scale_factor)
5    %This function reconstructs a hologram using a
6    %convolution algorithm and returns the reconstructed
7    %hologram matrix.
8    %Hr1 is the reconstruction using the explicit formula
9    %for the Fourier transform.
10   %Hr1 has been removed as an output because it
11   %does not work correctly.
12   %Hr2 uses the numerically calculated impulse response.
13   %reconstruction_distance is in meters,
14   %wavelength is in meters, and
15   %pixel size is in meters.
16   %Magnification will default to the best magnification
17   %available if this
18   %field and remaining fields are left blank, or if this
19   %field is set to 0;
20   %otherwise, the user must enter a magnification, which
21   %may be poorly
22   %selected. In this case, the function will compute a
23   %suggested magnification to use.
24   %If in_line is set to true, the hologram will rescale
25   %with distance about the zeroth order (use full for
26   %inline holograms), defaults to 0 (false).
27   %horiz_shift shifts the image horizontally, and
28   %vert_shift shifts the image vertically.
29   %THE SHIFT IS APPLICABLE ONLY TO THE IMPULSE RESPONSE
30   %RECONSTRUCTION[ HR2].
31   %phase_mask should be the same size as the hologram
32   %(i.e., taken on the same camera).
33   %If either one is not square, they will be cropped to
34   %square.
35   %If a scalar value is entered for phase_mask,
36   %a constant array of that value is used.
37   %scale_factor will reduce the size of the image by
38   %a factor between 0 to 1.
39   %scale_factor defaults to 1.
40   %Adjusting the scaling factor will automatically adjust
41   %the magnification to compensate; accordingly,
42   %reducing the scale factor too much (<1/2 or so) will
43   %begin vignetting the image significantly, losing the
44   %higher spatial freqency information due to resampling
45   %losses.
46   %%%%%Begin function
47   A = size(hologram);
48   if nargin < 10
49   scale_factor = 1;
50   end
51   if nargin < 9
52   phase_mask = ones(A);
53   end
54   if nargin < 8
```

(continued)

Table 4.7 *(Continued)*

```
55  vert_shift = 0;
56  end
57  if nargin < 7
58  horiz_shift = 0;
59  end
60  if nargin < 6
61  in_line = 0;
62  end
63  if nargin < 5
64  magnification=min(size(hologram))*pixel_size^2...
65  /(wavelength*reconstruction_distance);
66  elseif magnification == 0
67  magnification=min(size(hologram))*pixel_size^2...
68  /(wavelength*reconstruction_distance);
69  end
70  if nargin < 4
71  error('Not enough input arguments')
72  end
73  str=sprintf('Best magnification should be (%d)', ...
74  min(size(hologram))*pixel_size^2/...
75  (wavelength*reconstruction_distance));
76  disp(str);
77  disp('for n=1,2,4,8,16 etc.')
78  if length(phase_mask) == 1
79  phase_mask = ones(A)*phase_mask;
80  end
81  B = phase_mask;
82  H = hologram;
83  d = reconstruction_distance;
84  w = wavelength;
85  dx = pixel_size;
86  m = magnification;
87   sk=horiz_shift;                    %Shifts only for impulse
88                                      %response reconstruction
89  sl=vert_shift;
90  %If the image is not square, crop to be square
91  %along the smallest dimension.
92  %This cropping is done manually (i.e., without the
93  %imcrop function) and should be fairly robust.
94  if A(1,1)<A(1,2)
95  %Crop the x axis of the image to match the y axis
96  %crops symmetrically about the center
97  H = H(:,round(A(1,2)/2+1-A(1,1)/2):...
98  round(A(1,2)/2+A(1,1)/2));
99  B = B(:,round(A(1,2)/2+1-A(1,1)/2):...
100 round(A(1,2)/2+A(1,1)/2));
101 end
102 if A(1,1)>A(1,2)
103 %Crop the y axis of the image to match the x axis
104 H = H';                             %Transpose
105 B = B';
106 C = size(H);   %This is the line that fixes this part.
107 %After transposing, the sizes did not match anymore
108 H = H(:,round(C(1,2)/2+1-C(1,1)/2):...
109 round(C(1,2)/2+C(1,1)/2));   %Crop
```

(continued)

Table 4.7   (*Continued*)

```
110  B = B(:,round(C(1,2)/2+1-C(1,1)/2):...
111  round(C(1,2)/2+C(1,1)/2));  %Crop
112  H = H';                              %Transpose back
113  B = B';
114  %Not sure if this works perfectly yet – have not had
115  %to try it
116  end
117  %d_xi=w*d/(min(A)*dx)                %The "resolution" in the
118                                       %reconstruction space
119  %m=dx/d_xi                %Calculation of "correct" magnification
120                            %uses double precision to allow for
121                            %complex numbers
122  H = double(H);
123  B = double(B);
124  %If the image is too large to compute efficiently,
125  %scale it. Scale is from 0 to 1 in percentage.
126  %It must also scale other parameters to compensate.
127  if scale_factor ~= 1
128  H = imresize(H, scale_factor,'bicubic');
129  B = imresize(B, scale_factor,'bicubic');
130  dx = dx*length(hologram)/length(H);
131  m = m/scale_factor;
132  end
133  dp = d*m;
134  f = 1/(1/d + 1/dp);                  %Focal distance
135  n = length(H);                       %Size of hologram matrix nxn
136  H=double(H)-mean(mean(H));               %Must be class double
137                                           %for imaginary numbers
138  dy = dx;
139  Hr = complex(zeros(n));              %Reconstructed H
140  E = complex(zeros(n));               %Exponential term.
141  %This n/2 style does not work well with convolution
142  %Hr2 with shift,
143  %but it does work well with Hr2 without the XXYY
144  %shift in the meshgrid.
145  k = -n/2:1:n/2-1;%1:1:n;                 %Array with the same
146                                           %dimensions as the hologram
147  l = -n/2:1:n/2-1;%1:1:n;
148  %This works best with Hr2
149  %k = 1:1:n;                           %Array has the same
150                                        %dimensions as the hologram.
151  %l = 1:1:n;
152  %If the range is from -n/2 to n/2-1, then fftshift
153  %must be used.
154  %Set up the meshgrid for the numerical impulse
155  %response g.
156  g = double(zeros(n));
157  [XX,YY] = meshgrid((dx^2)*((k-n/2+sk).^2),...
158  (dy^2)*((l-n/2+sl).^2));
159  %[XX,YY] = meshgrid((dx^2)*(k.^2),(dy^2)*(l.^2));
160  %without n/2 term.
161  %n/2 term eliminates the need for fftshift if
162  %fft2(g) is computed;
163  %%does nothing if g is used in calculation
164  g = (i/w)*(exp((-i*2*pi/w)*sqrt(dp^2+XX+YY)))./...
165  (sqrt(dp^2+XX+YY));
```

(*continued*)

Table 4.7 (*Continued*)

```
166  %Set up meshgrid for lens functions
167  [KK,LL] = meshgrid(k*dx,l*dy);
168  L = exp((i*pi/(w*f)).*(XX + YY));                    %Lens transmission
169                                                        %factor, XX,YY already squared
170  P = exp((i*pi/(w*f)).*((KK).^2+(LL).^2));                    %Lens phase
171                                                        %correction factor.
172  %Correction factor P can be neglected if only
173  %the intensity is plotted.
174  %Set up meshgrid for g, if used (explicitly
175  %calculated Fourier transform).
176  %%%%%%%%%%%%%%%%%%%%%%%%%%%%%%
177  %k = 1:1:n;                                           %Array has the same dimensions
178                                                        %as the hologram
179  %l = 1:1:n;
180  %[NN,MM] = meshgrid(k,l);
181  %G = exp((-i*2*pi*dp/w).*sqrt(1-...
182  %(((w.^2).*(NN+(n.^2.*dx.^2/(2*dp*w))).^2)/...
183  %(n.^2.*dx.^2))-(((w.^2).*(MM+(n.^2.*dy.^2/...
184  %(2*dp*w))).^2)/(n.^2.*dy.^2))));
185  %%Reconstruct using the explicitly calculated
186  %Fourier transform.
187  %[Hr1] = (P.*ifft2(fft2(H.*L).*G);
188  %%%%%%%%%%%%%%%%%%%%%%%%%%%%%%%%%%%%%%%%%
189  %%fftshift is not required, already accounted for in
190  %equation symmetry
191  %reconstruction using numerically calculated impulse
192  %response.
193  %Hr = abs(fftshift(fft2(fft2(h).*fft2(g))));
194  [Hr2] = (P.*ifft2(fft2(H.*L).*fft2(g)));
195  %This gives better reconstruction at 512,
196  %but it is sensitive to changes in sign of d and m.
197  %Scale for distance to the Fresnel reconstruction.
198  %Crop the reconstruction about the center
199  %based upon the distance scale factor.
200  %Object "feature" size=lambda*d/(N*dx).
201  %Scale by CCD size/object feature size=number of
202  %pixels to keep
203  %rescales based on the zeroth-order size only.
204  %Rescaling for inline holograms ONLY.
205  if in_line == true
206  N=min(A);                                             %Smallest dimension of the
207                                                        %original hologram
208  obj_f=w*d/(N*dx);
209  P = round(N*dx/obj_f);                                %Should be the size of the
210                                                        %center region.
211  %If P is odd, make it even.
212  if (mod(P,2) == 1)                                    %If the first dimension has
213                                                        %an odd number of rows
214  P = P+1;
215  end
216  %End rescaling of reconstruction
217  if (P<N)
218  Hr1 = Hr1([N/2+1-P/2:N/2+P/2],[N/2+1-P/2:N/2+P/2]);
219  Hr2 = Hr2([N/2+1-P/2:N/2+P/2],[N/2+1-P/2:N/2+P/2]);
220  end
221  end
```

Table 4.8 MATLAB code "Reconstruction_Examples.m" for hologram reconstruction using the Fresnel and convolution techniques [see Figs. 4.18(a)–(f)].

```
1   %%Examples of various reconstruction methods.
2   %First, reconstruct native hologram via the Fresnel
3   %transform.
4   format compact
5   %Physical recording parameters for lensless Fresnel
6   %hologram of the newportmlogo at 39 cm, using argon @
7   %496.5 nm
8   d =. 39;                          %Reconstruction distance in m
9   lambda = 496.5e-9;                %Wavelength in m
10  pixel_size = 6.7e-6;              %Camera pixel size
11  N = 1024;                         %Number of pixels
12  load 'Saved_Raw_holo1.mat'
13  figure(1)
14  imagesc(h)
15  title('Recorded Hologram' )
16  axis square
17  colormap gray
18  C0 = myFresnel(h,d,lambda,pixel_size);
19  figure(2)
20  imagesc(abs(C0).^.5)              %The square root increases the
21                                    %apparent contrast
22  title('Native Reconstruction by Fresnel Transform' )
23  axis square
24  colormap gray
25  %%Next, reconstruct via the Fresnel transform using
26  %padding
27  in_line = 'false' ;
28  phase_mask = 1;                   %Uniform plane wave
29  scale_factor = 1;                 %No scaling
30  pad_size = 150;           %Zero pad around the perimeter by 512
31  figure(3)
32  %Pad the hologram outside the function for display
33  %purposes only; this step
34  %is not necessary for the function to automatically
35  %apply padding
36  imagesc(padarray(h,[ pad_size pad_size] ))
37  title('Zero padded hologram' )
38  axis square
39  colormap gray
40  C1 = myFresnel(h,d,lambda,pixel_size,in_line,...
41  phase_mask,scale_factor,pad_size);
42  figure(4)
43  imagesc(abs(C1).^.5)              %The square root increases
44                                    %the apparent contrast
45  title('Zero-Padded Reconst. by Fresnel Transform' )
46  axis square
47  colormap gray
48  %%Reconstruction by convolution
49  C2 = myConvolution(h,d,lambda,pixel_size);
50  figure(5)
51  imagesc(abs(C2).^.5)              %The square root increases the
52                                    %apparent contrast
```

(continued)

Table 4.8 (*Continued*)

```
53  title('Native Reconstruction by Convolution')
54  axis square
55  colormap gray
56  %%Shift the reconstructed object to the center of the
57  %image
58  %and magnify by 2x
59  magnification=0.2373918*2;               %Optimal mag*2,
60                                           %calculated by function
61  horiz_shift = 70;                        %150 pixels to the left
62  vert_shift= -40;                         %130 pixels down
63  C3 = myConvolution(h,d,lambda,pixel_size, ...
64  magnification, false, horiz_shift, vert_shift,...
65  phase_mask, scale_factor);
66  figure(6)
67  imagesc(abs(C3).^.5)                     %The square root increases the
68                                           %apparent contrast
69  title('Shifted Reconstruction by Convolution')
70  axis square
71  colormap gray
```

valid at any distance d, as opposed to both the Fresnel transform and convolution methods, which do not perform well below a certain minimum distance without preprocessing, as noted in the previous section. The function shown in Table 4.9, "myAngularSpectrum.m," is only valid for inline holograms and yields a fixed image resolution equal to that of the CCD resolution (i.e., $\Delta\xi = \Delta x$). Because of this, zero padding has no effect on the reconstruction, whereas scaling alters only the numeric value of $\Delta\xi$ in direct proportion to the scaling of Δx, again with less advantage than realized for the Fresnel transform. The function inputs operate similarly to the equivalent inputs for the "myFresnel.m" and "myConvolution.m" functions.

The example code "Filament_Reconstructions.m" provided in Table 4.10 was used to generate Figs. 4.16(a)–(d), as well as Fig. 4.19, which is the AS reconstruction of the hologram shown in Fig. 4.16(a). The AS method can directly reconstruct the hologram at $d = 2.5$ mm without preprocessing or scaling, and with an image resolution equal to the CCD resolution $\Delta\xi = \Delta x = 6.7$ µm. Note that the defocused twin image (due to the inline recording setup) is more strongly present using the AS method when compared to the rescaled Fresnel transform. The filament recording at $d = 10$ cm is also included on the CD, which has been used to generate Figs. 4.17(a)–(d) using zero padding. The "Filament_Reconstructions.m" sample code may be easily modified to replicate the reconstructions shown in Figs. 4.17(a)–(d).

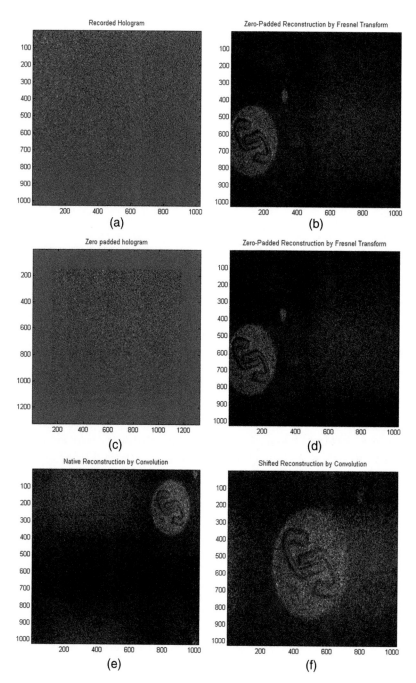

Figure 4.18 (a) Recorded hologram of the Newport logo, where $d = 39$ cm, $\lambda = 496.5$ nm, $\Delta x = 6.7$ μm, and $N = 1024$. (b) Fresnel reconstruction of the Newport logo using the native resolution in (a), where $\Delta\xi = 28.2$ μm/pixel. (c) The zero-padded hologram from (a) with pad size $= 150$ ($N = 1324$). (d) The reconstruction of the padded hologram resulting in a somewhat larger reconstructed image, where $\Delta\xi_{padded} = 21.8$ μm/pixel. (e) Reconstruction of (a) by the convolution method at the native resolution ($\Delta\xi = 28.2$ μm/pixel). (f) Reconstruction by convolution using the shift and magnification properties to place the image in the center, with $2\times$ magnification (i.e., $\Delta\xi_{mag} = 14.1$ μm/pixel). Note that the $2\times$ magnification shown in (f) causes image wrapping (i.e., aliasing), such that the defocused (blurry) twin image begins to overlap the focused image (on the right).

Table 4.9 MATLAB code "myAngularSpectrum.m" for hologram reconstruction using the angular spectrum technique.

```
1    function[Hr] = ...
2    myAngularSpectrum(hologram,reconstruction_distance,...
3    wavelength,pixel_size,phase_mask,scale_factor)
4    %NOTE: This function only works for Gabor (inline)
5    %holograms.
6    %Off-axis reconstructions will only return the
7    %zero order.
8    %This function reconstructs a hologram using the angular
9    %spectrum
10   %and returns the reconstructed hologram matrix.
11   %The angular spectrum method, as implemented here,
12   %reconstructs image
13   %pixels that are equal in size to the CCD pixels.
14   %Reconstruction_distance is in meters,
15   %wavelength is in meters, and
16   %pixel size is in meters.
17   %phase_mask defaults to a uniform phase of constant
18   %intensity (plane wave)
19   % (i.e., this can be used to reconstruct with some tilt
20   %or lens phase, etc.).
21   %scale_factor will change the size of the original
22   %hologram, which has little effect on the angular
23   %spectrum method but can be used to increase the
24   %apparent numerical resolution.
25   %scale_factor defaults to 1.
26   %Padding the hologram has no significant effect on
27   %this method and is therefore not included in this
28   %function.
29   %%%%%Begin function
30   A=size(hologram);
31   if nargin < 6
32   scale_factor=1;
33   end
34   if nargin < 5
35   phase_mask=1;
36   end
37   if nargin < 4
38   error('Not enough input arguments')
39   end
40   if length(phase_mask) == 1
41   phase_mask = ones(A).*phase_mask;
42   %phase_mask = 1;
43   end
44   B = phase_mask;
45   H = hologram;
46   d = reconstruction_distance;
47   w = wavelength;
48   dx = pixel_size;
49   %If the image is not square, crop to be square along
50   %the smallest dimension
51   if A(1,1)<A(1,2)
52   %Crop the x axis of the image to match the y axis
53   %crops symmetrically about the center
```

(*continued*)

Table 4.9 (*Continued*)

```
54  H = H(:,round(A(1,2)/2+1-...
55  A(1,1)/2):round(A(1,2)/2+A(1,1)/2));
56  B = B(:,round(A(1,2)/2+1-...
57  A(1,1)/2):round(A(1,2)/2+A(1,1)/2));
58  end
59  if A(1,1)>A(1,2)
60  %Crop the y axis of the image to match the x axis
61  H = H';                               %Transpose
62  B = B';
63  C = size(H);                %This is the line that fixes this part.
64  %After transposing, the sizes did not match anymore.
65  H = H(:,round(C(1,2)/2+1-C(1,1)/2):...
66  round(C(1,2)/2+C(1,1)/2));            %Crop
67  B = B(:,round(C(1,2)/2+1-C(1,1)/2):...
68  round(C(1,2)/2+C(1,1)/2));            %Crop
69  H = H';                               %Transpose back
70  B = B';
71  end
72  %Use double precision to allow for complex numbers
73  H = double(H);
74  B = double(B);
75  %If the image is too large to compute efficiently,
76  %scale it.
77  %Scale is from 0 to 1, in percentage.
78  %To scale above 1, the phase mask can cause problems
79  %because the phase
80  %does not scale well with bicubic resampling.
81  if scale_factor ~= 1
82  H=imresize(H, scale_factor,'bicubic');
83  if length(B(:,1)) > 1                 %Only rescale profile
84                                        %if it is not a scalar
85  B = imresize(B, scale_factor,'bicubic');
86  end
87  dx=dx/scale_factor;
88  end
89  Image_Pixel_Size = dx
90  n = length(H);                        %Size of hologram matrix nxn
91  H = double(H)-mean(mean(H));           %Must be class double for
92                                         %imaginary numbers
93  %%%%%Angular spectrum method
94  k0=2*pi/w;                            %k-vector
95  k = (-n/2:1:n/2-1)*dx; %Array same dimension as hologram
96  l = (-n/2:1:n/2-1)*dx;
97  [ XX,YY] = meshgrid(k,l);
98  step = k(2)-k(1);                     %Step size
99  k_max = 2*pi/step;                    %Maximum k vector
100 k_axis = linspace(0,k_max,n)-k_max/2;          %Confine
101                                       %reconstruction to k < k_max
102 [ Kx Ky] =meshgrid(k_axis,k_axis);
103 %Angular spectrum
104 E=B.*exp(-1i* sqrt(k0^2-Kx.^2-Ky.^2)*d-1i* k0* d);
105 Hf=fftshift(fft2(sqrt(H)));
106 [ Hr] =ifft2((Hf.*E));
107 end                                   %End function
```

Table 4.10 MATLAB code "Filament_Reconstructions.m" for hologram reconstruction of a filament using the angular spectrum technique (see Fig. 4.19).

```
1    %This example illustrates the resolution scaling
2    %properties of the Fresnel
3    %transform, compared to the angular spectrum method
4    load Filament_d_2_5mm
5    h = hraw1;
6    d = 0.0025;
7    lambda = 632.8e-9;
8    dx = 6.7e-6;
9    h = hraw1(625:825,700:900);          %Crop to size
10   figure(1)
11   imagesc(h);
12   colormap gray
13   title ('Native Hologram')
14   axis square
15   %%Try the native resolution Fresnel transform first
16   H0 = myFresnel(h,d,lambda,dx,true,1,1,0);
17    H0 = rot90(H0,2);                    %Image will be upside down,
18                                          %so flip it
19   figure(2)
20   imagesc(abs(H0).^2)
21   colormap gray
22   axis square
23   title ('Native Fresnel Reconstruction')
24   %%Try to increase the resolution via bicubic scaling.
25   %Scale the hologram but not the pixel size to get
26   %increased performance.
27   %Display the scaled version here (this step is not
28   %usually necessary).
29   scale = 6;
30   hs = imresize(h,scale,'bicubic');
31   figure(3)
32   imagesc(hs)
33   colormap gray
34   axis square
35   title ('6x Rescaled Hologram')
36   %Scaling is done directly in the function,
37   %using the original hologram
38   Hs = myFresnel(h,d,lambda,dx,false,1,scale);
39    Hs = rot90(Hs,2);                    %Image will be upside down,
40                                          %so flip it
41   figure(4)
42   imagesc(abs(Hs).^2)
43   colormap gray
44   axis square
45   title ('6x Rescaled Fresnel Reconstruction')
46   %%Compare to the angular spectrum method
47   scale=1;
48   H0 = myAngularSpectrum(h,d,lambda,dx,1,scale);
49   figure(3)
50   imagesc(abs(H0).^2)
51   colormap gray
52   axis square
53   title ('Angular Spectrum Reconstruction')
```

(continued)

Table 4.10 (*Continued*)

```
54   %%Angular spectrum method with upscaling
55   scale = 6;
56   H0 = myAngularSpectrum(h,d,lambda,dx,1,scale);
57   figure(3)
58   imagesc(abs(H0).^2)
59   colormap gray
60   axis square
61   title ('6x Scaled Angular Spectrum Reconstruction')
```

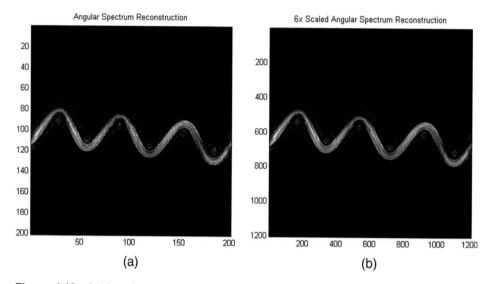

Figure 4.19 (a) Angular spectrum reconstruction of the hologram shown in Fig. 4.16(a), where $d = 2.5$ mm, $\lambda = 623.8$ nm, and $N = 1024 \times 1024$, cropped to 200×200, with an image resolution equal to the CCD resolution $\Delta\xi = \Delta x = 6.7$ µm. No rescaling of the hologram has been performed. (b) 6× upscaled angular spectrum reconstruction of the same hologram [Fig. 4.16(c)], with $\Delta\xi = \Delta x/6 = 1.12$ µm.

References

1. J. W. Goodman, *Introduction to Fourier Optics*, 3rd Ed., Roberts & Co., Englewood, CO (1996).

2. T. Kreis, *Holographic Interferometry: Principles and Methods*, Akademie Verlag, Berlin (1996).

3. U. Schnars and W. Jueptner, "Direct recording of holograms by a CCD target and numerical reconstruction," *Appl. Opt.* **33**(2), 179–181 (1994).

4. L. P. Yaroslavski and N. S. Merzlyakov, *Methods of Digital Holography*, Consultants Bureau, New York (1980).

5. U. Schnars and W. Jueptner, *Digital Holography*, Springer, Berlin (2005).

6. U. Schnars and W. Jueptner, "Digital recording and numerical reconstruction of holograms," *Meas. Sci. Technol.* **13**(9), R85–R101 (2002).

7. T. M. Kreis, M. Adams, and W. P. O. Jueptner, "Methods of digital holography: a comparison," *Proc. SPIE* **3098**, 224 (1997) [doi: 10.1117/12.281164].

8. T. M. Kreis and W. Jueptner, "Suppression of the dc term in digital holography," *Opt. Eng.* **36**(8), 2357–2360 (1997) [doi: 10.1117/1.601426].

9. U. Schnars, T. Kreis, and W. Jueptner, "Digital recording and numerical reconstruction of holograms: reduction of the spatial frequency spectrum," *Opt. Eng.* **35**(4), 977–982 (1996) [doi: 10.1117/1.600706].

10. G. Nehmetallah and P. P. Banerjee, "Digital holographic interferometry and microscopy for 3D object visualization," *Frontiers in Optics Conf.*, San Jose, CA (2011).

11. G. Nehmetallah and P. P. Banerjee, "Applications of digital and analog holography in 3D imaging," *Adv. Opt. Photon.* **4**(4), 472–553 (2012).

12. E. Cuche, F. Bevilacqua, and C. Depeursinge, "Digital holography for qualitative phase-contrast image," *Opt. Lett.* **24**(5), 291–293 (1999).

13. E. Cuche, P. Marquet, and C. Depeursinge, "Simultaneous amplitude-contrast and quantitative phase-contrast microscopy by numerical reconstruction of Fresnel off-axis holograms," *Appl. Opt.* **38**(34), 6994–7001 (1999).

14. F. Charrière, J. Kühn, T. Colomb, F. Montfort, E. Cuche, Y. Emery, K. Weible, P. Marquet, and C. Depeursinge, "Characterization of microlenses by digital holographic microscopy," *Appl. Opt.* **45**(5), 829–835 (2006).

Chapter 5
Digital Holographic Interferometry and Phase-Shifting Digital Holography

5.1 Digital Holographic Interferometry: Basic Principles

If the holograms of the object are *digitally* recorded using a CCD camera and they are compared by computing the phase difference of the digitally reconstructed images, then the process is called *digital holographic interferometry* (DHI). In current technology, commercial CCD cameras have pixel sizes around 5 μm, which can sometimes limit the spatial resolution required for large off-axis angles (<2 deg), which, in practice, limits DH to inline or near-inline configurations. In DHI, the recorded holograms are individually reconstructed by numerical methods, and the experimental setup is simpler compared to AHI. Due to the numerical reconstruction process, the interference phase, which represents the deformation field, can be calculated by subtracting the reconstructed phases of the undeformed and deformed object waves. Thus, there is no need to generate a macroscopic interference pattern. Additionally, the interference phase in DHI can be determined without sign ambiguity.

As already stated, in DHI, the holograms of the original and the displaced/deformed object are both recorded on the CCD camera, and the reconstruction is performed on each to yield the complex optical fields constituting the respective situations. Thereafter, the two complex fields are digitally compared to yield information about the displacement/deformation.[1-3] In DH, the intensity and the phase of the reconstructed hologram are computed as described in Chapter 4. Thus, using the reconstructed complex amplitudes

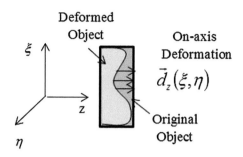

Figure 5.1   Schematic of deformation calculation.

$\Gamma_1(\xi,\eta)$ and $\Gamma_2(\xi,\eta)$ of the original and deformed objects, respectively, their corresponding phases are found to be[1–3]

$$\phi_1(\xi,\eta) = \arctan\left(\frac{\operatorname{Im}\Gamma_1(\xi,\eta)}{\operatorname{Re}\Gamma_1(\xi,\eta)}\right), \qquad (5.1a)$$

$$\phi_2(\xi,\eta) = \arctan\left(\frac{\operatorname{Im}\Gamma_2(\xi,\eta)}{\operatorname{Re}\Gamma_2(\xi,\eta)}\right). \qquad (5.1b)$$

The interference phase can be found by subtraction:

$$\Delta\phi(\xi,\eta) = \begin{cases} \phi_1(\xi,\eta) - \phi_2(\xi,\eta) & \text{if } \phi_1(\xi,\eta) \geq \phi_2(\xi,\eta), \\ \phi_1(\xi,\eta) - \phi_2(\xi,\eta) + 2\pi & \text{if } \phi_1(\xi,\eta) < \phi_2(\xi,\eta). \end{cases} \qquad (5.2)$$

Therefore, Eq. (5.2) calculates the interference phase directly from the digital holograms. After the fringes are obtained from Eq. (5.2), the next step is to perform phase unwrapping (discussed earlier). This step converts the unwrapped phase to the on-axis deformation (in this case, the z axis is defined by the surface normal of the CCD plane), as shown in Fig. 5.1 and derived in a similar fashion as in Section 2.3, according to the following equation:

$$d_z(\xi,\eta) = [\lambda/(4\pi)]\Delta\phi(\xi,\eta). \qquad (5.3)$$

The following tables and figures present some experimental results of deformation analysis using DHI and the phase retrieval scheme discussed earlier. Table 5.1 provides the MATLAB code "coin_tilt.m" to visualize the tilt of a coin object using DHI. The upper row in Fig. 5.2 shows two reconstructed DHs of a coin as recorded at two different tilting states, showing reconstructed intensities and wrapped phases. The phases are derived according to Eqs. (5.1a) and (5.1b), after digital reconstruction from the DHs based on the algorithm described in Chapter 4. The lower-left picture of Fig. 5.2(c) shows the subtraction of these two phases according to Eq. (5.2). Because the interference phase is unique only up to a multiple of 2π, the interference phase must be converted into a continuous phase distribution through the phase-unwrapping algorithm discussed earlier. The result is shown in the lower-right of Fig. 5.2(c) and confirms the fact that the coin was tilted between the two DH recordings. The phase reconstruction can also be performed dynamically if the holograms are recorded at different times

Table 5.1 MATLAB code "coin_tilt.m" to visualize the tilt of a coin object using digital holographic interferometry (see Fig. 5.2).

```
1    %%Coin-tilt digital holographic interferometry
2    clc
3    close all;
4    clear all;
5    %Input hologram
6    I1=imread('coindef1.bmp');
7    IH1=double(I1(:,:,1));
8    [Ny,Nx]=size(IH1);
9    I2=imread('coindef2.bmp');
10   IH2=double(I2(:,:,1));
11   %----Subtract dc from hologram
12   Im1=1/(Nx*Ny)*sum(sum(IH1));
13   IH1=IH1-Im1;
14   Im2=1/(Nx*Ny)*sum(sum(IH2));
15   IH2=IH2-Im2;
16   delx=9.8*10^-3;           %Pixel spacing in the y
17                             %direction in mm of the CCD
18   dely=9.8*10^-3;
19   lambda=0.514*10^-3;       %Wavelength in mm
20   k0=2*pi/lambda;           %Pixel spacing in the x
21                             %direction in mm of the CCD.
22   %%Reconstruction using the discrete Fresnel transform.
23   nx =[-Nx/2:1:Nx/2-1];
24   ny =[-Ny/2:1:Ny/2-1]';
25   X = nx*delx;
26   Y = ny*dely;
27   [XX,YY]=meshgrid(X,Y);
28   d=[850];                  %Distance from object to CCD in mm
29   w=exp(i*pi/(lambda*d)*(XX.^2+YY.^2));
30   Rec_image1=fftshift(ifft2(IH1.*w,Ny,Nx)); %Reconstruct
31                                      %the first hologram
32   Mag_Rec_image1=abs(Rec_image1).^2;
33   phase_Rec_image1=angle(Rec_image1);
34   B1=mylogim2(Mag_Rec_image1,3);
35   imagesc(B1);
36   colormap(gray(256))
37   title('Intensity of Recons. Hologram Before Tilt')
38   Rec_image2=fftshift(ifft2(IH2.*w,Ny,Nx)); %Reconstruct
39                                      %the second hologram
40   Mag_Rec_image2=abs(Rec_image2).^2;
41   phase_Rec_image2=angle(Rec_image2);
42   B2=mylogim2(Mag_Rec_image2,3);
43   figure,
44   imagesc(B2);
45   colormap(gray(256))
46   title('Intensity of Reconst. Hologram after Tilt')
47   %%
48   %In this section, the user must select the region
49   %of interest around the hologram, using the mouse
50   %to perform phase subtraction
51   disp('select the region of interest around')
52   disp('the coin using th mouse then double')
53   disp('click the left button of the mouse')
54   [Holrec,rec]=imcrop(B1);    %rec=[XMIN YMIN WIDTH HEIGHT]
```

(continued)

Table 5.1 *(Continued)*

```
55  colormap(gray(256))
56  imagesc(Holrec)
57  title('Intensity of Reconst. Hologram Before Tilt')
58  B3=imcrop(B2,rec);
59  figure
60  colormap(gray(256))
61  imagesc(B3)
62  title('Intensity of Reconst. Hologram After Tilt')
63  phase_Rec_image1=imcrop(phase_Rec_image1,rec);
64  h1crop=Rec_image1(round(rec(2)):round(rec(2)+...
65  rec(4)),round(rec(1)):round(rec(1)+rec(3)));
66  figure
67  imagesc(phase_Rec_image1)
68  title('Phase of Reconstructed Hologram Before Tilt')
69  colormap(gray(256))
70  phase_Rec_image2=imcrop(phase_Rec_image2,rec);
71  h2crop=Rec_image2(round(rec(2)):round(rec(2)+...
72  rec(4)),round(rec(1)):round(rec(1)+rec(3)));
73  figure
74  imagesc(phase_Rec_image2)
75  colormap(gray(256))
76  title('Phase of Reconstructed Hologram After Tilt')
77  %%----Compute the wrapped phase------------
78  %A first method to calculate the wrapped phase--
79  WrappedPhase= phase_Rec_image1-phase_Rec_image2;
80  WrappedPhase(find(phase_Rec_image1<...
81  phase_Rec_image2))= ...
82  WrappedPhase(find(phase_Rec_image1<...
83  phase_Rec_image2))+2*pi; %Wrap 2pi if needed.
84  %-A second method to calculate the wrapped phase:
85  %WrappedPhase = angle(h1crop.*conj(h2crop));
86  figure
87  colormap(gray(256))
88  imagesc(WrappedPhase);
89  title({ 'Difference of Reconstructed Phase',
90  'Before and After Tilt'})
91  %%
92  %%%---Unwrapping using the 2D_SRNCP algorithm:
93  %http://www.ljmu.ac.uk/GERI/90225.htm
94  %Instructions:
95  %Install the Microsoft Windows SDK 7.1.
96  %mex -setup
97  %Follow instructions: type Y then 1 then Y.
98  %Call the 2D phase unwrapper from C language.
99  %To compile the C code: in MATLAB command window,
100 %you have to run
101 %mex Miguel_2D_unwrapper.cpp
102 %This file has to be in the same directory as
103 %the script to work.
104 mex Miguel_2D_unwrapper.cpp
105 %The wrapped phase should have the single
106 %(float in C) data type
107 WrappedPhase = single(WrappedPhase);
108 UnwrappedPhase = Miguel_2D_unwrapper(WrappedPhase);
109 UnwrappedPhase=double(UnwrappedPhase);
110 h = fspecial('average',15);
```

(continued)

Table 5.1 (*Continued*)

```
111 UnwrappedPhase = imfilter(UnwrappedPhase,h);
112 figure
113 surfl(10^3*lambda/(4*pi)*UnwrappedPhase);
114 shading interp; colormap(gray); axis ij
115 grid on
116 zlabel('Tilt in \mum')
117 title('2D Unwrapped Phase Showing Tilt')
```

during deformation. As a second example, consider the setup in Fig. 5.3(a), where deformation is introduced to the object, shown in Fig. 5.3(b) (embossment on a metal foil), through the calibrated impact of a metal pin. In this case, two DHs have been recorded. The first exposure is before the impact, and the second exposure is after the pin has impacted the object and indented the surface by approximately 6 microns. Figure 5.4(a) shows two reconstructed holograms of the original and deformed objects. Figure 5.4(b) shows the corresponding phases, Fig. 5.4(c) shows the interference phase modulo 2π, and Fig. 5.4(d) shows the unwrapped phase. Note that for $\lambda = 0.514$ μm, a 2π change of phase corresponds to a depth of $d_z = \lambda/2$. Table 5.2 shows the MATLAB code "deformation.m" to visualize the deformation introduced to the metal foil object.

5.2 Two-Illumination-Point Technique

Another way to perform shape measurement is to use the two-illumination-point technique.[1] In this technique, two holograms of the same surface use two different object-illumination points, as shown in Fig. 5.5(a). Figure 5.5(b) shows a schematic of the interference geometry. The optical path difference between the two paths of illumination is

$$\delta = (\overline{S_1P} + \overline{PO}) - (\overline{S_2P} + \overline{PO}) = \overline{S_1P} - \overline{S_2P} = \vec{s}_1\overrightarrow{S_1P} - \vec{s}_2\overrightarrow{S_2P} = \vec{s} \cdot \overrightarrow{\Delta s}, \quad (5.4)$$

where it is assumed that $\vec{s}_1 \approx \vec{s}_2 = \vec{s}$, $\overrightarrow{S_1P} - \overrightarrow{S_2P} = \overrightarrow{\Delta s}$. After subtracting the reconstructed phases according to Eqs. (5.1a) and (5.1b), an interference phase map proportional to the object shape can be computed as

$$\Delta\phi = \frac{2\pi}{\lambda} \overrightarrow{\Delta s} \cdot \vec{s}. \quad (5.5)$$

The result is a wrapped-phase map with the distance between two adjacent 2π jumps given by

$$\Delta H = \frac{\lambda}{2\sin(\theta/2)} => d_z = \frac{\Delta\phi_{\text{Total}} \times \Delta H}{2\pi}, \quad (5.6)$$

where θ is the angle between the two illumination directions, and d_z is the depth. For example, if $\theta = 1$ deg, $\lambda = 514 \times 10^{-9}$ nm, and $\Delta\Phi = 100\pi$, then $\Delta H = 30$ μm, and $d_z = 50 \times 30 = 1.5$ mm. The setup is shown in Fig. 5.6.

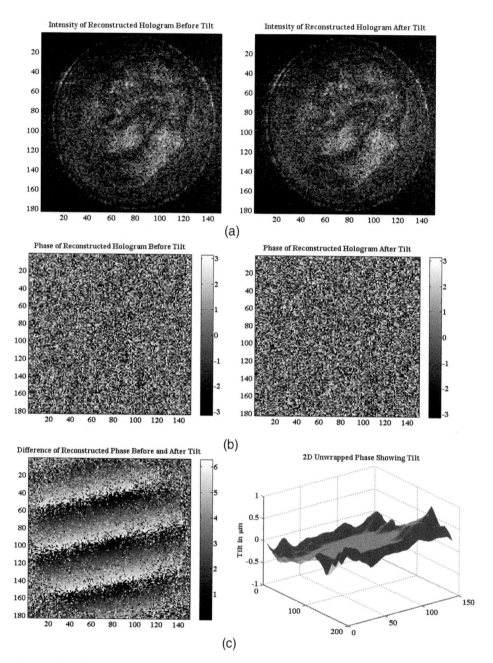

Figure 5.2 Digital holographic interferometry of a tilted coin: (a) intensities of the two reconstructed holograms, and (b) corresponding phases of the reconstructed holograms. (c) The wrapped-phase tilt (left) and the unwrapped 3D tilt (right). The *xy* axis units in all of the figures are in pixels (the pixel size of the camera is 10 μm, and on the image plane it is around $\Delta\xi = 100$ μm).

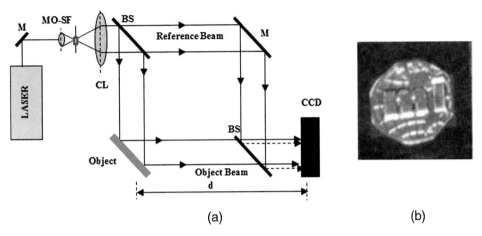

(a)   (b)

Figure 5.3 (a) Digital holographic interferometry setup, and (b) an object deformed by a pushing a pin.

5.3 3D Stress and Strain Sensors from Three Digital Hologram Recordings

In Section 5.2, the computed deformation is an out-of-plane (i.e., z axis) 3D deformation. In this section, the three deformation components x, y, and z of an object are measured simultaneously by using digital holography with a double-pulse ruby laser source. The object is illuminated from three different directions, each optically path-matched with three reference beams, such that three independent digital holograms are formed and added incoherently [due to delay lines (DLs) artificially introduced between the three object/reference pairs] in a single CCD image. The optical phase difference between the two recordings taken for each hologram is quantitatively evaluated by the Fourier-transform method so that a set of three phase maps is obtained, representing the deformation along three sensitivity vectors. The total object deformation is obtained as a vector resultant from the data of the three phase maps. By appropriate choice of spatial carriers with different directions for the three digital holograms, it is possible to separate the three components in the Fourier spectrum of the holographic image and to evaluate the phase difference along the three sensitivity vectors. This arrangement is usually referred to as digital holographic interferometry with spatial multiplexing (DHI-SM), where one CCD is used instead of three CCD arrays.

Let the three components of the deformation vector be (u,v,w). Let $P = (x_p, y_p, z_p)$ be the coordinates of a point of a solid object that is displaced by

$$d(P) = (d_x(P), d_y(P), d_z(P)) = (u,v,w). \tag{5.7}$$

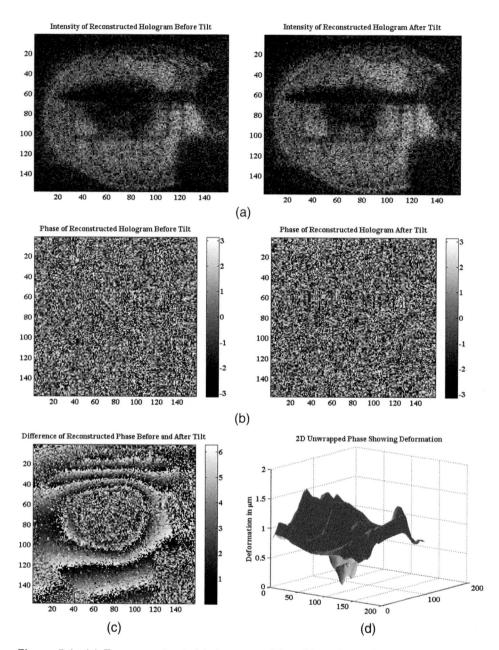

Figure 5.4 (a) Two reconstructed holograms of the object shown in Fig. 5.3(b), (b) the corresponding phases, (c) the interference phase modulo 2π, and (d) the unwrapped phase corresponding to the deformation immediately after the impact. The *xy* axis units in all of the figures are in pixels (the CCD pixel size is 10 μm, and on the image plane it is $\Delta\xi = 100$ μm).

Table 5.2 MATLAB code "deformation.m" to visualize the deformation introduced to the metal foil object (see Fig. 5.4).

```
1    %%Digital holographic interferometry of the object in
2    %Fig. 5.3(b)
3    clc
4    close all;
5    clear all;
6    %Input hologram
7    I1=imread('paper1.bmp');
8    IH1=double(I1(:,:,1));
9    [Ny,Nx]=size(IH1);
10   I2=imread('paper2.bmp');
11   IH2=double(I2(:,:,1));
12   %----Subtract dc from hologram
13   Im1=1/(Nx*Ny)*sum(sum(IH1));
14   IH1=IH1-Im1;
15   Im2=1/(Nx*Ny)*sum(sum(IH2));
16   IH2=IH2-Im2;
17   delx=9.8*10^-3;              %Pixel spacing of the CCD in
18                                %the y direction in mm
19   dely=9.8*10^-3;
20   lambda=0.514*10^-3;          %Wavelength in mm
21   k0=2*pi/lambda;              %Pixel spacing of the CCD in
22                                %the x direction in mm.
23   %%Reconstruction using the discrete Fresnel transform.
24   nx =[-Nx/2:1:Nx/2-1];
25   ny =[-Ny/2:1:Ny/2-1]';
26   X = nx*delx;
27   Y = ny*dely;
28   [XX, YY]=meshgrid(X,Y);
29   d=[850];                %Distance from the object to CCD in mm
30   w=exp(i*pi/(lambda*d)*(XX.^2+YY.^2));
31   %Reconstruct the first hologram
32   Rec_image1=fftshift(ifft2(IH1.*w,Ny,Nx));
33   Mag_Rec_image1=abs(Rec_image1).^2;
34   phase_Rec_image1=angle(Rec_image1);
35   B1=mylogim2(Mag_Rec_image1,4);
36   imagesc(B1);
37   colormap(gray(256))
38   %Reconstruct the second hologram
39   Rec_image2=fftshift(ifft2(IH2.*w,Ny,Nx));
40   Mag_Rec_image2=abs(Rec_image2).^2;
41   phase_Rec_image2=angle(Rec_image2);
42   B2=mylogim2(Mag_Rec_image2,4);
43   figure,
44   imagesc(B2);
45   colormap(gray(256))
46   %%
47   %In this section, the user has to select the region of
48   %interest around the hologram, using the mouse
49   %to perform phase subtraction
50   disp('select the region of interest around')
51   disp('the coin using th mouse then double')
52   disp(' click the left button of the mouse')
53   [Holrec,rec]=imcrop(B1); %rec=[XMIN YMIN WIDTH HEIGHT]
54   colormap(gray(256))
```

(continued)

Table 5.2 *(Continued)*

```
55  imagesc(Holrec)
56  title('Intensity of Reconst. Hologram Before Tilt')
57  B3=imcrop(B2,rec);
58  figure
59  colormap(gray(256))
60  imagesc(B3)
61  title('Intensity of Reconst. Hologram After Tilt')
62  phase_Rec_image1=imcrop(phase_Rec_image1,rec);
63  h1crop=Rec_image1(round(rec(2)):round(rec(2)...
64  +rec(4)),round(rec(1)):round(rec(1)+rec(3)));
65  figure
66  imagesc(phase_Rec_image1)
67  title('Phase of Reconstructed Hologram Before Tilt')
68  colormap(gray(256))
69  phase_Rec_image2=imcrop(phase_Rec_image2,rec);
70  h2crop=Rec_image2(round(rec(2)):round(rec(2)...
71  +rec(4)),round(rec(1)):round(rec(1)+rec(3)));
72  figure
73  imagesc(phase_Rec_image2)
74  colormap(gray(256))
75  title('Phase of Reconstructed Hologram After Tilt')
76  %%-Compute the wrapped phase------------
77  %-A first method to calculate the wrapped phase--
78  WrappedPhase= phase_Rec_image1-phase_Rec_image2;
79  WrappedPhase(find(phase_Rec_image1<...
80  phase_Rec_image2))= ...
81  WrappedPhase(find(phase_Rec_image1<...
82  phase_Rec_image2))+2*pi;%Wrap 2pi if needed.
83  %-A second method to calculate the wrapped phase---
84  %WrappedPhase = angle(h1crop.*conj(h2crop));
85  figure
86  colormap(gray(256))
87  imagesc(WrappedPhase);
88  title({'Difference of Reconstructed Phase',
89  'Before and After Tilt'})
90  %%
91  %%%---Unwrapping using the 2D_SRNCP algorithm:
92  %http://www.ljmu.ac.uk/GERI/90225.htm
93  %Instructions:
94  %Install the Microsoft Windows SDK 7.1.
95  %mex -setup
96  %Follow instructions: type Y then 1 then Y.
97  %Call the 2D phase unwrapper from C language.
98  %To compile the C code: in MATLAB command window,
99  %you have to run mex Miguel_2D_unwrapper.cpp.
100 %This file has to be in the same directory as the
101 %script to work.
102 mex Miguel_2D_unwrapper.cpp
103 %The wrapped phase should have the single
104 %(float in C) data type.
105 WrappedPhase = single(WrappedPhase);
106 UnwrappedPhase = Miguel_2D_unwrapper(WrappedPhase);
107 UnwrappedPhase=double(UnwrappedPhase);
108 h = fspecial('average',15);
109 UnwrappedPhase = imfilter(UnwrappedPhase,h);
110 min_UnwrappedPhase =min(UnwrappedPhase(:));
```

(continued)

Table 5.2 (*Continued*)

```
111  UnwrappedPhase=UnwrappedPhase -min_UnwrappedPhase;
112  figure
113  surfl(10^3*lambda/(4*pi)*UnwrappedPhase);
114  shading interp; colormap(gray); axis ij
115  grid on
116  zlabel('Deformation in \mum')
117  title('2D Unwrapped Phase Showing Deformation')
```

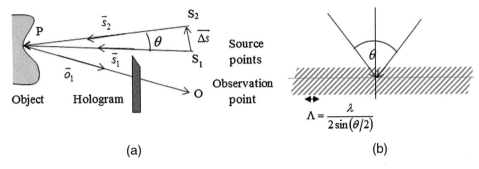

(a)   (b)

Figure 5.5 (a) Schematic of a shape measurement using the two-illumination-point technique,[1] and (b) schematic showing the interference geometry.

Section 5.2 only computed $d_z(P) = w$ (i.e., the out-of-plane deformation). At any point in a solid body, the three-dimensional components of *normal strain* are[2,4]

$$\varepsilon_{xx} = \frac{\partial u}{\partial x} = \frac{\partial d_x(P_i)}{\partial x} \approx \frac{d_x(P_{i+1}) - d_x(P_i)}{x_{i+1} - x_i},$$

$$\varepsilon_{yy} = \frac{\partial v}{\partial y} = \frac{\partial d_y(P_i)}{\partial y} \approx \frac{d_y(P_{i+1}) - d_y(P_i)}{y_{i+1} - y_i},$$

$$\varepsilon_{zz} = \frac{\partial w}{\partial z} = \frac{\partial d_z(P_i)}{\partial z} \approx \frac{d_z(P_{i+1}) - d_z(P_i)}{z_{i+1} - z_i}, \qquad (5.8)$$

which describe the change in length per unit length in each direction. The three independent *shear strains* are

$$\gamma_{xy} = \frac{\partial d_x}{\partial y} + \frac{\partial d_y}{\partial x}, \quad \gamma_{yz} = \frac{\partial d_y}{\partial z} + \frac{\partial d_z}{\partial y}, \quad \gamma_{zx} = \frac{\partial d_z}{\partial x} + \frac{\partial d_x}{\partial z}, \qquad (5.9)$$

which describe the decrease in the angle between two line segments that are initially orthogonal and parallel to the coordinate axes. Therefore, the strains are described as derivatives of the displacement components. Also, the *rotations* of a typical object about the x, y, and z axes, respectively, are

$$\omega_x = \frac{1}{2}\left(\frac{\partial d_z}{\partial y} - \frac{\partial d_y}{\partial z}\right), \quad \omega_y = \frac{1}{2}\left(\frac{\partial d_x}{\partial z} - \frac{\partial d_z}{\partial x}\right), \quad \omega_z = \frac{1}{2}\left(\frac{\partial d_y}{\partial x} - \frac{\partial d_x}{\partial y}\right). \qquad (5.10)$$

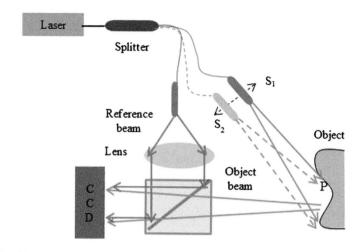

Figure 5.6 Shape-measurement setup of a two-illumination-point digital holography method.

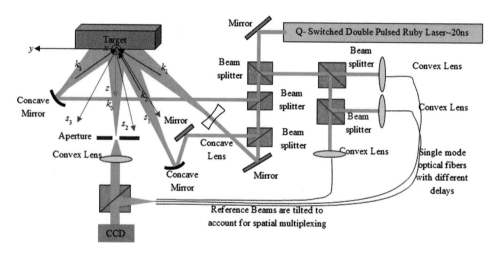

Figure 5.7 Experimental setup for 3D measurement with simultaneous recording of three digital holograms corresponding to the illumination directions k_1, k_2, and k_3, where s_1, s_2, and s_3 are the sensitivity vectors.

Therefore, this digital holography technique not only computes the normal strain but also the shear strain and the rotations of an object. A typical setup for the 3D deformation setup is shown in Fig. 5.7.

The relation between the phase $\phi(x,y)$ and the three deformations is given by

$$\phi(x,y) = \frac{2\pi}{\lambda}\bar{d} \cdot \bar{s}, \qquad (5.11)$$

where $\bar{d}$ is the desired displacement, and $\bar{s}$ is the sensitivity vector given by the geometry of the setup:

$$\bar{s} = \bar{k}_0 - \bar{k}_i, \qquad (5.12)$$

where $\bar{k}_i$ and $\bar{k}_0$ are the unit vectors of illumination and observation, respectively. To determine the three components of the deformation vector $\bar{d} = (u,v,w)$, it is necessary to measure the phase for three non-coplanar sensitivity vectorssensitivity vector $\bar{s}_1 = (s_{1x}, s_{1y}, s_{1z})$, $\bar{s}_2 = (s_{2x}, s_{2y}, s_{2z})$, $\bar{s}_3 = (s_{3x}, s_{3y}, s_{3z})$. The relationships among the phases, sensitivity vectors, and deformation vectors can be written in the following matrix form:

$$\begin{pmatrix} \phi_1 \\ \phi_2 \\ \phi_3 \end{pmatrix} = \frac{2\pi}{\lambda} \begin{pmatrix} s_{1x} & s_{1y} & s_{1z} \\ s_{2x} & s_{2y} & s_{2z} \\ s_{3x} & s_{3y} & s_{3z} \end{pmatrix} \begin{pmatrix} u \\ v \\ w \end{pmatrix}. \tag{5.13}$$

In matrix notation, Eq. (5.13) can be written as

$$\bar{\phi} = \frac{2\pi}{\lambda} \bar{\bar{S}} \cdot \bar{d}, \tag{5.14}$$

where $\bar{\bar{S}}$ is called the sensitivity matrix. $\phi_1(x,y)$, $\phi_2(x,y)$, $\phi_3(x,y)$ can be found from the three digital holograms recorded; the sensitivity vectors $\bar{s}_1 = (s_{1x}, s_{1y}, s_{1z})$, $\bar{s}_2 = (s_{2x}, s_{2y}, s_{2z})$, $\bar{s}_3 = (s_{3x}, s_{3y}, s_{3z})$ are determined from the setup configuration; and the displacement vector $\bar{d} = (u,v,w)$ can be determined by

$$\bar{d} = \frac{\lambda}{2\pi} \bar{\bar{S}}^{-1} \cdot \bar{\phi}, \tag{5.15}$$

where $\bar{\bar{S}}^{-1}$ is the inverse of the sensitivity matrix. Note that the sensitivity vectors can be generated either by illuminating the object from one direction and observing in three directions or illuminating from three directions and observing in one direction. The former setup is simple but requires three cameras and image rectification, whereas the latter requires a more-complicated setup but does not need rectification. After the displacement vector $\bar{d} = (u,v,w)$ is determined, the normal and shear strains can be found, as in Eqs. (5.8) and (5.9). A typical pulse time difference for deformation analysis is ~ 100 μs for deformation frequencies up to tens of kilohertz. The time delays between reference beams should be more than the coherence length of the laser, which is around 3 m in this case.

5.4 Phase-Shifting Digital Holography

Thus far, the chapter has discussed the process of numerical reconstruction of the object by using the Fresnel transformation of the recorded hologram on a CCD camera. Similar to the phase-shifting holography discussed in Section 2.6, phase-shifting digital holography (PSDH) is another technique used to visualize 3D objects or measure object deformation through multiple recordings of the interference patterns between the object beam and the reference beam. In each recording, the reference beam is shifted with respect to the object beam using several techniques. Phase-shifting holography uses a CCD instead of a PTP or PR crystal to record the different interference

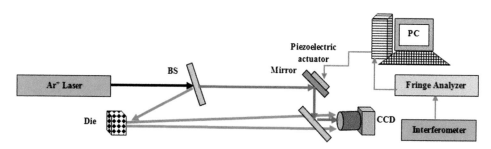

Figure 5.8 Phase-shifting digital holography (PSDH) setup.[8]

patterns and thus deduce the phase of the object. In the case of an off-axis hologram, the angle between the object wave and the reference wave causes additional fringes due to so-called "carrier" spatial frequency. For inline holograms, the Fresnel transformation produces superposed real and virtual images (as well as the DC term), and filtering is often required to separate them.[5] One way to find the Fresnel-propagated complex object wave on the plane of the recording medium (and thereby reconstruct the complex object) without the previously mentioned complications involves recording the intensity patterns by changing the phase of the reference wave by a predetermined quantity. The minimum number of phase shifts typically required is three, although the mathematical relationship for the phase resulting from four predetermined shifts is more straightforward.

Consider the two-beam interferometer setup shown in Fig. 5.8. The object and the reference wave can be defined as $E_O(x,y;d) = a_O(x,y)e^{-j\phi_O(x,y)}$ and $E_R(x,y) = a_R(x,y)e^{-j\phi_R(x,y)}$, respectively. The interference pattern on the CCD has the following form:

$$I(x,y) = |E_O(x,y;d) + E_R(x,y)|^2. \qquad (5.16)$$

Equation (5.16) can be rewritten as

$$I(x,y;\phi_R) = a_R^2 + a_O^2(x,y) + 2a_R a_O(x,y)\cos[\phi_R - \phi_O(x,y)]. \qquad (5.17)$$

Upon changing ϕ_R with values of 0, $\pi/2$, π, $3\pi/2$ (as an example) and recording the following holograms,

$$I_1(x,y;0) = a_R^2 + a_O^2 + 2a_R a_O \cos[\phi_O],$$
$$I_2(x,y;\pi/2) = a_R^2 + a_O^2 + 2a_R a_O \sin[\phi_O],$$
$$I_3(x,y;\pi) = a_R^2 + a_O^2 - 2a_R a_O \cos[\phi_O],$$
$$I_4(x,y;3\pi/2) = a_R^2 + a_O^2 - 2a_R a_O \sin[\phi_O], \qquad (5.18)$$

it is possible to calculate $\phi_O(x,y)$ using the relation[2,3,6,7]

$$\phi_O(x,y) = \arctan\left(\frac{I_4 - I_2}{I_1 - I_3}\right). \qquad (5.19)$$

A comprehensive table outlining the derivation of the propagated object phase on the recording plane for different imparted phase shifts between the object and reference waves is listed in Refs. 2, 3, and 6. With the phase determined, the amplitude $a_O(x,y)$ can be directly found by detecting the intensity $a_O^2(x,y)$ on the detector with the reference beam blocked. With knowledge of the amplitude and phase, or equivalently,

$$E_O(x,y;d) = a_O(x,y)e^{-j\phi_O(x,y)},\qquad(5.20)$$

the complex amplitude of the object wave can be determined in the recording (x,y) plane.

Note that the shift in the phase angle does not have to be $\pi/2$. To emphasize this point, Eq. (5.16) can be rewritten as

$$I(x,y;\phi_R) = A(x,y) + B(x,y)\cos[\Delta\phi(x,y)],\qquad(5.21)$$

where $A(x,y) = a_R^2 + a_O^2$, $B(x,y) = 2a_R a_O$, and $\Delta\phi(x,y) = \phi_R - \phi_O(x,y)$. For a general fixed and known angle α, the recorded intensities have the following form:[6,7]

$$I_1(x,y) = A(x,y) + B(x,y)\cos[\Delta\phi - \alpha],$$
$$I_2(x,y) = A(x,y) + B(x,y)\cos[\Delta\phi],$$
$$I_3(x,y) = A(x,y) + B(x,y)\cos[\Delta\phi + \alpha],\qquad(5.22)$$

which can be solved unambiguously for $\Delta\phi$ if the phase-shift angle α is known. After some algebra,

$$\Delta\phi(x,y) = \arctan\left\{\left(\frac{1-\cos(\alpha)}{\sin(\alpha)}\right)\left(\frac{I_1 - I_3}{2I_2 - I_1 - I_3}\right)\right\}$$
$$\overset{\alpha=\pi/2}{=} \arctan\left(\frac{I_1 - I_3}{2I_2 - I_1 - I_3}\right).\qquad(5.23)$$

The system can also be solved without knowledge of the phase-shift angle α. For a general fixed and unknown angle α, the recorded intensities have the following form:[6,7]

$$I_1(x,y) = A(x,y) + B(x,y)\cos[\Delta\phi],$$
$$I_2(x,y) = A(x,y) + B(x,y)\cos[\Delta\phi + \alpha],$$
$$I_3(x,y) = A(x,y) + B(x,y)\cos[\Delta\phi + 2\alpha],$$
$$I_4(x,y) = A(x,y) + B(x,y)\cos[\Delta\phi + 3\alpha],\qquad(5.24)$$

which, after some algebra, leads to

$$\Delta\phi(x,y) = \arctan\left(\frac{\sqrt{I_1 + I_2 - I_3 - I_4} \cdot \sqrt{3I_2 - 3I_3 - I_1 + I_4}}{I_2 + I_3 - I_1 - I_4}\right). \quad (5.25)$$

With knowledge of the amplitude and phase, or equivalently, $E_O(x,y)$, the Fresnel integral can be used to back-propagate the field to yield the original object. Because the hologram recording is described by[8]

$$E_O(x,y;d) = e^{-jk_0 d}\frac{jk_0}{2\pi d}\iint E_O(\xi,\eta) \times \frac{e^{-jk_0\sqrt{d^2+(\xi-x)^2+(\eta-y)^2}}}{\sqrt{d^2+(\xi-x)^2+(\eta-y)^2}}dxdy$$
$$= \Im_{x,y}^{-1}\{\Im_{x,y}\{E_O(\xi,\eta)\} \cdot \Im_{x,y}\{g_{PSF}(\xi,\eta,x,y)\}\}, \quad (5.26)$$

then

$$E_O(\xi,\eta) = \Im_{x,y}^{-1}\left\{\frac{\Im_{x,y}\{E_O(x,y;d)\}}{\Im_{x,y}\{g_{PSF}(\xi,\eta,x,y)\}}\right\}, \quad (5.27)$$

where

$$g_{PSF}(\xi,\eta,x,y) = \frac{j}{\lambda}\frac{e^{-jk_0\sqrt{((x-\xi)^2+(y-\eta)^2+d^2)}}}{\sqrt{((x-\xi)^2+(y-\eta)^2+d^2)}}. \quad (5.28)$$

Pertinent distances and coordinates are redrawn in Fig. 5.9.

A 3D diffuse object (die) 5 mm in size is positioned at a distance of $z_0 = 60$ cm. The images are reconstructed at $z = -60$ cm, as shown in Figs. 5.10(a) and 5.10(b) using the Fresnel and phase-shifting techniques, respectively. Note the advantage of the PSDH technique where the zero order can be eliminated.

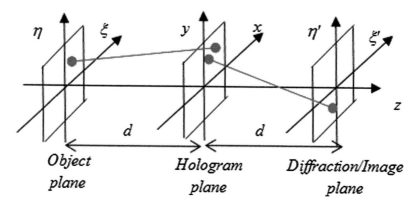

Figure 5.9 Coordinate system for DH reconstruction.

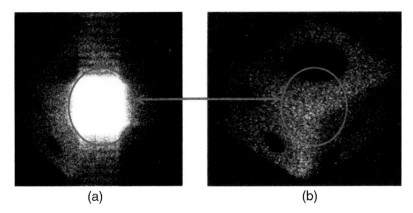

Figure 5.10 Numerically reconstructed intensity image of a die using the (a) Fresnel and (b) PSDH technique (adapted from Yamaguchi[8] with permission).

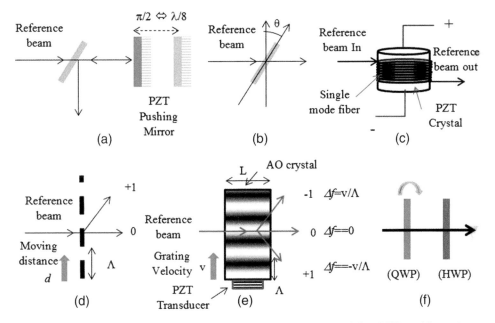

Figure 5.11 Different techniques to obtain a phase shift using (a) a PZT pushing mirror, (b) tilted glass, (c) an optical fiber wrapped on a PZT crystal, (d) a manually shifted diffraction grating, (e) an acousto-optic or Bragg cell, and (f) a half-wave plate (HWP) and a quarter-wave plate (QWP).

5.5 Techniques to Perform Phase-Shifting Digital Holography

There are several different techniques to introduce phase shifts in the reference beam to obtain digital phase-shifting interferometry (DPSI) interferograms. The first technique, which is by far the most common, is to translate one of the mirrors or optical surfaces in the interferometer using a piezoelectric transducer (PZT),[9] as shown in Fig. 5.11(a). These devices expand or contract with an externally applied voltage, thus introducing the phase shift. The phase of the reference beam is shifted by a reflecting mirror mounted on the PZT transducer, which can be controlled electrically with very high precision. A mirror shift of $\lambda/8$ corresponds to a path length change of $2\pi/8$ radians and, due to the double-pass results, in a phase shift of $\pi/2$ in the reflected wave.

The second technique uses a titled glass plate, as shown in Fig. 5.11(b). If a plane-parallel glass plate is tilted, the path through the plate changes, and a phase shift is produced that depends on the thickness of the plate, its refractive index, the wavelength, and the tilt angle. Because the exact phase shift is strongly influenced by the quality of the plate, this approach is not frequently used.

The third technique also uses a PZT crystal, albeit for when the reference wave is transmitted through an optical fiber. To perform the phase shift, a portion of the fiber is wrapped firmly around a PZT cylinder that expands and contracts depending on the applied voltage. The stretching of the fiber results in a phase shift that can be used to perform PSDH [shown in Fig. 5.11(c)].

The fourth technique uses a lateral displacement d of a diffraction grating that shifts the phase of the mth diffraction order by[9]

$$\alpha = \frac{2\pi m d}{\Lambda},\tag{5.29}$$

where Λ is the period of the grating. So, if a shift of $d = \Lambda/4$ occurs for the first order, then $\alpha = \pi/2$ [shown in Fig. 5.11(d)].

The fifth technique to introduce phase shifts uses acousto-optic modulators (AOMs). The frequency shift is realized by a diffraction grating moving with continuous velocity. An AOM or Bragg cell is a quartz material through which an ultrasonic wave propagates. Because this is a longitudinal (i.e., compression) wave, the index of refraction of the material varies sinusoidally with the same acoustic wavelength. Incident light that is diffracted or deflected into the Bragg angle receives a Doppler shift that is equal to the acoustic frequency [shown in Fig. 5.11(e)]. The interference between the reference and object wave including the time dependence in this case can be written as

$$E_O(x,y;d,t) = a_O(x,y)e^{-j[\phi_O(x,y)-2\pi ft]}$$

and

$$E_R(x,y) = a_R(x,y)e^{-j[\phi_R(x,y)-2\pi(f+\Delta f)t]},$$

where f and Δf are the light frequency and the shift in light frequency, respectively. The intensity pattern on the CCD can be expressed as

$$I_1(x,y) = A(x,y) + B(x,y)\cos[\Delta\phi(x,y)+\alpha(t)],\tag{5.30}$$

where $\alpha(t) = 2\pi\Delta f t$ is a linear phase shift that is time dependent,

$$\Delta f = \frac{mv}{\Lambda} = mf_a,$$

$m = \pm 1, 0$ is the diffraction order, f_a is the sound frequency (20–30 MHz), Λ is the period of the grating, and v is the velocity of the grating in the AO crystal. This technique is very useful when dynamic measurements are required, so the phase shift must be faster than the dynamic change in the object. If the AO cell has a width $L = (c/n)t$, where c/n is the velocity of light in the cell of refractive index n, and t is the time it takes for light to cross a distance L, then the phase shift is

$$\alpha = L\frac{2\pi n f_a}{c}. \tag{5.31}$$

The last technique to obtain different phase shifts through the rotation of wave plates uses the phenomenon known as the Pancharatnam–Berry phase, or the geometric phase. Let the field E_{in} be a 45-deg polarized-input reference field and consider four scenarios for the orientation of the wave plates:[2]

(a) Rotate both plates by 45 deg.
(b) Rotate the QWP by 45 deg and the HWP by −45 deg.
(c) Rotate both plates by −45 deg.
(d) Rotate the QWP by −45 deg and the HWP by 45 deg.

Using the Jones-matrices formalism for the four different cases produces the following:

(a) $E_{out1} = R^{-1}(45) \cdot HWP \cdot R(45) \cdot R^{-1}(45) \cdot QWP \cdot R(45) \cdot E_{in}$;
(b) $E_{out3} = R^{-1}(45) \cdot HWP \cdot R(45) \cdot R^{-1}(-45) \cdot QWP \cdot R(-45) \cdot E_{in}$;
(c) $E_{out2} = R^{-1}(-45) \cdot HWP \cdot R(-45) \cdot R^{-1}(-45) \cdot QWP \cdot R(-45) \cdot E_{in}$;
(d) $E_{out4} = R^{-1}(-45) \cdot HWP \cdot R(-45) \cdot R^{-1}(45) \cdot QWP \cdot R(45) \cdot E_{in}$;

where the rotation matrix is defined as

$$R = \frac{1}{\sqrt{2}}\begin{pmatrix} 1 & 1 \\ -1 & 1 \end{pmatrix},$$

the input field is linear polarized light at 45 deg is defined as

$$E_{in} = \frac{1}{\sqrt{2}}\begin{pmatrix} 1 \\ 1 \end{pmatrix},$$

the quarter-wave plate is defined as

$$QWP = \begin{pmatrix} 1 & 0 \\ 0 & j \end{pmatrix},$$

and the half-wave plate is defined as

$$HWP = \begin{pmatrix} 1 & 0 \\ 0 & -1 \end{pmatrix}.$$

Applying these matrices to the four cases above produces

$$E_{out1} = \frac{1}{\sqrt{2}} \begin{pmatrix} 1 & -1 \\ 1 & 1 \end{pmatrix} \begin{pmatrix} 1 & 0 \\ 0 & -1 \end{pmatrix} \frac{1}{\sqrt{2}} \begin{pmatrix} 1 & 1 \\ -1 & 1 \end{pmatrix} \frac{1}{\sqrt{2}} \begin{pmatrix} 1 & -1 \\ 1 & 1 \end{pmatrix} \begin{pmatrix} 1 & 0 \\ 0 & j \end{pmatrix}$$

$$\times \frac{1}{\sqrt{2}} \begin{pmatrix} 1 & 1 \\ -1 & 1 \end{pmatrix} \frac{1}{\sqrt{2}} \begin{pmatrix} 1 \\ 1 \end{pmatrix} = \frac{1}{\sqrt{2}} \begin{pmatrix} e^{j0} \\ e^{j0} \end{pmatrix} = \frac{1}{\sqrt{2}} \begin{pmatrix} 1 \\ 1 \end{pmatrix}; \qquad (5.32a)$$

$$E_{out2} = \frac{1}{\sqrt{2}} \begin{pmatrix} 1 & -1 \\ 1 & 1 \end{pmatrix} \begin{pmatrix} 1 & 0 \\ 0 & -1 \end{pmatrix} \frac{1}{\sqrt{2}} \begin{pmatrix} 1 & 1 \\ -1 & 1 \end{pmatrix} \frac{1}{\sqrt{2}} \begin{pmatrix} 1 & 1 \\ -1 & 1 \end{pmatrix} \begin{pmatrix} 1 & 0 \\ 0 & j \end{pmatrix}$$

$$\times \frac{1}{\sqrt{2}} \begin{pmatrix} 1 & -1 \\ 1 & 1 \end{pmatrix} \frac{1}{\sqrt{2}} \begin{pmatrix} 1 \\ 1 \end{pmatrix} = \frac{1}{\sqrt{2}} \begin{pmatrix} e^{j\frac{\pi}{2}} \\ e^{j\frac{\pi}{2}} \end{pmatrix} = \frac{1}{\sqrt{2}} e^{j\frac{\pi}{2}} \begin{pmatrix} 1 \\ 1 \end{pmatrix}; \qquad (5.32b)$$

$$E_{out3} = \frac{1}{\sqrt{2}} \begin{pmatrix} 1 & 1 \\ -1 & 1 \end{pmatrix} \begin{pmatrix} 1 & 0 \\ 0 & -1 \end{pmatrix} \frac{1}{\sqrt{2}} \begin{pmatrix} 1 & -1 \\ 1 & 1 \end{pmatrix} \frac{1}{\sqrt{2}} \begin{pmatrix} 1 & 1 \\ -1 & 1 \end{pmatrix} \begin{pmatrix} 1 & 0 \\ 0 & j \end{pmatrix}$$

$$\times \frac{1}{\sqrt{2}} \begin{pmatrix} 1 & -1 \\ 1 & 1 \end{pmatrix} \frac{1}{\sqrt{2}} \begin{pmatrix} 1 \\ 1 \end{pmatrix} = \frac{1}{\sqrt{2}} \begin{pmatrix} e^{j\frac{3\pi}{2}} \\ e^{j\frac{3\pi}{2}} \end{pmatrix} = \frac{1}{\sqrt{2}} e^{j\frac{3\pi}{2}} \begin{pmatrix} 1 \\ 1 \end{pmatrix}; \qquad (5.32c)$$

$$E_{out4} = \frac{1}{\sqrt{2}} \begin{pmatrix} 1 & 1 \\ -1 & 1 \end{pmatrix} \begin{pmatrix} 1 & 0 \\ 0 & -1 \end{pmatrix} \frac{1}{\sqrt{2}} \begin{pmatrix} 1 & -1 \\ 1 & 1 \end{pmatrix} \frac{1}{\sqrt{2}} \begin{pmatrix} 1 & -1 \\ 1 & 1 \end{pmatrix} \begin{pmatrix} 1 & 0 \\ 0 & j \end{pmatrix}$$

$$\times \frac{1}{\sqrt{2}} \begin{pmatrix} 1 & 1 \\ -1 & 1 \end{pmatrix} \frac{1}{\sqrt{2}} \begin{pmatrix} 1 \\ 1 \end{pmatrix} = \frac{1}{\sqrt{2}} \begin{pmatrix} e^{j\pi} \\ e^{j\pi} \end{pmatrix} = \frac{1}{\sqrt{2}} e^{j\pi} \begin{pmatrix} 1 \\ 1 \end{pmatrix}; \qquad (5.32d)$$

Therefor, the reference fields in the four cases are

$$E_{out1} = \frac{1}{\sqrt{2}} \begin{pmatrix} 1 \\ 1 \end{pmatrix}, \qquad E_{out2} = \frac{1}{\sqrt{2}} e^{j\frac{\pi}{2}} \begin{pmatrix} 1 \\ 1 \end{pmatrix},$$

$$E_{out3} = \frac{1}{\sqrt{2}} e^{j\frac{3\pi}{2}} \begin{pmatrix} 1 \\ 1 \end{pmatrix}, \qquad E_{out4} = \frac{1}{\sqrt{2}} e^{j\pi} \begin{pmatrix} 1 \\ 1 \end{pmatrix}, \qquad (5.33)$$

which is equivalent to $\alpha = 0$, $\pi/2$, $3\pi/2$, π, respectively. Therefore, Eq. (5.19) can be applied to compute $\Delta\phi$.

Consider the setup shown in Fig. 5.12. This setup performs PSDH using wave plates. Figure 5.13(a) shows the photo of an object (Newport logo). Figure 5.13(b) shows the recorded hologram for a 0-deg phase shift, Fig. 5.13(c) shows the result of a standard Fresnel reconstruction after reference-wave subtraction (equivelant to *dc* subtraction). Figure 5.13(d) shows the phase recovered from four sequential 90-deg phase shifts, and Fig. 5.13(e) shows the phase-shifting reconstruction using wave plates (PSDH-WP), as described earlier.

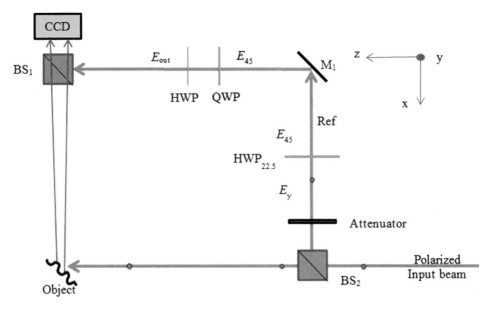

Figure 5.12 Setup for phase-shifting digital holography using wave plates. HWP: half-wave plate, and QWP: quarter-wave plate.

Note that the reference beam has been subtracted from each hologram at the time of recording, which is equivalent to performing dc subtraction (under plane-wave illumination). This was done because minor aberrations in the wave plate produce small variations in the reference beam as the wave plate is rotated, which serve to degrade the overall reconstruction if left uncorrected.

Table 5.3 shows the code for phase shifting digital holography using MATLAB. The script loads the phase-shifted holograms and calls the "myFresnel.m" function, which should all be in the same directory of the script. Note that numeric implementation of Eq. (5.25) may result in some invalid values (infinity, or not-a-number) for a few indices, which are addressed in the following example. Additionally, the accompanying CD includes some additional hologram recordings for alternative phase shifts for further exploration.

5.6 One-Shot Phase-Shifting Digital Holography Using Wave Plates

The setup in Fig. 5.14 uses wave plates. The reference beam is converted to right circular polarization (RCP) via a QWP. The RCP is converted to left circular polarization (LCP) by the first HWP (optional); it is then rotated by the second HWP by angle α and converted back to RCP, with a total additional Berry's phase of 2α, according to the following calculation:

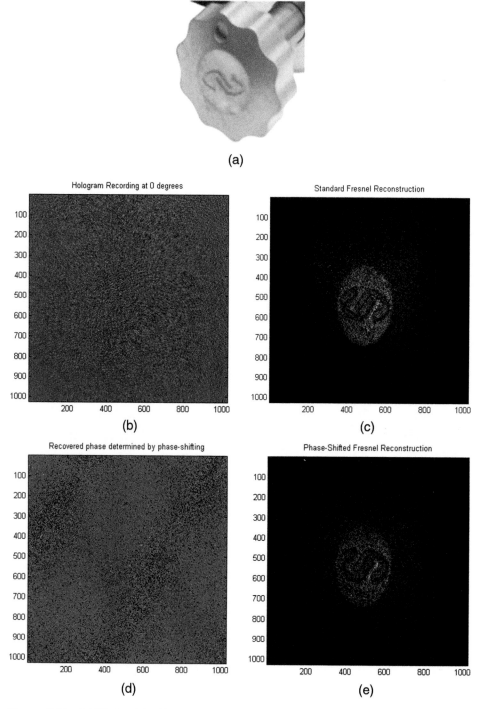

Figure 5.13 (a) Photo of the Newport logo object; (b) hologram recorded for a 0-deg phase shift, where $\lambda = 514.5$ nm, $\Delta x = 6.7$ μm, and $d = 30.5$ cm; (c) standard Fresnel transform reconstruction of the 0-deg hologram; (d) the recovered phase using four sequential phase shifts of 90 deg each (0 deg, 90 deg, 180 deg, and 270 deg); and (e) Fresnel reconstruction of the phase recovered via PSDH-WP.

Table 5.3 MATLAB code "Waveplate_PSDH_Reconstructions" for phase-shifting digital holography (see Fig. 5.13).

```
1   %%PSDH via wave plates (Berry phase) using four
2   %sequential phase shifts.
3   %Finds phase by phase shifting four holograms.
4   %The phase shift angle must be constant between
5   %each hologram.
6   clc
7   clear all
8   format compact
9   %Enter the pertinent reconstruction data
10  dx = 6.8e-6;              %Camera pixel size in m
11  w = 514.5e-9;            %Wavelength in m
12  d = -0.305;              %Reconstruction distance in m.
13  %Load the raw holos --> each phase is shifted 30 deg.
14  %In this case, all raw holos are stored to variable
15  %h, so they must be reassigned to I1,I2,I3,I4.
16  load raw_holo_0deg
17  I1 = h;
18  load raw_holo_90deg.mat
19  I2 = h;
20  load raw_holo_180deg.mat
21  I3 = h;
22  load raw_holo_270deg.mat
23  I4 = h;
24  %Loads the raw object wave with no reference
25  load raw_holo_ObjectOnly.mat
26  Iobj = h;
27  clear h              %Clear dummy h variable.
28  %%Construct the object phase via phase shifting.
29  %4-hologram del_phi Eq. (5.25)
30  del_phi = atan(sqrt(I1+I2-I3-I4).*...
31  sqrt(3.*I2-3.*I3-I1+I4)./sqrt(I2+I3-I4-I4));
32  %As computed, due to the atan function, del_phi
33  %may contain NaN values.
34  %Force del_phi to be a well-conditioned matrix
35  %(eliminate spurious values).
36  del_phi(find(isnan(del_phi)))=0; %Eliminate NaN entries
37  del_phi(find(isinf(del_phi)))=0; %Eliminate inf entries
38  del_phi(find(abs(del_phi) >= 2*pi)) = 0; %Eliminates
39                                  %nonphysical values.
40  %Plot the recovered object phase.
41  figure(1)
42  imagesc(abs(del_phi));
43  colormap(gray)
44  axis square
45  title('Recovered phase determined by phase-shifting')
46  %Construct the object wave from the calculated
47  %phase shift
48  Ao = sqrt(Iobj); %Raw object beam without reference
49  Eoxy = Ao.*exp(1i.*del_phi); %Eq. 5.20 (only gives
50                                  %modulo pi/2 results).
51  %Eoxy should be well-conditioned if del_phi is well-
52  %conditioned, but check for NaN entries anyway.
53  Eoxy(find(isnan(Eoxy))) = 0; %Eliminates NaN
54                                  %elements in Eoxy.
```

(continued)

Table 5.3 *(Continued)*

```
55  %%Phase-shifted reconstruction by the Fresnel method.
56  %Eq. (5.26) passing the Eoxy object field (rather
57  %than the recorded raw hologram) will
58  %generate the phase-shifted reconstruction
59  E0 = myFresnel(Eoxy,d,w,dx);
60  figure(2)
61  imagesc(abs(E0).^.7);
62  colormap(gray)
63  axis square
64  title('Phase-Shifted Fresnel Reconstruction')
65  %%Compare to the standard Fresnel reconstruction of
66  %a single hologram
67  E0 = myFresnel(I1,d,w,dx);
68  figure(3)
69  imagesc(I1)                    %Display the raw hologram, to
70                                 %compare with phase shift result
71  colormap(gray)
72  axis square
73  title('Hologram Recording at 0 degrees')
74  figure(4)
75  imagesc(abs(E0).^.7);
76  %logim(abs(rot90(del_phi,2)),1)  %Flip the
77                                   %reconstruction
78  colormap(gray)
79  axis square
80  title('Standard Fresnel Reconstruction')
```

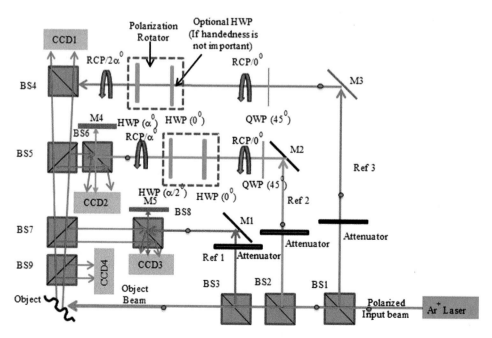

Figure 5.14   Setup of the phase-shifting reconstruction using wave plates (PSDH-WP).

$$E_{out} = \text{HWP} \times R(\alpha) \times \text{HWP} \times \text{QWP} \times R(45) \times E_y, \tag{5.34a}$$

$$E_{out} = \frac{1}{\sqrt{2}} \begin{bmatrix} \cos\alpha & -\sin\alpha \\ \sin\alpha & \cos\alpha \end{bmatrix} \begin{bmatrix} 1 & 0 \\ 0 & -1 \end{bmatrix} \begin{bmatrix} \cos\alpha & \sin\alpha \\ -\sin\alpha & \cos\alpha \end{bmatrix}$$

$$\times \begin{bmatrix} 1 & 0 \\ 0 & -1 \end{bmatrix} \begin{bmatrix} 1 & 0 \\ 0 & j \end{bmatrix} \begin{bmatrix} 1 & 0 \\ -1 & 1 \end{bmatrix} \begin{bmatrix} 0 \\ 1 \end{bmatrix} \propto e^{j2\alpha} \text{RCP}. \tag{5.34b}$$

Therefore, according to the schematic shown in Fig. 5.14, "reference 1" is the phase reference, "reference 2" has a delay of α, and "reference 3" has a delay of 2α with respect to "reference 1." The advantage of such a setup is that it is controllable depending on the rotation of the axis of the HWPs. After $\phi_O(x,y)$ is found according to an equation similar to Eq. (5.23), $a_O(x,y)$ can be found from CCD4 without trying to block the reference beam, which is usually done in static PSDH. The complex field of the object wave at the hologram plane can then be found according to

$$\Delta\phi(x,y) = \arctan\left(\frac{I_3 - I_2}{I_1 - I_2}\right). \tag{5.35}$$

The complex field of the object wave at the emitting plane can then be found according to Eq. (5.27).

5.7 General Functions for Digital Holographic Interferometry and Phase-Shifting Digital Holography Using MATLAB

Table 5.4 shows the function that calculates the digital interferogram between two input holograms using two alternative methods. The first method follows

Table 5.4 MATLAB code "myInterferogram.m" computes the wrapped-phase interference pattern due to deformation.

```
1   function[ Ps,Pr] = myInterferogram(h1,h2)
2   %Input = complex field of two already reconstructed
3   %holograms. Output = the digital phase interferogram
4   %between the two holograms.
5   %This function will output the digital interferogram
6   %computed using two different methods. The primary
7   %different in the results, between the two
8   %methods, is a pi phase shift in the fringe locations.
9   %Standard method:
10  phi1 = angle(h1);
11  phi2 = angle(h2);
12  del_phi = phi1-phi2;
13  del_phi(find(phi1<phi2))=del_phi(find(phi1<phi2))+2*pi;
14  %wrap 2pi if needed
15  [Ps] = del_phi;
16  %Alternate method:
17  del_phi = angle(h1.*conj(h2));
18  %The result is equal to the standard method, shifted
19  %by pi
20  [Pr] = del_phi;
21  end
```

Table 5.5 MATLAB code "Dime_Tilt_Reconstructions_v2.m" illustrates an example of the DHI of a tilted object (see Fig. 5.15).

```
1   %%Example of DHI using a dime that undergoes four waves
2   %of tilt @ 633 nm.
3   %Load previously reconstructed holograms,
4   %which are complex valued, via myFresnel.m
5   clc
6   clear all
7   load Saved_Holo_1
8   load Saved_Holo_2
9   %Flip right-side-up for viewing
10  h1 = flipud(h1);
11  h2 = flipud(h2);
12  %Display the holograms
13  figure(1)
14  imagesc(abs(h1))
15  colormap gray
16  axis square
17  %Display only the region of interest
18  axis ([300 600 190 540])
19  figure(2)
20  imagesc(abs(h2))
21  colormap gray
22  axis square
23  axis ([300 600 190 540])
24  %Compute the digital interferogram between the
25  %holograms
26  [P1,P2] = myInterferogram(h1,h2);
27  figure(3)
28  imagesc(P1)
29  colormap gray
30  axis square
31  axis ([300 600 190 540])
32  figure(4)
33  imagesc(P2)
34  colormap gray
35  axis square
36  axis ([300 600 190 540])
37  %%Try phase unwrapping
38  %the region of interest
39  wrapped_image = P1(220:451,340:571);
40  [R,C] =size(wrapped_image);
41  x=[-C/2:1:C/2-1];y=[-R/2:1:R/2-1];
42  [Y,X] =meshgrid(x,y);
43  r = sqrt(Y.*Y+X.*X);
44  z = zeros(size(r));
45  z(r<R/2)=1.0;
46  wrapped_image=wrapped_image.*z;
47  figure(5)
48  imagesc(wrapped_image)
49  colormap gray
50  axis square
51  %%
52  %%%---Unwrapping using the 2D_SRNCP algorithm:
53  %http://www.ljmu.ac.uk/GERI/90225.htm
54  %Instructions:
55  %Install the Microsoft Windows SDK 7.1.
```

(continued)

Table 5.5   (*Continued*)

```
56  %mex -setup
57  %Follow instructions: type Y then 1 then Y.
58  %Call the 2D phase unwrapper from C language.
59  %To compile the C code: in MATLAB command window,
60  %you have to run
61  %mex Miguel_2D_unwrapper.cpp
62  %This file has to be in the same directory as the
63  %script to work.
64  WrappedPhase=wrapped_image; %Read the wrapped phase
65  mex Miguel_2D_unwrapper.cpp
66  %The wrapped phase should have the single
67  % (float in C) data type
68  WrappedPhase = single(WrappedPhase);
69  UnwrappedPhase = Miguel_2D_unwrapper(WrappedPhase);
70  UnwrappedPhase=double(UnwrappedPhase);
71  UnwrappedPhase = medfilt2(UnwrappedPhase,[15,15]);
72  h = fspecial('average',5);
73  UnwrappedPhase = imfilter(UnwrappedPhase,h);
74  figure
75  surfl(z.*(UnwrappedPhase-min(UnwrappedPhase(:))));
76  shading interp; colormap(gray);
77  grid on
78  title('2D Unwrapped Phase Showing Tilt')
```

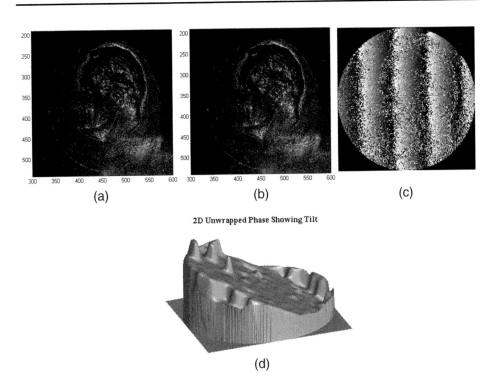

Figure 5.15   (a) Hologram reconstruction of a dime prior to tilt, (b) hologram reconstruction of a dime after a small horizontal tilt, (c) digital interferogram revealing the degree of tilt between conditions (a) and (b), and (d) 2D phase unwrapping showing tilt. For the recording wavelength of $\lambda = 632.8$ nm, one "fringe" of tilt in the phase reconstruction corresponds to $\lambda/2 = 316.4$ nm of physical tilt [from Eq. (5.3)].

Eqs. (5.1a), (5.1b), and (5.2), whereas the second method can be derived using the trigonometric identity

$$\left(\tan(A - B) = \frac{\tan A - \tan B}{1 + \tan A \tan B}\right)$$

to be

$$
\begin{aligned}
\Delta\phi(\xi,\eta) &= \arctan\left(\frac{\operatorname{Im}\Gamma_1(\xi,\eta)}{\operatorname{Re}\Gamma_1(\xi,\eta)}\right) - \arctan\left(\frac{\operatorname{Im}\Gamma_2(\xi,\eta)}{\operatorname{Re}\Gamma_2(\xi,\eta)}\right) \\
&= \arctan\left(\frac{\operatorname{Im}\{\Gamma_2(\xi,\eta)\Gamma_1^*(\xi,\eta)\}}{\operatorname{Re}\{\Gamma_1(\xi,\eta)\Gamma_2^*(\xi,\eta)\}}\right) \\
&= \arctan\left(\frac{\operatorname{Im}\{\Gamma_1(\xi,\eta)\Gamma_2^*(\xi,\eta)\}}{\operatorname{Re}\{\Gamma_1(\xi,\eta)\Gamma_2^*(\xi,\eta)\}}\right) \pm \pi.
\end{aligned}
$$

(5.36)

The results of each method differ only in a π phase shift in the location of the digital interferogram fringes.

Table 5.5 shows an example that uses the myInterferogram.m function, above, to compute the deformation of a dime, which was tilted by elevating one edge by approximately $\sim$1.25 μm between exposures. The results are illustrated in Fig. 5.15(a–c). Readers are encouraged to perform phase unwrapping on the wrapped-phase image shown in Fig. 5.15(c). Figure 5.15(d) shows the tilt after 2D phase unwrapping Fig. 5.15(c).

References

1. U. Schnars and W. Jueptner, *Digital Holography*, Springer, Berlin (2005).
2. T. Kreis, *Holographic Interferometry: Principles and Methods*, Akademie Verlag, Berlin (1996).
3. U. Schnars and W. Jueptner, "Direct recording of holograms by a CCD target and numerical reconstruction," *Appl. Opt.* **33**(2), 179–181 (1994).
4. M. De la Torre-Ibarra, F. Mendoza-Santoyo, C. Pérez-López, and S. A. Tonatiuh, "Detection of surface strain by three-dimensional digital holography," *Appl. Opt.* **44**(1), 27–31 (2005).
5. L. Onural and P. D. Scott, "Digital decoding of in-line holograms," *Opt. Eng.* **26**(11), 1124–1132 (1987) [doi: 10.1117/12.7974205].
6. P. Hariharan, *Optical Holography*, Cambridge University Press, Cambridge, UK (1984).
7. P. Hariharan, *Basics of Holography*, Cambridge University Press, Cambridge, UK (2002).
8. I. Yamaguchi and T. Zhang, "Phase-shifting digital holography," *Opt. Lett.* **22**(16), 1268–1270 (1997).
9. D. Malacara, *Optical Shop Testing*, 3rd Ed., Wiley-Interscience, Hoboken, NJ (2007).

Chapter 6
Digital Holographic Tomography

6.1 Introduction

The book has thus discussed both Gabor and Leith–Upatneiks digital holography with applications in digital holographic interferometry. While it is true that holography yields the 3D shape of the object, it is only possible to deduce this information from the surface of the object that is illuminated in order to produce the "object" beam. If a 360-deg 3D profile of the object is desired, illumination of the object from all angles is required; this can be achieved by illuminating the object from different angles, as in tomography, and recording multiple holograms.[1] The example provided here digitally reconstructs 3D profiles of amplitude and/or phase objects, such as lenses, water droplets, and dandelions, from recorded holograms formed from the illumination of the objects from multiple angles. This procedure is called digital holographic tomography (DHT). For experimental simplicity, only transmissive holograms (typically inline and Gabor) are considered.

Lenslets, like water droplets, are also translucent objects with large curvatures that can scatter light at very large angles. The use of traditional DH to determine the 3D shape by using the light transmitted through the lenslets or water droplets results in thousands of fringes per millimeter, which may easily exceed the resolution of CCD cameras. A novel single-beam holographic tomography (SHOT) technique was developed to record and reconstruct the 3D shapes of water droplets and lenslets, and their distribution.[1] Because the beamwidth is larger than several water droplets, the light that is transmitted between the droplets acts as the reference beam, which interferes with the "object" beam to record an inline Gabor hologram. In this case, the "object" beam comprises light scattered from the edges of the object because light passing through the droplet or lenslet converges and then diverges rapidly, and it is virtually absent on the recording plane. As stated earlier, single-beam (inline) holography reduces system complexity and allows

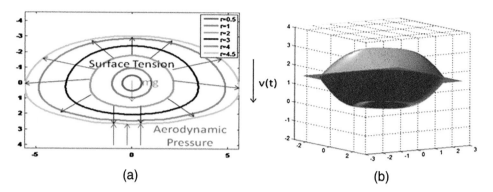

Figure 6.1 (a) Water-droplet falling shape and forces, and (b) 3D droplet falling.

us to determine the shape of the droplets or lenslets, albeit without details of the interior structure.

There are two forces acting on the falling-water-droplet case: the surface tension of the water, and the pressure of the air pushing against the bottom of the drop as it falls. When the drop is small, surface tension prevails and pulls the drop into a spherical shape. With increasing size, the fall velocity increases, and the pressure on the bottom increases, causing the raindrop to flatten and even develop a depression. Finally, when the radius exceeds ~5 mm, the depression grows almost explosively to form an annular ring of water before breaking into smaller drops. Thus, large spherical raindrops are deformed because of aerodynamic pressure as they fall at terminal velocity, as shown in Figs. 6.1(a) (2D representation) and 6.1(b) (3D representation). Drops tend to flatten at the base, with a droplet shape specified by[2]

$$r(\theta) = a\left[1 + \sum_{n=0}^{N} c_n \cos(\theta_n)\right], \tag{6.1}$$

where a is the radius of the undistorted sphere, and c_n are determined by curve fittings. The MATLAB code to simulate the droplet shape with respect to its size and the 3D falling-droplet shape are shown in Tables 6.1 and 6.2, respectively.

6.2 Single-Shot Optical Tomography Using the Multiplicative Technique (SHOT-MT)

This section specifically describes a nonintrusive technique for the recording and 3D-shape reconstruction of 3D objects, such as water droplets, lenslets, and dandelions, using the multiplicative technique (SHOT-MT) and the Radon transform technique (SHOT-RTT). Both of these techniques utilize the visualization of the 2D cross-section of objects along a certain line of sight. Thus, to visualize the 3D shape of an object, multiple projections from multiple directions (as in tomographic imaging systems) are required.

Table 6.1 MATLAB code "falling_droplet.m" to visualize the droplet shape with respect to size [see Fig. 6.1(a)].

```
1   %Fig 6.1(a): This script shows how the droplet shape
2   %changes with droplet radius
3   clc
4   clear all
5   N=800;
6   theta=linspace(-pi,pi,N);
7   a=[ 0.5,1,2,3,4,4.5,6];
8   c0=[ -28,-134,-481,-834,-1187,-1328,-843]*10^-4;
9   c=[ -30 -83 -22 -3 2 1 0 0 0 0;...
10  -118 -385 -100 -5 17 6 -1 -3 -1 1;...
11  -359 -1263 -244 91 99 15 -25 -16 2 10;...
12  -472 -2040 -240 299 168 -21 -73 -20 25 24;...
13  -482 -2650 -148 543 171 -100 -107 2 64 32;...
14  -403 -2889 -106 662 153 -146 -111 18 81 31;...
15  -472 -2040 -240 299 168 -21 -73 -20 25 24]*10^-4;
16  mc=[ 'b' ,' r' ,' g' ,' k' ,' m' ,' c' ,' y' ];
17  figure
18  for m=1:1:7
19  r=droplet_shape(theta,a(m),c0(m),c(m,:));
20  [ Y,X]=pol2cart(theta,r);
21  plot(X,Y,mc(m));
22  hold on
23  axis equal
24  axis ij
25  grid on
26  end
27  legend('r=0.5' ,' r=1' ,' r=2' ,' r=3' ,' r=4' ,' r=4.5' ,' r=6' )
28  function r=droplet_shape(theta,a,c0,c)
29  %Theta is the polar angle,
30  %a is the radius of the undistorted sphere, and
31  %c(n) are determined by curve fittings
32  r=a* (1+c0+c(1)* cos(theta)+c(2)* cos(2*theta)+c(3)* ...
33  cos(3*theta)+c(4)* cos(4*theta)+c(5)* cos(5*theta) ...
34  +c(6)* cos(6*theta)+c(7)* cos(7*theta)+c(8)* ...
35  cos(8*theta)+c(9)* cos(9*theta)+c(10)* cos(10*theta));
```

A holographic reconstruction may therefore be used for each 2D visualization along a certain projection, with the 3D shape subsequently reconstructed using the SHOT-MT or SHOTT-RTT.

The object is assumed to be a small 3D object at a distance d from the CCD camera. The diffraction of light is described by the Fresnel–Kirchhoff integral described in Eq. (4.2). Thus, the hologram process, using the Fresnel approximation formula, is computed using an inverse Fourier-transform formula

$$\Gamma = \hat{z}(\xi,\eta)\Im_{x,y}[hE_R^*w]\big|_{k_x=2\pi\xi/\lambda d, k_y=2\pi\eta/\lambda d},$$

defined in Eqs. (4.2) and (4.3).

In SHOT-MT, digital holograms $h_j(x,y)$ corresponding to each angular orientation θ_j about the y axis (coming out of the plane of the page) are recorded, as shown in Figs. 6.2(a) and 6.2(b). Thereafter, each $h_j(x,y)$ is

Table 6.2 MATLAB code "mupeanut3d.m" to visualize the changing shape of a falling droplet [see Fig. 6.1(b)].

```
1   %Fig 6.1(b): This script creates a 3D falling droplet
2   clc
3   clear all
4   N=100;
5   theta=linspace(-pi,pi,N);
6   scale=0.25;
7   %Create a movie of a falling droplet
8   vidObj=VideoWriter('droplet3d6.avi','Motion JPEG AVI');
9   open(vidObj)
10  figure('Renderer','zbuffer')
11  count=1;
12  for c=1:-.2:-3
13  a=8;b=.5;d=0.5;
14  %Create a simulation of a falling droplet
15  r=a+b*sin(theta)+c*cos(2*(theta-pi/2))+...
16  d*cos(3*(theta-pi/2));r=r*scale;
17  [X,Y]=pol2cart(theta,r);
18  X2=X(round(length(X)/4+1:round(length(X)/2)+1));
19  Y2=Y(round(length(Y)/4+1:round(length(Y)/2)+1));
20  X3=fliplr(X(round(length(X)/2):round(3*length(X)/4)));
21  Y3=fliplr(Y(round(length(Y)/2):round(3*length(Y)/4)));
22  x=X(N/2:end);
23  [XX,YY]=meshgrid(x,x);
24  x2=[-fliplr(X2),X2(1:end-1)];
25  y2=[fliplr(Y2),Y2(1:end-1)];
26  x3=[-fliplr(X3),X3(1:end-1)];
27  y3=[fliplr(Y3),Y3(1:end-1)];
28  [XX2,YY2]=meshgrid(x2,x2);
29  [XX3,YY3]=meshgrid(x3,x3);
30  [a,XI2,YI2]=gencircsym(Y2,max(Y2));
31  ap=a-min(a(:));
32  surfl(XX3,YY3,ap);
33  shading interp;
34  colormap(gray);hold on;
35  %Function to create a surface out of a curve by
36  %rotating that curve over a certain axis
37  [b,XI3,YI3] = gencircsym(Y3,min(Y3));
38  surfl(XX3,YY3,b+max(ap(:)));
39  shading interp;
40  colormap(gray);
41  axis equal
42  axis([-3 3 -3 3 -2 4])
43  view(30,-25)
44  currFrame = getframe;
45  writeVideo(vidObj,currFrame);
46  count=count+1;
47  hold off
48  end
49  close(vidObj)
```

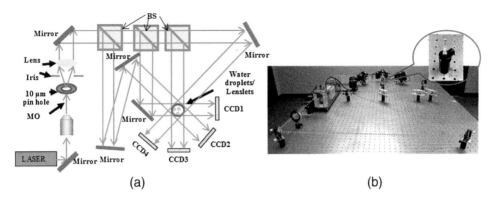

Figure 6.2 (a) Experimental setup of a typical SHOT-MT recording scheme. (b) Lab setup of an indigeneously pulsed frequency-doubled YAG laser, along with four high-speed cameras.

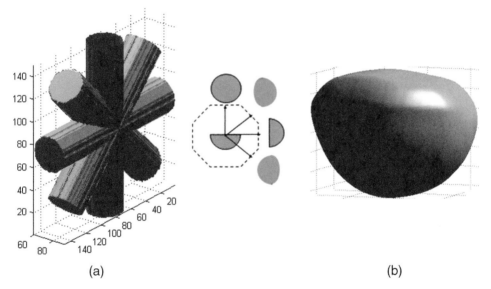

Figure 6.3 (a) Schematic showing the principle of SHOT-MT reconstruction, and (b) a typical reconstruction of a hemisphere.

numerically reconstructed, and the intensities I_j are computed on multiple planes, at multiple angles, and at a distance d surrounding the test volume wherein the object is located. The numerical reconstruction involves using the discretized form of the Fresnel diffraction formula. After some coordinate transformations, the 3D shape of this object can then be reconstructed by multiplying the multiple reconstructed intensities along each angular projection[3]

$$I = \prod_1^M I_j,$$ (6.2)

as shown in Fig. 6.3. Figure 6.3(a) is a computer simulation of the multiplication of several projections of a certain volume from different

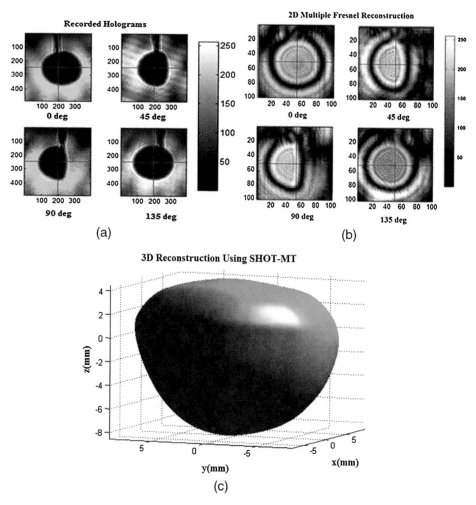

Figure 6.4 (a) Recorded inline holograms of a 5-mm hemisphere lens, (b) multiple 2D Fresnel reconstructions, and (c) 3D reconstruction using SHOT-MT.

angles. Figure 6.3(b) is the result of multiplication that is the intersection of the multiple views. Note that when very few projections are recorded, some postprocessing using a lowpass filter (i.e., smoothing) is typically needed.

The following provides an example of SHOT and reconstruction using SHOT-MT. Figures 6.4(a) and 6.4(b) show four holograms and their corresponding Fresnel reconstruction of a hemispherical lens mounted on a pin. The holograms are recorded at angles of 0 deg, 45 deg, 90 deg, and 135 deg, respectively, using a doubled YAG laser with a wavelength of 532 nm, a pulse width of 10 ns, and a pulse energy of 100 mJ. A pulsed laser is used to eliminate any motion blur produced while recording moving droplets. Figure 6.4(c) shows the reconstructed 3D shape. A similar reconstruction of two lenslets is shown in Fig. 6.5; here, the holder pins are removed in

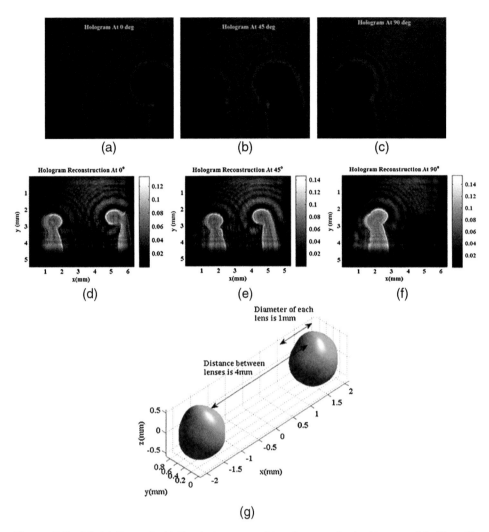

Figure 6.5 (a)–(c) Recorded inline holograms of two 3-mm spherical lenses, (d)–(f) multiple 2D Fresnel reconstructions, and (g) 3D reconstruction using SHOT-MT.

postprocessing by adaptively selecting specific regions of interest to reconstruct the 3D shapes. Note that postprocessing smoothing is also needed if the number of projection angles are small, e.g., 4. However, for more than 10–15 projection angles, no smoothing is typically needed.

Table 6.3 provides MATLAB code that demonstrates how SHOT-MT works on a fictitious object, which produces a tomographic reconstruction similar to Fig. 6.5(g) [shown in Figs. 6.6(a)–(e)].

The MATLAB code in Table 6.4 shows how SHOT-MT works on a water droplet. While running this code, there will be the opportunity to select four regions of interest for the four projections. Each region selection that uses the ellipse must be manually centered on the x and y axes. The results are shown in Fig. 6.7.

Table 6.3 MATLAB code "SHOT_MT_Ex1.m" of the SHOT-MT reconstruction algorithm applied to three examples (see Fig. 6.6).

```
1   %%Create one sphere: Example 1
2   close all;
3   clc
4   clear all
5   N=150
6   a=0;
7   [ x,y] = meshgrid(linspace(−12,12,N));
8   z = cyl((x−a)/5,y/5);        %Create a disk
9   z=logical(z);               %Transform it to 1 or 0
10  im(z);
11  hold on;
12  line([ N/2 N/2],[ 0 N] )
13  hold on;
14  line([ 0 N] ,[ N/2 N/2] )
15  %Loft the disk to become a cylinder
16  S0=repmat(z,[ 1 1 N] );
17  figure
18  isosurface(S0)              %Computes isosurface geometry
19                             %for data V at an isosurface value
20  axis equal
21  %Rotation 45 deg
22  S45=rigid3D(S0,45,0,0,0,0,0); %Function used to
23                                %perform 3D rotation
24  S45=logical(S45);
25  hold on;
26  isosurface(S45)
27  axis equal
28  %Rotation 90 deg
29  S90=rigid3D(S0,90,0,0,0,0,0);
30  S90=logical(S90);
31  hold on;
32  isosurface(S90)
33  axis equal
34  %Rotation 135 deg
35  S135=rigid3D(S0,135,0,0,0,0,0);
36  S135=logical(S135);
37  hold on;
38  isosurface(S135)
39  axis equal
40  grid on
41  view(30,60)
42  %- - - - - - - - - - - - - - - - - -
43  clear x y z
44  %Intersection of all the volumes using
45  %the multiplication technique
46  F=S0 & S45 & S90 & S135;
47  clear S0 S45 S135 S90
48  F2 = smooth3(F,'box',7);   %LP filter to smoothen edges
49  f=figure
50  isosurface(F2)
51  axis equal
52  xlabel('x')
53  ylabel('y')
54  zlabel('z')
55  grid on
```

(continued)

Table 6.3 (*Continued*)

```
56  view(30,60)
57  %%Create two spheres: Example 2
58  clc
59  clear all
60  N=180
61  [x,y] = meshgrid(linspace(-12,12,N));
62  a=7;
63  z1 = cyl((x+a)/4,y/4);
64  z2 = cyl((x)/4,(y)/4);
65  z=z1+z2;
66  im(z);
67  S0=repmat(z,[1 1 N]);
68  z1 = cyl((x+a/sqrt(2))/4,y/4);
69  z2 = cyl((x)/4,(y)/4);
70  z=z1+z2;
71  im(z);
72  S1=repmat(z,[1 1 N]);
73  S45=rigid3D(S1,45,0,0,0,0,0);
74  clear S1
75  z = cyl((x)/4,(y)/4);
76  im(z);
77  S2=repmat(z,[1 1 N]);
78  S90=rigid3D(S2,90,0,0,0,0,0);
79  clear S2
80  z1 = cyl((x-a/sqrt(2))/4,y/4);
81  z2 = cyl((x)/4,(y)/4);
82  z=z1+z2;
83  im(z);
84  S3=repmat(z,[1 1 N]);
85  S135=rigid3D(S3,135,0,0,0,0,0);
86  clear S3
87  for m=1:1:N
88  F(:,:,m) = S0(:,:,m).*S90(:,:,m).*...
89  S45(:,:,m).*S135(:,:,m);
90  end
91  clear x y J a m z1 z2 z S0 S45 S135 S90
92  [X,Y,Z]=meshgrid(linspace(-12,12,N),...
93  linspace(-12,12,N),linspace(-12,12,N));
94  F2= smooth3(F,'box',9);
95  figure,isosurface(X,Y,Z,F2)
96  axis equal
97  grid on
98  view(30,15)
99  %%Create two ellipsoids: Example 3
100 close all;
101 clc
102 clear all
103 N=150
104 S0=zeros(N,N,N);
105 S1=S0;S2=S0;S3=S0;S45=S0;S90=S0;S135=S0;
106 [x,y] = meshgrid(linspace(-12,12,N));
107 a=3.5;
108 z1 = cyl((x+a)/5,y/3);
109 z2 = cyl((x-a)/3,(y)/5);
110 z=z1+z2;
```

(*continued*)

Table 6.3 (*Continued*)

```
111  z=logical(z);
112  figure
113  imshow(z);
114  S0=repmat(z,[ 1 1 N] );
115  z1 = cyl((x+a/sqrt(2))/5,y/3);
116  z2 = cyl((x-a/sqrt(2))/3,(y)/5);
117  z=z1+z2;
118  z=logical(z);
119  figure
120  imshow(z);
121  S1=repmat(z,[ 1 1 N] );
122  S45=rigid3D(S1,45,0,0,0,0,0);
123  S45=logical(S45);
124  clear S1
125  z1 = cyl((x)/5,y/3);
126  z2 = cyl((x)/3,(y)/5);
127  z=z1 | z2;
128  z=logical(z);
129  figure
130  imshow(z);
131  S2=repmat(z,[ 1 1 N] );
132  S90=rigid3D(S2,90,0,0,0,0,0);
133  S90=logical(S90);
134  clear S2
135  z1 = cyl((x+a/sqrt(2))/3,y/5);
136  z2 = cyl((x-a/sqrt(2))/5,(y)/3);
137  z=z1+z2;
138  z=logical(z);
139  figure
140  imshow(z);
141  S3=repmat(z,[ 1 1 N]);
142  S135=rigid3D(S3,135,0,0,0,0,0);
143  S135=logical(S135);
144  clear S3
145  %- - - - - - - - - - - - - - - - - -
146  clear x y z z1 z2
147  F=S0 & S45 & S90 & S135;
148  clear S0 S45 S135 S90
149  F2= smooth3(F,'box',7);
150  f=figure
151  isosurface(F2)
152  axis equal
153  xlabel('x')
154  ylabel('y')
155  zlabel('z')
156  grid on
```

6.3 Single-Shot Optical Tomography Using the Radon Transform Technique

In SHOT-RTT (shown in Fig. 6.8), the projection 3D matrix of all of the numerically reconstructed holograms from different angles $\theta_j = [0{:}j\pi/M{:}\pi]$, $j = 1,2,\ldots,M$ is formed, and then the inverse 3D Radon transform is

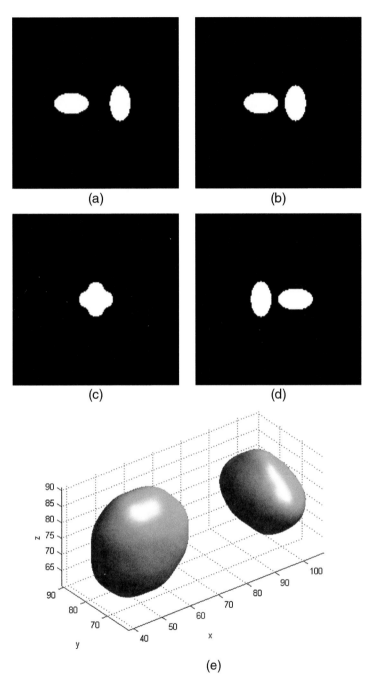

Figure 6.6 (a)–(d) 2D projections of two fictitious elliptical objects at 0 deg, 45 deg, 90 deg, and 135 deg, and (e) the 3D tomographic reconstruction via Eq. (6.2).

.

Table 6.4 MATLAB code "SHOT_MT_Ex2.m" used to compute the 3D shape of a droplet (see Fig. 6.7).

```
1   %%Reading holograms and subtracting DC term
2   clc
3   clear all;
4   %Input hologram
5   M1=1;
6   R=[ 0 45 90 135];            %Four projections
7   %- - - - - - - - - - - - - - - - -Read the holograms- - - -
8   ind=1;
9   for m=1:1:length(R)
10  I=imread(strcat('large_drop_',num2str(R(m)),'.JPG'));
11  IH1=rgb2gray(I);        %Transform to grayscale.
12  %Ensure that the hologram rows and columns are
13  %the same.
14  [ rows,cols]=size(IH1);
15  D_max=max(rows,cols);
16  D_min=min(rows,cols);
17  if cols>rows
18  rect_crop=[ floor(D_max/2)-floor(D_min/2)...
19  0 D_min-1 D_min];
20  else
21  rect_crop=[ 0 floor(D_max/2)-floor(D_min/2)...
22  D_min D_min-1];
23  end
24  IH1=imcrop(IH1,rect_crop);
25  %Resize hologram if needed for computation purposes
26  IH1=imresize(IH1,M1);
27  [ Ny,Nx]=size(IH1);
28  subplot(2,2,ind)
29  subimage(IH1)
30  title(strcat('Angle is:',num2str(R(m))))
31  hold on
32  line([ round(Nx/2) round(Nx/2)],[ 0 round(Ny)])    %Lines
33                                  %used for centering purposes
34  line([ 0 round(Nx)],[ round(Ny/2) round(Ny/2)])    %Lines
35                                  %used for centering purposes
36  %- - - -Subtract dc from hologram
37  Im1=1/(Nx*Ny)*sum(sum(IH1));
38  IH(:,:,ind)=IH1-Im1;
39  ind=ind+1;
40  end
41  IH=double(IH);
42  [ Ny,Nx,depth]=size(IH)
43  lambda0=0.532*10^-3;        %Wavelength in mm
44  k0=2*pi/lambda0;
45  delx=5.2*10^-3;             %Pixel spacing in the x
                                %direction in mm of the CCD
46  dely=5.2*10^-3;             %Pixel spacing in the y
                                %direction in mm of the CCD
47  %%Reconstruction using the discrete Fresnel transform
48  clc
49  nx =[ -Nx/2:1:Nx/2-1];
50  ny =[ -Ny/2:1:Ny/2-1]';
51  X = nx*delx;
52  Y = ny*dely;
```

(continued)

Table 6.4 (*Continued*)

```
53  [ XX, YY] =meshgrid(X,Y);
54  d0=[ 70] ;                  %Reconstruction distance
55  %Distance from the object to CCD in mm
56  d=d0*M1
57  w=exp(i*pi/(lambda0*d)*(XX.^2+YY.^2));
58  for m=1:1:depth
59  Rec_image(:,:,m)=fftshift(ifft2(IH(:,:,m).*w,Ny,Nx));
60  Mag_Rec_image(:,:,m)=abs(Rec_image(:,:,m));
61  end
62  %Visualize all holograms
63  my_image_subfigure(Mag_Rec_image)
64  resolution_mm_in_x=lambda0*d/(Nx*delx*M1); %Hologram
65                                             %resolution
66  resolution_mm_in_y = lambda0*d/(Ny*dely*M1);
67  npixelsx=5/resolution_mm_in_x
68  npixelsy=5/resolution_mm_in_y
69  %%Cropping images
70  close all
71  xmid=round(Nx/2);
72  ymid=round(Ny/2);
73  M2=1/10;
74  HR=imresize(Mag_Rec_image,M2);
75  my_image_subfigure(HR)
76  %%Creating masks
77  clc
78  disp('Since the holograms are intentionally not')
79  disp('centered properly in this case')
80  disp('when you select the region of interest you')
81  disp('have to manually drag the')
82  disp('ellipse and center it on the x and y axes')
83  disp('for each figure then double click');
84  close all
85  %If there are many droplets, then num_droplet is not one
86  num_droplet=1;
87  %Manually select the shaded region of each
88  %reconstructed hologram by dragging the mouse, then
89  %manually center the ellipse on the blue axes
90  for m=1:1:length(R)
91  [ Ro,Co] =size(HR(:,:,m));
92  im(HR(:,:,m))
93  hold on
94  line([ round(Co/2) round(Co/2)] ,[ 0 round(Ro)] )
95  line([ 0 round(Co)] ,[ round(Ro/2) round(Ro/2)] )
96  bw(:,:,m)=zeros(Ro,Co);
97  for n=1:1:num_droplet
98  %h=imfreehand;              %Use this function if the
99                              %object is not elliptic
100  h = imellipse;
101  vertices = wait(h);
102  X=vertices(:,1);
103  Y=vertices(:,2);
104  axis equal
105  G=zeros(Ro,Co);
106  [ J,b] = roifill(G,X,Y);
107  bw(:,:,m) = bw(:,:,m) | b;
```

(*continued*)

Table 6.4 (*Continued*)

```
108   end
109   end
110   close all
111   my_image_subfigure(bw)
112   %%- - - - - - - - - - - - - - - - - - - -Creating cylinders
113   %- - - - - - - - - - - - - - - - - - - - -Rotating matrices
114   clear F0
115   for m=1:1:length(R)
116   S=repmat(bw(:,:,m),[1 1 Ro]);
117   F0(:,:,:,m)=rigid3D(S,R(m),0,0,0,0,0);
118   end
119   %%Finding the intersecting volume
120   close all
121   clear X Y XX YY ans d* p Nx Ny h ind m n
122   clear cols rows D* G H* I* J* Mag* Rec* S*
123   clear b* k* num* nx ny rect* v* w* xm* ym*
124   F=ones(Ro,Co,Ro);
125   for m=1:1:length(R)
126   F= F & F0(:,:,:,m);
127   end
128   figure
129   isosurface(F)
130   axis equal
131   grid on
132   %%Drawing the 3D shape
133   resolution_mm_in_xf=resolution_mm_in_x/M2;
134   resolution_mm_in_yf=resolution_mm_in_y/M2;
135   [ X Y Z]= meshgrid(-Ro/2:Ro/2-1,...
136   -Co/2:Co/2-1, -Ro/2:Ro/2-1);
137   X = X*resolution_mm_in_xf;
138   Y = Y*resolution_mm_in_yf;
139   Z = Z*resolution_mm_in_xf;
140   F2 = smooth3(F,'box',15);
141   close all
142   figure
143   isosurface(X,Y,Z,F2)
144   axis equal
145   xlabel('x(mm)')
146   ylabel('y(mm)')
147   zlabel('z(mm)')
148   title('3D shape')
149   grid on
```

calculated by computing the inverse 2D Radon transform of each slice using the Fourier slice theorem.[4] Finally, some morphological image-processing techniques are applied to the inverted 3D matrix to produce the final 3D shape of the object. Specifically, an inline single-beam hologram $h_j(x,y)$ is recorded for each orientation for $\theta_j = [0 \text{ deg} : 360 \text{ deg} / M : 360 \text{ deg}]$, where $j = 1,2,3,4,\ldots,M$, respectively. Also, for each orientation, the corresponding hologram is reconstructed, and its intensity I_j is computed according to Eq. (4.3) on a single plane at the distance d, which corresponds to the middle of the test volume wherein the objects are located.

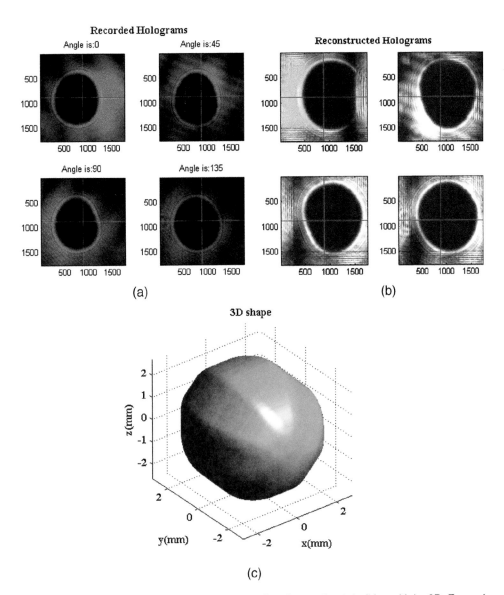

Figure 6.7 (a) Recorded inline holograms of a 5-mm droplet, (b) multiple 2D Fresnel reconstructions, and (c) 3D reconstruction using the SHOT-MT algorithm.

The algorithm works as follows:

1. Construct the 3D projection matrix of all of the reconstructed holograms according to Eq. (4.3) from M different angles, as shown in Fig. 6.9(a).
2. Compute the inverse Radon transform (RT) of the 3D matrix, as shown in Fig. 6.9(b), by computing the inverse 2D RT of each slice using the Fourier slice theorem, which states that the Fourier transform (FT) of a projection is a *slice* of the 2D FT of the region from which the projection was obtained [Figs. 6.9(a) and 6.9(b)].

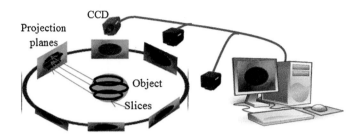

Figure 6.8   Schematic of the RTT setup.

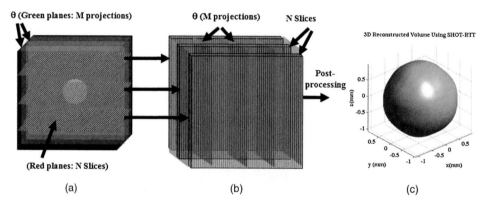

Figure 6.9   (a) Projection matrix, (b) inverse Radon transform matrix, and (c) 3D shape.

3. Some morphological image-processing techniques are applied to the 3D matrix obtained from step 3 to obtain the 3D shape, as shown in Fig. 6.9(c).[5]

The inverse RT is computed according to the following formula:

$$G(\omega,\theta) = \int_{-\infty}^{\infty} g(\rho,\theta)e^{-j2\pi\omega\rho}d\rho$$
$$= [F(k_x,k_y)]_{k_x=2\pi\omega \cos \theta, k_y=2\pi\omega \sin \theta}$$
$$= F(2\pi\omega \cos \theta, 2\pi\omega \sin \theta), \qquad (6.3)$$

where $F(k_x,k_y)$ is the 2D Fourier transform of $f(x,y)$,

$$\Re\{f(x,y)\} = g(\rho,\theta) = \int_{-\infty}^{\infty}\int_{-\infty}^{\infty} f(x,y)\delta(x \cos \theta + y \sin \theta - \rho)dxdy$$

is the Radon transform of a function $f(x,y)$, and $x \cos(\theta) + y \sin(\theta) = \rho$ (see Gonzalez and Woods[4]).

A second example of SHOT and reconstruction using SHOT-RTT is provided next. Figure 6.10(a) shows multiple inline holograms of a water droplet hanging from a syringe needle, recorded using $M = 10$. A CW Ar

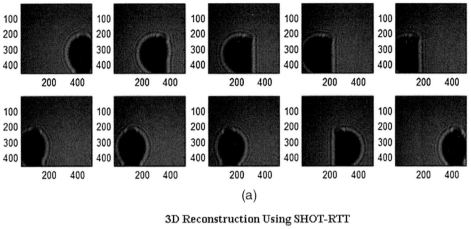

(a)

3D Reconstruction Using SHOT-RTT

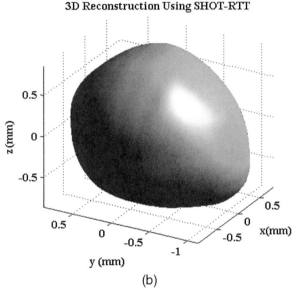

(b)

Figure 6.10 (a) Recorded inline holograms of a water droplet suspended from a syringe along several orientations, with $M = 10$. The numbers on the horizontal and vertical axes are pixel numbers. (b) The 3D reconstruction (the pixel size of the CCD is 10 μm).[3]

laser operating at 514 nm has been used for illumination. Figure 6.10(b) shows the 3D reconstructed image using SHOT-RTT, where the needle is eliminated by postprocessing by interactively selecting the region of interest. The MATLAB code in Table 6.5 shows how SHOT-RTT works on a fictitious object.

In summary, the provided examples of inline digital holographic tomography using multiplicative and Radon transform techniques for reconstruction demonstrate that SHOT-MT is easier to set up and use than SHOT-RTT, and it typically requires a greater number of samples (i.e., angles θ_j) to be recorded. Applications of pulsed SHOT techniques are likely to find applications for high-speed moving objects.

Table 6.5 MATLAB code "SHOT_RTT.m," which implements SHOT-RTT for 3D visualization of an ellipsoid (see Fig. 6.11).

```
1    %%Reconstruction of 3D object from multiple
2    %projections
3    clear all
4    close all
5    clc
6    %Creating a fictitious elliptical object
7    thetas=linspace(0,180,60);  %Number of projections
8    length_theta=length(thetas);
9    N=250;
10   slices = 1:1:N;                    %Number of slices
11   [x,y] = meshgrid(linspace(−14,14,N));
12   Z1 = cyl(x/2,y,6);
13   im(Z1);
14   %%Creating the projection; see the green vertical
15   %planes in Fig. 6.9(a).
16   %The I_proj 3D matrix[Fig. 6.9(a)]has dimensions
17   %rows = # slices, col = # slices, depth = #
18   %projections: (N x N x length(theta)).
19   for m=1:1:length_theta
20   I_proj(:,:,m)=Z1;
21   %I_proj(:,:,m)=eval(strcat('Z',num2str(m)));
22   imshow(I_proj(:,:,m))
23   %pause(0.5)
24   end
25   %%Creating the slices; see the red horizontal
26   %planes in Fig. 6.9(a).
27   %The R2 3D matrix[Fig. 6.9(b)]has dimensions
28   %rows = # slices, col = # projections,
29   %depth = # slices: (N x length(theta)x N).
30   for slice = slices
31   slice;
32   for m = 1:1:length(thetas)
33   R2(:,m,slice) = I_proj(slice,:,m);
34   end
35   end
36   %%Perform the inverse Radon transform at each slice
37   %of the 3D matrix R2
38   clear I_proj
39   close all
40   clc
41   for slice = slices
42   slice;
43   F(:,:,slice) = iradon(R2(:,:,slice),thetas);
44   %Figure
45   %imshow(F(:,:,slice),[min(min(F(:,:,slice)))
46   %max(max(F(:,:,slice)))])
47   F0 = F(:,:,slice) > max(max(F(:,:,slice)))-...
48   16*std(std(F(:,:,slice)));
49   %Figure
50   %imshow(F0)
51   se=strel('disk',32);       %Perform some morphological
52                                %image processing
53   F0=imclose(F0,se);
54   %Figure
55   imshow(F0)
```

(*continued*)

Table 6.5 *(Continued)*

```
56  axis equal
57  pause(0.1)
58  F1(:,:,slice)=F0;
59  end
60  %%3D reconstruction
61  close all
62  F2= smooth3(F1,'box',3);
63  f=figure
64  isosurface(F2)
65  axis equal
66  xlabel('x')
67  ylabel('y')
68  zlabel('z')
69  title('3D reconstruction using the SHOT-RTT technique')
70  grid on
```

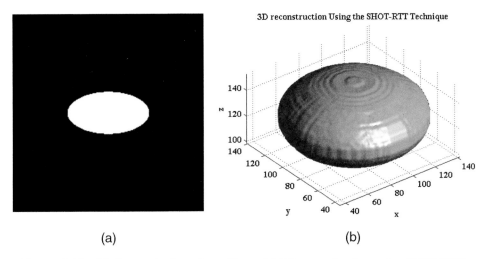

(a)   (b)

Figure 6.11 (a) One projection of an ellipse, (b) 3D reconstruction using SHOT-RTT.

6.4 Recording Considerations for Holographic Tomography

Hologram recordings for tomography may be obtained from several different configurations, including Michelson and Mach–Zehnder configurations, which may also employ holographic microscopy and/or multiple-angle illumination. Each configuration has both advantages and disadvantages, such that the specific application will dictate which setup is required.

6.4.1 Multiple-angle, single-exposure methods

In many practical applications, it is necessary to capture 3D tomographic data in a single image recording. This factor is primarily applicable to moving objects (e.g., particle distributions flowing through turbulent media, etc.), but it can be equally applied to static objects. Although many techniques have been proposed to perform single-projection tomography (notably compressive

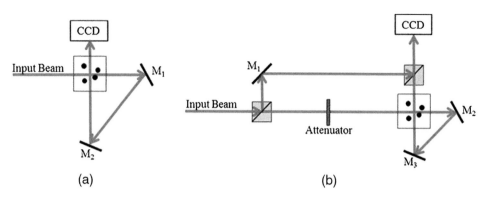

Figure 6.12   (a) A multiple-angle, single-exposure inline (Gabor) and a (b) multiple-angle Mach–Zehnder recording configuration, either allowing off-axis holography or control of the reference wave intensity.

holography, which is examined further in Chapter 9), it is also possible to perform multiple-projection tomography with a single recording. In this method, after passing once through the object, the beam is redirected via mirrors to pass through the object again at some alternate angle, as shown in Figs. 6.12(a) and 6.12(b). However, after the initial pass through the object, the beam picks up the "shadow" of the object cross-section projected at that angle. This shadow is present in the beam during the second pass through the object, and the effect compounds as the number of passes increases. Therefore, this recording geometry is limited to relatively sparse transmissive object volumes that use relatively few projection angles (in this case, only two), in which the final recorded hologram can still be unambiguously interpreted. The low number of projection angles is generally not sufficient to determine the 3D object shape with high fidelity; therefore, this technique is typically employed to determine the instantaneous location of small particles within a 3D volume. The inline recording configuration is the most convenient, but it does not allow control of the reference or object wave intensities; thus, a Mach–Zehnder configuration may be modified to allow for multiple-angle illumination while controlling the intensity ratio between the object and reference beams.

Although a single hologram is recorded, the reconstruction is performed separately for each angle recorded, using the appropriate CCD-to-object distance (d_1 or d_2 given by the unfolded path length), as shown in Fig. 6.13. Each image plane is separated by numerical defocus, in which the interplane signal rejection must be high enough to adequately distinguish the data in plane d_1 from that of d_2. Assuming that the unfolded path length between each image plane is large and/or the object is weakly scattering, only the desired image plane will be in focus, whereas the undesired image planes will be sufficiently out-of-focus to not contribute significantly.

If the unfolded path length between each image plane is small and/or the object is strongly scattering, then the unsharp image remnants (i.e., out-of-focus images) from the remaining image planes will contribute significantly,

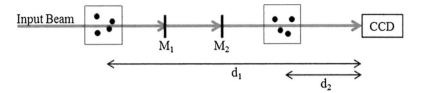

Figure 6.13 Unfolded path lengths d_1 and d_2 used in reconstruction.

resulting in a cluttered reconstruction with low interplane signal rejection. In practice, the distance between any two reconstruction planes using the multi-angle technique is typically much greater than the Rayleigh range z_R of the sparse objects being illuminated in either plane, such that the data at d_1 can be easily thresholded and separated from the data at d_2 using numerical methods. Therefore, interplane signal rejection is assumed to be sufficiently high, under reconstruction by Fresnel transform, if the following condition is met:

$$|d_2 - d_1| \gg z_R = \frac{\pi w^2}{\lambda}, \qquad (6.4)$$

where w is the "feature size" of the object. It should be noted that the Rayleigh range of the object is simply the range at which the Fresnel number is equal to $1/\pi$, thus ensuring that the distance z_R resides within the far field. Indeed, this is the standard range under which the Fresnel transform has been shown to be valid. However, should the distance between reconstruction planes be spaced on the order of $\sim z_R$ or less, which is common in single-projection tomography, the data cannot be easily distinguished as belonging to one plane or another because both data sets will appear to be "in focus" simultaneously.[6]

An example of this technique is illustrated in Fig. 6.14, in which two small air bubbles in a liquid medium were imaged using the single-capture configuration of Fig. 6.12(a). Illumination of the bubbles from two angles represents the simplest case of the single-exposure method. Due to the double pass of the beam, each bubble present in the sample forms two holograms, seen side by side in Fig. 6.14. The larger diffraction patterns represent a longer path (approximately 61.8 cm) after scattering from the bubble to the CCD, while the smaller diffraction patterns represent a shorter path (approximately 20.6 cm) after scattering from the bubble to the CCD.

The reconstruction at 61.8 cm gives the locations of the bubbles in the yz plane, and the 20.6-cm reconstruction gives their locations in the xy plane; thus, the 3D coordinates of the bubbles are uniquely determined through this tomographic process, as shown in Figs. 6.15(a) and 6.15(b).

The axial separation of the bubble centers along the z axis is 0.76 mm and can be measured directly from the recorded hologram (i.e., the diffraction pattern center-to-center). The two-angle tomographic reconstruction shows

Composite Hologram

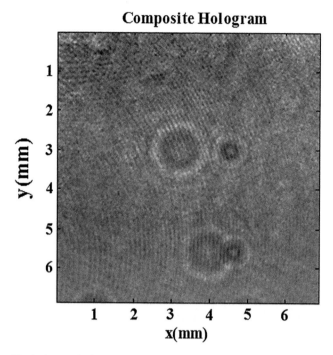

Figure 6.14 Single-beam hologram of two air bubbles in a liquid media. The top two conjugate shadows are for the first bubble, and the bottom two are for the second bubble.

the axial separation to be 0.78 mm with an axial resolution (z axis) equal to 48.9 μm. The yz and xy projections of the 3D reconstruction in Fig. 6.15(b) are again shown in Figs. 6.15(d) and 6.15(f), in comparison to the Fresnel transform reconstruction shown in Figs. 6.15(c) and 6.15(e). The results are identical to those expected.

The axial resolution of the multi-angle method is defined by the reconstructed pixel size $\Delta\xi$, which is based on the lateral resolution of each reconstruction plane. At the 20.6-cm distance, $\Delta\xi = 16.3$ μm, which defines the resolution of the x and y axes of the 3D volume. The 61.8-cm reconstruction sets the resolution of the y and z axes of the 3D volume to be $\Delta\xi = 48.9$ μm. Conservatively, the reconstruction is assumed to be limited by the greatest value (i.e., worst resolution) of $\Delta\xi$ (e.g., 48.9 μm). It should be noted that the resolution of all of the reconstruction planes may be set to be equal using the zero-padding technique (discussed in Chapter 7), although this was not performed for this experiment. Example software to implement this reconstruction is included in Section 6.5.

6.4.2 Multiple-angle, multiple-exposure methods

The multiple-angle, multiple-exposure method rotates the object (or, equivalently, the illumination source and detector) through a range of several angles and records a new hologram at each angle. The multiple projections are

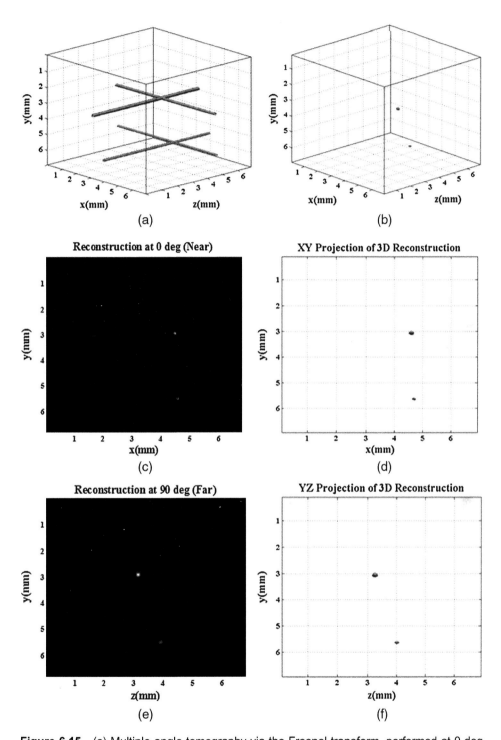

Figure 6.15 (a) Multiple-angle tomography via the Fresnel transform, performed at 0 deg and 90 deg, using only the planes of best focus for reconstruction. (b) 3D reconstruction, where $\lambda = 543$ nm, with 6.7-μm pixels; (c) reconstructed hologram at 61.8 cm; (d) *yz* projection of the 3D view in (b); (e) reconstructed hologram at 20.6 cm; and (f) *xy* projection of the 3D view in (b). Longitudinal positions are uniquely determined within the recording volume with accuracy on the order of $\Delta\xi$.

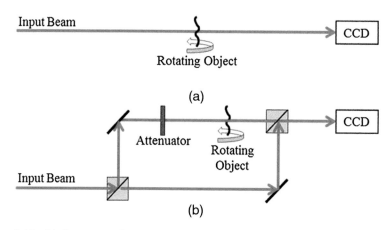

Figure 6.16 Various recording geometries: (a) inline (Gabor) and (b) Mach–Zehnder.

then used to reconstruct the 3D shape of the object using the multiplicative method, as previously described. This method does not employ multiple passes of the same beam but rather sequential single passes using multiple CCD exposures.

This technique dramatically improves upon single-projection methods by unambiguously determining both the longitudinal positions of various objects and/or object distributions as well as the gross 3D shape of each object.[3,5,7] Additionally, this technique is applicable to a significantly wider range of recording geometries, including near- or far-field object placement, strongly scattering objects, and holographic microscopy, using almost any reconstruction algorithm.

To improve the axial resolution under such conditions, either an inline or Mach–Zehnder configuration may be employed, with the object mounted on a rotation stage, as in Fig. 6.16. This configuration is equivalent to a fixed object about which the illumination source and CCD array rotate, as in conventional medical CT imaging.[1] The Mach–Zehnder configuration allows (a) the intensity of both the reference and object waves to be controlled by inserting an attenuator in one arm of the interferometer, and (b) off-axis geometries to be implemented by introducing an angular tilt to the reference beam.

The following experiments illustrate the multiple-exposure tomography method for some macroscopic objects. In the first experiment, a 3D scattering object [e.g., the spring of a ballpoint pen, shown in Fig. 6.17(a)] has been imaged at 13 angles in 15-deg increments, spanning 0–180 deg, using the inline geometry of Fig. 6.17(a). Figures 6.17(c) and 6.17(d) show two holograms and their reconstructions, respectively, captured from two directions (90 deg and 180 deg at 33 cm) recorded by rotating the object. A 480×508, 9.8-μm Spiricon camera has been used with illumination of $\lambda = 632.8$ nm without subtraction of the beam profile. Figures 6.17(e) and 6.17(f) show the 3D reconstruction resulting from 7 and 13 views, respectively, using the multiplicative method given by Eq. (6.2). The

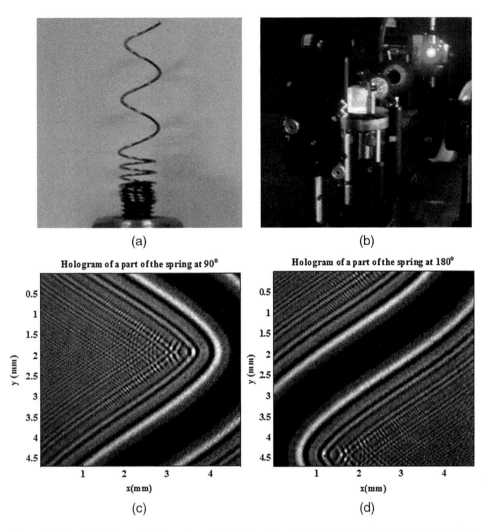

Figure 6.17 (a) 450-μm-thick spring, (b) photograph of a lab setup, (c) two representative holograms at angles 0 deg and 90 deg, (d) 2D reconstructions at 90 deg and 180 deg, (e) tomographic reconstruction using 7 angles (0–180 deg) at 30-deg increments, and (f) 13 angles (0–180 deg) at 15-deg increments.[8]

primary advantage of rotating the object using a single beam is the simplicity of the recording configuration with no upper limit on the number of angular projections possible.

The cross-section radius of the spring (i.e., the wire, not the helix radius) is 0.225 mm, and the hologram resolution $\Delta\xi$ is 14.4 μm/pixel at a reconstruction distance of 33 cm. Thus, according to Eqs. (6.7)–(6.10) (discussed in Section 6.4.4), the object must ideally be rotated 40 deg or less between successive recordings for accurate reconstruction, which corresponds to 4.5 rotations over a 180-deg range. In this experiment, however, 13 projections from 0–180 deg at 15-deg increments were necessary to provide adequate 3D

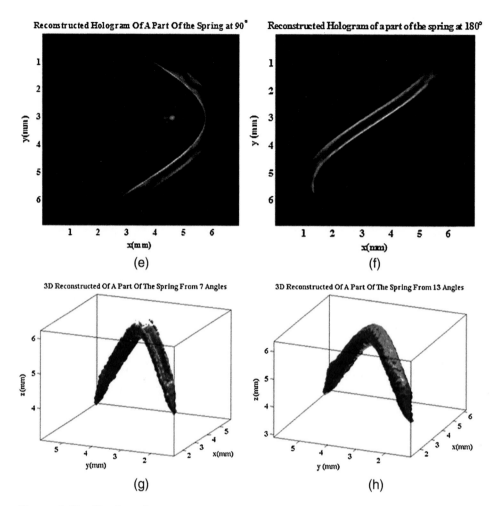

Reconstructed Hologram Of A Part Of the Spring at 90°

Reconstructed Hologram of a part of the spring at 180°

(e)

(f)

3D Reconstructed Of A Part Of The Spring From 7 Angles

3D Reconstructed Of A Part Of The Spring From 13 Angles

(g)

(h)

Figure 6.17   (Continued).

reconstruction. These additional projections help increase the SNR during tomographic reconstruction by compensating for nonuniformity in the illumination profile and allowing for deviation from the assumption of a circular cross-section, which underlies Eqs. (6.7)–(6.10), e.g., the horizontal cross-section of the spring is actually elliptical due to the helical shape. The code necessary to perform the reconstructions shown in Fig. 6.17 is given in Section 6.5.

The tomographic reconstruction of the spring has been calculated by assuming out-of-plane scattering along the z axis is small during recording, such that the "best focus" 2D reconstruction for a given angle accurately reflects the object cross-section at the reconstruction distance. Each 2D reconstruction is then lofted to form a 3D volume and multiplied at the appropriate angles, as given by Eq. (6.2). Due to computational memory limitations, each 2D projection (after reconstruction) has been resized to 96×96 pixels, via bicubic interpolation, prior to lofting into a $96 \times 96 \times 96$ voxel volume. The corresponding image resolution is thus rescaled to 72 μm/pixel, which is the cause of the excess surface roughness shown in Figs. 6.17(g) and 6.17(h). In the absence of such computational limitations, the 3D voxel resolution would be equal to the original $\Delta \xi = 14.4$ μm/pixel for each x, y, z component. However, if the original hologram resolution is used, the total number of voxels in the 3D reconstruction is 480^3, which is over 110 million voxels.

To illustrate the generalizability of this technique, similar tomographic reconstructions were performed for a dandelion seed parachute, shown in Fig. 6.18(a), using a Lumenera camera (LU-120M) with a pixel size $\Delta x = 6.7$ μm. Nineteen holograms were initially recorded ($\lambda = 632.8$ nm) from 0–180 deg at angular increments of 10 deg, although not all holograms were used for 3D reconstruction. To overcome computational limitations while still achieving a robust 3D reconstruction, several scaling and thresholding steps are performed, as illustrated in Figs. 6.18(b)–6.18(d). First, the 1024×1024 pixel holograms are padded by 1000 pixels on each edge to increase the numerical resolution to $\Delta \xi = 11.5$ μm. The reconstruction is then cropped to a 400×400 pixel region containing the data of interest and then thresholded to remove any background noise that falls below 20% of the maximum image intensity. The remaining pixels then undergo a binary conversion to simplify the tomographic multiplication process, which also allows the double-precision data values to be demoted to unsigned 8-bit integers to conserve computer memory. The 400×400 pixel image is then rescaled to 50% of its original size via bilinear resampling. Bilinear resampling is preferred over bicubic resampling in this case due to its ability to operate more reliably on binary images (i.e., it does not introduce binary interpolation errors). The resulting 201×201 pixel postprocessed holograms then undergo the tomographic multiplication procedure resulting in the 3D reconstruction shown in Figs. 6.18(e) and 6.18(f). The resulting lateral voxel resolution is $\Delta \xi = 23$ μm/voxel, and the total volume encompasses a 4.7 mm $\times$ 4.7 mm $\times$ 4.7 mm 3D space consisting of $\sim$8.12 million voxels. For this object, the optimal tomographic reconstruction shown in Figs. 6.18(e) and 6.18(f) was achieved using only five angles: 0 deg, 30 deg, 40 deg, 90 deg, and 130 deg. However, the angles are chosen such that there are two sets of orthogonal angles (0 deg and 90 deg, 40 deg and 130 deg), which are separated by roughly 45 deg. One additional "skew" angle, $\sim$10 deg separated from any of the other angles, helps remove excess noise from the 3D reconstruction. This pattern of five carefully chosen angles appeared to work well for several other angular choices as well (not shown).

6.4.3 Microscopic tomography methods

The tomographic techniques previously described are readily extended to a digital holographic microscopy (DHM) configuration to reconstruct

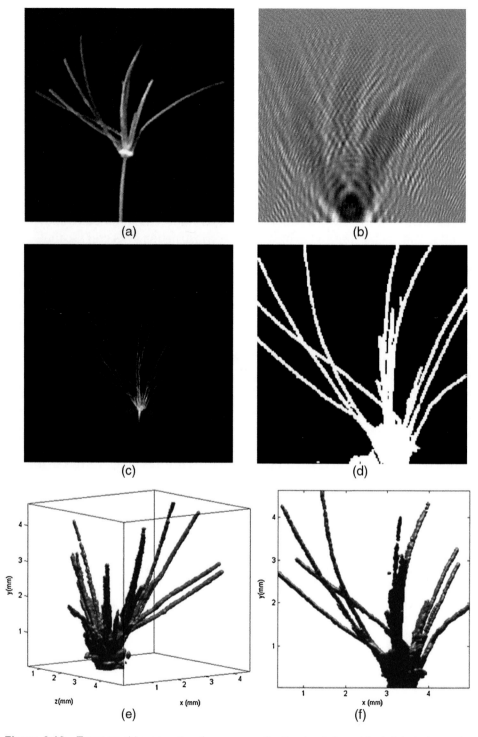

Figure 6.18 Tomographic reconstruction process for the dandelion object: (a) photograph,
(b) 0-deg hologram, (c) 0-deg hologram reconstruction with a *pad size* = 1000, (d) cropped
and scaled reconstruction with binary conversion applied at the 20% intensity threshold,
(e) 3D reconstruction of the dandelion volume (4.7 mm per side), consisting of ∼8.1 million
voxels, and (f) the *xy* projection of the 3D reconstruction that matches the profiles shown in
(a)–(d).

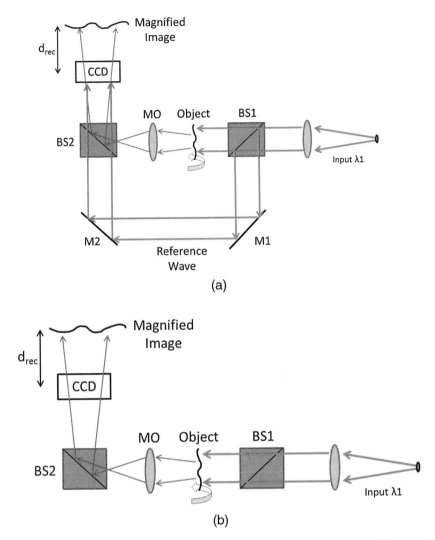

Figure 6.19 (a) Off-axis transmissive DHM configuration and (b) on-axis transmissive DHM configuration for multiple-exposure, multiple-angle micro-tomography. Note that under magnification, the reconstruction distance d_{rec} is the distance from the CCD plane to the magnified geometric image.

microscale 3D structures. Transmissive microscopy may be combined with multiple-exposure, multiple-angle tomography using the off-axis or inline DHM configurations of Figs. 6.19(a) and 6.19(b). Multiple holograms are recorded as the object is rotated over a range of angles, and the magnified 3D volume is reconstructed using the previously described tomographic techniques.

The primary difference between the DHM configurations and those previously described is the reconstruction method used for the magnified

Figure 6.20 Photograph of the tungsten lightbulb filament used for microtomography reconstruction.

images. Under plane-wave illumination, the object magnification M is given by the standard geometric-optics relationship

$$M = d_i/d_o, \tag{6.5}$$

with a magnified pixel resolution $\Delta\xi_{mag}$ after Fresnel transformation given by

$$\Delta\xi_{mag} = \frac{\Delta\xi}{M} = \frac{\lambda d_{rec}}{N \cdot dx \cdot M}. \tag{6.6}$$

This relationship between $\Delta\xi_{mag}$ and M is intuitively understood by realizing the reconstruction is of the geometric image of the object, rather than the object itself. If the object is magnified by a factor of M, the pixel size in the reconstructed image plane must be reduced by M such that the physical object size is accurately represented.

The off-axis configuration is used to demonstrate the differences between off-axis tomographic reconstruction and the inline configurations previously used for macroscopic tomography. In this experiment, multiple-exposure, multiple-angle holographic tomography of a tungsten lightbulb filament, shown in Fig. 6.20, is performed using the off-axis configuration of Fig. 6.19(a). The filament outer-coil diameter is 667 µm and is recorded using a wavelength of $\lambda = 632.8$ nm and a MO of focal length $f_{MO} = 10$ cm. The filament was geometrically imaged such that $M = 5.51$ and reconstructed at $d_{rec} = 83$ cm with zero padding of *pad size* = 250, which results in $\Delta\xi_{mag} = 9.33$ µm/pixel. Section 6.5 lists the software used to perform this reconstruction.

The filament was holographically recorded at 25 angles, in 15-deg increments spanning 0–360 deg, although not all angular projections were needed for reconstruction. It should be noted that reconstruction of inline transmission holograms occur within the zero-order area of the reconstruction (with the actual zero-order terms numerically eliminated) and generally result in positive images (i.e., the object intensity values are higher than the background) due to the contrast-reversal effect that occurs as a result of subtracting either the *dc* term or beam profile. For an opaque object in a transmissive geometry, the physical scattering occurs at the edges, with zero scattering from "within" the object. In the absence of contrast reversal (e.g., by not subtracting the *dc* term), the holographic reconstruction faithfully represents this by generating a negative image that is dark in the object region (where no scattering occurred and thus no signal was generated) against a bright background.

Due to the standard practice of *dc* subtraction, contrast reversal is the norm rather than the exception. Positive images are expected for inline recording of opaque objects; however, off-axis transmissive holograms of sparse objects tend to result in negative images (i.e., the object intensity is low against a lighter background) because the angular spectrum containing the off-axis object image is encoded with a high-spatial-frequency carrier (i.e., the off-axis reference wave), which, in the Fourier domain, is located far from the *dc* (low-frequency) portion of the spectrum. Removal of the *dc* term will not affect the reconstruction stemming from this higher-frequency portion of the Fourier spectrum.

Indeed, this behavior has been confirmed by band-pass filtering the off-axis contributions in the Fourier domain, thereby removing all spectral components except for those encoded with the high-frequency carrier prior to reconstruction. This portion of the spectrum results in a faithful reconstruction of the scattered object wave, which contains zero signal originating from "within" the object, i.e., a negative image. Because off-axis transmissive holograms result in negative images (i.e., the object intensity is zero against a lighter background), the "in-focus" image must be cropped and numerically inverted as a precondition for tomography. This process is demonstrated in Figs. 6.21(a)–6.21(d) for the 0-deg projection. Close inspection of Fig. 6.21(b), for which the *dc* term has been removed, reveals that contrast reversal occurs in the central (zero-order) portion of the figure but not for either of the off-axis reconstructions.

The cropped region of the hologram, which is 211×211 pixels, is resized to 106×106 to overcome computational memory limitations. The previously described tomographic procedure is used to assemble 3D reconstructions of the filament using different numbers of projections. Figure 6.22(a) illustrates the angular undersampling error that results from using only two angles (0 deg and 90 deg). Note that using only two orthogonal angles still allows the gross structure of the filament to be reconstructed rather well. A high-fidelity 3D

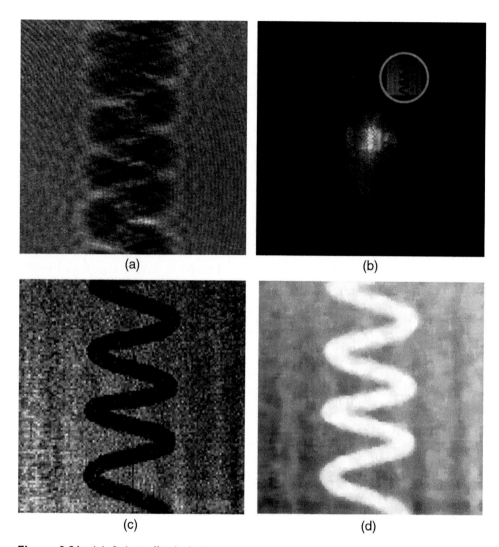

Figure 6.21 (a) 0-deg off-axis hologram projection of a tungsten filament, (b) off-axis intensity reconstruction showing the real (upper-right, circled) and virtual (lower-left, out-of-focus) images, (c) cropped real-image region of interest, and (d) numerically inverted intensity image.

reconstruction is shown in Fig. 6.22(b), using 13 angles spanning 0–180 deg in 15-deg increments. Note that the voxel resolution is reduced to $\Delta\xi_{mag} = 18.57$ μm per side due to the 50% downsampling, which again produces some excess surface roughness.

6.4.4 Angular sampling considerations

In general, to avoid angular undersampling, the minimum number of recording angles for accurate reconstruction should be determined by the geometry of the object. However, an approximation can be determined from

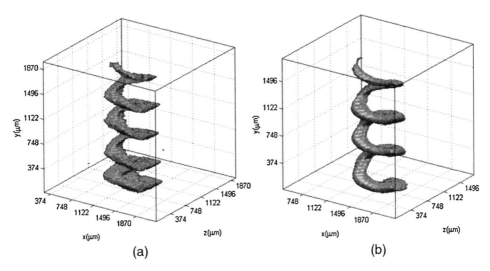

Figure 6.22 (a) Two-angle (0 deg and 90 deg, with an 85% intensity threshold) and (b) 13-angle (0 deg to 180 deg in 15-deg increments, with a 40% intensity threshold) tomographic reconstructions of the tungsten filament. Note that the angular undersampling error results in a quadrangular circumference in (a), whereas the 13-angle reconstruction results in a circular circumference in (b).

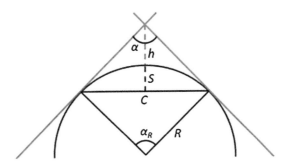

Figure 6.23 Geometry of the multi-angle illumination of an object with a circular cross-section, where α_R is the illumination angle (angle of object rotation); α is the angle between adjacent illumination beams ($\alpha = 180$ deg $-\alpha_R$; R is the cross-section radius; C is the chord length $[C = 2R \sin(\alpha_R/2)]$; S is the sag height of the arc ($S = R - \sqrt{R^2 - (C/2)^2}$); and h is the excess height (tomographic measurement error).[8]

the geometry of Fig. 6.23 by assuming a circular cross-section and requiring the excess height h to be less than or equal to the resolution of the holographic reconstruction $\Delta\xi$, $\Delta\eta$, given by Eq. (4.6). Following the geometry of Fig. 6.23, the chord length C and the circular sag height S are well-known geometric equations given by

$$C = 2R \sin(\alpha_R/2) \qquad (6.7)$$

and

$$S = R - \sqrt{R^2 - (C/2)^2}, \tag{6.8}$$

respectively. These equations allow the excess height and the illumination angle to be related by

$$\tan\left(\frac{\alpha}{2}\right) = \frac{C}{2(h+S)}, \tag{6.9}$$

such that the excess height h is given by

$$h = \frac{C}{2\tan(\alpha/2)} - S, \tag{6.10}$$

where α is the angle between adjacent beams (or equivalently, the rotation angle of the object), R is the cross-section radius, C is the chord length, and S is the sag height of the arc.

An example of angular undersampling is shown in Fig. 6.24, in which four projections (simulated) of a cylindrical cross-section are used to perform tomographic reconstruction by the SHOT-MT. The reconstructed 3D image exhibits an octagonal shape, rather than circular, circumscribing the lateral dimensions of the cylinder due to undersampling. Ideally, *a priori* knowledge of the object geometry may be applied, in a manner similar to that illustrated in Fig. 6.23, to determine the optimal angular sampling requirements.

The limitations of the multiplicative method become apparent if the object becomes overly complex, with many deep features that cannot be illuminated sufficiently from any projection angle, or if information regarding the internal

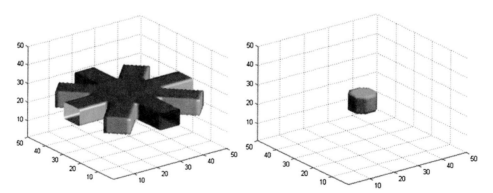

Figure 6.24 Simulation of multi-angle tomography using Eq. (6.2). Here, four projections (0 deg, 45 deg, 90 deg, and 135 deg) of a cylindrical cross-section are multiplied (left) to produce a 3D cylinder (right). Note that the angular undersampling errors circumscribing the cylinder result in an octagonal shape. The figure dimensions are in pixels (voxels).

Table 6.6 MATLAB code "Two_angle_single_capture_bubbles.m" for the 3D capturing of bubbles (see Fig. 6.15).

```
1   %Tomographic reconstruction of two air bubbles in
2   %water using the multiple-angle, single-exposure
3   %method
4   format compact
5   close all
6   clear all
7   %Load the hologram recording
8   load h2.mat                      %Loads to a variable h.
9   %Relevant reconstruction parameters.
10  d_near = 0.206;    %Near distance for 2-angle tomography
11  d_far = 0.618;              %Far distance, in meters
12  w = 543e-9;
13  dx = 6.7e-6;
14  %Display the original hologram recording
15  figure(1)
16  imagesc(h)
17  colormap gray
18  title('Recorded Multi-Angle Hologram')
19  %Reconstruct and display the near reconstruction plane
20  [ C0] = myFresnel(h,d_near,w,dx,true);
21  C0 = C0.*conj(C0);           %Display the intensity image
22  figure(2)
23  %Flip the image right-side up
24  imagesc(flipud(fliplr(C0)))
25  colormap(gray)
26  title('Near reconstruction (d2 = 20.6 cm)')
27  %Reconstruct and display the far reconstruction plane
28  [ C90] = myFresnel(h,d_far,w,dx,true);
29  C90 = C90.*conj(C90);
30  figure(3)
31  imagesc(flipud(fliplr(C90)))
32  colormap(gray)
33  title('Far reconstruction (d1 = 61.8 cm)')
34  %%Reconstruct the 3D volume
35  sum_threshold = 0.3;        %Illustrate the concept
36  product_threshold = 0.2;   %For actual tomographic
37                              %multiplication
38  if size(C0) ~= size(C90)    %Resize the matrices to match
39  C90 = imresize(C90, length(C0)/length(C90),'bicubic');
40  end
41  %Loft and rotate the holograms at appropriate angles
42  D0=myLoftAndRotate(C0,0.25,0); %Loft at 0 deg
43  D90=myLoftAndRotate(C90,0.25,90);     %Loft at 90 deg
44  D = D0.*D90;                %Multiplicative technique.
45  %Permute the 3D volumes to display more intuitively.
46  D0=permute(D0,[ 2 3 1]);
47  D90=permute(D90,[ 2 3 1]);
48  %Plot the (summation) superposition of lofted
49  %reconstructions for illustration purposes only
50  figure(4)
51  myDisplay3d(D0,sum_threshold)
52  hold on
53  myDisplay3d(D90,sum_threshold)
```

(continued)

Table 6.6   (*Continued*)

```
54  hold off
55  xlabel('z')
56  ylabel('x')
57  zlabel('y')
58  grid on
59  title('Superposition of multiple-angle projections')
60  %%Plot the superposition product (true tomography)
61  figure(5)
62  myDisplay3d(D,product_threshold)
63  title('Tomographic reconstruction at 2 angles')
```

Table 6.7   MATLAB code "large_spring_tomography.m" to reconstruct a spring tomographically (see Fig. 6.17).

```
1   %This code reconstructs the 13-angle spring tomography
2   format compact
3   close all
4   %Reconstruction parameters
5   scale = .20;                 %Scale to resize the holograms
6                                % (conserves memory)
7   d = 0.33;
8   w = 632.8e-9
9   dx = 9.8e-6;
10  padsize = 500;        %Size of zero padding (increases
11                           %resolution)
12  wtbr=waitbar(0,' Reconstructing Tomog. Projections');
13  steps = 13; %13 projection angles
14  H0 = abs(myFresnel(rot90(imread...
15  ('1_spring_0deg_480.bmp','bmp'),2)...
16  ,d,w,dx,false,1,1,padsize));
17  H0 = myLoftAndRotate(H0,scale,0);   %Lofts H0 but
18                                       %does not rotate
19  step = 1;
20  waitbar(step / steps)
21  H15 = abs(myFresnel(rot90(imread...
22  ('1_spring_15deg_480.bmp','bmp'),2)...
23  ,d,w,dx,false,1,1,padsize));
24  H15 = myLoftAndRotate(H15,scale,15);      %Lofts H0 but
25                                             %does not rotate
26  H30 = abs(myFresnel(rot90(imread...
27  ('1_spring_30deg_480.bmp','bmp'),2)...
28  ,d,w,dx,false,1,1,padsize));
29  H30 = myLoftAndRotate(H30,scale,30);      %Lofts and
30                                             %rotates by 45 deg
31  step = 3;
32  waitbar(step / steps)
33  H45 = abs(myFresnel(rot90(imread...
34  ('1_spring_45deg_480.bmp','bmp'),2)...
35  ,d,w,dx,false,1,1,padsize));
36  H45 = myLoftAndRotate(H45,scale,45);      %Lofts and
37                                             %rotates by 45 deg
38  H60 = abs(myFresnel(rot90(imread...
39  ('1_spring_60deg_480.bmp','bmp'),2)...
```

(*continued*)

Table 6.7 (*Continued*)

```
40  ,d,w,dx,false,1,1,padsize));
41  H60 = myLoftAndRotate(H60,scale,60);      %Lofts H0 but
42                                            %does not rotate
43  step = 5;
44  waitbar(step / steps)
45  H75 = abs(myFresnel(rot90(imread...
46  ('1_spring_75deg_480.bmp','bmp'),2)...
47  ,d,w,dx,false,1,1,padsize));
48  H75 = myLoftAndRotate(H75,scale,75);      %Lofts H0 but
49                                            %does not rotate
50  H90 = abs(myFresnel(rot90(imread...
51  ('1_spring_90deg_480.bmp','bmp'),2)...
52  ,d,w,dx,false,1,1,padsize));
53  H90 = myLoftAndRotate(H90,scale,90);
54  step = 7;
55  waitbar(step / steps)
56  H105 = abs(myFresnel(rot90(imread...
57  ('1_spring_105deg_480.bmp','bmp'),2)...
58  ,d,w,dx,false,1,1,padsize));
59  H105 = myLoftAndRotate(H105,scale,105);
60  H120 = abs(myFresnel(rot90(imread...
61  ('1_spring_120deg_480.bmp','bmp'),2)...
62  ,d,w,dx,false,1,1,padsize));
63  H120 = myLoftAndRotate(H120,scale,120);
64  step = 9;
65  waitbar(step / steps)
66  H135 = abs(myFresnel(rot90(imread...
67  ('1_spring_135deg_480.bmp','bmp'),2)...
68  ,d,w,dx,false,1,1,padsize));
69  H135 = myLoftAndRotate(H135,scale,135);
70  H150 = abs(myFresnel(rot90(imread...
71  ('1_spring_150deg_480.bmp','bmp'),2)...
72  ,d,w,dx,false,1,1,padsize));
73  H150 = myLoftAndRotate(H150,scale,150);
74  step = 11;
75  waitbar(step / steps)
76  H165 = abs(myFresnel(rot90(imread...
77  ('1_spring_165deg_480.bmp','bmp'),2)...
78  ,d,w,dx,false,1,1,padsize));
79  H165 = myLoftAndRotate(H165,scale,165);
80  H180 = abs(myFresnel(rot90(imread...
81  ('1_spring_180deg_480.bmp','bmp'),2)...
82  ,d,w,dx,false,1,1,padsize));
83  H180 = myLoftAndRotate(H180,scale,180);
84  close(wtbr)                %Closes the wait bar.
85  %%Multiply the various angles.
86  H13 = H0.*H15.*H30.*H45.*H60.*H75.*H90.*...
87  H105.*H120.*H135.*H150.*H165.*H180;
88  figure(1)
89  myDisplay3d(H13,0.0003)    %All 13 angles (0.0003
90                             %threshold is best)
91  view(-68,28); axis tight
92  grid on
93  title('13 Angle Tomographic Reconstruction')
```

(*continued*)

Table 6.7   (*Continued*)

```
94   %save 13_angle_spring.mat H13
95   %%Multiply the various angles
96   figure(2)
97   H7 = H0.*H30.*H60.*H90.*H120.*H150.*H180;    %7 angles
98   myDisplay3d(H7,0.06) %7 angles (0.06 threshold is best)
99   view(-68,28); axis tight
100     grid on
101     title('7 Angle Tomographic Reconstruction')
102     %save 7_angle_spring.mat H7
103     %%Reconstruct with alternate angles (as desired).
104     %H4 = H0.*H45.*H90.*H135.*H180; %4 angles (best
105     %threshold 0.2)
106     %H2 = H0.*H90;              %2 angles (best threshold 0.4)
107     %%Automatically set tick marks on the axis of
108     %the figures
109     s = length(H0);
110     Inc = (w*d/((480+2*padsize)*(dx)))/scale; %480 is
111                       %the original hologram size
112     Inc = Inc.*1000;        %Change increment to (mm) for
113                             %plotting
114     tickmarksx = 1:floor(s/6):s;
115     tickmarksy = 1:floor(s/6):s;
116     tickmarksz = 1:floor(s/6):s;
117     scalex = 0:floor(s/6)*Inc:(Inc*length(H0));
118     scaley = 0:floor(s/6)*Inc:(Inc*length(H0));
119     scalez = 0:floor(s/6)*Inc:(Inc*length(H0));
120     set(gca,'XTick',tickmarksx)
121     set(gca,'XTickLabel',scalex)
122     set(gca,'YTick',tickmarksy)
123     set(gca,'YTickLabel',scaley)
124     set(gca,'ZTick',tickmarksz)
125     set(gca,'ZTickLabel',scalez)
126     ylabel('y (mm)')
127     xlabel('x (mm)')
128     zlabel('z (mm)')
```

Table 6.8   MATLAB code "dandelion_tomography.m" to reconstruct a dandelion tomographically (see Fig. 6.18).

```
1    %This code reconstructs a dandelion tomography
2    %%%%%%%%%%%%%%%%%%%%%%%%%%%%%%%%%%%%
3    %Note: This example uses a specialized function
4    %"Dandelion_reconstruct.m"
5    %that is NOT A GENERALIZED FUNCTION and works ONLY
6    %for this example.
7    %The specialized function performs the Fresnel
8    %transform, filtering, and
9    %binary conversion of the hologram prior to lofting.
10   format compact
11   close all
12   scale = 1;              %No scaling in the main
                 %example code reconstruction paramters
13   d_rec = 0.37;         %Reconstruction distance (meters)
```

(*continued*)

Table 6.8 (*Continued*)

```
14  w = 632.8e-9;               %Wavelength
15  dx = 6.7e-6;                %Lumenera camera pixel size
16  N=1024;
17  pad = 1000;          %Pad size to increase resolution
18  rescale = . 5;             %Scaling performed in the
19                             %specialized function
20  threshold = 0.2;     %Threshold for 3D visualization.
21  %%Begin tomographic reconstructions.
22  wtbr = waitbar(0,' Reconstructing Tomog. Projections' );
23  load Dandelion_raw_0deg.mat
24  H0 = Dandelion_reconstruct(h,threshold,pad,rescale);
25  %(input, thresh,pad,scale)
26  H0([ 1:11] ,[ 86:112]) = 0;   %Crop some noise out of this
27                             %projection
28  H0 = myLoftAndRotate(H0,scale,0);      %Lofts H0 but
29                                    %does not rotate
30  waitbar(1/19)
31  %%Display the binary conversion reconstruction,
32  %if desired.
33  %figure(1)
34  %imagesc(rot90(H0,2))
35  %axis image
36  %colormap gray
37  %%Commented sections are not used for the 5-angle
38  %reconstruction.
39  %load Dandelion_raw_10deg.mat
40  %H10 = Dandelion_reconstruct(h,threshold,pad,rescale);
41  %H10 = myLoftAndRotate(H10,scale,10);    %Lofts H10 but
42                                    %does not rotate
43  %load Dandelion_raw_20deg.mat
44  %H20 =Dandelion_reconstruct(h,threshold,pad,rescale);
45  %H20 = myLoftAndRotate(H20,scale,20);    %Lofts H20 but
46                                    %does not rotate
47  waitbar(3/19)
48  load Dandelion_raw_30deg.mat
49  H30 =Dandelion_reconstruct(h,threshold,pad,rescale);
50  H30 = myLoftAndRotate(H30,scale,30);    %Lofts H30 but
51                                    %does not rotate
52  waitbar(4/19)
53  load Dandelion_raw_40deg.mat
54  H40 =Dandelion_reconstruct(h,threshold,pad,rescale);
55  H40 = myLoftAndRotate(H40,scale,40);    %Lofts H40 but
56                                    %does not rotate
57  waitbar(5/19)
58  %load Dandelion_raw_50deg.mat
59  %H50 =Dandelion_reconstruct(h,threshold,pad,rescale);
60  %H50 = myLoftAndRotate(H50,scale,50);    %Lofts H50 but
61                                    %does not rotate
62  %load Dandelion_raw_60deg.mat
63  %H60 =Dandelion_reconstruct(h,threshold,pad,rescale);
64  %H60 = myLoftAndRotate(H60,scale,60);    %Lofts H60 but
65                                    %does not rotate
66  %waitbar(7/19)
67  %load Dandelion_raw_70deg.mat
68  %H70 =Dandelion_reconstruct(h,threshold,pad,rescale);
```

(*continued*)

Table 6.8 (*Continued*)

```
69   %H70 = myLoftAndRotate(H70,scale,70);      %Lofts H70 but
70                                             %does not rotate
71   %load Dandelion_raw_80deg.mat
72   %H80 =Dandelion_reconstruct(h,threshold,pad,rescale);
73   %H80 = myLoftAndRotate(H80,scale,80);      %Lofts H80 but
74                                             %does not rotate
75   waitbar(9/19)
76   load Dandelion_raw_90deg.mat
77   H90 = Dandelion_reconstruct(h,threshold,pad,rescale);
78   H90([ 1:8],[ 85:110]) = 0;
79   H90([ 1:8],[ 140:166]) = 0;
80   H90 = myLoftAndRotate(H90,scale,90);       %Lofts H90 but
81                                             %does not rotate
82   waitbar(10/19)
83   %load Dandelion_raw_100deg.mat
84   %H100 = Dandelion_reconstruct(h,threshold,pad,rescale);
85   %H100 = myLoftAndRotate(H100,scale,100);   %Lofts H100
86                                             %but does not rotate
87   %waitbar(11/19)
88   %load Dandelion_raw_110deg.mat
89   %H110 = Dandelion_reconstruct(h,threshold,pad,rescale);
90   %H110 = myLoftAndRotate(H110,scale,110);   %Lofts H110
91                                             %but does not rotate
92   %load Dandelion_raw_120deg.mat
93   %H120 =Dandelion_reconstruct(h,threshold,pad,rescale);
94   %H120 = myLoftAndRotate(H120,scale,120);   %Lofts H0 but
95                                             %does not rotate
96   waitbar(13/19)
97   load Dandelion_raw_130deg.mat
98   H130 =Dandelion_reconstruct(h,threshold,pad,rescale);
99   H130 = myLoftAndRotate(H130,scale,130);    %Lofts H130
100                                            %but does not rotate
101  waitbar(14/19)
102  %load Dandelion_raw_140deg.mat
103  %H140 =Dandelion_reconstruct(h,threshold,pad,rescale)
104  %H140 = myLoftAndRotate(H140,scale,140);   %Lofts H140
105                                            %but does not rotate
106  %waitbar(15/19)
107  %load Dandelion_raw_150deg.mat
108  %H150 =Dandelion_reconstruct(h,threshold,pad,rescale)
109  %H150 = myLoftAndRotate(H150,scale,150);   %Lofts H0
110                                            %but does not rotate
111  %load Dandelion_raw_160deg.mat
112  %H160=Dandelion_reconstruct(h,threshold,pad,rescale)
113  %H160=myLoftAndRotate(H160,scale,160);  %Lofts H160
114                                            %but does not rotate
115  %waitbar(17/19)
116  %load Dandelion_raw_170deg.mat
117  %H170=Dandelion_reconstruct(h,threshold,pad,rescale)
118  %H170=myLoftAndRotate(H170,scale,170);  %Lofts H170
119                                            %but does not rotate
120  %load Dandelion_raw_180deg.mat
121  %H180=Dandelion_reconstruct(h,threshold,pad,rescale)
122  %H180=myLoftAndRotate(H180,scale,180);     %Lofts H0
123                                            %but does not rotate
```

(*continued*)

Table 6.8 (*Continued*)

```
124   waitbar(19/19)
125   close(wtbr)
126   %%
127   %Close all
128   H=H0.*H90.*H30.*H40.*H130;   %(Best threshold is 0.1)
129   H=permute(H,[ 3 2 1]);          %Permute to display
                                       %right-side up
130   figure(3);
131   myDisplay3d(H,0.1,3,1)          %(Data input, threshold,
132                                    %smoothing, alpha)
133   view(-39,6);
134   axis square
135   grid on
```

Table 6.9 MATLAB code "DHM_off_axis_tomography.m" to reconstruct a microfilament tomographically (see Fig. 6.22).

```
1    %This code reconstructs the 13-angle microfilament
2    %tomography.
3    %Note the postprocessing that occurs between the
4    %Fresnel reconstruction and lofting/rotating the volume.
5    format compact
6    close all
7    scale = 0.5;     %Downsamples when lofting to save memory
8    d_rec = 0.83;                %Reconstruction distance in m
9    w = 632.8e-9;                %Wavelength
10   dx = 6.7e-6;                 %Lumenera camera pixel size
11   N=1024;
12   filter_size = 5;            %Filter size
13   %%
14   %Reconstruction with no padding
15   padsize = 0;
16   x1 = 600;
17   x2 = 720;
18   y1 = 200;
19   y2 = 320;
20   %Reconstruction with padding of 250.
21   %padsize = 250;
22   %x1 = 625;
23   %x2 = 835;
24   %y1 = 11;
25   %y2 = 221;
26   load Saved_Raw_holo_0deg.mat
27   H0 = myFresnel(hraw1,d_rec,w,dx,false,1,1,padsize);
28   H0 = abs(H0([ y1:y2],[ x1:x2]));    %Crops to pertinent area
29   H0 = (max(max(H0))-H0)./max(max(H0));  %Inverts and
30                                          %normalizes the image
31   H0 = medfilt2(H0,[ filter_size filter_size]);    %Filter to
32                                          %smooth the intensity.
33   %Display the 0-deg projection.
34   figure(1)
35   imagesc(H0)
36   axis image
```

(*continued*)

Table 6.9 (*Continued*)

```
37   colormap gray
38   wtbr = waitbar(0,' Reconstructing Tomog. Projections');
39   H0 = myLoftAndRotate(H0,scale,0); %Lofts H0 but
40                                      %does not rotate
41   waitbar(1/13)
42   load Saved_Raw_holo_15deg.mat
43   H15 = myFresnel(hraw1,d_rec,w,dx,false,1,1,padsize);
44   %Crops to the pertinent area
45   H15 = abs(H15([ y1:y2],[ x1:x2]));
46   H15 = (max(max(H15))-H15)./max(max(H15)); %Inverts and
47                              %normalizes the image filter
48                              %to smooth the intensity
49   H15 = medfilt2(H15,[ filter_size filter_size]);
50   H15 = myLoftAndRotate(H15,scale,15);   %Lofts H15 but
51                                     %does not rotate
52   waitbar(2/13)
53   load Saved_Raw_holo_30deg.mat
54   H30 = myFresnel(hraw1,d_rec,w,dx,false,1,1,padsize);
55   %crops to pertinent area
56   H30 = abs(H30([ y1:y2],[ x1:x2]));
57   H30 = (max(max(H30))-H30)./max(max(H30)); %Inverts and
58                              %normalizes the image filter
59                              %to smooth the intensity
60   H30 = medfilt2(H30,[ filter_size filter_size]);
61   H30 = myLoftAndRotate(H30,scale,30);   %Lofts H30 but
62                                     %does not rotate
63   waitbar(3/13)
64   load Saved_Raw_holo_45deg.mat
65   H45 = myFresnel(hraw1,d_rec,w,dx,false,1,1,padsize);
66   %Crops to the pertinent area
67   H45 = abs(H45([ y1:y2],[ x1:x2]));
68   H45 = (max(max(H45))-H45)./max(max(H45));  %Inverts and
69                              %normalizes the image filter
70                              %to smooth the intensity
71   H45 = medfilt2(H45,[ filter_size filter_size]);
72   H45 = myLoftAndRotate(H45,scale,45);   %Lofts H45 but
73                                     %does not rotate
74   waitbar(4/13)
75   load Saved_Raw_holo_60deg.mat
76   H60 = myFresnel(hraw1,d_rec,w,dx,false,1,1,padsize);
77   %Crops to the pertinent area
78   H60 = abs(H60([ y1:y2],[ x1:x2]));
79   H60 = (max(max(H60))-H60)./max(max(H60));  %Inverts and
80                              %normalizes the image filter
81                              %to smooth the intensity
82   H60 = medfilt2(H60,[ filter_size filter_size]);
83   H60 = myLoftAndRotate(H60,scale,60);   %Lofts H60 but
84                                     %does not rotate
85   waitbar(5/13)
86   load Saved_Raw_holo_75deg.mat
87   H75 = myFresnel(hraw1,d_rec,w,dx,false,1,1,padsize);
88   %crops to pertinent area
89   H75 = abs(H75([ y1:y2],[ x1:x2]));
90   H75 = (max(max(H75))-H75)./max(max(H75));     %Inverts and
91                              %normalizes the image filter
92                              %to smooth the intensity
```

(*continued*)

Table 6.9 *(Continued)*

```
93   H75 = medfilt2(H75,[ filter_size filter_size]);
94   H75 = myLoftAndRotate(H75,scale,75);    %Lofts H75 but
95                                           %does not rotate
96   waitbar(6/13)
97   load Saved_Raw_holo_90deg.mat
98   H90 = myFresnel(hraw1,d_rec,w,dx,false,1,1,padsize);
99   %crops to pertinent area
100  H90 = abs(H90([ y1:y2],[ x1:x2]));
101  H90 = (max(max(H90))-H90)./max(max(H90));    %Inverts &
102                                 %normalizes the image filter
103                                 %to smooth the intensity
104  H90 = medfilt2(H90,[ filter_size filter_size]);
105  H90 = myLoftAndRotate(H90,scale,90); %Lofts H90 but
106                                 %does not rotate
107  waitbar(7/13)
108  load Saved_Raw_holo_105deg.mat
109  H105 = myFresnel(hraw1,d_rec,w,dx,false,1,1,padsize);
110  %Crops to the pertinent area
111  H105 = abs(H105([ y1:y2],[ x1:x2]));
112  H105 = (max(max(H105))-H105)./max(max(H105));
113  %Inverts and normalizes the image filter
114  %to smooth the intensity
115  H105 = medfilt2(H105,[ filter_size filter_size]);
116  H105 = myLoftAndRotate(H105,scale,105); %Lofts H0
117                                 %but does not rotate
118  waitbar(8/13)
119  load Saved_Raw_holo_120deg.mat
120  H120 = myFresnel(hraw1,d_rec,w,dx,false,1,1,padsize);
121  %Crops to the pertinent area
122  H120 = abs(H120([ y1:y2],[ x1:x2]));
123  %Inverts and normalizes the image
124  H120 = (max(max(H120))-H120)./max(max(H120));
125  %Filter to smooth the intensity
126  H120 = medfilt2(H120,[ filter_size filter_size]);
127  H120 = myLoftAndRotate(H120,scale,120); %Lofts H0
128                                 %but does not rotate
129  waitbar(9/13)
130  load Saved_Raw_holo_135deg.mat
131  H135 = myFresnel(hraw1,d_rec,w,dx,false,1,1,padsize);
132  %Crops to pertinent area
133  H135 = abs(H135([ y1:y2],[ x1:x2]));
134  %Inverts and normalizes the image
135  H135 = (max(max(H135))-H135)./max(max(H135));
136  %Filter to smooth the intensity
137  H135 = medfilt2(H135,[ filter_size filter_size]);
138  H135 = myLoftAndRotate(H135,scale,135); %Lofts H0
139                                 %but does not rotate
140  waitbar(10/13)
141  load Saved_Raw_holo_150deg.mat
142  H150=myFresnel(hraw1,d_rec,w,dx,false,1,1,padsize);
143  %Crops to the pertinent area
144  H150 = abs(H150([ y1:y2],[ x1:x2]));
145  %Inverts and normalizes the image
146  H150 = (max(max(H150))-H150)./max(max(H150));
```

(continued)

Table 6.9 (*Continued*)

```
147  %Filter to smooth the intensity
148  H150 = medfilt2(H150,[ filter_size filter_size]);
149  H150 = myLoftAndRotate(H150,scale,150); %Lofts H0
150                                      %but does not rotate
151  waitbar(11/13)
152  load Saved_Raw_holo_165deg.mat
153  H165 = myFresnel(hraw1,d_rec,w,dx,false,1,1,padsize);
154  %Crops to pertinent area
155  H165 = abs(H165([ y1:y2],[ x1:x2]));
156  %Inverts and normalizes the image
157  H165 = (max(max(H165))-H165)./max(max(H165));
158  %Filter to smooth the intensity
159  H165 = medfilt2(H165,[ filter_size filter_size]);
160  %Lofts H0 but does not rotate
161  H165 = myLoftAndRotate(H165,scale,165);
162  waitbar(12/13)
163  load Saved_Raw_holo_180deg.mat
164  H180 = myFresnel(hraw1,d_rec,w,dx,false,1,1,padsize);
165  %Crops to pertinent area
166  H180 = abs(H180([ y1:y2],[ x1:x2]));
167  %Inverts and normalizes the image
168  H180 = (max(max(H180))-H180)./max(max(H180));
169  %Filter to smooth the intensity
170  H180 = medfilt2(H180,[ filter_size filter_size]);
171  H180 = myLoftAndRotate(H180,scale,180); %Lofts H0
172                                      %but does not rotate
173  waitbar(13/13)
174  close(wtbr)
175  %%
176  %Close all
177  %13 angles (0.3 threshold)
178  H = H0.*H15.*H30.*H45.*H60.*H75.*H90.*H105.*...
179  H120.*H135.*H150.*H165.*H180;
180  %H = H0.*H30.*H60.*H90.*H120.*H150.*H180; %7 angles
181                                      % (threshold 0.45)
182  %H = H0.*H90;    %2 angles (best threshold 0.85).
183  %Permute for correct viewing angle.
184  H = permute(H,[ 2 3 1]);
185  % (data input, threshold, smoothing, alpha)
186  myDisplay3d(H,0.3,3,1)
187  view(-55,22);
188  axis square
189  %Axis tight
190  grid on
191  %Save 13_angle_spring.mat H
```

composition of the object is desired. However, this is a common disadvantage of all tomographic techniques when used to measure opaque objects. For such objects, more-complex tomographic methods must be employed, such as the previously discussed back-projection by the Radon transform, combined with imaging at a wavelength that both renders the object semi-transparent and minimizes diffraction (e.g., x-rays).

Table 6.10 MATLAB code "Undersampling_Example.m" for the tomographic angular undersampling error assessment of a cylinder (see Fig. 6.24).

```
1   %%Example of tomographic angular undersampling
2   %error for a cylinder.
3   %This is a basic tomography example without
4   %holography.
5   close all
6   clear all
7   %Make a simple image of a square (cylinder cross-
8   %section)
9   H = zeros(50,50);
10  H(21:29,21:29) = 1; %Draw a box in an arbitrary location
11  figure(1)
12  imagesc(abs(H))
13  colormap gray
14  %Loft and rotate images, or just use the same one for
15  %simplicity
16  %and rotate them to 4 angles
17  scale = 1;                 %No resizing
18  H0 = myLoftAndRotate(H,scale,0);
19  H45 = myLoftAndRotate(H,scale,45);
20  H90 = myLoftAndRotate(H,scale,90);
21  H135 = myLoftAndRotate(H,scale,135);
22  %Compute the tomographic reconstruction at 4 angles
23  H_3D = H0.*H90.*H45.*H135; %Multiplicative technique
24  H_sum = H0+H45+H90+H135;    %Sum technique (for
25                              %illustration only)
26  H_sum(find(H_sum>1))=1; %Do this so that the
27                              %isosurface works correctly
28  figure(2)
29  isosurface(H_sum);
30  %Force full axes
31  axis([ 1 length(H) 1 length(H) 1 length(H)])
32  grid on
33  %Change the viewing direction using permute
34  H_permute=permute(H_sum,[ 2 3 1]);    %This is the one
35                                         %we typically use
36  figure(3)
37  isosurface(H_permute);
38  axis([ 1 length(H) 1 length(H) 1 length(H)])
39  grid on
40  %View the multiplicative version (real tomography)
41  figure(4)
42  isosurface(permute(H_3D,[ 2 3 1]));
43  axis([ 1 length(H) 1 length(H) 1 length(H)])
44  grid on
```

6.5 Examples of Digital Holographic Tomography Using MATLAB

Various software examples of holographic tomography are included in Tables 6.6–6.10, including the code used to produce Figs 6.15, 6.17, 6.18, 6.22, and 6.24.

References

1. A. C. Kak and M. Slaney, *Principles of Computerized Tomographic Imaging*, IEEE Press, New York (1988).
2. O. N. Ross and S. G. Bradley, "Model for optical forward scattering by nonspherical raindrops," *Appl. Opt.* **41**(24), 5130–5141 (2002).
3. G. Nehmetallah and P. P. Banerjee, "SHOT: single-beam holographic tomography," *Proc. SPIE* **7851**, 785101 (2010) [doi: 10.1117/12.873083].
4. R. C. Gonzalez and R. E. Woods, *Digital Image Processing*, Prentice Hall, Harlow, NJ (2007).
5. G. Nehmetallah, P. P. Banerjee, and S. Praharaj, "Digital holographic tomography for 3D visualization," Digital Holography and 3D Imaging, Tokyo, Japan (2011).
6. L. Tian, J. Lee, and G. Barbastathis, "Compressive holographic inversion of particle scattering," Digital Holography and 3D Imaging, Tokyo, Japan (2011).
7. G. Nehmetallah and P. P. Banerjee, "Applications of digital and analog holography in 3D imaging," *Advances Opt. Photon.* **4**(4), 472–553 (2012).
8. L. Williams, G. Nehmetallah, and P. P. Banerjee, "Digital tomographic compressive holographic reconstruction of three-dimensional objects in transmissive and reflective geometries," *Appl. Opt.* **52**(8), 1702–1710 (2013).

Chapter 7
Multiwavelength Digital Holography

7.1 Holographic Contouring

Another application of HI is the generation of a fringe pattern corresponding to contours of constant elevation with respect to a reference plane (see Fig. 7.1). Such contour fringes can be used to determine the shape of a 3D object. Holographic contour interferograms can be generated by[1-3]

- the two-illumination-point method (discussed in Section 5.2);
- the two-refractive-index technique, which is generally not practical because the refractive index of the medium wherein the object is located must be changed; and
- the two-wavelength method, which is discussed in this chapter.

Consider the schematic in Fig. 7.2(a). The phase at a point $P(x,y,z)$ relative to the phase at point $P_O(0,0,z)$ can be calculated from the difference in the optical paths:[3]

$$\phi = \left(\frac{2\pi}{\lambda}\right)(SP - SP_0)$$

$$= \left(\frac{2\pi}{\lambda}\right)\{[(x - x_1)^2 + (y - y_1)^2 + z^2]^{1/2} - [x_1^2 + y_1^2 + z^2]^{1/2}\}$$

$$= \left(\frac{2\pi}{\lambda}\right)z\left\{\left[1 + \frac{(x - x_1)^2 + (y - y_1)^2}{z^2}\right]^{1/2} - \left[1 + \frac{x_1^2 + y_1^2}{z^2}\right]^{1/2}\right\}. \quad (7.1)$$

If z is large compared to x, y, x_1, y_1, then

$$\phi \approx \left(\frac{2\pi}{\lambda}\right)\left(\frac{1}{2z}\right)(x^2 + y^2 - 2xx_1 - 2yy_1) \quad (7.2)$$

257

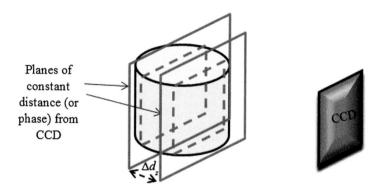

Figure 7.1 Holographic contouring.

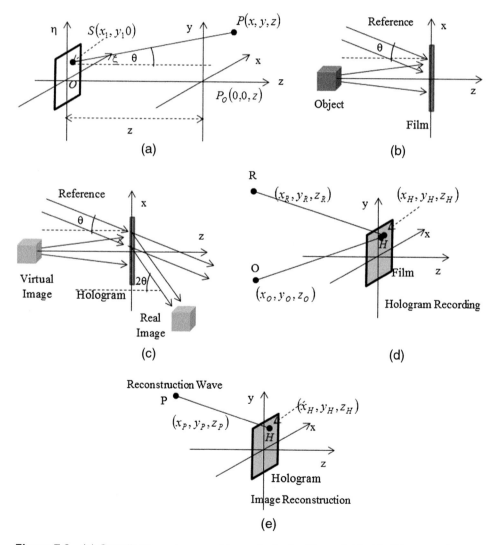

Figure 7.2 (a) Coordinate system used to evaluate the Fresnel–Kirchhoff integral, (b) off-axis hologram recording, and (c) image reconstruction with an off-axis reference. Coordinate system of (d) a hologram recording, and the (e) image reconstruction.[3]

Consider the off-axis hologram recording schematic shown in Fig. 7.2(b). Let the reference and object beam be defined as

$$E_R(x,y) \propto E_R e^{j\frac{2\pi}{\lambda}\sin(\theta)x}, \quad E_O(x,y) \propto |E_O(x,y)|e^{-j\phi_O(x,y)} \tag{7.3}$$

The recorded hologram, as shown in Fig. 7.2(c), can be written as

$$h(x,y) = |E_R(x,y) + E_O(x,y)|^2$$
$$= |E_R(x,y)|^2 + |E_O(x,y)|^2 + E_R^*(x,y)E_O(x,y) + E_R(x,y)E_O^*(x,y). \tag{7.4}$$

The off-axis reconstructed hologram can be written as

$$E_{Reconst}(x,y) = E_R(x,y)h(x,y)$$
$$= E_1(x,y) + E_2(x,y) + E_3(x,y) + E_4(x,y), \tag{7.5}$$

where

$$E_1(x,y) \propto E_R^3 e^{j\frac{2\pi}{\lambda}\sin(\theta)x},$$
$$E_2(x,y) \propto E_R|E_O(x,y)|^2 e^{j\frac{2\pi}{\lambda}\sin(\theta)x},$$
$$E_3(x,y) \propto E_R^2|E_O(x,y)|e^{-j\phi_O},$$
$$E_4(x,y) \propto E_R^2 e^{j\frac{4\pi}{\lambda}\sin(\theta)x}|E_O(x,y)|e^{j\phi_O}. \tag{7.6}$$

According to the schematic shown in Fig. 7.2(d), and Eq. (7.2), the complex amplitude of the object wave at point $O(x_O,y_O,z_O)$ is $E_O = |E_O|e^{-j\phi_O}$. The complex amplitude of the object wave at a point $H(x_H,y_H,z_H)$ is then

$$\phi_O(x_H,y_H,z_H) \approx \left(\frac{\pi}{\lambda_1 z_O}\right)(x_H^2 + y_H^2 - 2x_H x_O - 2y_H y_O), \tag{7.7a}$$

where λ_1 is the recording wavelength. Similarly, the complex amplitude of the reference wave at point $R(x_R,y_R,z_R)$ is $E_R = |E_R|e^{-j\phi_R}$. The complex amplitude of the reference wave at a point $H(x_H,y_H,z_H)$, shown in Fig. 7.2(d), is then

$$\phi_R(x_H,y_H,z_H) \approx \left(\frac{\pi}{\lambda_1 z_R}\right)(x_H^2 + y_H^2 - 2x_H x_R - 2y_H y_R). \tag{7.7b}$$

As shown in Figure 7.2(e), assuming that the reconstruction wavelength is λ_2, the reconstructed wave at point P has the form $E_P = |E_P|e^{-j\phi_P}$. The complex amplitude of the reconstruction wave at a point $H(x_H,y_H,z_H)$ is

$$\phi_P(x_H,y_H,z_H) \approx \left(\frac{\pi}{\lambda_2 z_P}\right)(x_H^2 + y_H^2 - 2x_H x_P - 2y_H y_P). \tag{7.7c}$$

From Eq. (7.6), the reconstructed term $E_3(x,y)$ is

$$E_3(x,y) \propto E_P E_R^* E_O = |E_P||E_R||E_O|e^{-j[\phi_P - \phi_R + \phi_O]} = |E_3|e^{-j\phi_3}$$

$$\Rightarrow \phi_3 = [\phi_P - \phi_R + \phi_O]. \tag{7.8}$$

Substituting the values of $\phi_{O,R,P}$ from Eqs. (7.7a)–(7.7c) into Eq. (7.8) produces

$$\phi_3(x_H, y_H, z_H) = \left(\frac{\pi}{\lambda_2}\right)\left[(x_H^2 + y_H^2)\left(\frac{1}{z_P} + \frac{\mu}{z_O} - \frac{\mu}{z_R}\right)\right.$$
$$\left. - 2x_H\left(\frac{x_P}{z_P} + \frac{\mu x_O}{z_O} - \frac{\mu x_R}{z_R}\right) - 2y_H\left(\frac{y_P}{z_P} + \frac{\mu y_O}{z_O} - \frac{\mu y_R}{z_R}\right)\right], \tag{7.9}$$

where $\mu = \lambda_2/\lambda_1$. Because the wave represented by E_3 produces a point image, it must be a spherical wave, so the phase at $H(x_H, y_H, z_H)$ is then approximately

$$\phi_3(x_H, y_H, z_H) \approx \left(\frac{\pi}{\lambda_2 z_3}\right)(x_H^2 + y_H^2 - 2x_H x_3 - 2y_H y_3). \tag{7.10}$$

Equate the coefficients of similar terms in Eqs. (7.9) and (7.10):

$$x_3 = \frac{x_P z_O z_R + \mu x_O z_P z_R - \mu x_R z_P z_O}{z_O z_R + \mu z_P z_R - \mu z_P z_O},$$

$$y_3 = \frac{y_P z_O z_R + \mu y_O z_P z_R - \mu y_R z_P z_O}{z_O z_R + \mu z_P z_R - \mu z_P z_O},$$

$$z_3 = \frac{z_P z_O z_R}{z_O z_R + \mu z_P z_R - \mu z_P z_O}. \tag{7.11}$$

Let $z_O = z$ and $z_p = z_R$ tend to infinity; then,[1,2]

$$z_3 = \frac{z_P z_O z_R}{z_O z_R + \mu z_P z_R - \mu z_P z_O} = \frac{z z_R^2}{z z_R + \mu z_R^2 - \mu z z_R} \approx z\frac{\lambda_1}{\lambda_2}. \tag{7.12}$$

As shown in Fig. 7.3, the axial displacement of the image recorded with λ_1 and reconstructed with λ_2, with respect to the image recorded and reconstructed with λ_2, is[2]

$$\Delta d_z = z_3 - z = z\frac{|\lambda_1 - \lambda_2|}{\lambda_2}. \tag{7.13}$$

The path difference of the light rays on their way from the source to the surface and from the surface to the hologram is $2\Delta d_z$. Therefore, the phase shift is

$$\Delta\phi(x,y) = \frac{2\pi}{\lambda_1}2\Delta d_z = 4\pi z\frac{|\lambda_1 - \lambda_2|}{\lambda_1\lambda_2}, \tag{7.14}$$

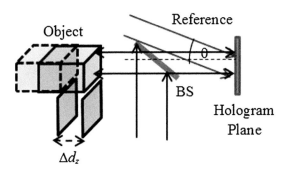

Figure 7.3 Holographic contouring.[2]

which means that the phase shift depends on the distance z between the object and the hologram plane. The height jump between two adjacent fringes is

$$\Delta H = z(\Delta\phi = (n+1) \times 2\pi) - z(\Delta\phi = n \times 2\pi) = \frac{\lambda_1\lambda_2}{2|\lambda_1 - \lambda_2|} = \frac{\Lambda}{2}, \quad (7.15)$$

where Λ is known as the synthetic wavelength, or the beat wavelength, between λ_1 and λ_2. Pixel matching should be performed when applying the two-wavelength technique, as explained in Section 7.4.

7.2 Principle of Multiwavelength Digital Holography

Chapters 4 and 5 considered holography and holographic interferometry using a single illumination wavelength. The maximum size of deformation that can be tracked is on the order of tens of microns, or tens of wavelengths, which is limited by the current resolution of the CCD arrays. For larger deformations or depths along the direction of propagation of the light, the phase changes could be hundreds of multiples of 2π, and thus the single-wavelength technique is not as advantageous due to large fringe densities. Multiwavelength illumination, however, encodes the object height in terms of 2π multiples of the synthetic wavelength, which is generally much longer (tens of microns, or more) than either fundamental wavelength. This relationship allows larger object deformations to be measured by multiwavelength illumination *as if* illuminated by the single-wavelength method, where the single wavelength is now given by the synthetic wavelength Λ. In many practical recording configurations (i.e., in the presence of noise, vibration, laser instability, etc.), the realizable depth resolution is limited to $\sim 1/100$ of the synthetic wavelength. Digital holographic interferometry (or holographic topography) is sometimes called holographic profilometry due to the frequent practice of analyzing only a cross-section of a given topography (generally due to the ease of 1D phase unwrapping compared to 2D unwrapping).

Multiwavelength digital holography (MWDH) may be used to quantify surface topography and displacement measurements for both fixed objects and time-varying objects.[4,5] Visible or IR fundamental wavelengths are typically used, where the difference between the two wavelengths $\Delta\lambda$ is on the order of 8 nm to 40 nm, yielding synthetic wavelengths Λ of approximately 30 μm to 10 μm, respectively. The assumption that the topographic resolution is typically on the order of $1/100$ of Λ allows feature heights on the order of 1–3 μm to be resolved reasonably well.[5,6] However, some work has also been performed using much-longer synthetic wavelengths to measure millimeter-scale features, whereas nanometer-scale measurements can be performed using phase-shifting DH or very short synthetic wavelengths.[4,7]

Digital holographic interferometry, using a dual-wavelength method, is shown schematically in Figs. 7.4(a) and 7.4(b), where two holograms are recorded with different wavelengths λ_1 and λ_2, and stored electronically, as in DH, rather than on photographic plates. Both holograms can be reconstructed separately at the correct fundamental wavelengths λ_1 or λ_2, according to the theory discussed in Section 4.2. The phases are calculated from the resulting complex amplitudes $\Gamma_{\lambda_1}(\xi,\eta)$ and $\Gamma_{\lambda_2}(\xi,\eta)$:

$$\phi_{\lambda_{1,2}}(\xi,\eta) = \arctan\left(\frac{\mathrm{Im}\Gamma_{\lambda_{1,2}}(\xi,\eta)}{\mathrm{Re}\Gamma_{\lambda_{1,2}}(\xi,\eta)}\right). \tag{7.16}$$

The phase difference is now calculated directly by subtraction

$$\Delta\phi = \begin{cases} \phi_{\lambda_1} - \phi_{\lambda_2} & \text{if } \phi_{\lambda_1} \geq \phi_{\lambda_2} \\ \phi_{\lambda_1} - \phi_{\lambda_2} + 2\pi & \text{if } \phi_{\lambda_1} < \phi_{\lambda_2} \end{cases}. \tag{7.17}$$

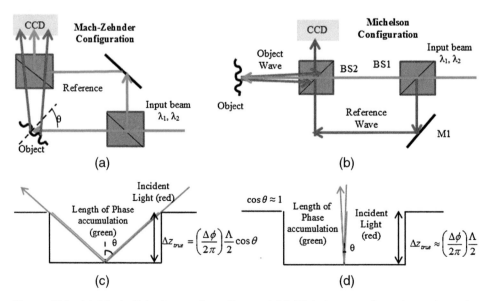

Figure 7.4 (a) Mach–Zehnder configuration and (b) Michelson configuration, where the illustration of the true height Δz_{true} is relative to the path of phase accumulation for the (c) Mach–Zehnder and (d) Michelson configurations.

This phase map (i.e., digital interferogram) is equivalent to the phase distribution of a hologram recorded with the *synthetic wavelength*

$$\Lambda = \left[\frac{\lambda_1 \lambda_2}{|\lambda_1 - \lambda_2|}\right]. \tag{7.18}$$

At normal incidence, a 2π phase jump corresponds to a height step of $\Lambda/2$, and the change in longitudinal distance or height Δz is given by[2]

$$\Delta z = \left(\frac{\Delta\phi}{2\pi}\right)\frac{\Lambda}{2} = \frac{\Delta\varphi}{2\pi}\left[\frac{\lambda_1 \lambda_2}{2|\lambda_1 - \lambda_2|}\right] = \left(\frac{\Delta\phi}{2\pi}\right)\Delta H. \tag{7.19}$$

Note that the transverse resolution is the same as in DH, namely, $\Delta\xi = \lambda d/N\Delta x$ is the reconstructed pixel size, N is the number of pixels (assume an $N \times N$ layout), Δx is the physical size of camera pixels, and d is the reconstruction distance (object to camera).

According to Figs. 7.4(c) and 7.4(d), the true height measurement in the Mach–Zehnder and Michelson configuration are, respectively,

$$\Delta z_{true,Mach-Zehnder} = \left(\frac{\Delta\phi}{2\pi}\right)\frac{\Lambda}{2}\cos\theta, \tag{7.20}$$

$$\Delta z_{true,Michelson} \approx \left(\frac{\Delta\phi}{2\pi}\right)\frac{\Lambda}{2}. \tag{7.21}$$

7.3 Hierarchical Phase Unwrapping

The use of a synthetic wavelength is advantageous when the depth variation is much larger than a single wavelength. On the other hand, it turns out that the use of larger synthetic wavelengths leads to larger phase noise because the phase noise scales as a percentage of Λ. In practice, the phase noise limits the achievable measurement resolution to $\sim 1/100$ of the synthetic wavelength. One way to recover the accuracy in the measurement is to carry out a systematic reduction in the synthetic wavelength, using the information from the larger synthetic wavelength measurements to remove 2π ambiguities in the shorter synthetic wavelength data.[4] This process is known as *hierarchical phase unwrapping* and is especially useful when the object contains sharp/discrete height variations.[2] Four steps are usually sufficient for reliable and precise demodulation of complicated modulo 2π phase maps.

The procedure is as follows:[2]

1. Start with a synthetic wavelength Λ_1 that is larger than twice the h_{max} variation of the object:

$$z_1 = \frac{\Delta\phi_1}{2\pi}\left(\frac{\Lambda_1}{2}\right). \tag{7.22}$$

This result is unambiguous but strongly disturbed by noise.
2. Reduce the synthetic wavelength to Λ_2:

$$\hat{z}_2 = \frac{\Lambda_2}{2}\frac{\Delta\phi_2}{2\pi}. \tag{7.23}$$

This result is **not** unambiguous and is indicated by the hat.
3. Compute:

$$\Delta z = z_1 - \hat{z}_2. \tag{7.24}$$

4. Compute:

$$N = \text{floor}\left[2\frac{\Delta z}{\Lambda_2} + \frac{1}{2}\right]. \tag{7.25}$$

5. The right value of the height is

$$z_2 = \hat{z}_2 + \Lambda_2 N/2; \tag{7.26}$$

z_2 is unambiguous like z_1 but with better accuracy.
6. For $n = 3$ to N hierarchical phase measurements, compute:

$$z_n = \hat{z}_n + \frac{\Lambda_n}{2}\text{floor}\left[2\frac{z_{n-1} - \hat{z}_n}{\Lambda_n} + \frac{1}{2}\right], \tag{7.27}$$

where

$$\hat{z}_n = \frac{\Lambda_n}{2}\frac{\Delta\phi_n}{2\pi},$$

and

$$\Lambda_{n+1} = \Lambda_n\left(\frac{\varepsilon_n}{1 - \varepsilon_{n+1}}\right), \quad \varepsilon_n \approx \varepsilon_{n+1} \approx 0.2 \text{ to } 0.3.[1]$$

7.4 Multiwavelength Digital Holography

A typical example of a 3D profile using the MWDH technique is shown in Fig. 7.5; an actual laboratory setup is shown in Fig. 7.6. Because the two holograms are recorded sequentially for each wavelength, this technique needs two sequential CCD recordings (i.e., two "shots"). This "two-shot" method will obviously not work for dynamic objects. Figure 7.7(a) shows the Newport logo test object, and Fig. 7.7(b) shows the reconstructed hologram of the Newport logo at one of the wavelengths used ($\lambda_1 = 496.5$ nm). Figure 7.7(c) shows the wrapped phase, and Fig. 7.7(d) shows the unwrapped 3D surface profile. Figure 7.8 shows hierarchical phase measurements for the same object.

One important detail that must be considered when applying the two-wavelength technique is pixel matching. Recall from Eq. (4.6) that the pixel

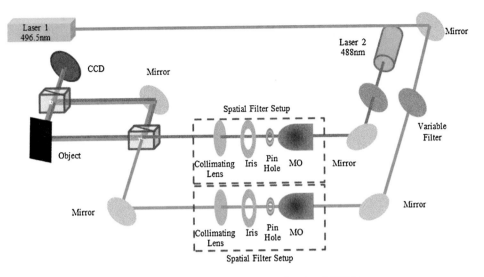

Figure 7.5 Shape measurement using MWDH.

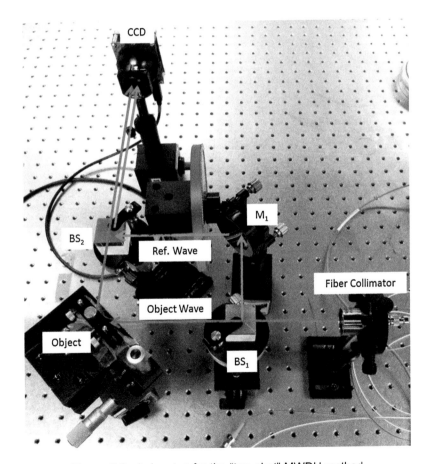

Figure 7.6 Lab setup for the "two-shot" MWDH method.

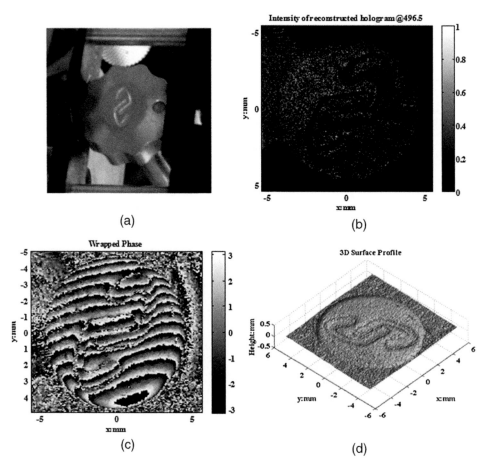

(a)   (b)

(c)   (d)

Figure 7.7 (a) Newport logo, (b) reconstructed hologram at $\lambda_1 = 496.5$ nm, and (c) wrapped phase and (d) unwrapped phase (or 3D surface profile). The two wavelengths used are $\lambda_1 = 496.5$ nm and $\lambda_2 = 488$ nm, and the synthetic wavelength is $\Lambda = 28.5$ μm.

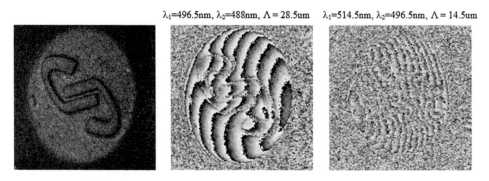

Figure 7.8 Hierarchical phase measurements for the same object.

resolution $\Delta\xi$ of each hologram is dependent on the fundamental recording wavelength (λ_1 or λ_2). In order for the reconstruction to be successful, the subtraction described by Eq. (7.17) must be performed on a pixel-by-pixel basis, in which the pixel sizes match (and are well aligned) between each hologram (i.e., $\Delta\xi_1 = \Delta\xi_2$). This can be accomplished by zero padding the holograms to alter the numerical resolution, according to the following procedure: One hologram is zero-padded prior to reconstruction such that its value of $\Delta\xi$ matches that of the second hologram. The second hologram is then either zero-padded after reconstruction, or the first hologram (which is now larger) is cropped, such that the total sizes of each image are again equal. If it is assumed that $\lambda_1 > \lambda_2$ then the degree of padding applied to both the λ_1 hologram prereconstruction and the λ_2 hologram postreconstruction is

$$padsize = \text{round}\left[\frac{N}{2}\left(\frac{\lambda_1}{\lambda_2} - 1\right)\right], \qquad (7.28)$$

where *padsize* is the number of zero elements to be added symmetrically to each edge (top, bottom, left, right) of the hologram matrix, rounded to the nearest integer value. It should be noted that rounding to the nearest integer value potentially introduces a quantization error, although this error is typically negligible in practice because the per-pixel error is approximately $\Delta\xi/2N$, where typically $N \sim 1000$. That is, the total quantization error due to the zero-padding method will not exceed one half of a pixel total over the full extent of the hologram. Stated alternatively, the lateral error in any single pixel is on the order of only $\sim 0.05\%$, which is typically negligible in practice. To summarize, the procedure is as follows, assuming that λ_1 is larger than λ_2:

- The hologram recorded using λ_1 must be padded prior to reconstruction;
- The hologram recorded using λ_2 must be padded after reconstruction;
- The pad size applied to each side of the hologram matrix is $\text{round}\left[\frac{N}{2}\left(\frac{\lambda_1}{\lambda_2} - 1\right)\right]$; and
- The overlapping holograms are subtracted pixel by pixel, with negligible error due to padding.

The MATLAB code in Table 7.1 shows an example of the MWDH two-shot reconstruction method, which reproduces images of the Newport logo similar to Figs. 7.7 and 7.8.

7.5 Multiwavelength Digital Holography with Spatial Heterodyning

The spatial-heterodyne technique is employed to capture both wavelength measurements in a single composite holographic exposure,[4,8] which is accomplished by introducing a different angular tilt to the λ_1 and λ_2 reference

Table 7.1   MATLAB code "Example1_MWDH_Topography2.m" performs two-shot MWDH topography reconstruction of the Newport logo object (see Figs. 7.7 and 7.8).

```
1    %This example performs MWDH phase reconstructions of
2    %the Newport logo holograms, with a recording/
3    %reconstruction distance of 0.39 meters.
4    %%Reconstruct the holograms
5    format compact
6    clear all
7    close all
8    d = .39;                          %Reconstruction distance in m
9    lambda1 = 496.5e-9;               %Wavelengths in m
10   lambda2 = 488.0e-9;
11   pixel_size = 6.7e-6;              %Lumenera pixel size
12   N = 1024;                         %Number of CCD pixels
13   SW = lambda1*lambda2/abs(lambda1-lambda2)     %Synthetic
14                                                 %wavelength.
15   %Pad size for pixel matching.
16   padsize = round(0.5*(lambda1/lambda2-1)*N);
17   %Load and pad the lambda1 hologram prior to
18   %reconstruction
19   S = load('Saved_Raw_holo1.mat');
20   hpad=padarray(S.h,[padsize padsize]);
21   h1 = myFresnel(hpad,d,lambda1,pixel_size);
22   clear S
23   %Load the lambda 2 hologram and pad after
24   %reconstruction
25   S = load('Saved_Raw_holo2.mat');
26   h2 = myFresnel(S.h,d,lambda2,pixel_size);
27   h2 = padarray(h2,[padsize padsize]);
28   clear S                          %Recover memory.
29   %%Display reconstructions and find the phase
30   %difference.
31   %Display one of the reconstructions (full field
32   %of view).
33   figure(1)
34   imagesc(abs(rot90(h1,2)).^.5)          %The square root
35                                          %increases apparent contrast
36   %logim(abs(rot90(h1,2)),2)             %Flip the reconstruction
37                                          %for viewing
38   colormap(gray)
39   axis square
40   %axis ([ 675 990 244 610])             %This crops to the area of
41                                          %interest.
42   %The phase difference can found by calling a function.
43   del_phi = myInterferogram(h1,h2);
44   %%Alternatively, find the phase difference manually.
45   %phi1 = angle(h1);
46   %phi2 = angle(h2);
47   %del_phi = phi1-phi2;
48   %%wrap 2pi if needed
49   %del_phi(find(phi1<phi2)) = ...
50   %del_phi(find(phi1<phi2))+2*pi;
51   %Display the phase difference image.
52   figure(2)
53   imagesc(rot90(del_phi,2))
54   %logim((rot90(del_phi,2)),1)           %Flip the reconstruction
```

(continued)

Table 7.1 (*Continued*)

```
55  colormap(gray)
56  axis square
57  %axis ([ 675 990 244 610] )              %View only the region of
58                                           %interest.
59  %Optionally, the phase image may be prefiltered.
60  %This may be necessary
61  %if the wrapped phase image is exceptionally noisy.
62  %However, this is not necessary for this example.
63  %figure;
64  %B = myDHIfilter(del_phi);
65  %imagesc(flipud(fliplr(B)))
66  %colormap(gray)
67  %axis square
68  %%axis ([ 675 990 244 610] )
69  %%Select/crop a smaller region of interest for phase
70  %unwrapping.
71  del_phi2 = del_phi(444:796,87:353);          %Region of interest.
72  %Optional plotting to visually verify the correct region
73  %of interest.
74  figure;
75  imagesc(del_phi2)
76  colormap(gray)
77  axis square
78  %%
79  %%%- - -Unwrapping using the 2D_SRNCP algorithm:
80  %http://www.ljmu.ac.uk/GERI/90225.htm
81  %Instructions:
82  %Install the Microsoft Windows SDK 7.1.
83  %mex -setup
84  %Follow instructions: type Y then 1 then Y.
85  %Call the 2D phase unwrapper from C language.
86  %To compile the C code: in MATLAB command window,
87  %you have to run
88  %mex Miguel_2D_unwrapper.cpp
89  %This file has to be in the same directory as the
90  %script to work.
91  WrappedPhase=del_phi2;              %Read the wrapped phase
92  mex Miguel_2D_unwrapper.cpp
93  %The wrapped phase should have the single
94  %(float in C) data type
95  WrappedPhase = single(WrappedPhase);
96  UnwrappedPhase = Miguel_2D_unwrapper(WrappedPhase);
97  UnwrappedPhase=double(UnwrappedPhase);
98  min_UnwrappedPhase=min(UnwrappedPhase(:));
99  surfl(UnwrappedPhase-min_UnwrappedPhase);
100 shading interp; colormap(gray);
101 title('UnFiltered Solution' );
102 size = 5;
103 unwph=UnwrappedPhase-min_UnwrappedPhase;
104 unwph_filter = medfilt2(unwph,[ size size] );
105 figure;
106 surfl(unwph_filter);shading interp; colormap(gray);
107 title('Filtered Solution' );
108 figure;
```

(*continued*)

Table 7.1 (*Continued*)

```
109  imagesc(unwph_filter)
110  colormap(gray)
111  %%Display the 3D surface with proper physical scales.
112  %Image pixel size
113  Feature_size = lambda1*d/(N*pixel_size)
114    theta = 45;                        %45-deg illumination in
115                                        %Mach-Zehnder configuration
116    height_factor = cosd(theta)*SW/(4*pi);         %Approx cos45
117                                           %for Mach-Zehnder
118  unwph2 = unwph_filter(:,:).*height_factor;         %Convert
119                                        %radians to meters.
120  %Create a new meshgrid for physical scaling.
121  x = 1:1:length(unwph2(1,:));
122  y = 1:1:length(unwph2(:,1));
123  %Multiply by a factor of 10^3 to convert meters to
124  %millimeters
125  [II,JJ] = meshgrid(x*Feature_size*10^3,...
126  y*Feature_size*10^3);
127  figure(3);
128  surfl(II,JJ,unwph2*10^3); shading interp;
129  colormap(gray);
130  xlabel('x (mm)')
131  ylabel('y (mm)')
132  zlabel('z (mm)')
133  xlim([ 0 8.3] )
134  ylim([ 0 10.2] )
135  view(45,30)
```

beams. These angular tilts in the spatial domain introduce linear phase shifts in the frequency domain of the recorded composite hologram. When reconstructed, the different phase shifts result in spatially separated object locations in the image that each correspond to their respective λ_1 and λ_2 recordings. One of these reconstructed objects may be cropped and digitally overlaid on the other to perform the required phase subtraction. A typical recording configuration using mutli-wavelength digital holography with the spatial heterodyning (MWDH-SH) method is shown in Fig. 7.9; an actual laboratory setup is shown in Fig. 7.10. Because the two holograms are recorded for each wavelength at the same time using spatial heterodyning, this technique needs only one CCD exposure (i.e., "one-shot").[8,9] This method is well suited for dynamic objects that change relatively quickly, albeit at a rate slower than the integration time of the CCD. Figure 7.11 shows the reconstructed Newport-logo test object. The reconstructed image resolution = 32 μm/pixel. Note that two separate reconstructions are required (λ_1 and λ_2) from the single hologram, although only one reconstruction is shown here.

In order to align the two phase images, a block-matching algorithm (BMA) is used. After cropping the two reconstructed holograms, it is necessary to slide one image (the reference image) over the other image (the target image) to produce the best correlation (minimum difference), as shown

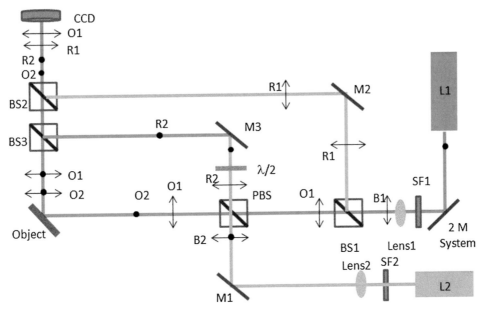

Figure 7.9 Shape measurement using MWDH-SH[8] with the following features: half-wave plate (λ/2), spatial filter (SF), periscope mirrors (2M), laser (L), beamsplitter (BS), polarized beamsplitter (PBS), mirror (M), laser beam 1 and 2 (B1, B2), object beam 1 and 2 (O1, O2), reference beam 1 and 2 (R1, R2).

in Fig. 7.12. Unfortunately, BMA algorithms can only match to within one half of a pixel; given the typically rapid variation in object phase, BMA matching will generally underperform the two-shot method. After aligning the images, the phase difference is calculated by phase subtraction similar to the two shot technique. The example shown in Fig. 7.13 features a synthetic wavelength $\Lambda \sim 150$ μm.

An alternative method of matching the two images introduces a phase "tilt" to either one of or both holograms during reconstruction, which causes lateral shifts in the position of each image. This process is typically referred to as introducing a phase mask $\Psi(m,n)$ during reconstruction, and it can generally take any form, although the most commonly used are tilt phases and lens phases. Proper selection of the phase mask (typically found via multiple iterations) can position one hologram reconstruction directly over the other, and phase subtraction may then be performed in a matter analogous to the "two-shot" method previously described, including appropriate resolution matching via zero padding. Example tilt and lens phases are given by Eqs. (7.29) and (7.30), respectively. The hologram matrix is simply multiplied by the phase mask Ψ prior to reconstruction:

$$\Psi(m,n) = \exp\left\{ -j\frac{2\pi}{\lambda} [(\sin \theta_x n\Delta x) + (\sin \theta_y m\Delta y)] \right\}, \qquad (7.29)$$

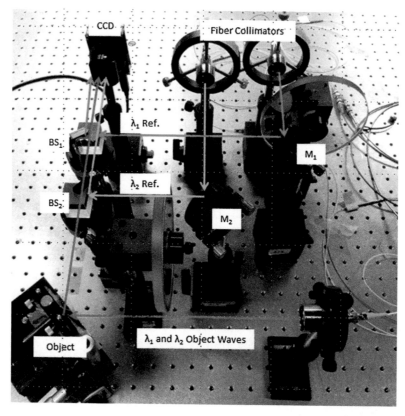

Figure 7.10   Lab setup for MWDH-SH using the Mach–Zehnder configuration.

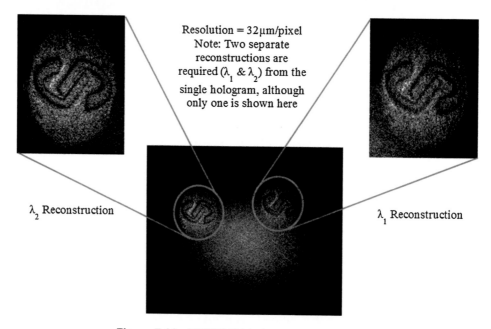

Resolution = 32 μm/pixel
Note: Two separate
reconstructions are
required (λ_1 & λ_2) from the
single hologram, although
only one is shown here

λ_2 Reconstruction

λ_1 Reconstruction

Figure 7.11   MWDH-SH hologram reconstruction.

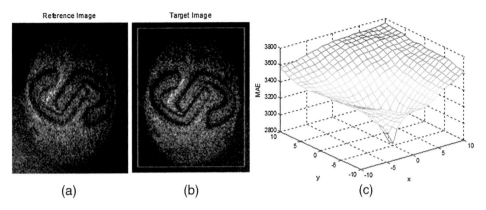

Figure 7.12 BMA slides (a) the reference image over (b) the target image to produce (c) correlation. This result is for a 10-pixel shift range, and the best correlation occurs at X_{shift}: 0, Y_{shift}: −4 pixels.

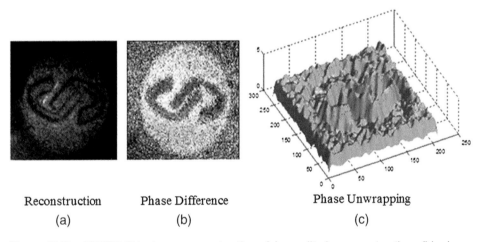

Reconstruction   Phase Difference   Phase Unwrapping
   (a)   (b)   (c)

Figure 7.13 MWDH-SH phase reconstruction: (a) amplitude reconstruction, (b) phase difference, and (c) phase unwrapping for $\Lambda \sim 150$ μm.

$$\Psi(m,n) = \exp\left\{-j\frac{\pi}{\lambda}\left[\frac{1}{d_i}\left(1 + \frac{d_o}{d_i}\right)(n^2\Delta x^2 + m^2\Delta y^2)\right]\right\}, \tag{7.30}$$

where (m,n) are discrete indices corresponding to the sampled (x,y) coordinates of the hologram matrix, and $\theta_{x,y}$ are the tilt angles. Although the phase mask method is typically more difficult to implement, requiring multiple iterations to arrive at the correct phase mask, it does not suffer from the inherent mismatch error of up to one-half pixel, as the BMA process does. However, the overlap accuracy will now depend upon the accuracy of the modeled phase mask $\Psi(m,n)$.

The MATLAB code in Table 7.2 provides an example of the MWDH-SH reconstruction method using a silicon-wafer object containing photoresist

Table 7.2 MATLAB code "BMA_Reconstructions1.m" is an example of the MWDH-SH reconstruction method using BMA matching for the silicon-wafer object containing photoresist bumps [shown in Fig. 7.15(c)].

```
1   %This function performs two-wavelength MWDH using the
2   %spatial heterodyne
3   %method, with reconstruction from a single composite
4   %hologram.
5   %The BMA shifting method is used to match images of two
6   %holograms.
7   %The object is a silicon wafer containing rows of
8   %photoresist bumps.
9   format compact
10  close all
11  clear all
12  %Load a single composite hologram
13  load Saved_Raw_holo1.mat
14  h = hraw1;
15  figure(1)
16  imagesc(abs(h))                       %Raw hologram
17  colormap(gray)
18  axis square
19  title ('Composite Hologram Recording')
20  %Reconstruction parameters
21  dx =6.7e-6;
22  d = 0.48;
23  lambda1 = 543.5e-9;%496.5e-9; %514.5e-9%488.0e-9;
24  lambda2 = 514.5e-9;
25  padsize = round(0.5*(lambda1/lambda2-1)*length(h));
26  %%Reconstruct for lambda1
27  %(PAD FIRST, THEN RECONSTRUCT)
28  hpad=padarray(h,[padsize padsize]);
29  %Pads in an array so that the correct pixels will
30  %overlap when subtracted from phase2.
31  [h1] = myFresnel(hpad,d,lambda1,dx);
32  figure(2)
33  logim(abs(h1),2)
34  phi1 = angle(h1);
35  title ('\lambda_1 (Top) Object in Focus')
36  %axis ([200 400 260 460])
37  %Top holo is in focus for lambda1.
38  h1crop = h1(260:460,200:400);
39  phi1crop = angle(h1crop);
40  figure(3)
41  logim(abs(h1crop),2)
42  %%Reconstruct for lambda2
43  %(RECONSTRUCT FIRST, THEN PAD).
44  [h2] = myFresnel(h,d,lambda2,dx,false);
45  h2pad=padarray(h2,[padsize padsize]);       %Pad for resizing
46                                              %to match phase1
47  figure(4)
48  logim(abs(h2pad),2)
49  phi2 = angle(h2pad);
50  %axis ([218 418 468 668])
51  %Bottom holo is in focus for lambda2.
52  title ('\lambda_2 (Bottom) Object in Focus')
53  h2crop = h2pad(468:668,218:418);
```

(continued)

Table 7.2 (*Continued*)

```
54  phi2crop = angle(h2crop);
55  figure(5)
56  logim(abs(h2crop),2)
57  %%Block matching algorithm (BMA)
58  ref = abs(h1crop);                    %First input(reference image)
59  out = abs(h2crop);                     %Second input image (target image)
60  max_shift = 15;                     %Maximum pixel shifting range for BMA
61  figure(3)
62  logim(ref,2);
63  title('Reference Image' );
64  figure(5)
65  logim(out,2)
66  mask = zeros(size(out));
67  mask(max_shift+1:end-max_shift,max_shift+1:...
68  end-max_shift)=1;
69  hold on
70  contour (mask, 1, 'r-' );
71  title('Target Image' );
72  target = out(max_shift+1:end-max_shift,...
73  max_shift+1:end-max_shift);
74  %%%%Start search%%%%
75  w = waitbar(0,' Please wait...' );
76  shx =[-max_shift: max_shift] ;
77  shy =[-max_shift: max_shift] ;
78  numx = length (shx);
79  numy = length (shy);
80  mae = zeros (numy, numx);
81  for idxx = 1: numx
82  for idxy = 1: numy
83  sty = max_shift + 1 + shy(idxy);
84  edy = sty + size (target, 1) - 1;
85  stx = max_shift + 1 + shx(idxx);
86  edx = stx + size (target, 2) - 1;
87  err = dif2(ref(sty:edy,stx:edx),target);
88  mae(idxy,idxx) = err.mae;
89  end
90  waitbar(idxx/numx,w)
91  end
92  close(w)
93  %Display the correlation
94  figure(6)
95  mesh(shx,shy,mae)
96  xlabel('x' )
97  ylabel('y' )
98  zlabel('MAE' )
99  title ('BMA Error' )
100 [min_mae, min_idx] = min(mae(:))
101 [min_idxy, min_idxx] = ind2sub(size(mae),min_idx);
102 bma_shx = shx (min_idxx)
103 bma_shy = shy (min_idxy)
104 %%After running BMA code, shift holo2 as needed
105 %to align with holo1.
106 %Shift the holo.
107 h2shift = circshift(abs(h2crop),[bma_shy bma_shx] );
```

(continued)

Table 7.2 (*Continued*)

```
108  %Shift the phase, too
109  phi2shift = circshift(phi2crop,[bma_shy bma_shx]);
110  %%Perform phase subtraction on the aligned images
111  del_phi = phi1crop-phi2shift;
112  %Wrap 2pi if needed
113  del_phi(find(phi1crop<phi2shift)) =...
114  del_phi(find(phi1crop<phi2shift))+2*pi;
115  [Ro,Co] =size(del_phi)
116  del_phi=del_phi(round(Ro/4):Ro-round(Ro/4),...
117  round(Co/4):Co-round(Co/4));
118  figure(7)
119  imagesc(del_phi)
120  colormap(gray)
121  axis square
122  title('Phase Reconstruction')
123  size = 3;
124  del_phi_filt = medfilt2(del_phi,[size size]);
125  figure(8)
126  imagesc(del_phi_filt)
127  colormap(gray)
128  axis square
129  title('Filtered Phase Reconstruction')
130  %%Phase unwraping using PUMA (if desired)(only
131  %works for 32-bit MATLAB).
132  %p=2;                              %Clique potential exponent.
133  %figure;
134  %[unwph,iter,erglist] = puma_ho(del_phi,p);
135  %%%
136  %figure;
137  %surfl(unwph);shading interp; colormap(gray);
138  %title('Puma solution');
139  %%
140  %%%- - -Unwrapping using the 2D_SRNCP algorithm:
141  %http://www.ljmu.ac.uk/GERI/90225.htm
142  %Instructions:
143  %Install the Microsoft Windows SDK 7.1.
144  %mex -setup
145  %Follow instructions: type Y then 1 then Y.
146  %Call the 2D phase unwrapper from C language.
147  %To compile the C code: in MATLAB command window, you
148  %have to run
149  %mex Miguel_2D_unwrapper.cpp
150  %This file has to be in the same directory as the
151  %script to work.
152  WrappedPhase=(del_phi_filt); %Read the wrapped phase
153  mex Miguel_2D_unwrapper.cpp
154  %The wrapped phase should have the single
155  %(float in C) data type
156  WrappedPhase = single(WrappedPhase);
157  UnwrappedPhase = Miguel_2D_unwrapper(WrappedPhase);
158  UnwrappedPhase=double(UnwrappedPhase);
159  min_UnwrappedPhase=min(UnwrappedPhase(:));
160  %mesh(UnwrappedPhase-min_UnwrappedPhase);
161  figure
162  surfl(UnwrappedPhase);shading interp;
```

(*continued*)

Table 7.2 (*Continued*)

```
163  colormap(gray);
164  grid on
165  title('2D Unwrapped Phase Using 2D-SRNCP Algorithm')
166  ylabel('y')
167  xlabel('x')
168  zlabel('\psi: (rad)')
169  %%
170  size = 5;
171  unwph_filter = medfilt2(UnwrappedPhase,[size size]);
172  figure;
173  surfl(unwph_filter);shading interp; colormap(gray);
174  title('Filtered Solution');
175  figure;
176  imagesc(unwph_filter)
177  colormap(gray)
178  %%
179  figure
180  H = fspecial('average');
181  Ihp = imfilter(unwph_filter,H);
182  %logim(Ihp)
183  surfl(Ihp);shading interp; colormap(gray);
184  title('Filtered Solution');
```

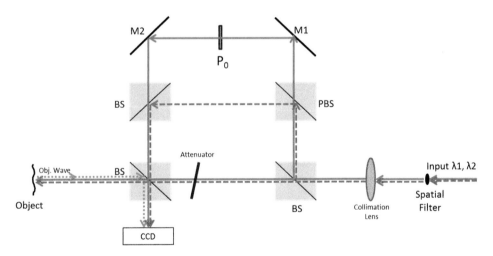

Figure 7.14 Practical lab setup (Michelson configuration) for macroscopic, spatial heterodyne MWDH using coaxial beams and a single spatial filter and collimation lens. The collimation lens should ideally be achromatic at the λ_1 and λ_2 wavelengths.

bumps. This example is interesting to examine because the phase reconstruction reveals residual phase rings that are not due to object curvature because the silicon wafer is known to be perfectly flat. Rather, these phase rings are due to a slight mismatch in collimation between the λ_1 and λ_2 beams, which causes circularly symmetric phase beating because at least one wavefront is not well collimated. This situation often arises in physical lab setups in which

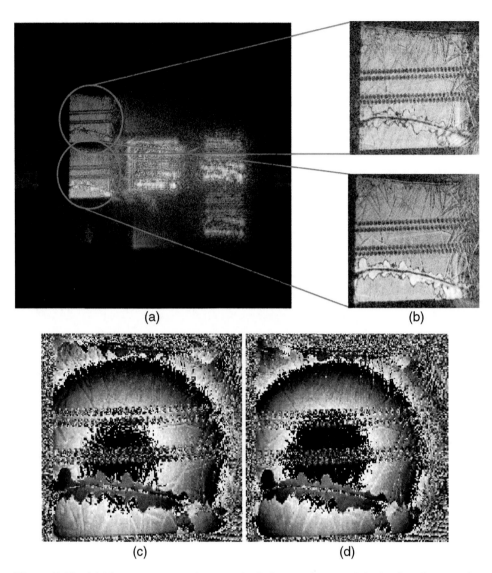

Figure 7.15 (a) The reconstructed composite hologram (at λ_1 only) of a flat silicon-wafer object, revealing that the object was recorded twice, with (b) close-up views of both the λ_1 (top) and λ_2 (bottom) reconstructions in focus. (c) The phase-difference image after BMA matching, and (d) the phase difference after overlapping the reconstructions using the phase mask $\Psi(m,n)$ of Eq. (7.29) (employing vertical/horizontal phase tilt) during reconstruction. Note the residual phase rings due to poor collimation of at least one of the reference beams.

both beams are coaxially aligned and filtered using the same pinhole prior to using a single collimation lens. Chromatic dispersion in the lens will prevent both wavelengths from being collimated simultaneously unless an achromatic lens is used. A practical example of such a setup is shown in Fig. 7.14, with the object measurements shown in Fig. 7.15.

Table 7.3 MATLAB code "Phase_Mask_Reconstructions.m" is an example that employs the MWDH-SH reconstruction method using the phase mask [see Fig. 7.15(d)].

```
1   %This function performs 2-wavelength MWDH using the
2   %spatial heterodyne
3   %method, with reconstruction from a single composite
4   %hologram.
5   %The phase mask method is used to center the images
6   %of two holograms prior to phase subtraction.
7   %The object is a silicon wafer containing rows of
8   %photoresist bumps.
9   clear all
10  close all
11  format compact
12  %Load the single hologram(composite of two holograms)
13  load Saved_Raw_holo1
14  h1 = hraw1;
15  h2 = hraw1;
16  dx =6.7e-6;
17  d = 0.48;
18  lambda1 = 543.5e-9;%496.5e-9;%514.5e-9;
19  lambda2 = 514.5e-9;%496.5e-9;%488.0e-9;
20  padsize = round(0.5*(lambda1/lambda2-1)*length(h1));
21  %First, pad h1 for pixel matching prior to
22  %reconstruction
23  h1 = padarray(h1,[ padsize padsize]);
24  %Introduce tilt phase directly into the myFresnel
25  %function as a phase mask.
26  %The magnitude of the horizontal and vertical tilt
27  %used in myTiltPhase for
28  %each reconstruction were determined by trial
29  %and error, although an
30  %iterative loop could be written to perform this
31  %action.
32  C1 = myFresnel(h1,d,lambda1,dx,false,...
33  myTiltPhase(size(h1),1.41,-1.10));
34  C2 = myFresnel(h2,d,lambda2,dx,false,...
35  myTiltPhase(size(h2),1.4,.1));
36  %Then pad the second hologram after reconstruction to
37  %be the same size as C1
38  C2 = padarray(C2,[ padsize padsize]);
39  %Visualize the shifted reconstructions
40  figure(1)
41  imagesc(abs(C1).^.5)
42  title('\lambda_1 Hologram Centered')
43  axis square
44  colormap gray
45  figure(2)
46  imagesc(abs(C2).^.5)
47  title('\lambda_2 Hologram Centered')
48  axis square
49  colormap gray
50  %Crop arrays to the region of interest
51  h1crop = C1(440:670,430:660);
52  h2crop = C2(440:670,430:660);
53  %Compute the phase difference
```

(continued)

Table 7.3 *(Continued)*

```
54  [ Ps,Pr] = myInterferogram(h1crop,h2crop);
55  %Visualize the reconstructed phase
56  figure(3)
57  imagesc(Ps)
58  colormap(gray)
59  axis square
```

The MATLAB code "Phase_Mask_Reconstructions.m" in Table 7.3 is an example of the MWDH-SH reconstruction method using the phase mask $\Psi(m,n)$ of Eq. (7.29) (employing vertical/horizontal phase tilt) during reconstruction for the silicon-wafer object shown in Fig. 7.15(d). Note that the required vertical/horizontal phase tilts were determined by trial and error for this example, although an iterative loop could be written to perform the same task.

7.6 Multiwavelength Digital Holographic Microscopy

This section presents an example of the multiwavelength digital holography technique using a microscopy setup similar to the one described in Chapter 4 (abbreviated as MWDHM). Figure 7.16(a) shows the MWDHM Michelson recording configuration using achromatic optics, which may be operated in either the "one-shot" or "two-shot" configuration. Figure 7.16(b) is a photograph of the object consisting of four bars of photoresist, each 50 μm wide, on a silicon-wafer substrate; Fig. 7.16(c) is the intensity reconstruction of the λ_1 hologram only; Fig. 7.16(d) shows the wrapped-phase difference between λ_1 and λ_2 reconstructions; Fig. 7.16(e) shows the unwrapped phase (via PUMA[10]) with the residual MO quadratic phase curvature; and Fig. 7.16(f) is the 3D topogram after removing the MO phase. The relevant reconstruction parameters are $d = 22.7$ cm, $\lambda_1 = 632.8$ nm, $\lambda_2 = 488.0$ nm, $\Lambda = 2.13$ μm, $\Delta x = 6.7$ μm, $N = 1024$, and $M = 2.75$.

The MATLAB code in Table 7.4 shows an example of the MWDHM method using the physical configuration of Fig. 7.16(a) and will reproduce the remaining images shown in Figs. 7.16(c)–7.16(f), as well as a few other figures relevant to the example. The last section of the code computes the volume displacement of the four bar-shaped features, which will be discussed in the next section. Another example is the MATLAB code "Microscopic_MWDHM.m" found on the CD-ROM.

7.7 Multiwavelength Digital Holographic Microscopy with Spatial Heterodyning

Table 7.5 provides a MATLAB example using the multiwavelength digital holography technique with the microscopy setup of Fig. 7.16(a), operating in the spatial heterodyne configuration (MWDHM-SH). The object is a set of

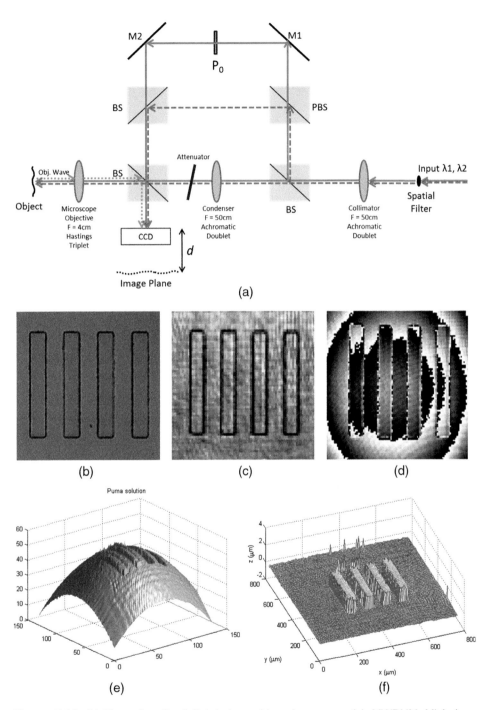

Figure 7.16 Multiwavelength digital holographic microscopy: (a) MWDHM Michelson recording configuration using achromatic optics; (b) photograph of the object, consisting of four bars of photoresist on a silicon wafer substrate; (c) amplitude reconstruction of the λ_1 hologram only; (d) wrapped-phase difference between λ_1 and λ_2 reconstructions; (e) unwrapped phase (via PUMA) that shows residual MO curvature; and (f) the flattened topogram after removing the MO phase.

Table 7.4 MATLAB code "Microscopic_MWDHM2.m" is an example that performs MWDHM on a test target [see Figs. 7.16(c)–7.16(f)].

```
1   %This example performs MWDH microscopy (MWDHM)
2   %using a test target
3   %consisting of four photoresist bars on a silicon-wafer
4   %substrate
5   format compact
6   close all
7   clear all
8   clc;
9   %Load both captured holograms (two-shot capture)
10  load Saved_Raw_holo1            %hraw1
11  load Saved_Raw_holo2            %hraw2
12  d = 0.227;                      %CCD to image distance (drec)
13  dx = 6.7e-6;                    %CCD pixel size
14  N = length(hraw1(:,1));
15  lambda1 = 632.8e-9;             %Wavelength in SI units
16  lambda2 = 488.0e-9;
17  SW = lambda1.*lambda2./abs(lambda1-lambda2)
18  padsize = round(0.5*(lambda1/lambda2-1)*N);
19  %%Reconstruct the holograms:
20  %Pad hologram 1 prior to reconstruction for
21  %pixel matching
22  hraw1pad=padarray(hraw1,[padsize padsize]);
23  [h1] = myFresnel(hraw1pad,d,lambda1,dx);
24  [h2] = myFresnel(hraw2,d,lambda2,dx);
25  %Pad hologram 2 after reconstruction for
26  %pixel matching
27  h2pad = padarray(h2,[padsize padsize]); %For lambda 2
28  %Display the lambda 1 intensity image
29  figure(1)
30  imagesc(abs(h1))
31  colormap(gray)
32  title('HeNe \lambda_1 = 632.8nm Reconstruction')
33  axis([650 825 225 400]);        %Region of interest
34  axis square
35  %%Calculate and display the phase difference
36  del_phi = myInterferogram(h1,h2pad);
37  figure(2)
38  imagesc(del_phi)                %Flip the reconstruction
39                                  %because it will be upside down
40  colormap(gray)
41  %axis([650 825 225 400]);       %Display region of interest
42  title('Phase Subtraction Image for \Lambda = 2.13\mum')
43  axis square
44  %Crop del_phi to the region of interest
45  del_phi2 = del_phi(220:400,650:830);
46  figure(3)
47  imagesc(del_phi2)
48  axis image
49  colormap gray
50  title({'Phase Subtraction Image',...
51  'for \Lambda = 2.13\mum'})
52  %%
53  %%%-Unwrapping using the 2D_SRNCP algorithm:
54  %http://www.ljmu.ac.uk/GERI/90225.htm
```

(continued)

Table 7.4 *(Continued)*

```
55  %Instructions:
56  %Install the Microsoft Windows SDK 7.1.
57  %mex -setup
58  %Follow instructions: type Y then 1 then Y.
59  %Call the 2D phase unwrapper from C language.
60  %To compile the C code: in MATLAB command window,
61  %you have to run
62  %mex Miguel_2D_unwrapper.cpp
63  %This file has to be in the same directory as the
64  %script to work.
65  WrappedPhase=del_phi2;                    %Read the wrapped phase
66  mex Miguel_2D_unwrapper.cpp
67  %The wrapped phase should have the single
68  %(float in C) data type
69  WrappedPhase = single(WrappedPhase);
70  unwph = Miguel_2D_unwrapper(WrappedPhase);
71  unwph=double(unwph);
72  unwph=unwph(30:150,30:150);
73  surfl(unwph);shading interp; colormap(gray);
74  title('UnFiltered Solution');
75  size = 5;
76  Bias=min(unwph(:));
77  unwph= medfilt2(unwph,[size size])-Bias;
78  figure;
79  surfl(unwph);shading interp; colormap(gray);
80  title('Filtered Solution');
81  %%Flatten the unwrapped phase synthetically with a
82  %reference surface.
83  %Correct the quadratic phase first by introducing a
84  %reference surface.
85  x = 1:1:length(unwph(1,:));
86  y = 1:1:length(unwph(:,1));
87  [XX,YY] = meshgrid(x,y);                   %Create meshgrid for
88                                             %quadratic surface
89  %Parameters a, b, and c were determined iteratively
90  %and manually
91  a = 0.0054;%.0054;                         %x slope
92  b = 0.0054;                                %y slope
93  c = 43.1%52.6;
94  xshift = 61.1;%65.2;
95  yshift = 65.9%65.1;
96  %Calculate the quadratic phase surface
97  z = -(a*(XX-xshift).^2 + b*(YY-yshift).^2) + c;
98  unwph2 = unwph-z;                          %Subtract the quadratic
99                                             %curvature from the surface.
100 %Any remaining deviations from flat are due to
101 %higher-order aberrations.
102 %%Display the reconstructed surface and
103 %quadratic correction.
104 figure(5);
105 surfl(unwph);shading interp; colormap(gray);
106 hold on
107 h = surf(XX,YY,z,'FaceAlpha',0.4);
108 shading interp;                            %colormap(gray)
109 set(h,'FaceLighting','phong','FaceColor','red',...
```

(continued)

Table 7.4 (*Continued*)

```
110  'AmbientStrength',0.7)
111  light('Position',[40 40 500],'Style','infinite');
112  title('Quadratic Correction');
113  view([-30 30])
114  hold off
115  xlabel('x')
116  ylabel('y')
117  unwph2=unwph2(5:end-5,5:end-5);
118  figure(6);
119  surfl(unwph2);shading interp; colormap(gray);
120  title('Flattened Surface');
121  %save unwph_flat.mat unwph2                %Save the flattened
122                                             %surface
123  %%
124  %To correctly scale the hologram slice, the
125  %magnified pixel size must be
126  %known, meaning the magnification factor
127  %must be known.
128  %M may be calculated or measured (in this
129  %case, measured using a calibrated object)
130  M = 2.75; %Magnification factor (geometric imaging)
131  %Magnified resolution
132  Image_pixel_size = (lambda1*d/((N+2*padsize)*dx))./M
133  theta = 0;                        %Michelson configuration
134  height_factor = cosd(theta)*SW/(4*pi);          %Approx. cos45
135                                                  %for Mach-Zehnder
136  %unwph3 = unwph_filter(:,:).*height_factor;
137  %Use filter result, if desired.
138  unwph3 = unwph2(:,:).*height_factor;
139  %Fix unwrapping error, if known.
140  %Sometimes, if the synthetic wavelength is near the
141  %height of the object,
142  %there will be a loss of pi (if the object is
143  %greater than 1/2 Lambda but
144  %less than 1 Lambda), and this needs to be corrected.
145  %Unwrapping errors can be detected via hierarchical
146  %phase unwrapping using multiple measurements,
147  %or by using a priori knowledge (as in this case).
148  unwph3(find(unwph3>.18e-6))=...
149  unwph3(find(unwph3>.18e-6))+.5*SW;
150  unwph3(find(unwph3<-.25e-6))=...
151  unwph3(find(unwph3<-.25e-6))+1.*SW;
152  size = 5;
153  unwph4= medfilt2(unwph3,[size size]);
154  x = 1:1:length(unwph4(1,:));
155  y = 1:1:length(unwph4(:,1));
156  [XX,YY] = meshgrid(x,y);                %Create meshgrid for
157                                          %quadratic surface
158  figure(7)
159  mesh(XX.*Image_pixel_size.*1e6,YY.*...
160  Image_pixel_size.*1e6,(unwph4).*1e6);
161  xlabel('x (\mum)')
162  ylabel('y (\mum)')
163  zlabel('z (\mum)')
164  view([-20 60])
```

Table 7.5 MATLAB code "Microscopic_MWDHM_SH.m" is an example of MWDH spatial heterodyne microscopy (MWDHM_SH) using a test target [see Figs. 7.17(a)–(d)].

```
1   %This example performs MWDH spatial heterodyne
2   %microscopy (MWDHM)
3   %using a test target consisting of four photoresist
4   %bars on a silicon-wafer substrate.
5   format compact
6   clear all
7   close all
8   load Saved_Raw_holo1.mat
9   h = hraw1;
10  %Reconstruction parameters
11  d = 0.23;                %CCD-to-image distance (drec) for M = 2.7
12  dx = 6.7e-6;                 %CCD pixel size
13  lambda1 = 632.8e-9;          %Wavelength in SI units
14  lambda2 = 488.0e-9;
15  N = length(hraw1(:,1));
16  SW = lambda1.*lambda2./abs(lambda1-lambda2);   %Synthetic
17                                                 %wavelength
18  padsize = round(0.5*(lambda1/lambda2-1)*N);
19  figure(1)
20  imagesc(abs(h))              %Raw hologram
21  colormap(gray)
22  axis square
23  title('Composite Hologram Recording')
24  %%Reconstruct for lambda 1 (PAD FIRST,
25  %THEN RECONSTRUCT)
26  hpad=padarray(h,[padsize padsize]);
27  %Pads array so the correct pixels will overlap when
28  %subtracted from phase 2
29  [h1] = myFresnel(hpad,d,lambda1,dx,false);
30  figure(2)
31  imagesc(abs(h1));
32  phi1 = angle(h1);
33  %axis ([1000 1150 600 750])    %Region of interest
34  title('\lambda_1 Reconstruction')
35  axis square
36  %Crop to the region of interest
37  h1crop = h1(600:750,1000:1150);
38  phi1crop = angle(h1crop);    %Phase angle
39  figure(3)
40  logim(abs(h1crop),2)
41  title('Cropped \lambda_1 Reconstruction')
42  %%Reconstruct for lambda 2 (RECONSTRUCT FIRST,
43  %THEN PAD)
44  [h2] = myFresnel(h,d,lambda2,dx,false);
45  h2pad=padarray(h2,[padsize padsize]);    %Pad for resizing
46                                           %to match phase 1
47  figure(4)
48  imagesc(abs(h2pad))
49  phi2 = angle(h2pad);
50  %axis ([900 1050 300 475]) %Region of interest
51  title(' \lambda_2 Reconstruction')
52  axis square
53  h2crop = h2pad(315:465,920:1070); %Region of interest
```

(continued)

Table 7.5   (*Continued*)

```
54  phi2crop = angle(h2crop);      %Phase angle
55  figure(5)
56  logim(abs(h2crop),2)
57  title('Cropped \lambda_2 Reconstruction')
58  %%Block-matching algorithm
59  ref = abs(h1crop);             %First input(reference image)
60  out = abs(h2crop);
61  max_shift = 10;
62  figure(6)
63  logim(ref,2);
64  title('Reference Image');
65  figure(7)
66  logim(out,2)
67  mask = zeros(size(out));
68  mask(max_shift+1:end-max_shift,...
69  max_shift+1:end-max_shift)=1;
70  hold on
71  contour(mask, 1, 'r-');
72  title('Target Image');
73  target = out(max_shift+1:end-max_shift,...
74  max_shift+1:end-max_shift);
75  %%%%Start search%%%%
76  w = waitbar(0,'Please wait...');
77  shx =[-max_shift: max_shift];
78  shy =[-max_shift: max_shift];
79  numx = length(shx);
80  numy = length(shy);
81  mae = zeros(numy, numx);
82  for idxx = 1: numx
83  for idxy = 1: numy
84  sty = max_shift + 1 + shy(idxy);
85  edy = sty + size(target, 1) - 1;
86  stx = max_shift + 1 + shx(idxx);
87  edx = stx + size(target, 2) - 1;
88  err = dif2(ref(sty:edy, stx:edx), target);
89  mae(idxy,idxx) = err.mae;
90  end
91  waitbar(idxx/numx,w)
92  end
93  close(w)
94  figure(8)
95  mesh(shx,shy,mae)
96  xlabel('x')
97  ylabel('y')
98  zlabel('MAE')
99  [min_mae, min_idx] = min(mae(:))
100 [min_idxy, min_idxx] = ind2sub(size(mae),min_idx);
101 bma_shx = shx(min_idxx)
102 bma_shy = shy(min_idxy)
103 %%After running the BMA code, additional shifting
104 %may be needed.
105 %Because the images are noisy, the correlation is
106 %poor, so shift hologram 2 as needed to align with
107 %hologram 1 manually.
```

(*continued*)

Table 7.5 (*Continued*)

```
108  bma_shy = 0;
109  bma_shx = 2;
110  %Shift the hologram
111  h2shift = circshift(abs(h2crop),[bma_shy bma_shx]);
112  figure(9)
113  logim(h2shift,2)
114  %Shift its phase, too
115  phi2shift = circshift(phi2crop,[bma_shy bma_shx]);
116  %%Perform phase subtraction on the aligned images
117  del_phi = phi1crop-phi2shift;
118  %Wrap 2pi, if needed
119  del_phi(find(phi1crop<phi2shift)) =...
120  del_phi(find(phi1crop<phi2shift))+2*pi;
121  figure(10)
122  %Flip the reconstruction because it will be
123  %upside down.
124  %logim(abs(rot90(del_phi,2)),1)
125  %logim(abs(del_phi),1)
126  imagesc(del_phi)
127  colormap(gray)
128  axis square
129  title({ 'Phase Subtraction Image' ,...
130  '(via Spatial Heterodyne)'})
131  %%Phase unwrapping using PUMA
132  %%only works in 32-bit MATLAB.
133  %
134  %p=2;                          %Clique potential exponent.
135  %figure;
136  %[unwph,iter,erglist] = puma_ho(del_phi,p);
137  %%save unwph_1shot.mat unwph
138  %%Plot 3D topogram
139  load unwph_1shot.mat
140  figure(11);
141  surfl(unwph);shading interp; colormap(gray);
142  title('Puma solution' );
143  %%Flatten the unwrapped phase synthetically
144  %with a %reference surface.
145  %Correct the quadratic phase first by introducing a
146  %reference surface.
147  x = 1:1:length(unwph(1,:));
148  y = 1:1:length(unwph(:,1));
149  [XX,YY] = meshgrid(x,y);          %Create meshgrid
150                                    %for quadratic surface.
151  %Parameters a, b, and c were determined iteratively
152  %and manually.
153  a =. 0057;                %x slope
154  b = a;                    %y slope
155  c = 92;
156  xshift = 66;
157  yshift = 82.2;
158  %Calculate the quadratic phase surface
159  z = -(a*(XX-xshift).^2 + b*(YY-yshift).^2) + c;
160  unwph2 = unwph-z;          %Subtract the quadratic
161                             %curvature from the surface.
```

(*continued*)

Table 7.5 (*Continued*)

```
162  %Any remaining deviations from flat are due to
163  %higher-order aberrations.
164  %Display the reconstructed surface and quadratic
165  %correction.
166  figure(12);
167  surfl(unwph);shading interp; colormap(gray);
168  hold on
169  h = surf(XX,YY,z,'FaceAlpha',0.4); shading interp;
170  %colormap(gray)
171  set(h,'FaceLighting','phong','FaceColor','red',...
172  'AmbientStrength',0.7)
173  light('Position',[40 40 500],'Style','infinite');
174  title('Quadratic Correction');
175  view([-30 30])
176  hold off
177  xlabel('x')
178  ylabel('y')
179  %Fix unwrapping error, if known.
180  %Sometimes, if the synthetic wavelength is near the
181  %height of the object, there will be a loss of pi
182  %(if the object is greater than 1/2 Lambda but
183  %less than 1 Lambda), and this needs to be
184  %corrected.
185  %Unwrapping errors can be detected via hierarchical
186  %phase unwrapping using
187  %multiple measurements or by using a priori
188  %knowledge (as in this case).
189  unwph3 = unwph2(20:120,20:120);      %Region of interest
190  bias = mean2(unwph3);          %Correct/remove noise bias
191  unwph3(find(unwph3<-0.5))=...
192  unwph3(find(unwph3<-0.5))+2*pi;
193  unwph3(find(unwph3>1.5))=...
194  unwph3(find(unwph3>1.5))+2*pi;
195  unwph3 = unwph3-bias;
196  %Lowpass filter the noisy reconstruction
197  filtersize = 5;
198  unwph3 = medfilt2(unwph3,[filtersize filtersize]);
199  figure(13);
200  %surfl(unwph3);shading interp; colormap(gray);
201  mesh(unwph3)
202  title('Unscaled Surface Topography');
203  xlabel('x (pixels)')
204  ylabel('y (pixels)')
205  zlabel('z (Radians of \Lambda)')
206  %Save the flattened surface.
207  %save unwph_flat.mat unwph2
208  %%Plot the topogram using correct physical scales.
209  M = 2.75; %Magnification factor (geometric imaging)
210  Image_pixel_size = (lambda1*d/((N+2*padsize)*dx))./M
211  %Magnified resolution
212  theta = 0;                %Michelson configuration.
213  %Approx. cos45 for Mach-Zehnder.
214  height_factor = cosd(theta)*SW/(4*pi);
215  unwph4 = unwph3(:,:).*height_factor;
```

(*continued*)

Table 7.5 *(Continued)*

```
216  %Need a new meshgrid for the region of interest
217  x = 1:1:length(unwph4(1,:));
218  y = 1:1:length(unwph4(:,1));
219  %Create meshgrid for a quadratic surface
220  [XX,YY] = meshgrid(x,y);
221  figure(14)
222  mesh(XX.*Image_pixel_size.*1e6,YY.*...
223  Image_pixel_size.*1e6,(unwph4).*1e6);
224  %surfl(XX.*cal_pixel_size.*1e6,YY.*...
225  %Image_pixel_size.*1e6,(unwph3).*1e6);
226  %shading interp; colormap(gray);
227  xlabel('x (\mum)')
228  ylabel('y (\mum)')
229  zlabel('z (\mum)')
230  title('Corrected MWDHM-SH Surface Topography')
231  view([-20 60])
232  %%Volume calculations for microscopic features.
233  %Carefully adjust the height of the reference flat
234  %surface to calculate the correct volume.
235  a = 0;                    %x slope
236  b = 0;                    %y slope
237  c = 0.07;                 %Vertical height (z)
238  xshift = 65.2;
239  yshift = 65.1;
240  %Quadratic phase
241  z = -(a*(XX-xshift).^2 + b*(YY-yshift).^2) + c;
242  z_scaled = z.*height_factor;
243  unwph_scaled = unwph4;    %Already multiplied by the
244                            %height factor
245  figure(9);
246  surfl(unwph_scaled);shading interp; colormap(gray);
247  hold on
248  h = surf(XX,YY,z_scaled,'FaceAlpha',0.4);
249  shading interp; %colormap(gray)
250  set(h,'FaceLighting','phong','FaceColor','red',...
251  'AmbientStrength',0.7)
252  light('Position',[40 40 500],'Style','infinite');
253  title('Volume Calculation');
254  view([-20 60])
255  hold off
256  xlabel('x (pixels)')
257  ylabel('y (pixels)')
258  zlabel('z (m)')
259  %Find the volume in pixel-by-pixel-by-meters
260  Vol_unscaled = sum(sum(unwph_scaled-z_scaled));
261  %Find the volume in cubic meters, then convert to
262  %cubic microns
263  Vol_scaled = Vol_unscaled.*...
264  (Image_pixel_size.^2).*(1e6)^3
265  %The last term.*(1e-6)^3 converts the volume to
266  %cubic microns
267  Analytic_Vol = 3.*(290.8e-6.*...
268  73.4e-6.*1.33e-6).*(1e6)^3
```

three rectangular photoresist bars, each 75 μm wide, on a silicon wafer. In this case, the object is simultaneously illuminated by two wavelengths at normal incidence, and only a single composite hologram is recorded by the CCD (i.e., "one-shot"). The single hologram is reconstructed twice, one at each fundamental wavelength, and the block-match algorithm is used to alight the images prior to phase subtraction. The remaining steps are similar to the previous example, including a volume-displacement calculation.

Figure 7.17(a) shows the intensity reconstruction of the λ_1 hologram only (with the region of interest circled), Fig. 7.17(b) shows the wrapped-phase difference between the λ_1 and λ_2 reconstructions after block matching and phase subtraction, Fig. 7.17(c) shows the unwrapped phase (via PUMA) with

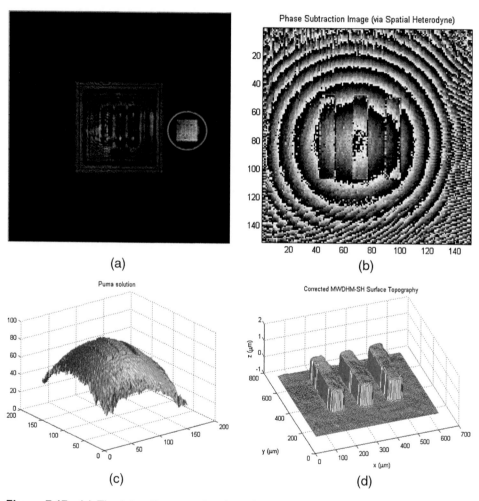

Figure 7.17 (a) The intensity reconstruction of the λ_1 hologram only, with the region of interest circled; (b) the wrapped-phase difference between λ_1 and λ_2 reconstructions after block matching and phase subtraction; (c) the unwrapped phase (via PUMA) with the residual MO quadratic phase curvature; and (d) the 3D topogram after removal of the MO phase and correction of phase errors.

the residual MO quadratic phase curvature, and Fig. 7.17(d) is the 3D topogram after removal of the MO phase and correction of phase errors. As previously discussed, the phase errors may be identified and corrected via multiple measurements using hierarchical phase unwrapping or by using *a priori* knowledge of the object (as in this case). The relevant reconstruction parameters are $d = 23$ cm, $\lambda_1 = 632.8$ nm, $\lambda_2 = 488.0$ nm, $\Lambda = 2.13$ μm, $\Delta x = 6.7$ μm, $N = 1024$, and $M = 2.75$.

7.8 Holographic Volume-Displacement Calculations via Multiwavelength Digital Holography

Multiwavelength digital holography is also applied to calculate the volume displacement of various topographic surface features. To accurately measure the volume displacement of macroscopic features, long synthetic wavelengths up to several millimeters are generated using tunable IR laser sources.

This section extends the applicability of MWDH to measure the surface topography on the scale of several millimeters using very long synthetic wavelengths with the intent of calculating the total volume displacement of various surface features. Additionally, 3D surface maps and 2D contour plots of topographic features can be generated from MWDH data. Note that other volumetric calculations based on moiré topography are also used (see Dirckx and Decraemer[11] and Xenofos and Jones[12]).

As previously discussed, the 2D phase map generated by two-wavelength phase subtraction yields surface topography with longitudinal feature resolution roughly on the order of Λ, which are viewed as fringe contours of constant elevation distributed across the object surface. Thus, proper choice of λ_1 and λ_2, such that $\lambda_1 \sim \lambda_2$, will yield very long synthetic wavelengths, as illustrated in Fig. 7.18.

The amount of synthetic phase accumulation is proportional to the object-surface feature height and the illumination angle θ, as shown in Fig. 7.4, which is typically either 0 deg or 45 deg, depending upon implementation of either Michelson or Mach–Zehnder recording geometries, respectively. Thus, the 2D phase map of the surface may be translated to the true object height z_{true} by using Eqs. (7.20) and (7.21). The digital interferogram resulting from phase subtraction is a 2D map of the wrapped phase, exhibiting modulo 2π fringe spacing of the synthetic wavelength Λ, which must be unwrapped to yield the absolute synthetic phase.

As λ_1 approaches λ_2, the synthetic wavelength Λ becomes infinite (see Fig. 7.18). However, in practice, λ_1 and λ_2 cannot be made equal due to various sources of wavelength error, including spectral broadening, wavelength drift, and mode competition. Generating the highly stable yet subtly different wavelengths required for such long synthetic wavelengths is thus a key challenge. Previous work has demonstrated the applicability of using

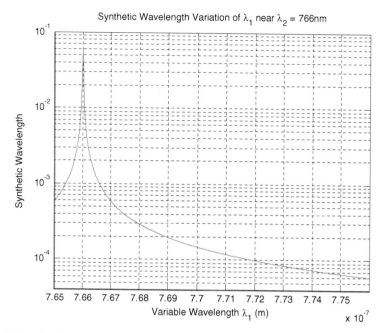

Figure 7.18 Synthetic wavelength as a function of the variable wavelength λ_1, with $\lambda_2 = 766$ nm.

Fabry–Pérot étalons to perform mode selection/stabilization at the laser output.[13] For this work, however, two semiconductor lasers are used: λ_2, fixed at 766.00 nm, and λ_1, tunable from 764.00–781.00 nm. The spectral accuracy, stability, and repeatability of both lasers have been characterized via spectrometer to reveal an expected error in λ_1 and λ_2 of approximately ± 0.0085 nm and ± 0.0092 nm, respectively.

To analyze this wavelength-selection error, consider that each wavelength is generated by a separate laser source; therefore, λ_1 and λ_2 are independent variables with zero covariance. The normalized covariance of λ_1 and λ_2 was experimentally verified to be approximately zero (i.e., less than 10^{-5}), as determined by 50 spectrometer measurements. In this case, the expected error in Λ due to wavelength selection can be determined by the well-known error propagation relationship

$$\sigma_\Lambda^2 = \left(\frac{\partial \Lambda}{\partial \lambda_1}\right)^2 \sigma_{\lambda_1}^2 + \left(\frac{\partial \Lambda}{\partial \lambda_2}\right)^2 \sigma_{\lambda_2}^2, \tag{7.31}$$

where σ_Λ is the expected error in Λ, and $\sigma_{\lambda_{1,2}}$ is the error in $\lambda_{1,2}$.[14] In this case,

$$\frac{\partial \Lambda}{\partial \lambda_1} = \frac{\lambda_2(\lambda_1 - \lambda_2) - \lambda_1\lambda_2}{(\lambda_1 - \lambda_2)^2}, \tag{7.32}$$

and

$$\frac{\partial \Lambda}{\partial \lambda_2} = \frac{\lambda_1(\lambda_1 - \lambda_2) + \lambda_1 \lambda_2}{(\lambda_1 - \lambda_2)^2}. \tag{7.33}$$

Substituting Eqs. (7.32) and (7.33) into Eq. (7.31) yields

$$\sigma_\Lambda^2 = \left(\frac{-\lambda_2^2}{(\lambda_1 - \lambda_2)^2}\right)^2 \sigma_{\lambda_1}^2 + \left(\frac{\lambda_1^2}{(\lambda_1 - \lambda_2)^2}\right)^2 \sigma_{\lambda_2}^2 = \left(-\Lambda^2 \frac{\sigma_{\lambda_1}}{\lambda_1^2}\right)^2 + \left(\Lambda^2 \frac{\sigma_{\lambda_2}}{\lambda_2^2}\right)^2, \tag{7.34}$$

where the error is found to increase quadratically with Λ, given by

$$\sigma_\Lambda = \Lambda^2 \sqrt{\left(\frac{\sigma_{\lambda_1}}{\lambda_1^2}\right)^2 + \left(\frac{\sigma_{\lambda_2}}{\lambda_2^2}\right)^2}. \tag{7.35}$$

This wavelength-selection error can lead to significant uncertainty in the synthetic wavelength as λ_1 approaches λ_2, as shown in Fig. 7.19. Thus, for short synthetic wavelengths, any single topographic measurement can be assumed to have reasonably high accuracy, limited primarily by shot and coherence noise.[15] However, wavelength selection error quickly begins to dominate at long synthetic wavelengths. Note that the percent error, which is proportional to σ_Λ / Λ, increases linearly with Λ. The measured λ_1 and λ_2 error distributions are approximately Gaussian; therefore, multiple measurements of the same object may be averaged to yield a more accurate result. For this example, multiple measurements at different Λ values within the region of $\sim 10\%$ or less error were used to compute the mean depth and volume displacement for various sample surfaces.

Volume-displacement calculations can be readily determined via holographic topography by first calculating the unwrapped/scaled 3D topographic

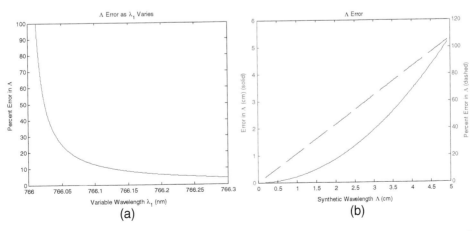

Figure 7.19 Error in Λ as a function of (a) λ_1 and (b) Λ for the measured values of $\sigma_{\lambda_1} = \pm 0.0085$ nm and $\sigma_{\lambda_2} = \pm 0.0092$ nm.[16]

map, as previously described, and then defining a reference surface bounding both the lateral extent and either the upper or lower surface of the desired volume. The unwrapped phase image is then numerically integrated over this lateral extent and subtracted from the reference volume. The difference yields the volume displacement of interest, which is given by

$$volume = \left| \int_A \phi_\Lambda dA \pm \int_A \rho dS \right|, \tag{7.36}$$

where A denotes the laterally bounded surface, ϕ_Λ is the unwrapped/scaled synthetic wavelength phase image (i.e., topogram), and ρ is the reference surface.

The sign of the second integral in Eq. (7.36) is determined by the placement of the reference surface either above or below the ϕ_Λ surface. This process is simulated in Figs. 7.20(a) and 7.20(b) using a tilted, asymmetric Gaussian surface. The unwrapped-phase image can also be used to generate a contour map describing the surface, either before or after numerical flattening, which is of interest in several practical applications.

In practice, the reconstructed surface is often tilted, as shown in Fig. 7.20(a), because the longitudinal axis (z axis) of the hologram surface is defined by the CCD plane normal. Therefore, if the tilt angle between the surface normal of the sample and the z axis is larger than a few degrees, then numerical flattening can help generate more-intuitive contour maps, although the volume calculation remains unaffected. Figure 7.20(c) shows a contour map of the tilted surface, and Fig. 7.20(d) shows a contour map determined from Fig. 7.20(c) after numerical flattening, i.e., reducing the average "bias" incline to zero.

For example, a series of dents in the surface of an aluminum plate is characterized via long-synthetic-wavelength topography, and the volume displacement is calculated, using a variable ($\lambda_1 = 765$–781 nm) and fixed IR source ($\lambda_2 = 766.00$ nm). A Lumenera (model LU120M) camera with 1024×1024 pixels and a 6.7-μm pixel size is used to record the holograms. Using the modified Michelson configuration shown in Fig. 7.4, two holograms of each sample are captured, one at each wavelength (λ_1, λ_2), and the MWDH reconstruction process is performed as previously described for a given synthetic wavelength. The modified Michelson configuration shown in Fig. 7.4(b) is used to illuminate the target at normal incidence, which eliminates the "shadow effect" caused by the 45-deg illumination angle in the Mach–Zehnder configuration [Fig. 7.4(a)], possibly causing parts of the sample to be poorly illuminated. Illumination at normal incidence also eliminates the need to correct the image perspective by $1/\cos\theta$ along the horizontal axis, as required by the Mach–Zehnder configuration.

Figures 7.21(a)–7.21(h) illustrate the MWDH reconstruction process for one of the aluminum samples, including the volume-displacement calculation for the depressed portion of the dent. The mean of eight measurements,

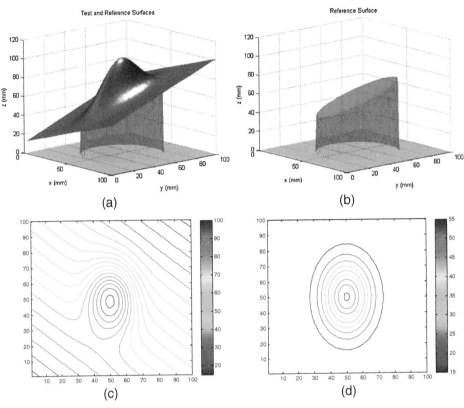

Figure 7.20 Illustration of holographic volume calculation: (a) the unwrapped phase surface (e.g., an asymmetric Gaussian surface) with the region of integration bounding the area of interest; (b) the reference volume, which is then subtracted from the volume found in (a) to yield only the volume of the Gaussian cap; (c) contour map of the tilted surface; and (d) contour map determined from (c) after numerical flattening, i.e., reducing the average "bias" incline to zero.

spanning $\Lambda = 1.869$ mm to $\Lambda = 7.930$ mm, yields a volume of 37.31 mm^3 ± 0.95 mm^3. The holographically measured mean depth of the dent is 1.63 mm ± 0.05 mm, which compares favorably to the depth measurement performed via caliper, which is 1.57 mm ± 0.13 mm. Note that the relatively large error of the caliper measurement is due to performing repeated measurements on the sample, which exhibits a rather pitted and rough surface, reducing the absolute repeatability of each measurement. Furthermore, the feature depth is measured from the planar surface of the aluminum sample, which is below the "ridge" of ejected material surrounding the dent, as illustrated in Fig. 7.21(g). Because the aluminum dent is approximately spherical, it is possible to compare the measured volume to the volume analytically calculated for a spherical cap of equal size. Assuming a mean caliper-measured depth and radius of 1.57 mm and 3.80 mm, respectively, the volume of the spherical cap is 37.63 mm^3. Although this comparison is not expected to be exact (because the aluminum surface is

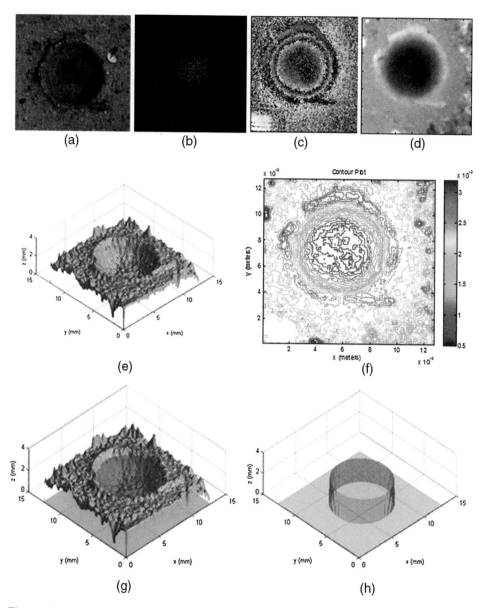

Figure 7.21 Illustration of the MWDH volume calculation process for $\Lambda = 1.869$ mm: (a) photograph of the dent in an aluminum test surface, (b) one of the reconstructed holograms, (c) the wrapped 2D phase map after phase subtraction, (d) the unwrapped 2D phase map via the PUMA algorithm, (e) distance-scaled 3D topographic map, (f) contour map illustrating topography, (g) 3D topographic map including the reference surface (red circular area), and (h) the reference volume without topographic map.

rough), it does reveal that the holographic calculation closely matches the nearest available analytical comparison.

Note that the wrapped-phase map typically exhibits a great deal of noise, as seen in Fig. 7.21(c), which is not eliminated by the PUMA algorithm.[10]

Indeed, PUMA was initially chosen for phase unwrapping because of its ability to perform well in the presence of such noise. Thus, for subsequent noise reduction, the unwrapped-phase maps have been subjected to 7×7 pixel median filtering prior to volume calculation or contour mapping. Topographic and volumetric measurements have been performed by the authors for a variety of additional objects, consisting primarily of additional depressions in an aluminum surface, with similar accuracy. For approximately spherical test features, the resulting accuracy was typically within a few percent of the analytically calculated volume (assuming a spherical cap). These measurements have also been repeated using the single-exposure spatial heterodyne method briefly discussed earlier. The spatial heterodyne method has been generally successful, although the resulting error tends to be larger due to ambiguity in pixel matching when the two object reconstructions are overlaid via a BMA prior to phase subtraction. In general, such pixel matching is only accurate to within one-half of a pixel, which causes additional phase aberration/noise in the reconstruction.

The MATLAB code in Table 7.6 shows an example of the volume calculation illustrated in Fig. 7.21 for a large depression in an aluminum plate. For this sample code, it is only necessary to begin from the unwrapped-phase reconstruction; however, the accompanying CD includes the original hologram recordings if the reader is interested in performing the complete reconstruction process, which is essentially identical to the processes given by the previous examples. This sample measurement should yield a volume of 37.46 mm^3.

7.9 Multiwavelength Digital Holography: Image-Type Setup and Results

The dual-wavelength-with-spatial-heterodyning method described earlier can also be used to digitally record image-plane holograms from different objects; each one is recorded with its own dedicated wavelength, where their respective references have unique angles of incidence on the CCD camera so long as their transforms are spatially separated in the Fourier plane. The setup is illustrated in Fig. 7.22. As shown in Fig. 7.22(a), image holograms are simultaneously superposed and recorded on the CCD at the two wavelengths. When the composite intensity profile recorded on the CCD is numerically Fourier transformed, the resulting intensity picture shows the Fourier transforms in all four quadrants [see the inset in Fig. 7.22(b)]. Quadrants I and III denote a pair corresponding to one wavelength, whereas quadrants II and IV denote the other pair (corresponding to the second wavelength). This quadrant separation is made possible because the references at two wavelengths travel at different angles with respect to the object beam. Incidentally, in lidar terminology, the inset showing the Fourier transform is referred to as the pupil or Fourier plane.

Table 7.6 MATLAB code "Volume_Reconstruction.m" is an example that calculates the volume of some phase-unwrapped image [see Figs. 7.21(c)–(7.21(g))].

```
1    %This code calculates the volume of some phase-
2    %unwrapped image
3    %by bounding the volume with a circular plane and
4    %integrating from the
5    %unwrapped surface to the surface of the plane.
6    %First: Read in (or calculate) a phase-unwrapped
7    %image. The raw holograms are provided if the reader
8    %is interested in performing the full reconstruction
9    %process; however, for this example, only the
10   %unwrapped surface needs to be imported for volume
11   %calculation.
12   load delphi.mat              %Wrapped-phase image
13   load unwph.mat               %Unwrapped-phase image
14   del_phi = rot90(del_phi,2);    %Rotate to match physical
15                                  %viewing perspective
16   unwph = rot90(unwph,2);
17   figure(1)
18   imagesc(medfilt2(del_phi,[ 3 3] ))  %Filter and display
19                                       %the wrapped image
20   colormap(gray)
21   axis square
22   title('Wrapped Phase Image' )
23   %%Filter and display the unwrapped image
24   size = 9;
25   unwph2 = ((medfilt2(unwph,[ size size] )));
26   unwph2 = unwph2(10:270,20:280);
27   figure(2);
28   %surfl(fliplr(unwph2));
29   %shading interp; colormap(gray);
30   %light('Position',[ -50 50 20] ,' Style' ,' infinite' );
31   %displays with depth coded colormap
32   mesh(fliplr(unwph2))
33   colorbar
34   title('Unwrapped (PUMA) solution' );
35   xlabel('x (pixels)' )
36   ylabel('y (pixels)' )
37   zlabel('z (radians)' )
38   view([ -158 76] )                    %Perspective view
39   %view([ 180 0] )           %Side view to show the depth profile
40   figure(3);
41   imagesc(unwph2)
42   colormap(gray)
43   axis square
44   title('Unwrapped (PUMA) solution' );
45   %%Calculate feature sizes based on the incident
46   %illumination angle.
47   %Reconstruction parameters.
48   lambda1 = 766.12e-9;                 %766.12 nm
49   correction = 0.194e-9;               %Fixed bias (measured via
50                                        %spectrometer)
51   lambda1 = lambda1+correction;
52   lambda2 = 766e-9;                    %766.0 nm
53   N = 1024;
```

(continued)

Table 7.6 (*Continued*)

```
54  dx = 6.7e-6;
55  d = 0.35;                            %Reconstruction distance
56  theta = 0;                           %Incident angle (0 deg for
57                          %Michaelson, 45 deg for Mach-Zehnder)
58  Feature_size = lambda1*d/(N*dx);  %Image pixel size
59  Synth_wavelength = lambda1.*lambda2./...
60  abs(lambda1-lambda2);
61  height_factor = cosd(theta)*Synth_wavelength/(4*pi);
62  %%Correct object aspect ratio by cos(45) from
63  %recording geometry.
64  %%If using the Mach-Zehnder configuration, run this
65  %section:
66  %unwph3 = unwph2;
67  %unwph3 = (resample(unwph3',141,100))'; %141/100 is
68  %approx 1/cosd(45)
69  %unwph3 = unwph3(:,:).*height_factor;
70  %%If using the Michelson (normal incidence),
71  %run this section; it converts radians of height
72  %into SI units (meters):
73  unwph3 = unwph2(:,:).*height_factor;
74  %%Plot with either surfl or mesh
75  figure(4)
76  %h = surfl(fliplr(unwph3)); shading interp;
77  %colormap(gray);
78  %set(h,'FaceLighting','phong','AmbientStrength',0.7)
79  %light('Position',[0 0 1],'Style','infinite');
80  %light('Position',[-50 50 20],'Style','infinite');
81  mesh(fliplr(unwph3))
82  xlabel('x (pixels)')
83  ylabel('y (pixels)')
84  zlabel('z (meters)')
85  view([-158 76])                      %Perspective view
86  %view([180 0])                   %Side view to show depth profile
87  title('Unwrapped height in meters')
88  colorbar
89  %%Find/place the integration plane
90  x = 1:1:length(unwph3(1,:));
91  y = 1:1:length(unwph3(:,1));
92  [XX,YY] = meshgrid(x,y);
93  [II,JJ] = meshgrid(y*Feature_size,y*Feature_size);
94  a = -.005;                           %x slope
95  b = -.001;                           %y slope
96  c = 15.8;
97  z = a*XX + b*YY + c;
98  dx = Feature_size; %6.7e-6; %Camera pixel size
99  dy = dx;
100 %Unscaled reference surface
101 S2 = myDrawCircle(length(x),90,-5,0);
102 %Height-scaled reference surface
103 S = S2.*z.*height_factor;
104 figure(5);
105 %surfl(II,JJ,fliplr(unwph3)); shading interp;
106 %colormap(gray);
107 mesh(II,JJ,fliplr(unwph3));
```

(*continued*)

Table 7.6 (*Continued*)

```
108  hold on
109  h = surf(II,JJ,fliplr(S),' FaceAlpha' ,0.4);
110  shading interp; %colormap(gray)
111  set(h,' FaceLighting' ,' phong' ,' FaceColor' ,' red' ,...
112  'AmbientStrength' ,0.7)
113  light('Position' ,[ -50 50 500] ,' Style' ,' infinite' );
114  %view([ -130 64] )
115  %view([ -180 90] )
116  view([ 140 25] )
117  hold off
118  xlabel('x (meters)' )
119  ylabel('y (meters)' )
120  zlabel('z (meters)' )
121  title({ 'Physically Scaled Topogram (m)' ,...
122  'with Bounded Reference Plane'} )
123  colorbar
124  %%Draw contours using MATLAB. Modify by
125  %unwph3+Diff to flatten the data for contouring
126  z_flat = 0*XX + 0*YY + c; %Ref plane for flattening
127  Diff = (z_flat-z).*height_factor;
128  %It just so happens that this data is already mostly
129  %flat/level, so no correction needs to be applied.
130  %Hence the zero %multipliers in z_flat.
131  figure(6)
132  values =[ .5e-3:.1e-3:3.5e-3] ;
133  contour(II,JJ,(flipud(unwph3+Diff)),values)
134  xlabel('x (meters)' )
135  ylabel('y (meters)' )
136  colorbar
137  title('Contour Plot' )
138  %%Scale distances to (mm) for more intuitive
139  %plotting.
140  %Plot with either mesh or surfl
141  figure(7);
142  [ II,JJ]  = meshgrid(y* Feature_size* 10^3,...
143  y* Feature_size* 10^3);
144  %surfl(II,JJ,fliplr(unwph3* 10^3)); shading interp;
145  %colormap(gray);
146  mesh(II,JJ,fliplr(unwph3* 10^3));
147  hold on
148  h = surf(II,JJ,fliplr(S* 10^3),' FaceAlpha' ,0.4);
149  shading interp;                    %colormap(gray)
150  set(h,' FaceLighting' ,' phong' ,' FaceColor' ,' red' ,...
151  'AmbientStrength' ,0.7)
152  light('Position' ,[ -50 50 500] ,' Style' ,' infinite' );
153  %view([ -158 76] )                  %Perspective view
154  view([ 140 25] )
155  hold off
156  xlabel('x (mm)' )
157  ylabel('y (mm)' )
158  zlabel('z (mm)' )
159  title({ 'Physically Scaled Topogram (mm)' ,...
160  'with Bounded Reference Plane'} )
161  colorbar
```

(*continued*)

Table 7.6 *(Continued)*

```
162  %%Calculate the volume integral by performing
163  %discrete sums
164  Range = find(S);                    %Find the nonzero values
165  Vol1 = sum(S(Range));
166  %feature^2 puts in square meters
167  Vol2 = sum(unwph3(Range));
168  %Volume in SI units (m^3)
169  Volume_SIunits = abs((Vol1-Vol2)*dx*dy)
170  Volume_cubic_mm = abs(Volume_SIunits*1000^3)
171  %%Analytical volume of spherical cap
172  a = 3.8;                            % (mm) measured radius
173  h = 1.57;                           % (mm) caliper measured depth
174                                      % (not including ridge)
175  V = pi*h*(3*a^2+h^2)/6              %volume of a spherical cap
```

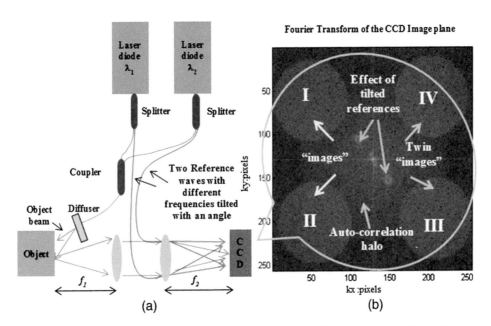

(a)   (b)

Figure 7.22 (a) Schematic of dual-wavelength DH with tilted references. The object is illuminated with two different wavelengths $\lambda_{1,2}$. The scattered light is combined with the tilted reference wave, and the resulting intensity is recorded on a CCD. The reference beams are distinguished by different angular offsets. (b) The inset on the right is the Fourier transform of the image hologram captured on the CCD, showing the Fourier transforms of the two-wavelength images (simply called "images" in the inset) and their twins appearing in complementary quadrants. The effect of the tilted references appears as two bright spots in the quadrants labeled I and III.

The CCD is a low-bandwidth receiver that creates a digital hologram by detecting the overall intensity pattern resulting from the mixing of the input signals with the matched frequencies of the reference waves. The frequency of a particular reference mixes favorably with one particular signal frequency, and all other signals appear as a weak background contribution to the CCD noise.

Assume, for instance, that the complex electric field in the pupil (focal) plane (the Fourier transform of the image plane, which is recorded on the CCD) can be written as

$$E(x,y) = \sum_{n=1,2} E_{R_n} e^{j\omega_n t - j(k_{x_n} x + k_y y)} + \sum_{m=1,2} E_{S_m}(x,y) e^{j\omega_m t}, \qquad (7.37)$$

where E_{R_n} is the nth reference wave at the $\omega_n{}^{th}$ frequency, E_{S_m} is the mth signal wave at the $\omega_m{}^{th}$ frequency. The two selected reference waves have the same wavelength as the signals labeled S_1 and S_2. The two reference beams are assumed to be plane waves in this expression, with a tip and tilt given by (k_{x_n}, k_y); the two can be offset in angle by changing the sign of the wavevector component, such that $k_{x_1} = -k_{x_2}$. The difference in tilts places the reconstructions from the digital holograms of the two signals in adjacent quadrants, and their twin images occupy diagonal quadrants, as shown on the right in Fig. 7.23. The recorded digital hologram is the integrated irradiance:

$$I(x,y) = \sum_{n=1,2} \left| E_{R_n} \right|^2 + 2\,\mathrm{Re}\{E_{R_1} E_{R_2}^* e^{-j2k_{x_1}x} T(e^{j(\omega_2 - \omega_1)t})\}$$

$$+ T(e^{j(\omega_n - \omega_m)t}) \left(\left| \sum_{m=1,2} E_{S_m}(x,y) e^{j(\omega_\alpha - \omega_m)t} \right|^2 \right)$$

$$+ \left\{ \sum_{n=1,2} E_{R_n} e^{-j(k_{x_n}x + k_y y)} \left(E_{S_n}^* + \sum_{m \neq n} E_{S_n}^* T(e^{j(\omega_n - \omega_m)t}) \right) + c.c. \right\}, \quad (7.38)$$

where T is the integration time of the CCD camera [also called the focal plane array (FPA)]. The first term above is the contribution of two plane-wave references, which appears as the central spot in the focal plane. The second term is a time average of the product reference fields; it has a large wavevector on the x axis that serves as a beam tilt along the x axis in the focal plane, and the signal amplitude is weakened by the time average. The time averages in Eq. (7.38) are represented by the integral denoted by

$$T(\ldots) = \frac{1}{T_0} \int_0^{T_0} \ldots dt,$$

where T_0 is the integration time of the CCD. The angular frequency difference between the nth reference and the mth signal is denoted by $\Delta\omega_{nm}$, which is the temporal frequency in the integral. Further analysis reveals that the two frequency-shifted references have only weak cross-correlation contributions with the signals. The amplitude of the time-averaged integral is inversely proportional to $\Delta\omega_{nm}T_0$, which is the product of the frequency offset and the camera integration time. The third term is a time average of the additional signals with one another; this is a very weak contribution leading to additional noise in the hologram. In the pupil plane, this contribution is separated from

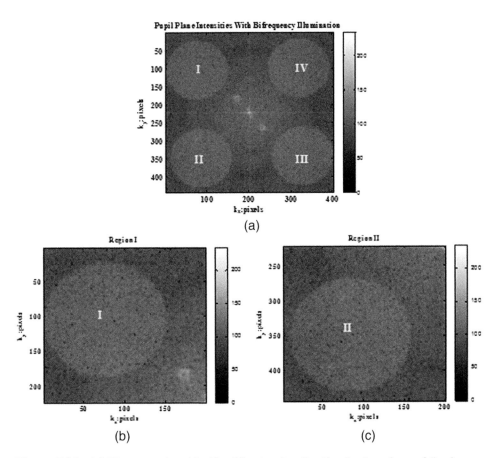

Figure 7.23 (a) The same inset in Fig. 22, showing the Fourier transform of the image on the CCD due to object illumination with two wavelengths using spatial heterodyning. (b)–(c) Cropped and zoomed regions I and II of (a).

the desired image and appears as an autocorrelation halo around the center in the inset of Fig. 7.22(b). The fourth term (in brackets) contains several contributions: The desired recorded hologram is the first element in the brackets. The second mixing element is a sum over all other signals, and its strength is determined by a time-averaged contribution of the frequency-detuned signals. The frequency difference between the references and the other signals suppresses their contribution to the signal. The complex conjugate (*c.c.*) denotes the twin images and the complex conjugate of the time-averaged signals. For more details and examples of dual-wavelength holographic microscopy, see Kuhn et al.[15]

The inset of Fig. 7.22 is reproduced in Fig. 7.23(a) to show how it can be processed to reconstruct the original object illuminated using dual wave-lengths. The difference frequencies have been tuned from 10 MHz to 1 GHz; all show similar results. Figures 7.23(b) and 7.23(c) show zoomed versions of the Fourier transforms appearing in quadrants I and II. Applying an inverse Fourier transform will reconstruct the original object illuminated with the two

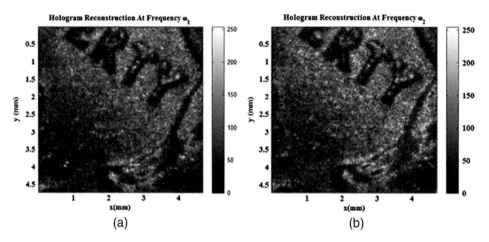

Figure 7.24. Reconstructed objects illuminated using two wavelengths and spatial heterodyning. Intensity profiles show part of a coin after averaging 32 different speckle realizations for (a) λ_1 and (b) λ_2. The pixel size of the CCD camera is around 10 μm.

wavelengths, both in amplitude and phase. The intensities of the reconstructed object (a coin) are shown in Fig. 7.24. The reconstructed phases, when subtracted, should yield information about the profile (height) of the object similar to what was demonstrated earlier, as in Fig. 7.21.

References

1. J. C. Wyant, "Testing aspherics using two-wavelength holography," *Appl. Opt.* **10**(9), 2113–2118 (1971).
2. U. Schnars and W. Jueptner, Digital Holography, Springer, Berlin (2005).
3. P. Hariharan, Optical Holography; Principles, *Techniques, and Applications*, Cambridge University Press, Cambridge, UK (1996).
4. T. Kreis, *Handbook of holographic Interferometry*, Wiley, Weinheim, Germany (2005).
5. C. Mann, P. Bingham, V. Paquit, and K. Tobin, "Quantitative phase imaging by three-wavelength digital holography," *Opt. Exp.* **16**(13), 9753–9764 (2008).
6. D. Abdelsalam, R. Magnusson, and D. Kim, "Single-shot, dual-wavelength digital holography based on polarizing separation," *Appl. Opt.* **50**(19), 3360–3368 (2011).
7. Y. Morimoto, T. Matui, M. Fujigaki, and N. Kawagishi, "Subnanometer displacement measurement by averaging of phase difference in windowed digital holographic interferometry," *Opt. Eng.* **46**(2), 025603 (2007) [doi: 10.1117/1.2538709].
8. J. Haus, B. Dapore, N. Miller, P. Banerjee, G. Nehmetallah, P. Powers, and P. McManamon, "Instantaneously captured images using multi-wavelength digital holography," *Proc. SPIE* **8493**, 84930W (2012) [doi: 10.1117/12.932280].

9. J. Kühn et al., "Real-time dual-wavelength digital holographic microscopy with a single hologram acquisition," *Opt. Exp.* **15**(12), 7231–7242 (2007).

10. J. Bioucas-Dias and G. Valadão, "Phase unwrapping via graph cuts," *IEEE Trans. Image Process.* **16**(3), 698–709 (2007).

11. J. Dirckx and W. Decraemer, "Deformation measurements of the human tympanic membrane under static pressure using automated moire topography," *Proc. SPIE* **1429**, 34–38 (1991) [doi: 10.1117/12.44653].

12. S. Xenofos and C. Jones, "Theoretical aspects and practical applications of moiré topography," *Phys. Med. Biol.* **24**(2), 250–261 (1979).

13. E. Barbosa, E. Lima, M. Gesualdi, and M. Muramatsu, "Enhanced multiwavelength holographic profilometry by laser mode selection," *Opt. Eng.* **46**(7), 075601 (2007) [doi: 10.1117/1.2756817].

14. J. Taylor, *An Introduction to Error Analysis: The Study of Uncertainties in Physical Measurements*, University Science Books, Sausalito, CA (1997).

15. J. Kühn et al., "Real-time dual-wavelength digital holographic microscopy with a single hologram acquisition," *Opt. Exp.* **15**(12), 7231–7242 (2007).

16. L. Williams, P. Banerjee, G. Nehmetallah, and S. Praharaj, "Holographic volume displacement calculations via multiwavelength digital holography," *Appl. Opt.* **53**(8), 1597–1603 (2014).

Chapter 8
Computer-Generated Holography

8.1 A Brief History

Digital holography optically generates a hologram, which is then recorded on a CCD camera, and an image is reconstructed using digital techniques. This chapter discusses the converse, i.e., the hologram is digitally generated and the reconstruction is performed optically, a process known as computer-generated holography (CGH).

Thus, in CGH, holograms are created by calculations performed by a digital computer. The next step transfers the computer-generated hologram to a transparency by means of a plotting or printing device. Alternatively, the holographic image can be produced by a holographic 3D display (a display that operates on the basis of interference of coherent light) or displayed using a spatial light modulator (SLM), thus bypassing the need to fabricate a "hard copy" of the holographic interference pattern. Consequently, the term "computer-generated holography" is increasingly being used to denote the entire process chain of synthetically preparing holographic light wavefronts suitable for observation. Ultimately, CGH might serve all of the roles of current computer-generated imagery: holographic computer displays for a wide range of applications from CAD to gaming, holographic video and TV programs, automotive and communication applications (e.g., cellphone displays), and many more. In other words, CGH can create images of fictitious objects.

CGH consists of three main steps:

1. Calculating the complex fields that the object wave will produce on the hologram plane, which is usually taken to be the discrete Fourier transform of the complex amplitude of points in the object plane.
2. Choosing a suitable representation of the complex fields in the hologram plane. The computed complex (both amplitude and phase) discrete sample values of the DFT are usually used to produce a hologram "transparency" that reconstructs the object when lit by an appropriate laser source.

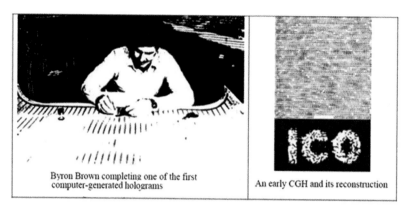

Byron Brown completing one of the first
computer-generated holograms

An early CGH and its reconstruction

Figure 8.1   One of the first CG holograms and its reconstruction.[5]

3. Transfering the encoded representation of the complex fields to a
   transparency through a printing or plotting process,[1,2] or onto a SLM.

There are many different methods for calculating the interference pattern
for a CG hologram. Many methods have been proposed in the fields of
holographic information and computational reduction, as well as computational and quantization techniques. In the field of computational techniques,
the reported algorithms can be categorized by two main concepts: Fourier-
transform holograms (cell oriented) and point-source holograms (point
oriented).[3,4] Figure 8.1 shows one of the first CG holograms.[5]

Depending on the material with which the CG hologram is to be
fabricated, there are typically three types of CG holograms:

(a) phase-only, where the material modulates only the phase of an incoming
    wavefront, and the transmittance amplitude is unity;
(b) amplitude-only, where the material modulates only the amplitude of an
    incoming wavefront, and the transmittance phase is constant; and
(c) complex-amplitude, where the material modulates both the phase and
    amplitude of an incoming wavefront.

8.2 Fourier Transform Holograms: Detour Method

The relationship between the complex optical field of the object and the
complex field at the hologram can be written as a discrete Fourier transform:[1]

$$h(p\Delta x,q\Delta y) = \sum_{m=0}^{N}\sum_{n=0}^{N} E_O(m\Delta\xi,n\Delta\eta) \exp\left[j2\pi\left(\frac{pm}{N}+\frac{qn}{N}\right)\right] \equiv |h_{pq}| \exp(j\phi_{pq}),$$

$$(8.1)$$

where $|h_{pq}|$ denotes the amplitude of the Fourier transform, and ϕ_{pq} denotes
its phase. In CGH, one of the best known methods for creating holograms

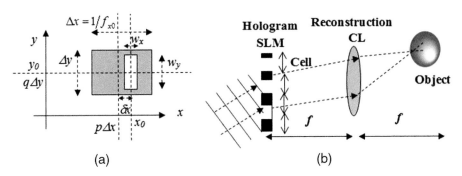

Figure 8.2 (a) A single cell in a detour-phase hologram, and (b) reconstruction of the CG hologram.

from computed complex fields is the detour method.[5–7] In this method, the hologram plane comprises an array of "cells" of size $\Delta x, \Delta y$ in the x and y directions. The $(p,q)^{th}$ cell, assumed to be located at $(p\Delta x, q\Delta y)$ on the hologram plane, comprises a rectangle with an area proportional to $|h_{pq}|$, and the position of the center of the rectangle within the cell is proportional to ϕ_{pq}, referred to as the detour phase. Therefore, the phase is encoded by moving the center of the plotted rectangle, as shown in Fig. 8.2. The procedure for Fresnel holograms is similar, but the Fresnel propagator is incorporated, as explained in previous chapters.

During reconstruction, the $N \times N$ hologram transparency is placed at the front focal plane of a lens and illuminated by a tilted reference (or reconstruction) wave of the form

$$E_R(x,y) \propto \exp(-jk_{x0}x), \qquad k_{x0} = k_0 \sin(\theta_{x0}) = (2\pi/\Delta x) = 2\pi f_{x0}, \quad (8.2)$$

where θ_{x0} is the angle between the propagation vector of the incident wave and the z axis. The Fourier transform hologram is therefore reconstructed at the back focal plane of the lens to yield the intended image.

Consider a rectangle within a cell in the hologram plane of dimensions (w_x, w_y), where $w_x \ll 2\pi k_{x0}^{-1}$, described as

$$t(x,y) = \text{rect}\left(\frac{x - x_0}{w_x}\right)\text{rect}\left(\frac{y - y_0}{w_y}\right), \quad (8.3)$$

where (x_0, y_0) is the center of the rectangle. If a rectangle (as an example) is in the center of the $(p,q)^{th}$ cell, $x_0 = p\Delta x, y_0 = q\Delta y$; however, in general, it can have a shift with respect to the center of the cell that is proportional to the encoded phase, as mentioned earlier. If this rectangle were illuminated with the plane wave defined earlier, the transmitted field just after the hologram is

$$E(x,y) = \exp(-jk_{x0}x)\text{rect}\left(\frac{x - x_0}{w_x}\right)\text{rect}\left(\frac{y - y_0}{w_y}\right). \quad (8.4)$$

At the back focal plane of the imaging lens of focal length f, the complex optical field becomes, after some algebra,

$$E(x,y) = \frac{jk_0}{2\pi f} \mathfrak{I}_{xy} \left[\exp(-jk_{x0}x)\mathrm{rect}\left(\frac{x-x_0}{w_x}\right)\mathrm{rect}\left(\frac{y-y_0}{w_y}\right) \right] \Bigg|_{\substack{k_x=k_0x/f \\ k_y=k_0y/f}}$$

$$= \frac{jk_0 w_x w_y}{2\pi f} \mathrm{sinc}\left(\frac{w_x k_0}{2\pi f}\left(x - \frac{2\pi f}{\Delta x k_0}\right)\right)\mathrm{sinc}\left(\frac{w_y k_0}{2\pi f} y\right)$$

$$\times \exp\left[j\frac{k_0 x_0}{f}\left(x - \frac{2\pi f}{\Delta x k_0}\right)\right]\exp\left[j\frac{k_0 y_0}{f} y\right]. \tag{8.5}$$

Assuming that w_x is sufficiently small $(w_x \ll \Delta x)$, Eq. (8.5) can be rewritten as

$$E(x,y) = \frac{jk_0 w_x w_y}{2\pi f} \exp\left[j\frac{k_0}{f}(xx_0 + yy_0)\right]\exp\left[-j\frac{2\pi x_0}{\Delta x}\right]. \tag{8.6}$$

The contribution to the image plane (back focal plane of the lens) from all cells that comprise rectangles of different widths $w_x, w_{y(p,q)}$ and positions $(x_0, y_0)_{(p,q)} = (p\Delta x + \delta x_{(p,q)}, q\Delta y)$ can be written as

$$E_{Total}(x,y) = \sum_{p=0}^{N}\sum_{q=0}^{N} \frac{jk_0 w_x w_{y(p,q)}}{2\pi f}\exp\left[-j2\pi\frac{\delta x_{(p,q)}}{\Delta x}\right]$$

$$\times \exp\left[j\frac{k_0}{f}(xp\Delta x + x\delta x_{(p,q)} + yq\Delta y)\right]. \tag{8.7}$$

Assuming that $\delta x_{(p,q)}$ is sufficiently small such that

$$\exp\left[j\frac{k_0 x\delta x_{(p,q)}}{f}\right] \approx 1,$$

Eq. (8.7) becomes

$$E_{Total}(x,y) = \sum_{p=0}^{N}\sum_{q=0}^{N} \frac{jk_0 w_x w_{y(p,q)}}{2\pi f}\exp\left[-j2\pi\frac{\delta x_{(p,q)}}{\Delta x}\right]$$

$$\times \exp\left[j\frac{k_0}{f}(xp\Delta x + yq\Delta y)\right]. \tag{8.8}$$

Because the goal is to reconstruct the hologram h through a Fourier transformation, the term in front of the second exponential in Eq. (8.8)

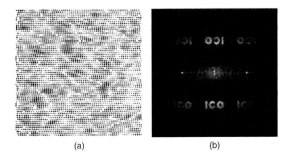

(a)   (b)

Figure 8.3 (a) Binary detour-phase hologram, and (b) an image digitally reconstructed from that hologram.[1]

should be proportional to the hologram function h. Accordingly, upon setting

$$E_{Total}(x,y) = \sum_{p=0}^{N} \sum_{q=0}^{N} |h_{pq}| \exp(j\phi_{pq}) \exp\left[j\frac{k_0}{f} (xp\Delta x + yq\Delta y) \right] \quad (8.9)$$

and comparing Eqs. (8.8) and (8.9), the following result is produced for the area and the displacement of each rectangle within the cell:

$$w_{y(p,q)} = \frac{2\pi f |h_{pq}|}{k_0 w_x}, \qquad \delta x_{(p,q)} = -\frac{\phi_{pq}}{2\pi}\Delta x, \quad (8.10)$$

respectively. Therefore, the detour-phase hologram has the capability to encode the amplitude and the phase of the complex hologram through the area and shift of the rectangle in each cell. The only drawback of the detour method is that the diffraction efficiency is low. Figure 8.3 shows (a) a binary detour-phase hologram and (b) an image reconstructed from that hologram using the fast Fourier transform algorithm in MATLAB. Although the reconstruction shown in Fig. 8.3(b) was performed digitally, this hologram can also be reconstructed optically. The code in Table 8.1 was used to generate Fig. 8.3(b). An exact implementation of the detour-phase method can be found in Poon and Liu,[8] and a generalized adapted code can be found in this book's CD-ROM under the script name "detour.m."

8.3 Phase-Only CG Hologram

A traditional phase-only CG hologram is called a kinoform. Currently, CG holograms are formed by lithographically recording a pattern that reconstructs a desired complex field when illuminated by a reference wave. The CG hologram is determined by the lithographic process used. For example, holograms created by etching glass are phase-only; multilevel phase holograms are created using multistep etching processes.

Table 8.1   MATLAB code "CGH_Reconstruction.m" for the digital reconstruction of a CG hologram (see Fig. 8.3).

```
1    %This file reads in the computer-generated hologram
2    %and computes the far-field diffraction pattern via
3    %the Fourier transform
4    clc;clear all
5    h = imread('CGH_ICO.bmp',' bmp');      %Read the image
6    h = imresize(h,0.5);            %Resize the image
7    h = h';                         %Transpose the image
8    H = fftshift(fft2(h));          %Compute the FFT
9    AH=abs(H);
10   [N,M]=size(AH);
11   AH=medfilt2(AH,[3 3]);          %Use to cancel the carrier
12                                   %frequencies and dc terms
13   figure(1)                       %Display the image
14   imshow(mat2gray(AH));
15   colormap gray
16   axis square
17   title('CGH Reconstruction')
```

If an object is illuminated by a diffused light, then the magnitude of the Fourier coefficients are neglected and the object is reconstructed using only the phase. The diffuser is an important component of CGH. For a typical object, a random phase pattern can be superposed without affecting the irradiance distribution. A digital random-phase or diffuser-phase distribution will spread the light energy uniformly on the hologram plane, thus improving the hologram's diffraction efficiency. The image information will be distributed around the hologram so that the hologram will be insensitive to errors. This diffused light is simulated by a random phase superposed on the object. If t_{pq} denotes the transmittance of the cell corresponding to the Fourier coefficient $|h_{pq}|$ and phase ϕ_{pq}, then[2,9]

$$t_{pq} = |h_{pq}| \exp(j\phi_{pq}) \approx \exp(j\phi_{pq}). \tag{8.11}$$

Therefore, the reconstructed object has the following form:

$$Obj = |\mathfrak{I}_{x,y}^{-1}\{e^{j\phi_{pq}}\}|. \tag{8.12}$$

A typical algorithm of the kinoform technique is shown in Fig. 8.4(a). The code shown in Table 8.2 was used to generate Figs. 8.4(b)–8.4(e). Figure 8.4(b) shows the original object; Fig. 8.4(c) and 8.4(d) show the amplitude and phase spectrum, respectively; and Fig. 8.4(e) shows the digitally reconstructed image from the phase part of the hologram. It is worth noting that the kinoform technique has a higher diffraction efficiency than the detour method, but the reconstructed object is noisy, as shown in Fig. 8.4(e).

Another method, the referenceless on-axis complex hologram (ROACH) technique, uses multilayer color films as recording media, where different layers of film are exposed to different colors, whereas other layers are

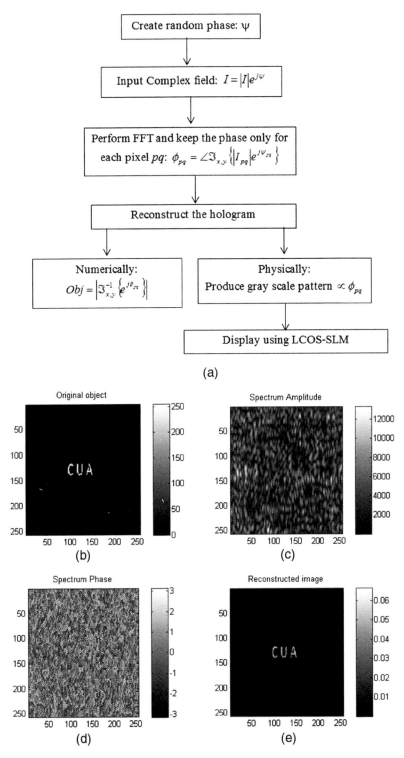

Figure 8.4 (a) Flowchart of the kinoform method, (b) original object, (c) amplitude spectrum, (d) phase spectrum, and (e) digitally reconstructed image from the phase hologram.

Table 8.2 MATLAB code "kinoform.m" for the digital reconstruction of a CG hologram (see Fig. 8.4).

```
1    %Kinoform technique, see Poon and Liu[ 8] .
2    clc;clear all;close all;
3    I=imread('CUA256.bmp' , 'bmp' );      %Input image
4    [ N,N] =size(I);
5    I=double(I);
6    ph_I=2*pi* (rand(N) −0.5);
7    IC=I.*exp(i*ph_I);                %Add a random phase
8    IF=fftshift(fft2(IC));            %Spectrum
9    Abs=abs(IF);
10   Ang=angle(IF);
11   %Reconstruction of the object by neglecting the
12   %amplitude and using only the phase
13   Obj=abs(ifft2(fftshift(exp(i*Ang))));
14   %Plot
15   figure;
16   imagesc(I)
17   colormap(gray(256))
18   title('Original object' )
19   colorbar
20   figure;
21   imagesc(Abs)
22   colormap(gray(256))
23   title('Spectrum Amplitude' )
24   colorbar
25   figure;
26   imagesc(Ang)
27   colormap(gray(256))
28   title('Spectrum Phase' )
29   colorbar
30   figure;
31   imagesc(Obj)
32   colormap(gray(256))
33   title('Reconstructed image' )
34   colorbar
```

transparent but affect the phase of the hologram. Thus, this type of hologram can directly control both the amplitude and phase of the transmitted beam.[2,10] For a detailed discussion of CGH techniques, refer to Goodman,[1] Poon and Liu,[8] and Lee.[11] Table 8.3 summarizes several of these techniques.

8.4 Gerchberg–Saxton Algorithm for Recording a CG Hologram

Computer-generated holograms have been widely used in optical information processing, interferometry, and diffractive optical elements, and can be manufactured via replication processes such as hot embossing (including UV embossing and injection molding), which are very important for mass production of microstructures and nanostructures. A typical flowchart of such a process is shown in Fig. 8.5.[12] Currently, CG holograms are transferred into polymer using e-beam lithography (EBL), which is the most commonly used technique for nanolithography. The resist is deposited by spin coating,

Table 8.3 Summary of different CGH techniques.[11]

Type	Preparation	Gray levels	Comments
Superimposed FZP	Multiexposure photo	Continuous	Limited number of points
Detour phase	Plotter output	Binary	Both the phase and amplitude are quantized separately
Delay sampling	CRT display	Continuous	Fourier hologram
Synthetic interferogram	CRT display	Binary	Phase only
Kinoform	Bleached photo of plotter output in the case of photographic film	Continuous. The final result is transparent.	Phase only. Wavefronts recorded as surface relief on photographic film or phase LCOS-SLM.
ROACH	Bleached photo on triple-emulsion film	Continuous	Both phase and amplitude. Requires special film and treatment.

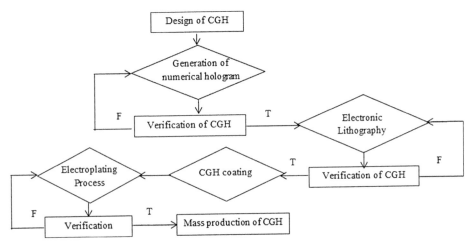

Figure 8.5 Algorithm for manufacturing microstructures: from design of the CG hologram to mass production.[12]

followed by electron-beam exposure and resist development.[13,14] A high-ratio metal mold is then created via electroforming, which is a process by which metal is deposited on the surface of a substrate. Although this process is often used for its excellent surface finishes and its ability to create uniform parts of varying thickness, electroforming has more recently been incorporated into the nanofabrication industry.[15,16] The completed mold can then be used to mass produce replicas using various different replication technologies: hot imprint, UV embossing, injection molding, etc.

The chapter has thus far discussed input/output-based techniques. Another class of techniques is based on iterative methods. Most iterative design techniques are based on the phase-retrieval algorithm suggested by Gerchberg and Saxton.[8,17–19] The original Gerchberg–Saxton (GS) algorithm is an iterative process in which Fourier and inverse Fourier transforms are

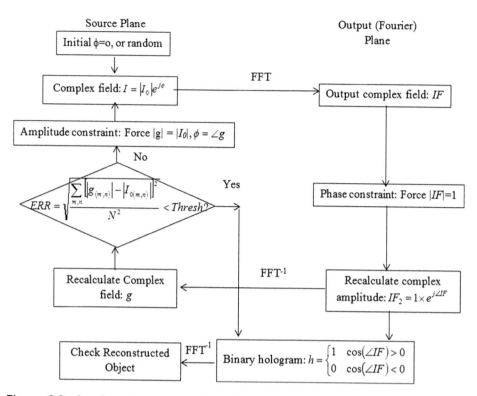

Figure 8.6 A schematic representation of the Gerchberg–Saxton algorithm used to compute a CG hologram.[8,20]

taken after substituting the intensity pattern of the input wave and the desired pattern at each iteration step while keeping the phase distribution unchanged. Therefore, the unknown phases on both the initial input wave and the final target plane will be computed at the end. For this version of the GS algorithm,[20] the phase constraint in Fig. 8.6 suggests that the element is phase-only (i.e., a phase hologram), whereas the amplitude is normalized to one at each iteration. The amplitude constraint forces the reconstructed object amplitude to match the desired input amplitude, leaving the phase unchanged.

The MATLAB code "CGH_GS.m," shown in Table 8.4, implements the GS algorithm from Fig. 8.6. Figure 8.7(a) shows the original object, Fig. 8.7(b) shows the root-mean-square error (RMSE), Fig. 8.7(c) shows the binary CG hologram, and Fig. 8.7(d) shows the image reconstructed from that hologram. More-advanced phase-retrieval methods can be found in Fienup.[18,19]

Finally, it can be proved that a CG hologram can be modeled on the basis of the following transmittance function:[11,21]

$$t(x,y) = \begin{cases} 1 & \text{if } \arg\left[\Im_{x,y}\{E_O(x,y)\}\big|_{k_x=\frac{k_0 x}{z},k_y=\frac{k_0 y}{z}}\right] > 0 \\ 0 & \text{otherwise.} \end{cases} \tag{8.13}$$

Table 8.4 MATLAB code "CGH_GS.m" for the digital reconstruction of a CG hologram using the GS algorithm (see Fig. 8.7).

```
1   %Script to use the GS algorithm to reconstruct a CG
2   %hologram according to the algorithm in Fig. 8.7
3   clc
4   clear all
5   close all
6   N=512;
7   %Load image
8   I0=imread('CUA_UD.bmp', 'bmp');
9   I0=imresize(I0,[N,N]);
10  I0=double(I0);
11  I0=I0/max(I0(:));           %Normalize
12  figure
13  colormap(gray(256))
14  imagesc(I0)
15  ampI0=abs(I0);
16  avI0=mean(I0(:));
17  title('Original Object')
18  %%---------------GS algorithm---------------
19  I=I0;
20  k=0;
21  err=1;
22  while err>0.087
23  k=k+1;
24  IF=fftshift(fft2(I));       %Going to the Fourier domain
25  angIF=angle(IF);
26  IF2=exp(j*angIF);           %Always force the amplitude to
27                              %1 and keep the computed phase
28  g=ifft2(fftshift(IF2));     %Going to the space domain
29  avg=mean(abs(g(:)));
30  g=g*avI0/avg;               %Adjust amplitude for error
31  ampg=abs(g);
32  angg=angle(g);
33  dif2=(ampg-ampI0).^2;       %Compute error
34  err(k)=sqrt(sum(dif2(:)/N^2));
35  %err(k)=sqrt(sum(dif2(:))/sum(ampI0(:)));
36  I=ampI0.*exp(j*angg);       %Recalculate the new object
37                              %through maintaining the
38                              %original amplitude and keep
39                              %the new computed phase
40  if k>150
41  break;
42  end
43  end
44  %Plot the RMS error
45  figure
46  plot(1:k,err)
47  grid on
48  xlabel('Iterations')
49  ylabel('error')
50  title('RMSE')
51  g=g./max(g(:));             %Normalize
52  %Plot the reconstructed object
53  figure;
```

(*continued*)

Table 8.4 (*Continued*)

```
54  imagesc(abs(g));
55  colormap(gray(256))
56  title('Reconstructed Object')
57  %%This section computes a binary CG hologram out of
58  %the phase of the converged solution of the Fourier
59  %transform of the object
60  for n=1:N
61  for m=1:N
62  h(m,n)=cos(angIF(m,n));
63  if h(m,n)>0
64  h(m,n)=1;
65  else
66  h(m,n)=0;
67  end
68  end
69  end
70  %Plot the binary computed-generated hologram
71  figure;
72  colormap(gray(256))
73  imagesc(h);
74  title('Binary Hologram')
75  %Check the computed reconstructed object
76  H=ifft2(fftshift(h));
77  AH=abs(H);
78  AH(1:5,1:5)=0;                    %Cancel dc
79  figure
80  subplot(121)
81  imagesc(AH)
82  colormap(gray(256))
83  subplot(122)
84  mesh(AH)
85  axis([ 1 N 1 N])
86  view(-15,80)
87  axis ij
```

The MATLAB code "myimaCGH.m," shown in Table 8.5, is based on Eq. (8.12). Figures 8.8(a)–8.8(c) show the original object, CG hologram, and image reconstructed from that hologram, respectively.

8.5 Point-Source Holograms and the Wavefront Recording Plane Method

The second computational strategy is based on the point-source concept, where the object is divided into self-luminous points. An elementary hologram is calculated for every point source and the final hologram is synthesized by superimposing all the elementary holograms. This concept was first reported by Waters[22] and assumes that a Fresnel zone plate (FZP, see Fig. 8.9) could be considered a special case of an inline Gabor hologram. However, for an arbitrary object that can be decomposed into point sources, the computational complexity of the point-source concept is much higher than

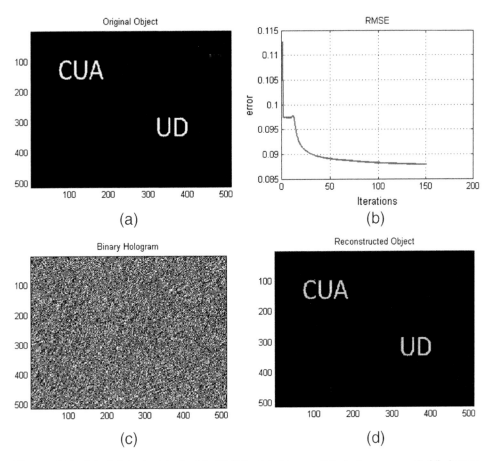

Figure 8.7 (a) Original object, (b) RMSE, (c) binary CG hologram, and (d) image reconstructed from (c).

in the Fourier-transformation concept. Another drawback is the size and viewing angle of reconstructed 3D objects. For example, there are 10^6 pixels for a typical hologram on a CCD (5 mm × 5 mm) with a pixel size of 5 μm × 5 μm; a typical 42-inch plasma screen has $1280 × 768$ pixels (983,040 pixels). In a modern HDTV, there are $\sim 10^6$ pixels in an area of 4784 cm^2, compared to 10^6 pixels in an area of 0.25 cm^2. In a future 42-inch holographic TV, the computational complexity will be at least 20,000 times greater, and 20 billion pixels will be needed.

Some have tried to overcome this drawback by predefining and storing all of the possible elementary holograms, using special data-storage techniques to circumvent the large capacity that is needed in this case, whereas others have used special hardware.[23,24] The point-source concept's major problem that must be circumvented is the competition between data storage capacity and computational speed. In particular, algorithms that minimize the computational speed usually need high data-storage capabilities, whereas algorithms that lower the need for data storage capacity lead to high computational

Table 8.5 MATLAB code "myimaCGH.m" for the digital reconstruction of a CG hologram (see Fig. 8.8).

```
1   clc
2   close all
3   clear all
4   load targetImage
5   [N,N]=size(targetImage);
6   figure
7   imshow(mat2gray(targetImage))
8   axis 'square';
9   colormap 'gray';
10  hologram=(sign(angle(fftshift(fft2(targetImage)))))+1)/2;
11  figure;
12  imshow(mat2gray(hologram))
13  axis 'square';
14  colormap 'gray';
15  %The scene observed through the hologram will be the
16  %Fourier transform of the holographic modulation
17  reconstruction=abs(fftshift(fft2(hologram)));
18  reconstruction(N/2+1,N/2+1)=0;    %Cancel the dc term
19  figure;
20  reconstruction = logim(reconstruction,2);
21  imshow(mat2gray(reconstruction))
22  axis 'square';
23  colormap 'gray';
```

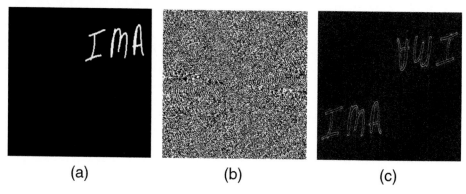

(a)   (b)   (c)

Figure 8.8 (a) Original object, (b) CG hologram, and (c) image reconstructed from that hologram.

complexity, although some optimizations can be achieved.[25,26] It is expected that digital holography will have a leading role in future 3D displays and 3D holographic TVs if practical techniques can be employed to decrease the computational complexity.[27]

Many techniques have been proposed to reduce the calculation complexity in CGH.[28,29] For example, a CG hologram was generated for a 3D object composed of polygons to calculate the diffraction from each polygon by using tilted-plane diffraction calculations.[4,30] A second approach

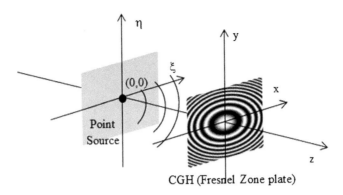

Figure 8.9   Point-source method for CGH.

uses an image hologram consisting of a real-time 3D color reconstruction similar to a CG hologram.[31] A third approach, based on the ray-tracing method, considers a 3D object to be a composite of several point sources that can then generate a CG hologram from a 3D object more precisely than the polygon model.

One of the promising techniques to reduce the computational complexity is the wavefront recording plane method (WRPM).[32–36] The WRPM employs a fast and simple calculation algorithm for CGH by introducing an intermediate wavefront recording plane (WRP). The WRP is placed between the object plane and a CGH. When the WRP is placed close to the object plane, the scattered object light passes through a small region on the WRP, which dramatically reduces the computational complexity for the object light. The CG hologram can be computed from the diffraction calculation from the WRP to the hologram, where the computational complexity is constant. Therefore, the total computational complexity is enormously reduced in comparison with conventional CGH calculations that do not employ a WRP.[32]

The intensity $I(x_i,y_i)$ of each pixel of the CG hologram using the ray-tracing algorithm can be written as[23]

$$I(x_i,y_i) = \sum_{j=1}^{N} \frac{A_j}{R_{ij}} \cos(k_0 R_{ij}), \tag{8.14}$$

where (x_i,y_i) is the coordinate of the ith point on the CG hologram plane $(I = 1,\ldots,N_x \times N_y)$, A_j is the intensity of the jth point source, $k_0 = (2\pi)/\lambda$ is the wavenumber of the laser light, N is the total number of pixels of the object, and $R_{ij} = \sqrt{(x_i - \xi_j)^2 + (y_i - \eta_j)^2 + z_j^2}$ is the radial distance between the jth point on the 3D object of coordinates (ξ_j,η_j,z_j) and a point of coordinates (x_i,y_i) on the CG hologram. Because there are $N_x \times N_y$ points on the CGH plane, the computational complexity is of the order: $O(\alpha N N_x \times N_y)$, where α is the number of additions and multiplications in Eq. (8.14). The setup is shown in Fig. 8.10.[32]

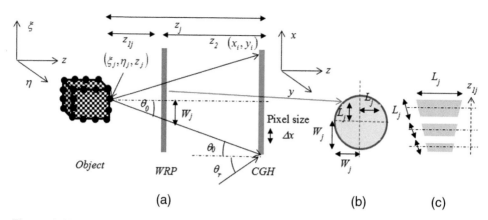

Figure 8.10 (a) The wavefront-recording-plane setup, (b) the rectangular region in WRP, and (c) a look-up table with a pyramidal structure.[32,33]

This computational complexity is hugely reduced in the WRPM. The algorithm works as follows. In the first step, the complex amplitude h_w of all of the point sources of the 3D object is recorded on the WRP plane using the diffraction of a point-source formula:

$$h_w(x_w, y_w) = \sum_{j=1}^{N} \frac{A_j}{R_{wj}} \exp(-jk_0 R_{wj}), \tag{8.15}$$

where $R_{wj} = \sqrt{(x_w - \xi_j)^2 + (y_w - \eta_j)^2 + z_{1j}^2}$, $z_{1j} = (z_j - z_2)$ is the radial distance between the jth point of the 3D object and the wth point (x_w, y_w) on the WRP plane such that $|x_w - \xi_j|$, $|y_w - \eta_j| < W_j$. Note in the setup that the distance $z_1 \ll z_2$, and the jth point of the object diffracts to a small region W_j on the WRP, which makes Eq. (8.15) dramatically less complex, computationally, than Eq. (8.14).

In the second step, the complex amplitude of the diffracted field h from the WRP plane to the CGH plane is computed using the Fresnel diffraction formula:[32]

$$
\begin{aligned}
h(x,y; z_2) &= \frac{jk_0}{2\pi z_2} e^{(-jk_0 z_2)} \iint h_w(x_w, y_w) e^{-j\frac{k_0}{2z_2}[(x-x_w)^2 + (y-y_w)^2]} dx_w dy_w \\
&= \frac{jk_0}{2\pi z_2} e^{(-jk_0 z_2)} \mathfrak{I}^{-1}\{\mathfrak{I}\{h_w(x,y)\} \cdot \mathfrak{I}\{g_{PSF}(x,y; z_2)\}\},
\end{aligned}
\tag{8.16}
$$

where

$$g_{PSF}(x,y; z_2) = \frac{jk_0}{2\pi z_2} \exp(-jk_0 z) \exp\left(-\frac{jk_0(x^2 + y^2)}{2z}\right)$$

is the impulse response of propagation defined in Eq. (1.38).

The third step, for an amplitude type of CG hologram, involves[33]

$$I(x,y) = |h(x,y; z_2) + R(x,y; z_2)|^2, \qquad (8.17a)$$

where $R(x,y; z_2)$ is the reference beam. For a phase type of CG hologram,[33]

$$\Theta(x,y) = \arg\{h(x,y; z_2)\}. \qquad (8.17b)$$

Similar to the derivation in Section 4.3, and as shown in Fig. 8.10(a), the maximum diffraction angle $\theta_{0\,max}$ for reconstructing a 3D object from the CG hologram is

$$\sin(\theta_{0\,max}) = \frac{\lambda}{2\Delta x}, \qquad (8.18)$$

where Δx is the pixel size on the hologram. The radius W_j of the WRP is

$$W_j = z_{1j} \tan\left[\sin^{-1}\left(\frac{\lambda}{2\Delta x}\right)\right] \approx z_{1j}\frac{\lambda}{2\Delta x}. \qquad (8.19)$$

In the first step of the algorithm mentioned earlier, the circular region of radius W_j can be approximated with a rectangular region [see Fig. 8.10(b)] in order to accelerate the algorithm. The length L_j of a side on the rectangular region is

$$L_j = \frac{2W_j}{\sqrt{2}} \approx \frac{z_{1j}\lambda}{1.4\Delta x}. \qquad (8.20)$$

It is worth noting that this WRP technique can be improved if a look-up table (LUT) is applied to the first step.[33] In the LUT method, the precalculated distributions of the complex amplitude

$$\frac{1}{R_{wj}} \exp(-jk_0 R_{wj}),$$

corresponding to all possible combinations of $|x_w - \xi_j|$, $|y_w - \eta_j|$ and z_{1j} in Eq. (8.15), are stored in the LUT. The distributions of the complex amplitude is found by referencing the LUT during the calculation of the first step. The memory usage of the LUT method [see Fig. 8.10(c)] can be computed as

$$memory = \sum_{\min[d_i]}^{\max[d_i]} L_j^2 \approx \sum_{\min[d_i]}^{\max[d_i]} \left[\frac{z_{1j}\lambda}{1.4\Delta x}\right]^2. \qquad (8.21)$$

As shown in Fig. 8.10(c), the areas of the rectangular regions on the WRP increase in proportion to z_{1j}, which gives the LUT a pyramidal structure. As an example, for a 3D object with a depth range 0.5 mm $< z_{1j} <$ 10.5 mm, the sampling pitch along the depth is 0.5 mm, $\Delta x = 8$ μm, $\lambda = 532$ nm, and the amount of memory needed is $\sim$2 Mb.

For computational complexity, let us define the average L_j to be

$$\bar{L} = \frac{1}{N} \sum_{j}^{N} L_j.$$

The average rectangular area is $\bar{L}^2$; thus, the computational complexity for the first step in the algorithm is approximately $2\alpha N \bar{L}^2$ [the factor 2 is for real and imaginary parts, and α is the arithmetic operation of addition and multiplication in the summation of Eq. (8.15)]. For the second step, which consists of two FFTs (note that the FFT of $g(x,y;z)$ can be found analytically), the complexity is around $2\beta N_x^2 \log N_x$, where the CG hologram size is $\approx N_x \times N_x$, where β is similar to α. The total computational complexity for both steps is

$$2\alpha N \bar{L}^2 + 2\beta N_x^2 \log N_x \approx 2\alpha N \bar{L}^2,$$

assuming that N (total number of pixels of the object) is very large compared to $\alpha N N_x^2$ where N_x is much larger than $\bar{L}$. Therefore, the computational complexity of the WRP technique is dramatically lower than traditional CGH.

8.6 Recent Developments in CGH

This section briefly discusses recent developments in CGH and their applications to interactive 3D visualization. It is widely accepted that CGH is the only technique with the potential to support full parallax 3D imaging capabilities with full depth cues, wide fields of view, and with high resolution. Although many methods to reduce the computational complexity for a high-resolution 3D imaging system have been proposed by many researchers,[37–40] practical systems able to compute and display high-definition CG holograms need more than 3.6 billion pixels for a 30-cm^2 area 3D TV. Thus, some additional tradeoffs are needed for a high-definition and affordable realization of a CGH system.

Some of the advances in CGH algorithms discussed here are the novel Fourier ping-pong (PP) algorithm, diffraction-specific (DS) algorithms, and parallel binarization techniques.[27] However, computer architectures for implementing these algorithms for interactive CGH calculation will be discussed in Chapter 11. Full-parallax (FP) 3D image generation is assumed for all of these techniques, but they can be modified to produce horizontal-parallax-only (HPO) holograms, which is more pertinent to the physiology of human eyes than vertical-parallax-only (VPO) holograms. Although HPO holograms are not as good as FP holograms, the computational resources are significantly reduced. Holographic stereogram techniques are not discussed in this section because they are not considered "true" holographic techniques, although they are briefly discussed in Chapter 11.

The common thread among all of these algorithms is the input 3D image. The 3D image is created using any commercially available 3D CAD tool and exported as a triangulated mesh with material properties, such as diffusivity and specular reflection based on the light properties and materials used. The exported mesh is filled with data points at a high resolution and then reconstructed holographically when the CG hologram is displayed.

8.6.1 Fourier ping-pong algorithm

Fourier ping-pong is a simple, Fourier-based CGH algorithm[41] that uses the Born approximation.[42] The Born approximation assumes that the 3D object is a nonabsorbing, self-luminous object. Wave propagation will produce a good reconstruction so long as there is not a high degree of overlap between the hidden surfaces and those selected for display.[42,43] An obscuration operator is introduced to allow hidden line-removal effects to be shown by the reconstructed 3D images. The first step in the PP algorithm slices the object into several planes perpendicular to the design plane. The next step propagates light through the image's first plane (plane 1), toward the design plane, until it meets the next plane (plane 2). The third step applies an occlusion operator that allows the selective attenuation and modulation of the light as it passes through plane 2. The fourth step adds light from plane 2 and continues propagation to plane 3. The process repeats for propagation through the other planes until the light reaches the design plane.

The physical simplification discussed here is called the lumped-element model (LEM) of propagation, wherein it is assumed that the absorption and transmission of the object is lumped into planes so that propagation occurs in three steps:

1. Free-space propagation: $u(x,y;\Delta z^-) = u(x,y;0) * g_{PSF}(x,y;\Delta z^-)$.
2. A transmission by a plane of the object:

$$u_0(x,y;\Delta z^+) = t(x,y;\Delta z)u(x,y;\Delta z^-).$$

3. Addition of a wave generated by sources at the surface:

$$u(x,y;\Delta z^+) = u_0(x,y;\Delta z^+) + u_1(x,y;\Delta z^+).$$

In the PP model, the propagation is performed in the Fourier domain and the transmission in the spatial domain. The majority of the computations, however, are in the Fourier transforms, going from spatial domain to Fourier domain and back (thus the term "ping-pong propagation"). Although the algorithm uses FFTs, it remains computationally intensive. Also, the drawback of such an algorithm is that it is limited to self-luminous 3D objects, which makes it an impractical approach for holographic displays.

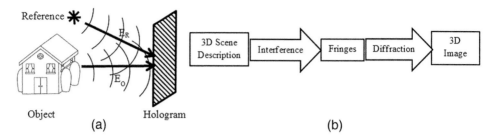

Figure 8.11   (a) Interference-based algorithm setup and (b) a traditional interference-based fringe computation algorithm that imitates the interference step in optical holography. Computed fringes are used to diffract light to form an image.[44]

8.6.2 Interference-based algorithms

Interference techniques are based on simulating an interferometric hologram recording process.[23] Figures 8.11(a) and 8.11(b) show the setup and process steps, respectively. This approach implements a 3D, scalar diffraction integral and is capable of generating very-high-definition images, including lighting effects and surface reflection properties. Therefore, it does not have the limitations of the PP technique. This algorithm is capable of reproducing all of the depth cues that the human visual system needs.[23] It is typically used as the benchmark by which other algorithms can be compared (see Section 8.5).

To decrease the computational complexity, a large array of elemental fringes can be precomputed and stored for later access during actual fringe computation. Each of the precomputed elemental fringe patterns represents the contribution of a single image element located at a certain 3D location of the 3D image volume. The assumption of linearity allows scaling a given elemental fringe (to represent the desired brightness of an image point) and then a summation at each applicable sample in the fringe.[44]

QinetiQ has developed this approach in its coherent raytrace (CRT) algorithm.[23] Their method uses a Fourier-transform geometry with an off-axis object and can incorporate rendering effects, such as shadowing and Phong shading of curved surfaces (i.e., an interpolation technique for surface shading in 3D computer graphics).[45] The name of the CRT comes from its requirement to calculate a phase along the ray. The main calculation can be performed as a double summation of all of the visible object points for each CGH pixel, as shown in Eq. (8.14). This many-to-many mapping between CG hologram pixels and object points results in a high computational complexity, and the WRP is a possible path forward.

8.6.3 Diffraction-specific algorithm

The original version of the diffraction-specific (DS) algorithm was created by Lucente.[44] The DS algorithm is a compromise between computational speed and image resolution. The CG hologram created using the DS algorithm renders high-resolution images that satisfy the requirements of the human

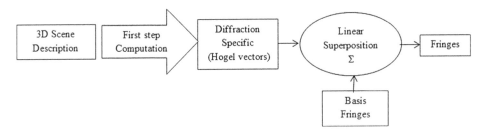

Figure 8.12 Schematic of diffraction-specific computing.[44]

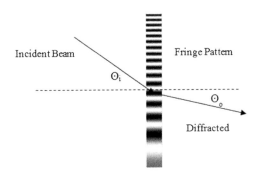

Figure 8.13 Diffraction grating.

visual system. Although the quality is not as good as the interference techniques discussed earlier, the computational speed is greater.

The previous technique involves summing elemental fringes to construct a hologram of a particular image. Each of these elemental fringes was precomputed using interference-based techniques to represent a particular image element. Because the fundamental job of a fringe pattern is to diffract light in a particular direction, DS computation provides a direct way of computing a fringe pattern by summing precomputed fringes that represent specific diffractive functions rather than specific image elements. In the previous technique, an array of elemental fringes was precomputed, where each element represents an image point. DS computation employs a precomputed set of basis fringes, where each basis fringe represents a specific diffractive purpose. Figure 8.12 shows a schematic of the DS technique. This algorithm separates the fringe computation from the 3D scene description through DS instructions.

The basis fringes are crucial in DS fringe computation. Each basis fringe diffracts light differently. Figure 8.13 shows local diffraction in the local region of a certain fringe pattern. The relationship between the angle of incidence and the diffracted beams is governed by

$$\frac{\lambda}{\Lambda} = \sin(\Theta_o) - \sin(\Theta_i), \tag{8.22}$$

where Θ_o and Θ_i are the diffracted and incident beam angles, respectively; λ is the wavelength of light; $\Lambda = 1/f$ is the fringe period; and f is the spatial frequency component. For a specific frequency f, light is diffracted in a specific direction. Looking at the problem in reverse, one can investigate which frequency f is needed to diffract a beam in a specific direction, which leads to a specific fringe pattern that yields a specific spectrum.

The DS algorithm to compute a CG hologram considers only the replay of a hologram using diffractive principles, rather than its interferometric formation, as in a CRT. Furthermore, an important part of the DS algorithm is controlling the information content of the final CG hologram, which is accomplished by spatially and spectrally quantizing the hologram. The spatial regions of the CG hologram are identified as "hogels;" each hogel is also spectrally quantized and identified as a hogel vector. The number of hogels and the number of hogel vector components determine the total information content (and thus the computational load of the hologram).[27,44] Therefore, a trade-off exists between the image resolution and computational load, depending on the number and size of hogels and hogel vectors.

The DS algorithm consists of four steps. There are two offline steps for a specific hologram and replay arrangement—(a) basis fringe generation and (b) diffraction table generation—and two online image-specific steps— (c) hogel vector generation and (d) hogel vector decoding.

(a) **Basis fringe generation:** A set of basis fringes are precomputed and used to map each DS or hogel vector to the corresponding fringe pattern or hogel. A basis fringe diffracts light at one given angle from a hogel. Basis fringes are the means by which the hologram diffracts light and constructs a 3D object.

(b) **Diffraction table generation:** The diffraction table maps the locations in the 3D image volume to a specific hogel and to its hogel vector components. In turn, the hogel vector selects which basis fringes from step (a) are required by a given hogel to construct the 3D image information.

(c) **Hogel vector generation:** The hogel vector of each hogel is constructed from the 3D input object data. The 2D image projections are rendered, and the z (depth) information associated with each pixel is recorded. The diffraction table from step (b) is used to fill the elements of the hogel vector.

(d) **Hogel vector decoding:** The DS hogel vectors from step (c) are combined with the precomputed basis fringes from step (a) to generate physical fringes or the final CG hologram.

Sampling the required wavefront at the center of the hogel results in some approximation in the wavefronts the hogel generates, which degrades the image quality. Some modifications of the previous algorithm are built on the spatial and temporal quantization to yield improved image quality (see Slinger et al.[27] and Lucente[44]).

8.6.4 Binarization algorithms

All of the previous techniques produce analog values for the CG hologram pixels. A quantization (binarization) stage is needed because many of the modulators used to reconstruct CG holograms are binary in nature. This binarization process introduces additional computational load and degradation in the replayed 3D image, which, with additional effort, should be minimized.

According to information theory, binarization has some adverse effects. The optical channel capacity C is a measure of the information contained in the CG hologram or the 3D image, and is defined as[27,46]

$$C = 8N_x N_y \log_2[Q]\log_2(1 + S/N), \qquad (8.23)$$

where N_x and N_y are the number of pixels along the x and y axes of the hologram, respectively; Q is the number of quantization levels; and S/N is the signal-to-noise ratio. Note that decreasing Q reduces the SNR in the image for a given image size. Therefore, for a given CG hologram, there is a trade-off in image quality and image size. Several algorithms can be used to binarize the hologram, including hard thresholding (HTh), error diffusion (ED), projection onto constrained sets (POCS), and simulated annealing direct binary search (SADBS). A standard metric to assess image quality is the normalized-mean-square error (NMRS), defined as[27]

$$NMSE = \frac{\sum\limits_{ROI} \|f(x,y) - \alpha h(x,y)\|^2}{\sum\limits_{ROI} |f(x,y)^2|}, \quad \text{where } \alpha = \frac{\sum\limits_{ROI} [f(x,y)h^*(x,y)]}{\sum\limits_{ROI} |h(x,y)^2|}, \quad (8.24)$$

and $f(x,y)$ and $h(x,y)$ are the desired and measured complex amplitudes of the image at the Fourier plane, respectively. Because the number of pixels is $>10^9$, binarization can be performed independently and in parallel by partitioning the CG hologram into subholograms.

Figure 8.14 illustrates the parallel-partitioned binarization method. One of the known drawbacks of such an approach is a reduction in image efficiency. The efficiency can be fixed by adjusting the solid state laser sources, which is adequate in most cases. Figure 8.15 shows a typical result of color binarization using optimized POCS. The mean NMRS value and efficiency of the binarized CGH output are 0.25 and 0.22, respectively.

8.7 CGH-based Display Systems

8.7.1 Advantages

CGH-based techniques are increasingly being used in 3D imaging displays, such as stereoscopic, autostereoscopic, and volumetric displays. CGH-based displays have unique features that are difficult to mimic using conventional approaches.[29]

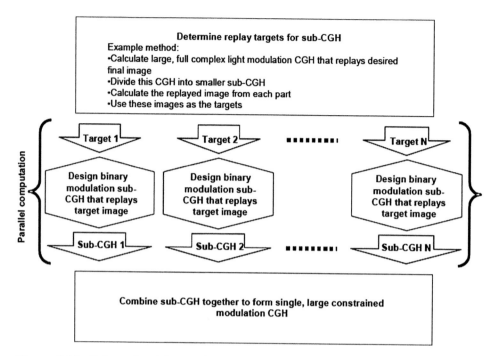

Figure 8.14 Schematic of the partitioned binarization technique, which is used for the efficient and parallel binarization of a large CG hologram.[27]

Figure 8.15 Results of color binarization using optimized POCS. Simulated replay from original analog CGH (left) and binarized CGH (right).[27]

(a) **Optical efficiency:** Due to the availability of the phase analog SLM, the diffraction efficiency is very high, contrary to traditional displays, which are highly inefficient because absorption or attenuation is used to vary pixels' gray levels.

(b) **Cascading:** CGH-based displays with a large number of pixels can be made by cascading multiple SLMs into a 2D array. Contrary to conventional displays, where pixel-level continuity is necessary to minimize the tiling effect, the CGH-based display's tiling effect is not an issue in the 3D projected image.

(c) **Tolerance to pixel defects:** Because every pixel in a 3D object/image affects all of the pixels in the hologram, defective pixels or even areas of pixels in a CGH do not cause noticeable degradation in the reconstructed image. However, in traditional displays based on one-to-one pixel mapping, even small numbers of dead pixels are noticeable, which has a tremendous impact on production cost.

(d) **Wide color range:** Existing display technologies use broadband color filters capable of displaying around 40 percent of the full color gamut. CGH-based systems use monochromatic lasers capable of displaying $\sim$90 percent of the color range that the human eye can detect.

(e) **Full depth cues:** Holographic techniques are the only 3D techniques that are capable of displaying a 3D image that contains all of the human visual system's depth cues. Other 3D techniques, such as stereoscopic, autostereoscopic, and volumetric displays, support some but not all of the depth cues. The lack of some of the depth cues or the presence of conflicting cues [such as vergence (eye rotation) versus accommodation (focusing)] that are coupled in the human visual system will induce discomfort and fatigue in some viewers. It is also important to note that truely 3D displays should be viewer-position dependent, i.e., different viewers at different locations should see different 3D images. Even advanced multiview autostereoscopic systems, such as integral imaging systems (which generate optical wavefront approximations), suffer from resolution limitations. Refer to Chapter 11 for a detailed description of several 3D display technologies.

(f) **Adjustable image resolution:** Traditional display technologies based on ray optics try to achieve diffraction-limited resolution or minimize diffraction and aberration as much as possible. CGH-based systems use the diffraction effect to record and reconstruct 3D images, with a variable resolution depending on the algorithm used.

(g) **Artifact-free binary modulation:** Current digital micromirror devices (DMDs), various ferroelectric liquid crystal microdisplays, and Silicon Light Machines' Grating Light Valve™ (GLV™) technology, are binary.[29] Grayscale is achieved through temporal multiplexing by running at high frame rates, which might produce image artifacts such as dithering. On the other hand, LCOS-based CGH can display grayscale images from binary fringe patterns without temporal multiplexing.

(h) **Aberration and distortion compensation:** Unlike traditional 3D display techniques, it is possible to precompensate the CGH pattern to prevent optical aberrations or imperfections due to the optical projection system used.[29]

8.7.2 Challenges

Despite of all of the advantages mentioned in the previous section, the main challenge of a CGH-based display technology is cost due to the need for a very high pixel count ($>10^9$) to achieve a high-resolution image of width I and field of view (FOV) $\Delta\theta$. Some of these disadvantages are as follows:[29]

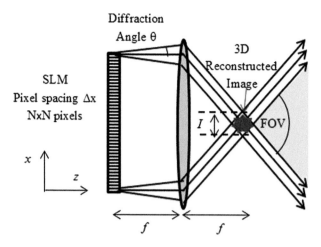

Figure 8.16 Relationship between image size (I) and FOV in true 3D image generation. $I \times \Delta\theta = N\lambda$ is independent of the focal length f.[29]

(a) **Image width and field of view**: In a direct-view CGH-based display, the product

$$I \times \Delta\theta = N\lambda \qquad (8.25)$$

is independent of the pixel size Δx. As an example, for $\lambda = 500$ nm, $I = 50$ cm, and $FOV = 60$ deg, the display requires $\sim 10^6$ pixels across the width or $\sim 10^{12}$ pixels for a full-parallax CG hologram with symmetrical horizontal and vertical specifications. For a horizontal-parallax-only (HPO) system, an acceptable pixel-count requirement is $\sim 10^{10}$, which is 1000 times higher than the pixel counts of current display systems. In addition to the pixel-count challenge, there is a need to update the SLM system at video rates. Both of these challenges remain major hurdles to overcome for widespread CGH systems.[29]

Consider the replay Fourier transform configuration setup in Fig. 8.16. The angle θ of the diffracted light from the CG hologram is governed by the grating equation; Eq. (8.22) can be rewritten as

$$\frac{\lambda}{\Lambda} = \sin\theta, \qquad (8.26)$$

where λ is the replay light wavelength, and Λ is the period of the fringe diffracting the light. According to Section 4.3 and Eq. (8.18), the largest value of θ is

$$\theta_{\text{max}} = \sin^{-1}\left(\frac{\lambda}{\Lambda}\right) = \sin^{-1}\left(\frac{\lambda}{2\Delta x}\right),$$

where Δx is the pixel spacing on the SLM displaying the CG hologram.

(b) **Image resolution:** For CGH-based 3D displays, the relation between the number of image points N_I in any plane perpendicular to the optical axis and the CG hologram's pixel count N_{CGH} is typically $N_{CGH} = 2N_I$. For many 3D display systems, meeting this constraint is less demanding than $I \times \Delta\theta/\lambda = N$.[29]

(c) **Image quality:** The CG hologram should always contain more information than the reconstructed image. The channel capacity C of a CGH-based optical system is determined by Eq. (8.23).[27,29,46] While maintaining $I \times \Delta\theta$, binary-quantized CGH fringe patterns can compromise the image quality by decreasing the amount of information passing through the system. In CGH systems, there always exists a trade-off between image resolution, size, FOV, and SNR.

(d) **Laser speckle:** To produce color images, the CG hologram must be illuminated with narrowband and spatially coherent laser light. However, laser speckle reduces the image quality. Therefore, speckle-reduction techniques, such as controlling laser system coherence or computing and time averaging different diffuser functions, are often used.[29]

8.7.3 Computational loads

For a detailed understanding of the computational load requirements in the CGH-based system described in this section, consider the following example. An HPO CG hologram with a spatial resolution comparable to high-definition television and a comfortable FOV requires ~400,000 horizontal and $N_y = 1{,}024$ vertical pixels. If each hogel contains $DT = 4{,}096$ pixels (diffraction table look-up entries), then around $N_{Hog} = 100$ hogels are needed. On average, each hogel will generate half of the possible image points $N_I = 1024$, so the total estimated multiplication and accumulation (MAC) load is

$$N_{Hog} \times N_I \times DT \times N_y = 430 \times 10^9 \text{ MACs.} \qquad (8.27)$$

In addition, temporal multiplexing can generate color, but it requires three times as many MACs. When converting a MAC to floating-point operations, the total computational load for a single frame is 2.6 teraflops. Moreover, this figure is for 1 frame per second; a 30-fps framerate needs 78 teraflops to guarantee a perceptually smooth image update during interactive operation.[29]

References

1. J. W. Goodman, *Introduction to Fourier Optics*, 2nd Ed., McGraw-Hill, New York (1996).
2. P. Hariharan, *Basics of Holography*, Cambridge University Press, Cambridge, UK (2002).

3. L. B. Lesem, P. M. Hirsch, and J. A. Jordan, "Scientific applications: Computer synthesis of holograms for 3D display," *J. Comm. ACM* **11**(10), 661–674 (1968).

4. D. Leseberg and C. Frère, "Computer-generated holograms of 3D objects composed of tilted planar segments," *Appl. Opt.* **27**(14), 3020–3024 (1988).

5. A. Lohmann, "A prehistory of computer-generated holography," *Opt. Photon. News* **19**(2), 36–41 (2008).

6. B. R. Brown and A. W. Lohmann, "Complex spatial filtering with binary masks," *Appl. Opt.* **5**(6), 967–969 (1966).

7. A. W. Lohmann and D. P. Paris, "Binary Fraunhofer holograms generated by computer," *Appl. Opt.* **6**(10), 1739–1748 (1967).

8. T. C. Poon and J. P. Liu, *Introduction to Modern Digital Holography*, Cambridge University Press, Cambridge, UK (2014).

9. L. B. Lesem, P. M. Hirsch, and J. A. Jordan, Jr., "The kinoform: a new wavefront reconstruction device," *IBM J. Res. Dev.* **13**(2), 150–155 (1969).

10. D. C. Chu, J. R. Fienup, and J. W. Goodman, "Multiemulsion on-axis computer-generated hologram," *Appl. Opt.* **12**(7), 1386–1388 (1973).

11. W. H. Lee, "Computer-Generated Holograms: Techniques and Applications," in *Progress in Optics XVI*, E. Wolf, ed., 119–232, Elsevier, Amsterdam (1978).

12. A. Palevičius, B. Narijauskaitė, and G. Janušas, "Generation and Replication of Computer-Generated Hologram," *Proc. World Congress Eng. Comp. Sci.* **I**, 621–623 (2012).

13. A. Palevičius, G. Janušas, B. Narijauskaitė, M. Mikolajunas, and D. Virzonis, "Implementation of computer-generated holograms using 3D electron beam lithography," *J. Vibroengineering* **11**(3), 407–414 (2009).

14. J. A. D. Caballero, S. Takahashi, S. J. Lee, and G. Barbastathis, "Design and Fabrication of Computer-Generated Holograms for Fresnel Domain Lithography," *Digital Holography and 3D Imaging*, Vancouver, BC (2009).

15. P. Spiro, *Electroforming*, 2nd Ed., Robert Draper, Teddington, UK (1971).

16. S. Tamulevicius et al., "Optical characterization of diffractive optical elements replicated in polymers," *J. Micro/Nanolith MEMS MOEMS* **5**(1), 013004 (2006) [doi: 10.1117/1.2170098].

17. R. W. Gerchberg and W. O. Saxton, "A practical algorithm for the determination of phase from image and diffraction plane pictures," *Optik* **35**(2), 237–246 (1972).

18. J. R. Fienup, "Phase retrieval algorithms: a comparison," *Appl. Opt.* **21**(15), 2758–2769 (1982).

19. J. R. Fienup, "Phase retrieval algorithms: a personal tour," *Appl. Opt.* **52**(1), 45–56 (2013).

20. L. G. Neto, P. S. P. Cardona, G. A. Cirino, R. D. Mansano, and P. Verdonck, "Implementation of Fresnel full complex-amplitude digital holograms," *Opt. Eng.* **43**(11), (2004) [doi: 10.1117/1.1805566].

21. D. Brady, *Optical Imaging and Spectroscopy*, John Wiley & Sons, Hoboken, NJ (2008).

22. J. P. Waters, "Holographic image synthesis utilizing theoretical methods," *Appl. Phys. Lett.* **9**(11), 405–407 (1968).

23. M. Lucente, "Interactive computation of holograms using a look-up table," *J. Electron. Imaging* **2**(1), 28–34 (1993) [doi: 10.1117/12.133376].

24. T. Ito, K. Yoshida, S. Takahashi, T. Yabe, and T. Kunugi, "Special-purpose computer for holography HORN-2," *Comp. Phys. Comm.* **93**(1), 13–20 (1996).

25. J. L. Juárez-Peréz, A. Olivares-Peréz, and L. R. Berriel-Valdos, "Nonredundant calculations for creating Fresnel holograms," *Appl. Opt.* **36**(29), 7437–7443 (1997).

26. H. Yoshikawa, S. Iwase, and T. Oneda, "Fast computation of Fresnel holograms employing difference," *Proc. SPIE* **3956**, 48–55 (2000) [doi: 10.1117/12.380022].

27. C. Slinger et al., "Recent developments in computer-generated holography: toward a practical electroholography system for interactive 3D visualization," *Proc. SPIE* **5290**, (2004) [doi: 10.1117/12.526690].

28. M. Lucente, "Interactive Three-dimensional Holographic Displays: Seeing the Future in Depth," *Comp. Graphics* **31**(2), 63–67 (1997).

29. C. Slinger, C. Cameron, and M. Stanley, "Computer-generated holography as a generic display technology," *Computer* **38**(8), 46–53 (2005).

30. K. Matsushima, "Computer-generated holograms for three-dimensional surface objects with shade and texture," *Appl. Opt.* **44**(22), 4607–4614 (2005).

31. H. Yoshikawa, T. Yamaguchi, and R. Kitayama, "Real-time generation of full color image hologram with compact distance look-up table," *Digital Holography and 3D Imaging*, Vancouver, BC (2009).

32. T. Shimobaba, N. Masuda, and T. Ito, "Simple and fast calculation algorithm for computer-generated hologram with wavefront recording plane," *Opt. Lett.* **34**(20), 3133–3135 (2009).

33. T. Shimobaba, H. Nakayama, N. Masuda, and T. Ito, "Rapid calculation algorithm of Fresnel computer-generated-hologram using look-up table and wavefront-recording plane methods for three-dimensional display," *Opt. Exp.* **18**(19), 19504–19509 (2010).

34. T. C. Poon, "On the fundamentals of optical scanning holography," *Am. J. Phys.* **76**(8), 739–745 (2008).

35. P. Tsang, W. K. Cheung, T. C. Poon, and C. Zhou, "Holographic video at 40 frames per second for 4-million object points," *Opt. Exp.* **19**(16), 15205–15211 (2011).

36. P. Tsang and T. C. Poon, "Review on theory and applications of wavefront recording plane framework in generation and processing of digital holograms," *Chinese Opt. Lett.* **11**(1), 010902 (2013).

37. P. St-Hilaire, S. A. Benton, M. Lucente, J. Underkoffer, and H. Yoshokawa, "Realtime holographic display: improvements using multichannel acousto-optic modulator and holographic optical elements," *Proc. SPIE* **1461**, 254–261 (1991) [doi: 10.1117/12.44734].

38. P. St-Hilaire, "Scalable optical architecture for electronic holography," *Opt. Eng.* **34**(10), 2900–2911 (1995) [doi: 10.1117/12.210756].

39. K. Maeno, N. Fukaya, O. Nishikawa, K. Sato, and T. Honda, "Electroholographic display using 15 Mega pixels LCD," *Proc. SPIE* **2652**, 15–23 (1996) [doi: 10.1117/12.236065].

40. C. Slinger et al., "Progress and prospects for practical electroholographic display systems," *Proc. SPIE* **4296**, 18–32 (2001) [doi: 10.1117/12.429455].

41. Y. Ichioka, M. Izumi, and Y. Suzuki, "Scanning halftone plotter and computer-generated continuous tone hologram," *Appl. Opt.* **10**(2), 403–411 (1971).

42. D. J. Dallas, "Computer-generated holograms," in *The Computer In Optical Research: Methods and Applications*, B. Frieden and R. Barakat, eds., Springer-Verlag, Berlin (1980).

43. T. C. Poon, *Digital Holography and Three-Dimensional Displays: Principles and Applications*, Springer, New York (2006).

44. M Lucente, "Diffraction-specific fringe computation for electroholography," Doctoral dissertation, MIT Dept. of Electrical Engineering and Computer Science, Cambridge, MA (Sept.1994).

45. B. T. Phong, "Illumination for computer-generated pictures," *Communications of ACM*, **18**(6), 311–317 (1975).

46. I. J. Cox and C. J. R. Sheppard, "Information capacity and resolution in an optical system," *J. Opt. Soc. Am. A* **3**(8), 1152–1158 (1986).

Chapter 9
Compressive Sensing and Compressive Holography

9.1 Compressive Sensing: Background

It is well known from communication theory that for a sampled signal, the sampling rate must be greater than twice the signal bandwidth for faithful reproduction of the original signal. The concept of sampling at the Nyquist rate was postulated by Shannon in 1949;[1] in the same year, Golay introduced the idea of artificial discrete multiplex coding in optical measurements.[2] More than 50 years later, Candes, Tao, and Romberg[3,4] and Donoho[5] have demonstrated that signals that are sparse in a certain basis and sampled by multiplex encodings may be accurately inferred with high probability using many fewer measurements than suggested by Shannon's sampling theorem[6] in a process referred to as *compressive sensing* (CS). This section summarizes the basic concept of CS and provides an example of its application to holography. As stated by Brady et al.,[6] holography can be considered as a complex encoding of a signal (recording both the amplitude and phase) to which CS may be applied. In conventional optical imaging, only the intensities (no phase information) can be recorded, which results in rather poor measurement conditioning.

The objective of CS is to recover an accurate representation of the signal from only a few samples. The keys to CS are sparsity, the l_1 norm, and the uncorrelated measurement scheme. The l_1 norm of a vector $\mathbf{c}$ is defined as

$$\left(\|\mathbf{c}\|_1 = \sum_i |c_i| \right),$$

where c_i are the components of the vector $\mathbf{c}$, whereas the l_2 norm adds the square of the absolute value of the components of the vector as

$$\left(\|\mathbf{c}\|_2 = \left(\sum_i |c_i|^2 \right)^{1/2} \right).$$

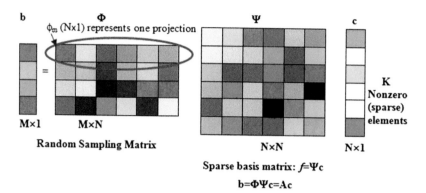

Figure 9.1 Schematic of the different matrices used for compressive sensing.

Samples f_i of a function f can be expressed as a linear combination of certain basis functions as

$$f_i = \psi_{ij}c_j, \tag{9.1}$$

where $\Psi = [\psi_{ij}]$ is an $N \times N$ matrix formed from basis functions such as those in the discrete cosine transform (DCT), commonly used for this purpose. The $N \times 1$ matrix (or vector) $[c_j]$ contains information regarding the content of the vector $[f_i]$ (which is an $N \times 1$ matrix) and is assumed to be K-sparse (i.e., with K nonzero entries). Consider that only a few random samples b_k of f are measured. The resulting vector $[b_k]$ (an $M \times 1$ matrix) can be expressed as

$$b_k = \phi_{ki}f_i, \tag{9.2}$$

where $\Phi = [\phi_{ki}]$ is a rectangular $M \times N$ matrix ($L < M \ll N$) that comprises a subset of the rows of the identity operator and represents the measurement process. The vector $[c_j]$ (an $N \times 1$ matrix) can be found by solving

$$A_{kj}c_j = b_k, A_{kj} = \phi_{ki}\psi_{ij}, \tag{9.3}$$

where $[A_{kj}]$ is an $M \times N$ matrix. If $[c_j]$ is known, then $[f_i]$ can be recovered. Figure 9.1 shows a typical schematic of the different matrices involved in compressive sensing.

Because $[\phi_{ki}]$ is a rectangular matrix, so is $[A_{kj}]$, with more columns than rows, which implies that Eq. (9.3) is an underdetermined system of simultaneous equations, with more unknowns than equations. Therefore, to recover $c'_j s$ (and thus $f'_i s$), a nonlinear regularizaton involving the l_1 norm (mentioned earlier) is imposed to find the closest approximation $\hat{c}'_j s$ to $c'_j s$ and, thus, the closest approximation $\hat{f}'_i s$ to $f'_i s$. A condition for this arrangement to work is[3–5]

$$M \approx K \log N \ll N. \tag{9.4}$$

Note that if $N \gg 1$, then the previous condition is consistent with the prior assumption $K < M \ll N$.

The CS theory ensures highly accurate reconstruction for multiplex encoders that sufficiently satisfy a condition called the restricted isometry property (RIP).[3-5] This condition implies that for any K-sparse $[c_j]$ to be reconstructed accurately and reliably, the corresponding $M \times K$ submatrices Φ_T, composed of K columns of the matrix Φ, must form a nearly isometric transformation. In other words, all of the eigenvalues of any Gram matrix $(G = [g_{ij}] = \langle g_j, g_i \rangle$, where $\langle g_j, g_i \rangle$ is the inner product of the jth and i^{th} columns $g_j, g_i)$ of any K-column submatrix Φ_T are distributed around 1, which ensures that any Φ_T is well conditioned.

After these conditions are satisfied, a precise reconstruction can be accomplished with high probability if the following is solved:

$$\hat{c} = \arg\min_c \|c\|_1, \quad \text{such that } b = \Phi f = \Phi \Psi c = Ac, \tag{9.5}$$

where $\|c\|_1 = \sum_i |c_i|$ is the l_1 norm.

Note that, based on the uncertainty principle, the two bases (Φ, Ψ) should be incoherent. The coherence coefficient can be found using either one of the two following equations:

$$\mu_1(\Phi, \Psi) = \sqrt{N} . \max_{\substack{1 \le k \le M \\ 1 \le j \le N}} |\langle \phi_k . \psi_j \rangle| \in \left[1, \sqrt{N}\right],$$

$$\mu_2(\Phi, \Psi) = \max_{1 \le i \ne j \le N} \left(\frac{|A_i^T . A_j|}{\|A_i\|_{l_2} . \|A_j\|_{l_2}} \right) = \max_{1 \le i \ne j \le N} \left(\frac{G_{i,j}}{\|G_j\|_{l_2}} \right). \tag{9.6}$$

Because coherence measures the largest correlation between any two elements of Φ and Ψ, μ_1 should be as close to 0 as possible. The complex nature of holography means that smaller values for the coherence coefficient can be obtained, which is advantageous for compressive sensing.

In summary, the following optimization problem—find c given that $b = Ac$—can be solved using the

- l_2 norm (minimum energy), which is fast but often wrong:

$$\hat{c} = \arg\min_{b=Ac} \|c\|_{l_2} = \arg\min_{b=Ac} \left(\sum_{i=1}^{N} |c_i|^2 \right)^{1/2} \xrightarrow{\text{solution}} \hat{c} = A^*(AA^*)^{-1}b; \tag{9.7a}$$

- l_0 norm, which is correct but slow due to computational complexity (for a Gaussian measurement matrix Φ, $M = K + 1 \ll N$):

$$\hat{c} = \arg\min_{b=Ac} \|c\|_{l_0} = \arg\min_{b=Ac} \left(\sum_{i=1}^{N} |c_i|^0 \right)$$

$$= \arg\min_{b=Ac} \# \{i : c(i) \ne 0\} \xrightarrow{\text{solution-NP}} \binom{N}{K}; \quad \text{or} \tag{9.7b}$$

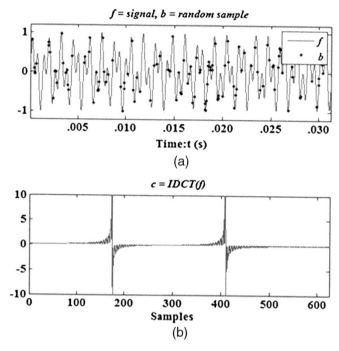

Figure 9.2 (a) Random samples of the original signal generated by the "1" key on a touchtone phone, and (b) the inverse discrete cosine transform of the signal.[7]

- l_1 norm, which is also correct but uses oversampling (for a Gaussian measurement matrix Φ, $M > CK \log(N/K) \ll N$):

$$\hat{c} = \arg\min_{b=Ac} \|c\|_{l_1} = \arg\min_{b=Ac} \left(\sum_{i=1}^{N} |c_i|\right) \xrightarrow{\text{solution}} \min\left(\sum_{i=1}^{N} |c_i|\right)$$

$$\text{such that } \|b - Ac\|_{l_2}^2 \leq \varepsilon \text{ or } \arg\min_{b=Ac} \|\nabla c\|_{l_1}, \tag{9.7c}$$

which can be solved using iterative techniques, such as basis pursuit, iterative greedy algorithms, iterative orthogonal-matching pursuit (OMP), and tree-matching pursuit (TMP).

Now consider the following example. The signal generated by the "1" key on a touchtone telephone is the sum of two sinusoids with incommensurate frequencies. Let $f(t) = \sin(1394\pi t) + \sin(3266\pi t)$.[7] This example uses the DCT as the basis. The sampling rate is 40 kHz, and the signal total time is 0.125 s. Figure 9.2(a) shows a portion of this signal along with the m random samples that are taken. Figure 9.2(b) shows the coefficients c_j, obtained by taking the inverse DCT of f_i, with two spikes at the appropriate frequencies. The compressed signal is now a vector $[b_k]$ of m samples from f_i using the matrix $[\phi_{ki}]$. The matrix A is constructed by multiplying $[\phi_{ki}]$ with $[\psi_{ij}]$. To reconstruct the signal, a solution to $A_{kj}\hat{c}_j = b_k$ must be found that minimizes

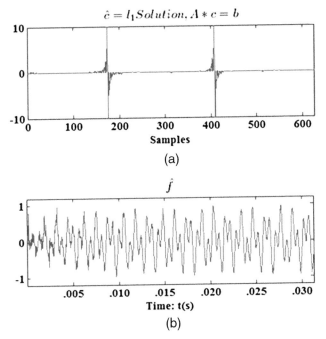

Figure 9.3 (a) The l_1 solution to $A_{kj}\hat{c}_j = b_k$, and (b) $\hat{f}$, a signal that is nearly identical to the original signal f.[7]

the l_1 norm of $\hat{c}_j$.[8] This is a nonlinear optimization problem, and there are several MATLAB-based programs available to solve it.

Figure 9.3 shows the resulting solution $\hat{c}_j$. Moreover, the DCT $\hat{f}_i$ of $\hat{c}_j$, shown in the lower plot, closely resembles the original signal f_i. For comparison, Fig. 9.4 is similar to Fig. 9.3, but it uses the traditional l_2, or least squares, solution computed by the pseudo-inverse function in MATLAB. As is obvious, it does not reproduce the original signal.

The MATLAB code CS.m, shown in Table 9.1, is used to perform this example. This script calls the l1eq_pd.m function found on the CD-ROM, which solves for $\hat{c} = \arg\min_{b=Ac} \|c\|_{l_1}$ such that $Ac = b$.

9.2 Compressive Holography

In compressive (sensing) holography (CsH), the "samples" f_i of a function (or object) f are voxels in a 3D volume. Gabor (or inline) holography can record a 3D object in 2D space; therefore, the measurement matrix Φ is related to the Fourier transform of the object. The matrix Φ generates uniformly distributed random samples over the spatial frequency domain and is assumed to satisfy the RIP with high probability. Holography is a comparatively effective encoder for compressive imaging because holographic multiplex measurement weights are complex valued.[6]

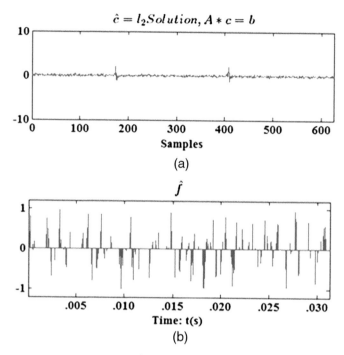

Figure 9.4 (a) The l_2 solution, and (b) $\hat{f}$, a signal that bears little resemblance to the original signal.[7]

Note that DH is not a 3D tomographic imaging technique because 3D object estimation from coherent scattering data is ill-posed.[9] (The solution to this problem is discussed in Chapter 6 regarding the holographic tomography technique.) Thus, in principle, decompression should enable 3D tomography from a single 2D digital hologram without needing multiple angles. Compressive sensing holography directly collects a smaller number of measurements M than the number of voxels N in the reconstruction (i.e., an underdetermined problem, as explained in Section 9.1). The word "compressive" means that the holographic sampling or sensing process encodes and compresses 3D datacube (i.e., voxel) information into 2D holographic measurements. This encoding is then inverted using CS theory.[3-5]

A Gabor-type setup is shown in Fig. 9.5. The irradiance recorded on the CCD has the following form [see Eq. (2.10)]:

$$I(x,y) = |E_R + E_O(x,y)|^2$$
$$= |E_R|^2 + |E_O(x,y)|^2 + E_R^* E_O(x,y) + E_R E_O^*(x,y)$$
$$\propto 2\,\mathrm{Re}\{E_O(x,y)\} + e(x,y), \tag{9.8}$$

where e is regarded as the error. The assumption in writing the last equality is that the reference beam and the diffracted field E_O from the

Table 9.1 MATLAB code "CS.m" showing the signal recovery from its samples using the l_1 and l_2 norms (see Figs. 9.2 to 9.4).

```
1   %"Magic" reconstruction: compressed sensing.
2   %Use "L1 magic" by Justin Romberg.
3   %f = signal = tone from "1" key on a touchtone phone.
4   %b = random subsample.
5   Fs = 40000;
6   t = (1:Fs/8)'/Fs;
7   f = (sin(2*pi*697*t) + sin(2*pi*1633*t))/2;
8   n = length(f);
9   m = ceil(n/10);
10  k = randperm(n)';
11  k = sort(k(1:m));
12  b = f(k);
13  %Plot f and b.
14  %Plot idct(f) = inverse discrete cosine transform.
15  axf =[ 0 max(t)/4 -1.2 1.2];
16  axd =[ 0 n/8 -10 10];
17  figure(1);
18  subplot(2,1,1)
19  plot(t,f,'b-',t(k),b,'k.')
20  axis(axf);
21  set(gca,'xtick',.005:.005:.030,'ytick',-1:1, ...
22  'xticklabel',{ '.005',' .010',' .015', ...
23  '.020',' .025',' .030'})
24  title('f = signal, b = random sample')
25  subplot(2,1,2)
26  plot(idct(f))
27  axis(axd);
28  set(gca,'xtick',0:100:600)
29  title('c = idct(f)')
30  drawnow
31  %A = rows of DCT matrix with indices of random sample
32  A = zeros(m,n);
33  for i = 1:m
34  ek = zeros(1,n);
35  ek(k(i)) = 1;
36  A(i,:) = idct(ek);
37  end
38  %y = l_2 solution to A*y = b.
39  y = pinv(A)*b;
40  %x = l_1 solution to A*x = b.
41  %Use "L1 magic".
42  x = l1eq_pd(y,A,A',b,5e-3,32);
43  %Plot x and dct(x).
44  %Good comparison with f.
45  figure(2)
46  subplot(2,1,1)
47  plot(x)
48  axis(axd);
49  set(gca,'xtick',0:100:600)
50  title('x = {\it l} _1 solution, A*x = b ')
51  subplot(2,1,2)
52  plot(t,dct(x))
53  axis(axf);
```

(continued)

Table 9.1 (*Continued*)

```
54  set(gca,'xtick',.005:.005:.030,'ytick',-1:1, ...
55  'xticklabel',{'.005','.010','.015',...
56  '.020','.025','.030'})
57  title('dct(x)')
58  %Plot y and dct(y).
59  %Lousy comparison with f.
60  figure(3)
61  subplot(2,1,1)
62  plot(y)
63  axis(axd);
64  set(gca,'xtick',0:100:600)
65  title('y={\it l}_2 solution, A*y=b ')
66  subplot(2,1,2)
67  plot(t,dct(y))
68  axis(axf);
69  set(gca,'xtick',.005:.005:.030,'ytick',-1:1, ...
70  'xticklabel',{'.005','.010','.015',...
71  '.020','.025','.030'})
72  title('dct(y)')
73  %Play three sounds
74  sound(f,Fs)
75  pause(1)
76  sound(dct(x),Fs);
77  pause(1)
78  sound(dct(y),Fs)
```

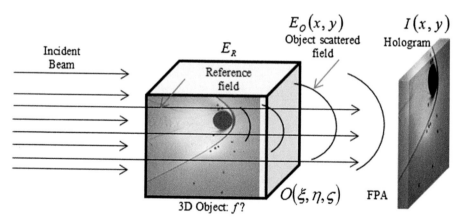

Figure 9.5 Typical Gabor-type setup using the transmissive geometry of an object surrounded by several smaller objects.

object(s) have approximately equal path lengths. If the objects are in a 3D volume, the composite scattered field from the object(s) can be generically expressed as

$$E_O(x,y;z) = \iiint O(\xi,\eta,\varsigma) g_{PSF}(x-\xi, y-\eta, z-\varsigma) d\xi d\eta d\varsigma, \qquad (9.9)$$

where $O(\xi,\eta,\varsigma)$ is the 3D object scattering density, and g_{PSF}, from Eq. (2.7), is the spatial impulse response, with a Fourier transform or spatial transfer function for propagation given by Eq. (2.4). Equation (9.9) represents the relation between the 3D object scattering density and the 2D measurement data. A typical Gabor-type setup using the transmissive geometry of an object surrounded by small objects is shown in Fig. 9.5.

Let N be the number of pixels of the detector and Δ_x, Δ_y, Δ_z be the sampling period in the x, y, and z axes, respectively. The 2D sampled field at the detector plane (with the sample spacing defined earlier) can be expressed by[6]

$$E_{n_1,n_2} = \Im_{x,y}^{-1}\left\{\sum_l \exp\left[-jl\Delta z\sqrt{k_o^2 - m_1^2\Delta_k^2 - m_2^2\Delta_k^2}\right] \cdot \tilde{O}_{m_1,m_2,l}\right\}, \qquad (9.10)$$

where $\tilde{O}$ is the Fourier transform of O, and Δ_k is the spatial frequency spacing. The indices in Eq. (9.10) can be viewed as a 2D slice of the 3D Fourier transform of O and can be canonically rewritten as

$$\bar{b} = \Im_{x,y}^{-1}P\Im_{x,y}f \equiv \Phi f, \qquad (9.11)$$

where $\Im_{x,y}$, $\Im_{x,y}^{-1}$ represent the forward and inverse (discrete, 2D) Fourier transform operators, respectively, and P represents the propagator or discretized transfer function in Eq. (9.10). Because the measured data is not the optical field but the intensity $I = 2\,\mathrm{Re}\{E_O\} + e$, Eq. (9.8) causes Eq. (9.11) to become

$$b = 2\,\mathrm{Re}\{\bar{b}\} = 2\,\mathrm{Re}\{\Im_{x,y}^{-1}P\Im_{x,y}f\} + e \equiv 2\,\mathrm{Re}\{\Phi f\} + e. \qquad (9.12)$$

Note that optical measurement over a finite aperture D is band-limited. The spatial resolution in imaging systems is assumed to be inversely proportional to the limits of the band volume, which yields the transverse resolution $\Delta_{x,y} = (\lambda z)/D$ [see Eq. (4.5)] and the longitudinal resolution $\Delta_z = \lambda[(2z)/D]^2$. The relationship between the transverse and longitudinal resolutions is identical to the relations between the transverse and longitudinal magnifications during holographic reconstruction.[10] An object feature of size w then produces a diffraction of size $\lambda z/w$. Assuming that this diffracted field fills the detector of size D, it is clear that $\Delta_{x,y} = w$, and thus $\Delta_z = 4w^2/\lambda$. Therefore, the longitudinal resolution also depends on the feature size of the object.[6]

Equation (9.12) is an ill-posed optimization problem and can be solved by minimizing an objective function $O(f)$ via the following:

(a) Selecting a basis Ψ, such as a wavelet basis on which f may be assumed to be sparse. Thus, f can be estimated as

$$\hat{f} = \arg\min_f O(f) = \arg\min_f \left[\frac{1}{2} \| b - 2\operatorname{Re}(\Phi f) \|_{l_2}^2 + \lambda \Gamma(f) \right]$$

$$= \arg\min_f \left[\frac{1}{2} \| b - 2\operatorname{Re}(\Phi f) \|_{l_2}^2 + \lambda \| \Psi f \|_{l_1} \right], \tag{9.13}$$

where $\Gamma(f)$ is a regularizer, and λ is the regularization parameter. Regularization introduces additional information to solve an ill-posed problem to prevent overfitting. Minimizing Eq. (9.13) is a compromise between the lack of fitness of a candidate estimate f to the observed data b, which is measured by $\| b - \Phi f \|^2$, and its degree of undesirability, given by $\| \Psi f \|_{l_1}$.

(b) Enforcing a sparsity constraint on f in the total variation (TV) domain is equivalent to finding f that minimizes the TV [using the two-step iterative shrinkage/thresholding (TwIST) algorithm].[6] Therefore, f can be estimated as

$$\hat{f} = \arg\min_f O(f) = \arg\min_f \left[\frac{1}{2} \| b - 2\operatorname{Re}(\Phi f) \|_{l_2}^2 + \lambda \Gamma(f) \right]$$

$$= \arg\min_f \left[\frac{1}{2} \| b - 2\operatorname{Re}(\Phi f) \|_{l_2}^2 + \lambda \| f \|_{TV} \right], \tag{9.14}$$

with $\| f \|_{TV}$ defined as

$$\| f \|_{TV} = \sum_l \sum_{n_1} \sum_{n_2} |\nabla(f_l)_{n_1,n_2}|$$

$$= \sum_l \sum_{n_1} \sum_{n_2} \sqrt{(f_{l,n_1+1,n_2} - f_{l,n_1,n_2})^2 + (f_{l,n_1,n_2+1} - f_{l,n_1,n_2})^2},$$

$$\tag{9.15}$$

where f_l is a 2D plane of the 3D object datacube. The TwIST algorithm[11–12] is usually adopted to solve this optimization problem; it minimizes a convex quadratic problem with the addition of a sparsity constraint. The sparsity constraint is enforced on the gradient of the object estimate. Table 9.2 explores several iterative algorithms to solve the regularization problem $\hat{c} = \arg\min_c [\frac{1}{2} \| Ac - b \|_{l_2}^2 + \lambda \Gamma(c)]$, with the shrinkage operator $\mathcal{T}_\lambda(x) = \arg\min_z \frac{1}{2} \| z - x \|_2^2 + \lambda \Gamma(z)$, where $\vec{\nabla}(\frac{1}{2} \| Ac - b \|_{l_2}^2) = A^T(Ac - b)$, and α and β are parameters.

The tomographic compressive holography (TCH) technique[13,14] is used to improve axial resolution for accurate 3D reconstruction of the targets and their distribution (see Fig. 9.6). In the transmissive case, because the illuminating beam "floods" the target, the light that is transmitted between

Table 9.2   Typical iterative algorithms.

Algorithm Name	Formula
Gradient descent: $\lambda = 0$	$c^{k+1} = c^k - A^T(Ac^k - b)$
Iterative shrinkage thresholding (IST): $\lambda \neq 0$	$c^{k+1} = (1 - \beta)c^k + \beta \mathcal{T}_\lambda(c^k - A^T(Ac^k - b))$
Two-step iterative method (TwSIM): $\lambda \neq 0$	$c^{k+1} = \alpha c^k + (1 - \alpha)c^{k-1} - \beta \mathcal{T}_\lambda(A^T(Ac^k - b))$
Two-step iterative shrinkage thresholding (TwIST): $\lambda \neq 0$	$c^{k+1} = (\alpha - \beta)c^k + (1 - \alpha)c^{k-1} + \beta \mathcal{T}_\lambda(c^k - A^T(Ac^k - b))$

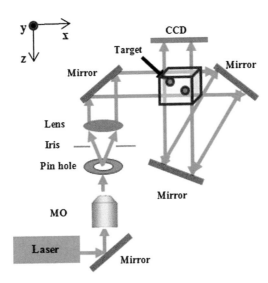

Figure 9.6   Typical TCH setup with transmissive geometry.

the object(s) acts like a reference beam that interferes with the object field and records the Gabor hologram. For reflective objects, a Leith–Upatnieks-type holographic setup can be employed. A tomographic technique for the recording and 3D shape reconstruction of water droplets and lenslets employing the SHOT-MT and based on Fresnel back-propagation is described in Chapter 6. Thus, to visualize the 3D shape, multiple projections from multiple directions (as in tomographic imaging systems) are required. Therefore, compressive holographic reconstruction for 3D volume reconstruction is used in each projection, and then the 3D shape is reconstructed using the SHOT-MT by multiplying the multiple reconstructed intensities $I = \prod_1^M I_j$, as shown in Chapter 6.

9.3 Experimental Setups and MATLAB Examples

As a first experimental setup of holographic tomography (see Fig. 9.6), the 3D reconstruction of a collection of small air bubbles (phase objects) in an aquarium is performed using the TCH-MT method, with different

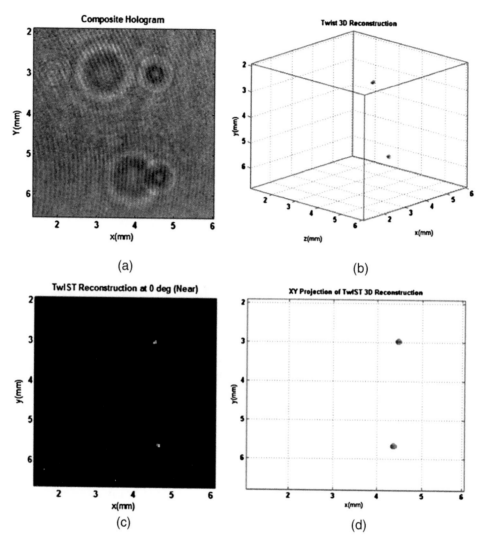

Figure 9.7 (a) Single-beam hologram of two bubbles. The top two are for the first bubble, and the bottom two are for the second bubble. The holograms to the left are from illumination of the bubbles along the *x* axis (90 deg with respect to the normal to the CCD), whereas the holograms to the right are from illumination of the bubbles along the *z* axis (0 deg with respect to the normal to the CCD). The left holograms look larger because the objects are farther from the CCD, whereas the right holograms are smaller because the objects are closer to the CCD. (b) TwIST 3D reconstruction, where $\lambda = 543$ nm with 6.7-μm pixels; (c) TwIST reconstructed hologram at 61.8 cm; (d) *yz* projection of the TwIST 3D view in (b); (e) TwIST reconstructed hologram at 20.6 cm; (f) *xy* projection of the TwIST 3D view in (b); (g) 3D sum of the 0-deg and 90-deg TwIST reconstructions, each of which exhibit a longitudinal resolution on the order of $\sim 1 - 2$ mm, compared to (h) the 3D sum of the 0-deg and 90-deg Fresnel reconstructions, which consist of a single in-focus plane each, lofted into a 3D volume.

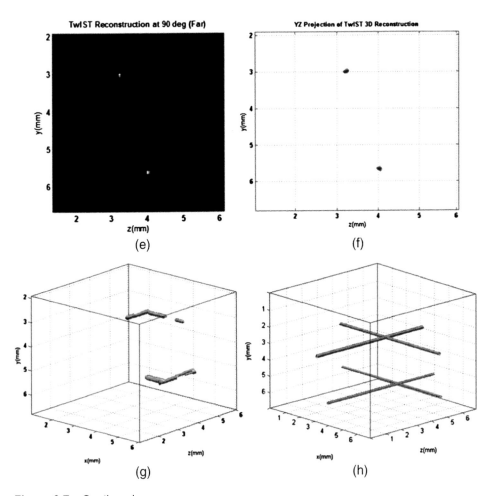

Figure 9.7 *Continued.*

sizes and distances from the detector. A green HeNe source ($\lambda = 543$ nm) and a Lumenera camera with 1024×1024 pixels (6.7 μm in size) is used.

Using the single-beam/single-CCD configuration shown in Fig. 9.6, the beam is passed through the air bubble sample at 90 deg and 0 deg with respect to the normal to the CCD, and a composite hologram is recorded in a single shot [Fig. 9.7(a)]. The illumination of the bubbles from two angles represents the simplest case of tomography. Due to the double pass of the beam, each bubble present in the sample forms two holograms, seen to be side by side, as in Fig. 9.7(a). The larger diffraction patterns represent a longer path (approximately 61.8 cm) after scattering from the bubbles to the CCD, whereas the smaller diffraction rings represent a shorter path (approximately 20.6 cm) after scattering from the bubbles to the CCD. Figure 9.7(b) shows the 3D reconstruction. Figures 9.7(c) and 9.7(e) show the reconstructed holograms using TwIST at distances of 20.6 cm and 61.8 cm, respectively. Because the reconstruction for 61.8 cm gives the

Table 9.3 MATLAB code "TwIST_Bubble_Reconstructions.m" shows how to obtain the results shown in Fig. 9.7.

```
1   %%TwIST 3D reconstruction of two-angle, single-
2   %capture tomography
3   format compact
4   close all
5   load h2.mat                    %Load the hologram.
6   %Crop the image prior to TwIST to avoid memory
7   %overrun while maintaining the
8   %maximum possible hologram fidelity.
9   h = double(h(281:980,201:900));
10  %Axis from 1.88 cm: 6.57 cm and 1.34 cm: 6.03 cm
11  figure(1)
12  imagesc(h)              %Flip only the image, not the matrix
13  colormap(gray)
14  title('Cropped Hologram')
15  axis image
16  %%TwIST parameters (compressive sensing).
17  %NOTE: all TwIST parameters must be in microns
18  d_near = 140000;            %Distancein um (starting distance)
19  total_pixels = length(h);
20  iterations = 50;            %Best reconstructions for
21                              %>= 50 iterations
22  slice_thickness = 10000;    %1-cm slices
23  number_of_planes = 12;      %Spans 12 cm
24  pad_size = 0;
25  w =. 542;                   %TwIST wavelength in um
26  pixel = 6.7;                %Pixel size in um
27  %%Reconstruct via TwIST for the near distance
28  % (compressive sensing)
29  [ M1] = myTWIST(h,d_near,w,pixel,...
30  total_pixels,iterations,slice_thickness,...
31  number_of_planes,pad_size);
32  %If the TwIST function overruns memory, just load
33  %the answer.
34  %load M1_fullcrop_14cm_to_26cm_1cm_inc_twist.mat
35  %Save the TwIST matrix.
36  %save M1_fullcrop_14cm_to_26cm_1cm_inc_twist.mat M1
37  %%Reconstruct via TwIST for the far distance
38  % (compressive sensing)
39  d_far = 550000;             %Change reconstruction
40                              %starting distance
41  [ M2] = myTWIST(h,d_far,w,pixel,...
42  total_pixels,iterations,slice_thickness,...
43  number_of_planes,pad_size);
44  %If the TwIST function overruns memory, just load
45  %the answer.
46  %load M2_fullcrop_55cm_to_62cm_1cm_inc_twist.mat
47  %Save the TwIST matrix.
48  %save M2_fullcrop_55cm_to_62cm_1cm_inc_twist.mat M2
49  %%View the slices in sequence to verify a good
50  %reconstruction.
51  for a = 1:1:12
52  a;
53  figure(2)
```

(continued)

Table 9.3 *(Continued)*

```
54  imagesc(abs(M1(:,:,a)))     %View either M1 or M2 here
55  title('TwIST Reconstruction Far')
56  colormap(gray)
57  pause(0.1)
58  end
59  %%Low-pass filter M1 and M2 to remove salt-and-pepper
60  %noise
61  M1s = M1.*conj(M1);     %Operate on the absolute magnitude
62  for a = 1:1:length(M1s(1,1,:))
63  M1f(:,:,a)=medfilt2(abs(M1s(:,:,a)),[ 1 1] );     %Filtered
64  end
65  M2s = M2.*conj(M2);
66  for a = 1:1:length(M2s(1,1,:))
67  M2f(:,:,a)=medfilt2(abs(M2s(:,:,a)),[ 1 1] );     %Filtered
68  end
69  %%View the filtered slices to verify a good
70  %reconstruction
71  for a = 1:1:12
72  a;
73  figure(2)
74  imagesc(abs(M1f(:,:,a)))
75  title('TwIST Reconstruction Far')
76  colormap(gray)
77  pause(0.1)
78  end
79  %%Resize the M1 and M2 TwIST matrices to avoid memory
80  %overrun
81  for a = 1:1:length(M1f(1,1,:))
82  M1r(:,:,a) = imresize(M1f(:,:,a),.14);     %scale = 14%
83  end
84  for a = 1:1:length(M2f(1,1,:))
85  M2r(:,:,a) = imresize(M2f(:,:,a),.14);     %scale = 14%
86  end
87  %Clear the unneeded matrices to free memory
88  %(if needed).
89  %clear M1 M1s M1f M2 M2s M2f
90  %%Loft M1 and M2 into square volumes.
91  M1_loft = myLoftAndRotate(M1r,1,180);     %Will fill in
92                                            %missing layers
93  M2_loft = myLoftAndRotate(M2r,1,90);     %Will fill in
94                         %missing layers and rotate.
95  %%Plot superposition of lofted reconstructions
96  sum_threshold = 0.3;
97  figure(3)
98  myDisplay3d(permute(M1_loft,[ 2 3 1] ),sum_threshold)
99  title('M1 loft')
100 view([ -138,20] )
101 hold on
102 figure(3)
103 myDisplay3d(permute(M2_loft,[ 2 3 1] ),sum_threshold)
104 title('M2 loft')
105 view([ -138,20] )
106 hold off
107 %%Condition the matrices for 3D viewing.
```

(continued)

Table 9.3 *(Continued)*

```
108 %Each index is 12 cm / 99 = 0.1212 cm = 1.212 mm.
109 %Indices must be shifted slightly because the
110 %original reconstruction range
111 %was only approximated.
112 M1_circ=circshift(M1_loft,[ 0 0 -3] );    %Shift 3
113                                            %indices (3.6 mm)
114 M2_circ=circshift(M2_loft,[ 0 -5 0] );    %Shift 5 indices
115                                            %(6 mm)
116 M2_circ(:,80:99,:) = 0;    %Clean some noise
117 sum_threshold = 0.2;
118 figure(4)
119 myDisplay3d(permute(M1_circ,[ 2 3 1] ),sum_threshold,3)
120 hold on
121 figure(4)
122 myDisplay3d(permute(M2_circ,[ 2 3 1] ),sum_threshold)
123 xlabel('x' );ylabel('z' ); zlabel('y' )
124 view([ -138,20] )
125 title('Two-Angle (Sum) TwIST Reconstruction' )
126 grid on
127 hold off
128 %%Plot the TwIST superposition product
129 D = zeros(size(M1_loft));
130 D = M1_loft.*M2_loft;
131 D = permute(D,[ 2 3 1] );
132 figure(5)
133 myDisplay3d(D)
134 view([ -138,20] )
135 title('Two-Angle (Product) TwIST Reconstruction' )
136 grid on
```

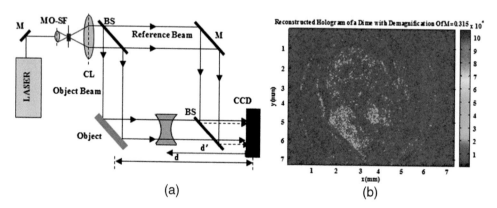

Figure 9.8 (a) Experimental setup with diverging lens to provide demagnification, and (b) CsH reconstruction of a dime using the TwIST algorithm in the reflective mode.

locations of the bubbles in the yz plane and the 20.6-cm reconstruction gives their locations in the xy plane, the 3D coordinates of the bubbles are uniquely determined through this tomographic process, which is used to generate Fig. 9.7(b). The yz and xy projections of the 3D

Table 9.4 MATLAB code "Twist_reflective_dime.m" shows how to obtain the results shown in Fig. 9.8.

```
1    %Reconstruct the reflective on-axis dime via
2    %TwIST %(compressive sensing)
3    close all;clc;clear all
4    load Dime_holo_31cm_633nm_zero      %Loads to variable h
5    g = double(h) - mean(mean(h));      %Subtract dc term
6    total_pixels=1024;     %Number of detector pixels
7    detector_size=6.7;     %Size of detector pixels (um)
8    lambda=0.6328;         %Wavelength (um)
9    iterations = 150;
10   %Distance between each axial plane (um)
11   slice_thickness=3000;
12   %Distance from detector to first reconst. plane (um)
13   %306000 w/3000 inc best for a 31-cm dime
14   reconstruction_distance=309000;
15   number_of_planes=2;   %Minimum 2 planes
16   %Number of zeroes to pad matrix by in each direction
17   pad_size=0;    %Minimal padding to accelerate algorithm
18   M = myTWIST(g,reconstruction_distance,lambda,...
19   detector_size,total_pixels,iterations,...
20   slice_thickness,number_of_planes,pad_size);
21   %%Display one of the slices
22   figure;
23   imagesc((abs(M(:,:,2))))
24   colormap(gray)
```

reconstruction in Fig. 9.7(b) are again shown in Figs. 9.7(d) and 9.7(f) and are identical to Figs. 9.7(c) and 9.7(e), as expected. The MATLAB code "TwIST_Bubble_Reconstructions.m," shown in Table 9.3, is used to perform the two-bubble 3D reconstruction example.

As a second example, a reflective-type setup is shown in Fig. 9.8(a). The divergent lens is used in a Mach–Zehnder configuration with zero reference tilt (i.e., equivalent to a Gabor-type setup) so that light from the demagnified virtual image, which acts as the effective object, writes an on-axis hologram on the CCD. Application of TwIST ensures that the resulting reconstruction fits within the area of the zeroth-order reference beam, albeit at the expense of lower resolution and excess noise. Figure 9.8(b) shows the CsH reconstruction of a dime using the TwIST algorithm in the reflective mode. The feature size in the reconstructed hologram is 28.6 μm for a CCD camera with a 6.7-μm pixel size, $\lambda = 633$ nm, $d = 31$ cm, and demagnification $M = 0.315$.

The MATLAB code "Twist_reflective_dime.m," shown in Table 9.4, is used to perform the reconstruction of a dime using the TwIST algorithm in the reflective mode. Note that the "myTWIST.m" function listed in Table 9.5 calls several additional functions; although they not included here, for brevity, they are included on the CD.

Table 9.5 MATLAB code "myTWIST.m" shows how to use the TwIST algorithm in hologram reconstruction.

```
1    function[M_reconstruct] = myTWIST(hologram,...
2    reconstruction_distance,wavelength,pixel_size,...
3    total_pixels,iterations,slice_thickness,...
4    number_of_planes,pad_size)
5    %%%%%%%%%%%%%%%%%%%%%%
6    %Type "help twist" at MATLAB prompt for lots of info
7    %%%%%%%%%%%%%%%%%%%%%%
8    %Reconstruction_distance in um.
9    %Wavelength in um.
10   %Pixel_size in um.
11   %Offset in um --plane to begin reconstruction slices.
12   %Slice_thickness in um.
13   %Number_of_planes--> reconstructing only one plane will
14   %be at exactly the reconstruction distance, and the
15   %slice thickness will be ignored.
16   %N = total array size along one dimension (assumed
17   %to be square).
18   %Ensure that all of the TwIST functions are in the
19   %directory.
20   %For the function, reconstruction_distance is the
21   %offset.
22   g = hologram;
23   g = double(g) - mean(mean(g));    %Subtract dc term.
24   %The number of ORIGINAL or CROPPED detector pixels.
25   %The pixel size will be scaled appropriately if
26   %downsampled.
27   pixel_num=total_pixels;
28   iterations = iterations;
29   %Size of detector pixels (um).
30   %detector_size=5.2;
31   detector_size=pixel_size;
32   %Wavelength (um)
33   lambda=wavelength;
34   %Distance between each axial plane (um)
35   deltaZ=slice_thickness;    %In um.
36   %Distance from the detector to the first reconstructed
37   %plane (um).
38   offsetZ=reconstruction_distance;    %In um from CCD.
39   %Number of axial planes
40   nz=number_of_planes;
41   %Number of zeroes to pad matrix by in each direction
42   pad_size=pad_size;    %Minimal padding to accelerate
43                         %algorithm.
44   %Scaling pixel sizes for proper reconstruction.
45   shrinkage_factor=pixel_num/size(g,1);
46   sensor_size=pixel_num*detector_size;
47   deltaX=detector_size*shrinkage_factor;
48   deltaY=detector_size*shrinkage_factor;
49   %figure;imagesc(abs(g));title('CapturedData');
50   %Axis image;
51   %pad the array to eliminate aliasing due to FFT wrap.
52   g=padarray(g,[pad_size pad_size]);
53   range=pad_size*2+pixel_num;
```

(continued)

Table 9.5 *(Continued)*

```
54  [nx ny]=size(g);
55  Nx=nx;
56  Ny=ny*nz*2;
57  Nz=1;
58  E0=ones(nx,ny);
59  [Phase3D Pupil]=MyMakingPhase3D(nx,ny,nz,lambda,...
60  deltaX,deltaY,deltaZ,offsetZ,sensor_size);
61  PhaseTmesPupil=Phase3D.*Pupil;
62  E=MyFieldsPropagation(E0,nx,ny,nz,Phase3D,Pupil);
63  g=MyC2V(g(:));
64  transf=MyAdjointOperatorPropagation...
65  (g,E,nx,ny,nz,Phase3D,Pupil);
66  transf=reshape(abs(MyV2C(transf)),nx,ny,nz);
67  %figure;imagesc(plotdatacube(transf));
68  %title('BackPropagation');axis image;drawnow;
69  A = @(f_twist) MyForwardOperatorPropagation...
70  (f_twist,E,nx,ny,nz,Phase3D,Pupil);
71  AT = @(g) MyAdjointOperatorPropagation...
72  (g,E,nx,ny,nz,Phase3D,Pupil);
73  tau = 0.01;      %Regularization parameter (non-neg, real)
74  piter = 4;
75  tolA = 1e-6;
76  %iterations = 10;           %195 default
77  Phi = @(f,weight,epsi) MyL1phi(f);
78  [M_reconstruct,dummy,obj_twist,...
79  times_twist,dummy,mse_twist] = ...
80  TwIST(g,A,tau,...
81  'AT', AT, ...
82  'Phi',Phi, ...
83  'Initialization',2,...
84  'Monotone',1,...
85  'StopCriterion',1,...
86  'MaxIterA',iterations,...
87  'MinIterA',iterations,...
88  'ToleranceA',tolA,...
89  'Verbose', 1);
90  [M_reconstruct]=reshape...
91  (MyV2C(M_reconstruct),nx,ny,nz);
92  %figure;imagesc(plotdatacube(abs(M_reconstruct)));
93  %title('Reconstruction');axis image;drawnow;
94  g=reshape(MyV2C(g),nx,ny);
```

References

1. C. E. Shannon, "Communications in the presence of noise," *Proc. IEEE* **86**(2), 447–457 (1998).
2. M. Golay, "Multi-slit spectrometry," *J. Opt. Soc. Am.* **39**, 437–444 (1949).
3. E. J. Candès, J. K. Romberg, and T. Tao, "Stable signal recovery from incomplete and inaccurate measurements," *Comm. Pure Appl. Math.* **59**(8), 1207–1223 (2006).

4. E. J. Candès and T. Tao, "Near-optimal signal recovery from random projections: Universal encoding strategies?" *IEEE Trans. Inform. Theory* **52**(12), 5406–5425 (2006).

5. D. L. Donoho, "Compressed sensing," *IEEE Trans. Inform. Theory* **52**(4), 1289–1306 (2006).

6. D. J. Brady, K. Choi, D. L. Marks, R. Horisaki, and S. Lim, "Compressive holography," *Opt. Exp.* **17**(15), 13040–13049 (2009).

7. C. Moler, "'Magic' reconstruction: Compressed sensing," MathWorks news and notes, http://www.mathworks.com/company/newsletters/articles/clevescorner-compressed-sensing.html.

8. E. J. Candès, J. Romberg, and T. Tao, "Robust uncertainty principles: Exact signal reconstruction from highly incomplete frequency information," *IEEE Trans. Inform. Theory* **52**(2), 489–509 (2006).

9. A. J. Devaney, "Nonuniqueness in the inverse scattering problem," *J. Math. Phys.* **19**(7), 1526–1531 (1978).

10. T. C. Poon and P. P. Banerjee, *Contemporary Optical Image Processing with MATLAB®*, Elsevier Science, Amsterdam (2001).

11. J. M. Bioucas-Dias and M. A. T. Figueiredo, "A new TwIST: Two-step iterative shrinkage/thresholding algorithms for image restoration," *IEEE Trans. Image Proc.* **16**(12), 2992–3004 (2007).

12. L. Tian, J. Lee, and G. Barbastathis, "Compressive holographic inversion of particle scattering," *Topical Meeting in Digital Holography and Three-Dimensional Imaging,* (2011).

13. L. Williams, G. Nehmetallah, and P. P. Banerjee, "Digital tomographic compressive holographic reconstruction of three-dimensional objects in transmissive and reflective geometries," *Appl. Opt.* **52**(8), 1702–1710 (2013).

14. G. Nehmetallah and P. P. Banerjee, "Applications of digital and analog holography in three-dimensional imaging," *Adv. Opt. Photon.* **4**(4), 472–553 (2012).

Chapter 10
Contemporary Topics in Holography

10.1 Transport-of-Intensity Imaging

All of the examples of holography thus far have involved the reconstruction of holograms that were generated and recorded using a reference wave. The recording of the hologram has been assumed to be at a certain plane, i.e., the detector or the CCD camera. The use of the reference allows for the recording of the phase (or depth information) of the object. However, as this chapter will demonstrate, the amplitude and phase of the optical field from an object are interrelated during propagation and obey the eikonal equations or the transport-of-intensity (TI) equations. It is therefore possible, in principle, to deduce the phase distribution of the original object if the amplitude (or intensity) is recorded at different distances during the propagation of the diffracting optical field. In fact, the amplitude and phase objects can be recorded and reconstructed using TI principles, as described in this section. Conventionally, phase-contrast microscopy is used to image weak phase objects. In cell biology, interferometric systems (along with phase-unwrapping algorithms) are usually employed to quantify the amplitude and phase of the field observed at a detector plane. If the complete 3D structure of the phase object is desired, then the data is acquired tomographically, and inversion algorithms are used to reconstruct the 3D complex index distribution of the object.[1] The interferometric systems are usually bulky, sensitive to perturbations and noise, and usually require phase unwrapping, which may introduce artifacts. Intensity-based phase retrieval techniques, in which both the amplitude and phase of a field are retrieved from defocused intensity measurements, offer an experimentally simple solution to determine the phase quantitatively without phase-unwrapping algorithms. TI principles can be applied to record and reconstruct an asymmetric bulk phase object in 3D.[2,3] Figures 10.1(a) and 10.1(b) show typical TI setups to tomographically record a 360-deg view for transmissive and reflective objects, respectively.

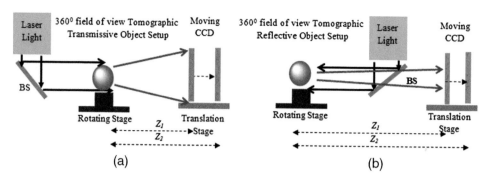

Figure 10.1 TI setups for 360-deg view: (a) transmissive and (b) reflective static.

Although the entire complex field can be determined in the spatial frequency domain [through Eq. (2.4)] or in the spatial domain [through Eq. (2.5) with Eq. (2.7)], it is also possible to determine the amplitude (or intensity) and phase of the propagating optical field directly by starting from the Helmholtz equation [Eq. (2.1)]. Conventionally, this leads directly to the so-called *eikonal equations* in the presence of diffraction. To see this, substitute

$$E(x,y,z) = \mathrm{Re}\{a(x,y,z)\exp[-j\phi(x,y,z)]\} \tag{10.1}$$

into Eq. (2.1) and separate the real and imaginary parts to produce, after some algebra,

$$(\vec{\nabla}\phi)\cdot(\vec{\nabla}\phi) = k_0^2 + \frac{1}{a}\nabla^2 a \tag{10.2a}$$

and

$$\vec{\nabla}\cdot(a^2\vec{\nabla}\phi) = 0, \tag{10.2b}$$

where $a(x,y,z)$ and $\phi(x,y,z)$ are the amplitude and phase of the complex field $E(x,y,z)$, respectively, and the operator

$$\vec{\nabla} = \left(\frac{\partial}{\partial x}, \frac{\partial}{\partial y}, \frac{\partial}{\partial z}\right).$$

Equation (10.2b) is a statement of the conservation of energy, as can be readily checked by integrating over a control volume. Equation (10.2a) is the eikonal equation in the presence of diffraction, which is represented by the last term on the right side. The amplitude and phase of the optical field can therefore be determined by solving Eqs. (10.2a) and (10.2b) simultaneously.

Because it is easier to monitor the intensity rather than the amplitude of the optical field, the eikonal equations can be alternatively recast in terms of the intensity and the phase: start from the paraxial wave equation, which can be derived from the Helmholtz equation by substituting $E(x,y,z) = E_e(x,y,z)\exp(-jk_0z)$, to get

$$\frac{\partial E_e}{\partial z} = \frac{1}{2jk_0}\nabla_\perp^2 E_e, \qquad (10.3)$$

where the operator

$$\nabla_\perp^2 = \left(\frac{\partial^2}{\partial x^2} + \frac{\partial^2}{\partial y^2}\right),$$

and the "slowly varying envelope approximation" (SVEA) is assumed for the envelope E_e. Note that

$$E_e(x,y,z) = \mathrm{Re}\{a(x,y,z)\exp[-j\psi(x,y,z)]\}, \qquad (10.4)$$

where $\psi(x,y,z)$ is the slowly varying part of the total phase $\phi(x,y,z)$ and is given by the relation $\phi(x,y,z) = \psi(x,y,z) + k_0 z$. Multiplying Eq. (10.3) by E_e^*, taking the complex conjugate of the resulting equation, and adding the two equations produces[4]

$$k_0\frac{\partial I}{\partial z} = -\frac{j}{2}\left(E_e^*\nabla_\perp^2 E_e - E_e\nabla_\perp^2 E_e^*\right), \qquad (10.5)$$

where $a(x,y;z) = \sqrt{I(x,y;z)}$. Substituting Eq. (10.4) in Eq. (10.5) and then simplifying it produces, after some algebra,

$$-k_0\frac{\partial I}{\partial z} = \vec{\nabla}_\perp \cdot (I\vec{\nabla}_\perp\psi). \qquad (10.6a)$$

After substituting Eq. (10.4) in Eq. (10.3), equating the real parts, and simplifying, a second equation interrelating I and ψ can be found to be

$$2k_0 I^2\frac{\partial\psi}{\partial z} = \frac{1}{2}I\nabla_\perp^2 I - \frac{1}{4}(\vec{\nabla}_\perp I)\cdot(\vec{\nabla}_\perp I) - I^2(\vec{\nabla}_\perp\psi)\cdot(\vec{\nabla}_\perp\psi). \qquad (10.6b)$$

Equations (10.6a) and (10.6b) are commonly referred to as the TI equations (TIE), first derived by Teague[4] and Streibl.[5–12]

If I is approximately constant as in a phase object, then Eq. (10.6a) becomes

$$\nabla_\perp^2\psi(x,y) = -\frac{k_0}{I(x,y)}\frac{\partial I(x,y)}{\partial z} \approx -\frac{k_0}{I(x,y)}\frac{I(x,y,\Delta z) - I(x,y,0)}{\Delta z}. \qquad (10.7)$$

If the FT is applied to both sides of Eq. (10.7), then

$$\tilde{\Psi}(k_x,k_y;z) \overset{I\text{ is const}}{\gg} -k_0\frac{\Im_{x,y}\left[\frac{1}{I(x,y)}\frac{\partial I(x,y)}{\partial z}\right]}{k_x^2 + k_y^2}. \qquad (10.8)$$

Performing the inverse FT on Eq. (10.8) produces the following phase of the object at the CCD:

$$\psi_{CCD}(x,y;z) = \Im_{x,y}^{-1}\{\tilde{\Psi}(k_x,k_y;z)\}, \qquad (10.9)$$

and the phase of the object at the object plane $\psi_{Obj}(x,y;0)$ is found with back propagation.

Another equivalent way to solve Eq. (10.6a) introduces a new scalar potential variable θ:

$$\vec{\nabla}_\perp\theta = I\vec{\nabla}_\perp\psi. \qquad (10.10)$$

It can be determined from Eq. (10.6a) that

$$\nabla_\perp^2\theta(x,y) = -k_0\frac{\partial I(x,y)}{\partial z} \approx -k_0\frac{I(x,y,\Delta z) - I(x,y,0)}{\Delta z}, \qquad (10.11)$$

which is a 2D Poisson's equation. The assumption in Eq. (10.10) is only valid if $\vec{\nabla}_\perp I \approx 0$, because

$$\vec{\nabla}\times(\vec{\nabla}_\perp\theta) = \vec{\nabla}\times(I\vec{\nabla}_\perp\psi) = I\vec{\nabla}\times(\vec{\nabla}_\perp\psi) + \vec{\nabla}_\perp I\times\vec{\nabla}_\perp\psi \Rightarrow \vec{\nabla}_\perp I\times\vec{\nabla}_\perp\psi = 0.$$

Equation (10.11) can be solved using the FT technique; it can be applied to both sides of Eq. (10.11) to produce

$$\tilde{\Theta}(k_x,k_y) = -k_0\frac{\Im_{x,y}[\partial I(x,y)/\partial z]}{k_x^2 + k_y^2} = -k_0\frac{[\partial\tilde{I}(k_x,k_y)/\partial z]}{k_x^2 + k_y^2}. \qquad (10.12)$$

When the inverse FT is performed on Eq. (10.12),

$$\theta(x,y;z) = \Im_{x,y}^{-1}\{\tilde{\Theta}(k_x,k_y;z)\}. \qquad (10.13)$$

Equation (10.10) can be written as follows to find the phase of the object at the CCD:

$$\psi_{CCD}(x,y;z) = \vec{\nabla}_\perp^{-1}\cdot\left(\frac{\vec{\nabla}_\perp\theta(x,y;z)}{I(x,y)}\right); \qquad (10.14a)$$

therefore, to solve Eq. (10.11), all of the previous steps can be expressed as[7]

$$\psi_{CCD}(x,y;z) = -k\nabla_\perp^{-2}\left\{\vec{\nabla}_\perp\cdot\left[\frac{1}{I(x,y;z)}\vec{\nabla}_\perp\left(\nabla_\perp^{-2}\left(\frac{\partial I(x,y;z)}{\partial z}\right)\right)\right]\right\}, \qquad (10.14b)$$

where the inverse Laplacian operator $\nabla_\perp^{-2}$ for an arbitrary function $\alpha(x,y)$ is defined by the relation

$$\nabla_\perp^{-2}(\alpha(x,y)) = -\Im_{x,y}^{-1}\left\{\frac{1}{k_x^2 + k_y^2}\Im_{x,y}\{\alpha(x,y)\}\right\}, \qquad (10.14c)$$

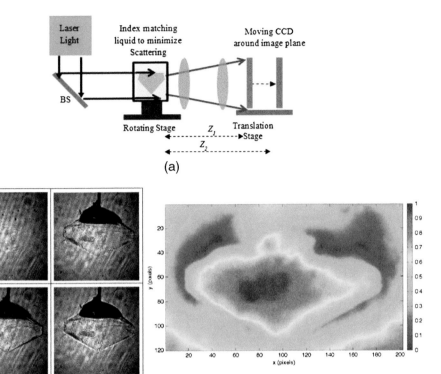

Figure 10.2 (a) Optical setup and (b) sample images clockwise from top left: background, in-focus, overfocused, and underfocused diamond. Background subtraction was applied via pixel-wise division by the background image before processing. (c) Phase map generated from the transport of intensity-based phase retrieval. Areas of higher intensity denote greater phase delay (estimated to linearly correlate with the depth of the object).[6]

where $\Im_{x,y}$ denotes the 2D Fourier transform operator, $\Im_{x,y}^{-1}$ is the inverse 2D Fourier transform, and k_x and k_y are the spatial frequencies in the Fourier domain. Equations (10.14b) and (10.9) are equivalent.

Finally, the phase of the object at the object plane $\psi_{Obj}(x,y;0)$ is found using back-propagation. Note that if I is not constant, such as with an interference pattern, a solution for the TI Eq. (10.6a) based on orthogonal series has been developed.[12]

For example, assume that a transparent object (Pyrex diamond) is placed in an index-matching fluid and imaged using the system shown in Fig. 10.2(a). The object is illuminated with a collimated plane wave from a 632.8-nm HeNe laser. Intensity measurements have been taken from 90 independent, 2-deg-spaced angles for a total of 180 deg of rotation. Three images have been taken at each angle: one corresponding to the in-focus image of the object, one corresponding to an overfocused image of the object via movement of the linear stage by $+10$ μm, and one corresponding to an underfocused image of the object obtained from movement of the linear stage by -10 μm. The object

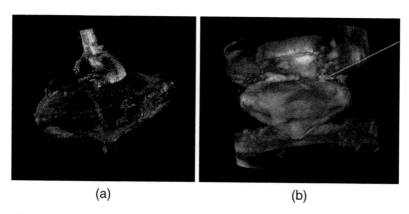

(a)   (b)

Figure 10.3 Volumetric reconstruction of the phase object. (a) Reconstruction from amplitude information alone (without the TIE), and (b) the reconstruction results from the TIE-retrieved phase.[6]

is rotated between each pair of image captures for tomographic acquisition. These images have been used to reconstruct maps of the phase depth for each projection angle.

Figure 10.2(b) shows sample images, proceeding clockwise from the top left, of the background, in-focus, overfocused, and underfocused diamond. A phase map generated from the transport of intensity-based phase retrieval is shown in Fig. 10.2(c). The resultant phase maps were then used in a filtered back-propagation algorithm and volumetrically rendered for verification, as shown in Fig. 10.3 (no attempt was made to account for diffraction).[6] It should be noted that this technique is truly referenceless because the object size is large and only the light passing through the object is recorded.

As a second example, two images were captured at distances z and $z + \Delta z$, and the TIE were applied to reconstruct the original phase of the object (the CUA logo). The MATLAB script, which needs the "mypropagation.m" and "imlin.m" functions, is shown in Table 10.1. Figure 10.4(a) shows the initial phase; Fig. 10.4(b) shows the intensities at distances z and $z + \Delta z$, respectively; Fig. 10.4(c) shows the difference between the intensities (at z and $z + \Delta z$); and Fig. 10.4(d) shows the initial phase and the retrieved phase.

Another method of using the TIE employs the iterative Fourier transform technique (shown in Fig. 10.5) to solve Eq. (10.6a).[8,9] Using Taylor expansion, the two intensities recorded by the CCD at positions $z_0 + \Delta z/2$ and $z_0 - \Delta z/2$ can be expressed as

$$I_1(x,y;z)\big|_{z_0+\Delta z/2} = I\big|_{z=z_0} + \frac{\partial I}{\partial z}\bigg|_{z=z0} \Delta z_0, \qquad (10.15a)$$

$$I_2(x,y;z)\big|_{z_0-\Delta z/2} = I\big|_{z=z_0} - \frac{\partial I}{\partial z}\bigg|_{z=z0} \Delta z_0, \qquad (10.15b)$$

Table 10.1 MATLAB code "TIE_ex_2.m" uses the TIE to construct the phase of a simulated object (see Fig. 10.4).

```
1    %%TIE example_2
2    clc; clear all; close all;
3    regparam = 0.5e-3;
4    %Load image
5    load ('cua.mat',' phase' );
6    I = phase;
7    [ N,~] = size(I);
8    sz = N/2;                          %Half of the CCD
9    z = 1000;
10   dz = 0.1;
11   L = sqrt(N);
12   lambda =.543e-3;k=2*pi/lambda;
13   %%Spatial domain
14   x = linspace(-L/2,L/2,N);y = x;
15   [ X,Y] = meshgrid(x,y);
16   %%Fourier domain
17   dx=L/N;                            %Sampling spacing
18   a=pi/dx;
19   kx=-a:2*a/N:a-2*a/N;               %Frequency vector
20   ky=kx;
21   [ KX,KY]=meshgrid(kx,ky);          %2D frequency grid
22   KK=KX.^2+KY.^2;
23   phase = imlin(phase,-0.2,0);
24   b = find(phase == 0);              %Boundary
25   m = find(abs(phase) <= 0.02);
26   phase(m) = 0;
27   figure;
28   imagesc(phase);colormap(gray);title('Initial Phase' );
29   axis image;colorbar
30   %%Generating wavefront
31   Ein =1*exp(1i*phase);
32   E1 = mypropagation(Ein,z,KK,k);
33   E2 = mypropagation(Ein,z+dz,KK,k);
34   I1=sqrt(E1.*conj(E1));I2=sqrt(E2.*conj(E2));
35   figure;
36   subplot(131);
37   imagesc(I1); colormap(gray);
38   title('Intensity at distance z' );axis image;
39   subplot(132);
40   imagesc(I2); colormap(gray);
41   title('Intensity at distance z + \Deltaz' );axis image;
42   I0 = (I1+I2)/2;
43   %%TIE_method
44   %derivertive dI/dz
45   dIdz = (I2-I1)/dz;
46   subplot(133);
47   imagesc(I1-I2); colormap(gray);
48   title('Difference between I1 and I2' );axis image;
49   %%Solve Poisson equation 1
50   D1 = fftshift(fft2(dIdz));
51   Z1 = (D1).*KK./((KK+4*pi^2*regparam).^2);
52   Z1 = -ifft2(ifftshift(Z1));        %Solution
53   phi1 = real(Z1);
```

(continued)

Table 10.1 (*Continued*)

```
54  %Gradient and divergence
55  [ Fx,Fy] = gradient(phi1,dx,dx);
56  Fx(b)=0;Fy(b)=0;
57  Fxx = Fx./(I0+eps);Fyy = Fy./(I0+eps);
58  del2phi = divergence(Fxx, Fyy)./dx;
59  %%Solve Poisson equation 2
60  D1 = fftshift(fft2(del2phi));
61  Z1 = (D1).*KK./((KK+regparam).^2);
62  Z1 = -ifft2(ifftshift(Z1));        %Solution
63  phi1 = real(Z1);
64  phi_K = k*phi1;
65  %figure; mesh(phi_K); title('Krenkel phase at CCD');
66  %%Back-propogation
67  e=sqrt(I0).*exp(1i*(phi_K));
68  [ Ek] = mypropagation(e,-(z+dz/2),KK,k);
69  angeK = angle(Ek);angeK(b) = max(angeK(:));
70  angeK(m) = max(angeK(:));
71  figure;
72  subplot(121);
73  imagesc(phase);colormap(gray(256));
74  title('Initial unwrap-phase');axis image;colorbar
75  subplot(122);
76  imagesc(angeK-max(angeK(:)));colormap(gray(256));
77  title('Retrieved initial phase');axis image; colorbar
```

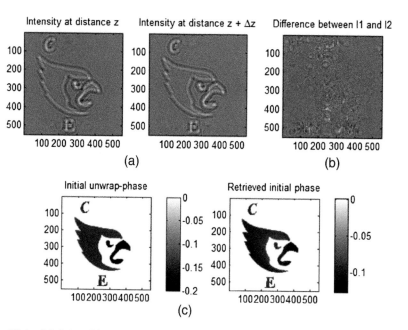

Figure 10.4 (a) Intensities at distance z and $z + \Delta z$, respectively; (b) the difference between intensities (at z and $z + \Delta z$); and (c) the initial phase and retrieved phase.

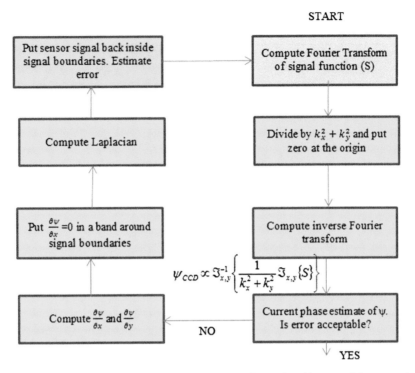

START

Put sensor signal back inside signal boundaries. Estimate error

Compute Fourier Transform of signal function (S)

Compute Laplacian

Divide by $k_x^2 + k_y^2$ and put zero at the origin

Put $\frac{\partial \psi}{\partial x} = 0$ in a band around signal boundaries

Compute inverse Fourier transform

$$\psi_{CCD} \propto \mathfrak{I}_{x,y}^{-1}\left\{\frac{1}{k_x^2+k_y^2}\mathfrak{I}_{x,y}\{S\}\right\}$$

Compute $\frac{\partial \psi}{\partial x}$ and $\frac{\partial \psi}{\partial y}$

Current phase estimate of ψ. Is error acceptable?

NO

YES

Figure 10.5 Flow chart of an iterative Fourier transform algorithm used to reconstruct a wavefront φ from the wavefront Laplacian measured from out-of-focus images.[8]

where z_0 is midway between the two CCD positions. A signal function S can be expressed as the following by using Eqs. (10.15a) and (10.15b):

$$S = \frac{I_1 - I_2}{I_1 + I_2} = \frac{I(x,y;z_0 + \frac{\Delta z}{2}) - I(x,y;z_0 - \frac{\Delta z}{2})}{I(x,y;z_0 + \frac{\Delta z}{2}) + I(x,y;z_0 - \frac{\Delta z}{2})} = \frac{-\frac{\partial I}{\partial z}\Delta z_0}{I_0}. \tag{10.16}$$

Using Eq. (10.16), Eq. (10.6a) can be written as

$$\psi_{CCD} \propto \mathfrak{I}_{x,y}^{-1}\left\{\frac{1}{k_x^2 + k_y^2}\mathfrak{I}_{x,y}\{S\}\right\}. \tag{10.17}$$

The signal S is sent to the iteration system, which follows the Fourier transform iterative method shown in Fig. 10.5.[8] Finally, after achieving an acceptable error in the phase, the phase of the object at the object plane $\psi_{Obj}(x,y;0)$ is found using back-propagation.

As a third example, two (simulated) images were captured at a distance z_1 and $-z_1$, and the TIE iterative FT algorithm was applied to reconstruct the original phase of the object, which possesses an astigmatism type of phase distribution. The MATLAB script, shown in Table 10.2m, needs the "TS.m," "mypropagation.m," and "My_TIE_Roddier.m" functions. Figure 10.6(a) shows the initial object phase (left) and sensor signal S (right); Fig. 10.6(b) shows the reconstructed phase at the CCD (left) and the subtraction of the

Table 10.2 MATLAB code "TIE_ex_3.m" uses the TIE to construct the phase of a simulated object (see Fig. 10.6).

```
1   %%TIE_example 3
2   clc; clear all; close all;
3   lambda=0.5*1e-3;k=(2*pi)/lambda;  %Wavelength, wavenumber
4   N = 512;                           %Half of the CCD size
5   sz = N/2;
6   rr= 200;                           %Radial of the wavefront
7   L = sqrt(N);
8   dx = L/N;
9   x = linspace(-sz,sz-1,N);
10  y = linspace(-sz,sz-1,N);
11  z = 3.5;
12  %%Fourier domain
13  a = pi/dx;
14  kx = -a:2*a/N:a-2*a/N;             %Frequency vector
15  ky = kx;
16  [ KX,KY] = meshgrid(kx,ky);        %2D frequency grid
17  KK = KX.^2+KY.^2;
18  %Pixel size
19  [ xwb,ywb]=meshgrid(dx*(-sz:sz-1),dx*(-sz:sz-1)); %Set up
20                                        %circular pupil
21  [ xw1,yw1]=meshgrid(-sz:sz-1,-sz:sz-1);  %Set up circular
22                                        %pupil
23  P=10;
24  %%Generating phase(astigmatism)
25  dis=3.5;                           %Distance propagation
26  [ X,Y]=meshgrid(x,y);
27  phase=(X.^2+Y.^2)/3000;
28  a= sqrt(xw1.^2+yw1.^2)>=rr;
29  phase(a)=0;
30  phase=phase-max(max(phase));
31  figure;
32  mesh(phase);axis tight;title('initial phase');
33  view(0,90);
34  %%Create wavefront
35  Uin=P.*exp(-1i*phase);
36  Iin=Uin.*conj(Uin);                %Intensity distribution
37  Uf=mypropagation(Uin,z,KK,k);      %Forward
38  Ub=mypropagation(Uin,-z,KK,k);     %Backward.
39  %Intensity distribution.
40  If=Uf.*conj(Uf);Ib = Ub.*conj(Ub);
41  b = find(If<0.02*max(If(:)));If(b) = 0;
42  c = find(Ib<0.02*max(Ib(:)));Ib(c) = 0;
43  %mesh(If);
44  [ phi]=My_TIE_Roddier(If,Ib,KK,dis,k,sz,dx);
45  figure;
46  mesh(real(phi));axis tight;title('phase at CCD');
47  view(0,90);
48  phisim = phase;
49  a=real(phi);
50  phiret=a-max(max(a));
51  figure
52  plot(phiret(sz,:));hold on
53  plot(phisim(sz,:),' r');hold off
```

(continued)

Table 10.2 (*Continued*)

```
54   title('Slice of simulated and retrieved phase ')
55   legend('Retrieved phase',' Simulation phase')
56   qw5b=find(sqrt(xw1.^2+yw1.^2)>=rr-11);
57   qw5=find(sqrt(xw1.^2+yw1.^2)<rr-11);
58   phiret(qw5b)=0;
59   phisim(qw5b)=0;
60   q=phisim-phiret;
61   figure;imagesc(q);colorbar;
62   title('Subtraction of simulation from retrieved phase ')
63   figure;subplot(121);imagesc(phiret);
64   colorbar;title('Retrieved phase ');axis square;
65   subplot(122);imagesc(phisim);
66   colorbar;title(' Simulation phase '); axis square;
```

simulated phase from the retrieved phase (right); Fig. 10.6(c) shows the retrieved phase using the TIE (left) and the simulated phase (right); and Fig. 10.6(d) shows a slice of the retrieved and simulated phases for comparison.

A fourth example reconstructs the phase from a real spherical-lens object. The MATLAB script is shown in Table 10.3; the recording setup is a $4f$ system with $f = 100$ mm (see Fig. 10.7). The phase information recorded on the CCD in this system is the same as the phase of the real spherical-lens object, with no need to perform back-propagation.

All of the TIE examples mentioned earlier require a translation of the CCD to capture multiple intensity images, rendering the technique unsuitable for dynamic or fast events. This issue can be solved by introducing a combination of an offset diverging lens and an electrically tunable lens (OL/ETL) in the back focal plane of lens L1 in the $4f$ system illustrated in Fig. 10.9.[10,11] Now consider why introducing the OL/ETL lenses into a $4f$ system is equivalent to translating the CCD. For example, a plane wave illuminating an object with a complex transparency function denoted by $t(x,y)$ is placed on the front focal plane of lens L1. The complex field at the back focal plane of lens L1 and just before the OL/ETL lens is a scaled version of the Fourier transform of $t(x,y)$, denoted as

$$\tilde{T}(k_x,k_y)|_{\substack{k_x=k_0x/f,\\k_y=k_0y/f}}$$

where $\tilde{T}(k_x,k_y) = \mathfrak{F}_{x,y}[t(x,y)]$.

The complex field just after the OL/ETL lens can be written as

$$w(x,y)\Big|_{\substack{\text{after}\\\text{OL/ETL}}} = \tilde{T}(k_x,k_y)|_{\substack{k_x=k_0x/f\\k_y=k_0y/f}} \cdot s_{fc}(x,y), \tag{10.18}$$

where

$$s_{fc}(x,y) = e^{\frac{jk_0(x^2+y^2)}{2f_c}}$$

is the phase transformation function of the OL/ETL lens with focal length $f_c = (f_{ETL}f_{OL})/(f_{ETL}+f_{OL}-d)$, and d is the axial distance between the OL

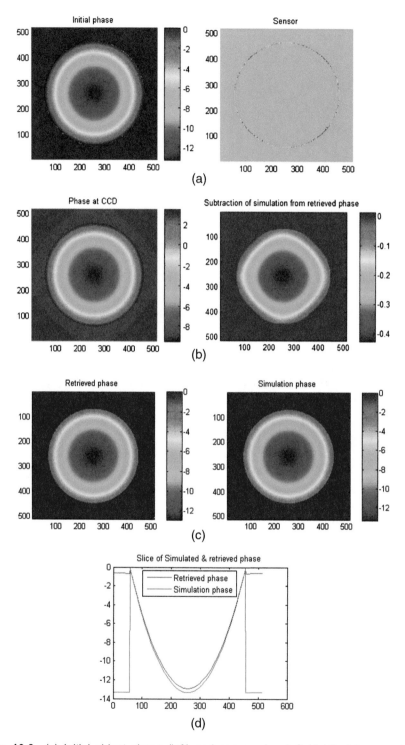

Figure 10.6 (a) Initial object phase (left) and sensor signal *S* (right), (b) reconstructed phase at CCD (left) and subtraction of simulation from retrieved phase (right), (c) the retrieved phase using the TIE (left) and simulated phase (right), (d) a slice of the retrieved phase and simulation phase for comparison.

Table 10.3 MATLAB code "TIE_ex_4.m" uses the TIE to reconstruct the phase of a real spherical-lens object (shown in Fig. 10.8).

```
1   %%TIE_ex_4
2   clc; clear all; close all;
3   regparam = 0.1e-3;
4   %Image
5   load ('s2.mat');
6   I1 = double(frames);
7   load ('s1.mat');
8   I2 = double(frames);
9   %I0 = double(frames);
10  I0 = (I1+I2)/2;
11  [N,~] = size(I1);
12  z = 0.5;
13  dz = 2*z;
14  L = sqrt(N);
15  dx = L/N;
16  lambda =.640e-3; k=2*pi/lambda;
17  d = 5.2e-3*N;
18  %Spatial domain
19  x = linspace(-L/2,L/2,N);y = x;
20  [X,Y] = meshgrid(x,y);
21  figure; imagesc(x,y,I1);colormap(gray(256));
22  title('Intensity-UnderFocusPlane');colorbar;
23  figure; imagesc(x,y,I2);colormap(gray(256));
24  title('Intensity-OverFocusPlane');colorbar;
25  figure; imagesc(x,y,I0);
26  colormap(gray(256));
27  title('Intensity-FocusPlane');colorbar;
28  %%Fourier domain.
29  %Sampling spacing.
30  a=pi/dx;
31  kx=-a:2*a/N:a-2*a/N;          %Frequency vector
32  ky=kx;
33  [KX,KY]=meshgrid(kx,ky);      %2D frequency grid
34  KK=KX.^2+KY.^2;
35  %%Solve Poisson equation.
36  %derivertive dI/dz
37  dIdz = (I2-I1)/dz;
38  figure;imagesc(x,y,I2-I1);
39  colormap(gray);axis square;colorbar;title('Difference');
40  %Solve Poisson equation 1
41  D1 = fftshift(fft2(dIdz));
42  Z1 = (D1).*KK./((KK+4*pi^2*regparam).^2);
43  Z1 = -ifft2(ifftshift(Z1));        %Solution
44  phi1 = real(Z1);
45  %Gradient and divergence
46  [Fx,Fy] = gradient(phi1,dx,dx);
47  %Fx(b)=0;Fy(b)=0;
48  Fxx = Fx./(I0+eps);Fyy = Fy./(I0+eps);
49  del2phi = divergence(Fxx, Fyy)./dx;
50  %Solve Poisson equation 2
51  D1 = fftshift(fft2(del2phi));
52  Z1 = (D1).*KK./((KK+4*pi^2*regparam).^2);
53  Z1 = -ifft2(ifftshift(Z1));        %Solution
54  phi1 = real(Z1);
55  phi_K = k*phi1;
56  %phi_K(m) = min(phi_K(:));
57  figure; mesh(X,Y,phi_K); axis tight; view(0,90);
58  colorbar;title('Phase Reconstruction');axis ij
```

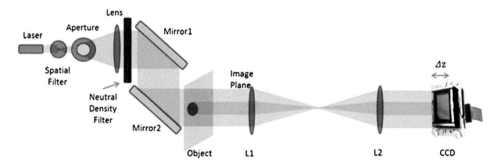

Figure 10.7 Schematic setup for a TIE 4*f* lens system that relays the phase from the front focal plane of lens L1 to the back focal plane of lens L2, which is the CCD plane.

and the ETL lenses. At the CCD plane, the complex field is again the Fourier transform of $w(x,y)$ and can be written as

$$w(x,y)\big|_{\substack{\text{back focal}\\\text{plane of L2}}} = \Im_{x,y}\{\tilde{T}(k_0 x/f, k_0 y/f) \cdot s_{fc}(x,y)\}\big|_{\substack{k_x=k_0 x/f\\k_y=k_0 y/f}} \tag{10.19}$$

or

$$w(x,y)\big|_{\substack{\text{back focal}\\\text{plane of L2}}} = \Im_{x,y}\{\tilde{T}(k_0 x/f, k_0 y/f)\}\big|_{\substack{k_x=k_0 x/f\\k_y=k_0 y/f}} * \tilde{S}_{fc}(k_x,k_y)\big|_{\substack{k_x=k_0 x/f\\k_y=k_0 y/f}}, \tag{10.20}$$

where $\tilde{S}_{fc}(k_x,k_y) = \Im_{x,y}[s_{fc}(x,y)]$. Equation (10.20) can be further simplified as

$$w(x,y)\big|_{\substack{\text{back focal}\\\text{plane of L2}}} \propto t(-x,-y) * \tilde{S}_{fc}(k_x,k_y)\big|_{\substack{k_x=k_0 x/f\\k_y=k_0 y/f}}, \tag{10.21}$$

$$w(x,y)\big|_{\substack{\text{back focal}\\\text{plane of L2}}} \propto t(-x,-y) * e^{\frac{-(k_x^2+k_y^2)}{2(-jk_0)/f_c}}\bigg|_{\substack{k_x=k_0 x/f\\k_y=k_0 y/f}}, \tag{10.22}$$

$$w(x,y)\big|_{\substack{\text{back focal}\\\text{plane of L2}}} \propto t(-x,-y) * e^{-j\frac{k_0 f_c}{2f^2}(x^2+y^2)}. \tag{10.23}$$

In the case where there is no OL/ETL lens, the complex field at the back focal plane of lens L2 can be written as

$$u(x,y)\big|_{\substack{\text{back focal}\\\text{plane of L2}}} \propto t(-x,-y).$$

Translating the CCD a distance of Δz according to the Fresnel diffraction theory is equivalent to convolving the object field with the impulse response of propagation. Therefore, the field at a distance Δz from the back focal plane of lens L2 can be written as

$$u(x,y,\Delta z) \propto t(-x,-y) * e^{-j\frac{k_0}{2\Delta z}(x^2+y^2)}. \tag{10.24}$$

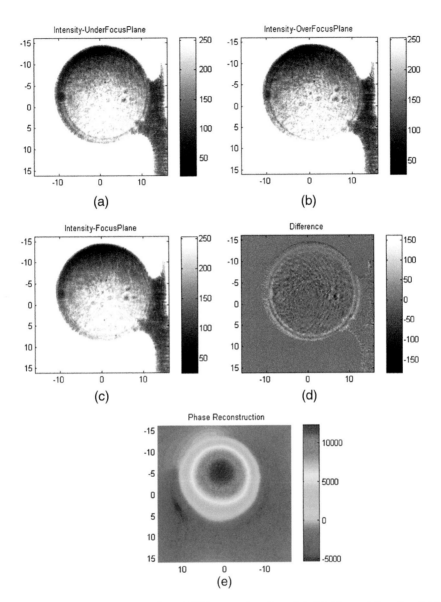

Figure 10.8 Experimental results of TIE-reconstruction: (a)–(c) Three intensity distributions of a lens object illuminated by a plane wave captured from both sides of CCD's plane, with $\Delta z = -0.5$ mm, $\Delta z = 0$ mm, and $\Delta z = +0.5$ mm, respectively; (d) the difference between two intensity distributions; and (e) the phase of the holographic reconstruction at the CCD camera.

It can be concluded that, in comparing the phase of Eq. (10.23) with Eq. (10.24),

$$w(x,y)\big|_{\substack{\text{back focal} \\ \text{plane of L2}}} \varpropto u(x,y,\Delta z) \quad \text{if } \Delta z = \frac{f^2}{f_c} = \frac{f^2(f_{ETL} + f_{OL} - d)}{f_{ETL} f_{OL}}. \tag{10.25}$$

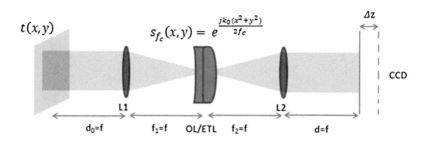

Figure 10.9   TIE 4*f* system using an OL/ETL.

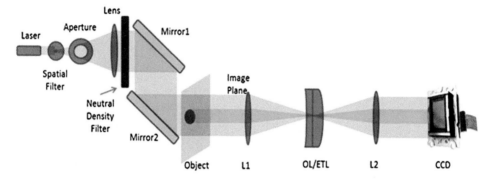

Figure 10.10   Schematic setup for a 4*f* system with an OL/ETL located in the Fourier plane of lens L1. The 4*f* system relays the object located at the front focal plane of lens L1 onto the image plane of the CCD.

Thus, electrically tuning the focal length f_{ETL} of the ETL replaces the need for a slower mechanical defocusing translation of the CCD camera by a distance Δz. Figure 10.10 shows the setup of the TIE using an OL/ETL. Figure 10.11 shows some experimental results of TIE reconstruction using the OL/ETL setup. Figures 10.11(a)–(c) show three intensity distributions of the object illuminated by a plane wave *as if* the CCD plane is translated by $\Delta z = \pm 1$ mm around the image plane $\Delta z = 0$ mm. Figure 10.11(d) shows the difference between the two intensity distributions at $\Delta z = \pm 1$ mm. Figure 10.11(e) shows the reconstructed phase of the phase object at the CCD camera.

10.2 Nonlinear Holography

It is widely known that one cannot image directly through a nonlinear medium because intensity-dependent phase changes distort signals as they propagate. Digital holography can be used to reconstruct an image when the complex optical field from an object travels through a nonlinear medium.[13] Benefits of this method include both increased field of view and super resolution while allowing imaging of the beam dynamics along the full propagation length.[13–15] Because the numerical reconstruction method requires knowledge of the full complex field exiting the sample, the digital

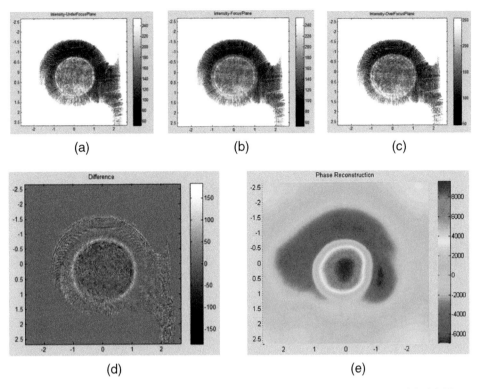

Figure 10.11 Experimental results of TIE reconstruction using an OL/ETL: (a)–(c) Three intensity distributions of the object illuminated by a plane wave captured at the CCD *as if* $\Delta z = -1$ mm, $\Delta z = 0$ mm, and $\Delta z = 1$ mm, respectively. (d) The difference between the overfocused and underfocused intensity distributions. (e) The reconstructed phase of the object at the CCD camera.

holography technique can be used for this purpose. A typical setup is shown in Fig. 10.12, where the output signal intensity is recorded directly in a camera, while the output object phase is measured using a standard phase-shifting algorithm, as explained in Chapter 5.[16]

Once the magnitude and phase of the output field is recorded, reconstruction can be implemented by numerical back-propagation through the nonlinear medium. The nonlinear medium used for demonstration is a photorefractive crystal SBN:75, in which the nonlinearity can be assumed to be similar to a Kerr nonlinearity, giving rise to a change in the refractive index given by $\Delta n(|E_e|^2) = -\gamma|E_e|^2$, where E_e denotes the envelope of the optical field $E = E_e \exp(-jk_0 z)$. Propagation through the "nonlinear" medium can then be modeled by the nonlinear Schrödinger (NLS) equation, given by[17]

$$\frac{\partial E_e}{\partial z} = \left[j\frac{1}{2k}\nabla_{\perp}^2 - j\Delta n(|E_e|^2) \right]\psi = [\mathcal{D} + \mathcal{N}(|E_e|^2)]\, E_e, \qquad (10.26a)$$

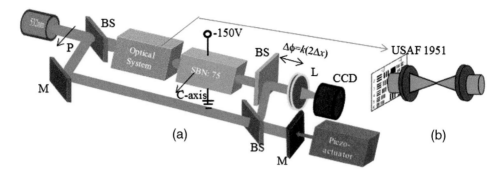

Figure 10.12 Typical experimental setup. Laser light (532 nm), polarized along the crystalline *c* axis, is split into two beams. (a) The object (upper) beam passes through the "optical system" to generate the input waveform, which is projected onto the crystal, and the reference (lower) beam is incremented in phase steps of $\Delta\phi = \pi/2$; both beams are imaged onto the CCD camera. (b) A USAF 1951 resolution chart, used as an object, along with the optical system.[13]

where $\mathcal{D}$ and $\mathcal{N}$ are the linear and nonlinear operators, respectively, and can be readily analyzed numerically using standard split-step beam propagation methods (BPMs).[17] In the split-step method, the linear and nonlinear operators act individually for each increment of propagation distance Δz as

$$E_e(z + \Delta z) \approx \exp(\Delta z \cdot \mathcal{D}) \exp(\Delta z \cdot \mathcal{N}(\psi)) E_e(z)$$
$$\rightarrow E_e(z) \approx \exp(-\Delta z \cdot \mathcal{D}) \exp(-\Delta z \cdot \mathcal{N}(\psi)) E_e(z + \Delta z). \quad (10.26b)$$

Note that when the nonlinear part is absent, Eqs. (10.26) reduces to the paraxial form of the Helmholtz equation [Eq. (2.1)]. Back-propagation through the nonlinear medium simply involves changing $z \rightarrow -z$.

As an example, Fig. 10.13 shows a comparison of linear (no applied voltage) and nonlinear reconstructions with the known (measured) output. The nonlinear reconstruction deconvolves this defocused image and recovers a portion of the object not available in the linear case (bar left of the vertical red line).[14]

An enhancement of 15% in the field of view is demonstrated from each side, for a total of 30%. As a second example, Fig. 10.14(a) shows the experimental results of the nonlinear digital reconstruction of a self-defocused USAF 1951 resolution chart. The first row shows the input intensity and phase, respectively; the middle row shows the nonlinear output intensity and phase, respectively; and the lower row is the numerically reconstructed input intensity and phase, respectively. Figure 10.14(b) shows a simulation of the experimental result in Fig. 10.14(a). The wavelength used is $\lambda = 0.532$ μm, with nonlinearity parameter $\gamma = 6 \times 10^{-4}$, longitudinal step size $\Delta z = 65$ μm, crystal length $d = 10$ mm, and pixel size $\Delta x = 2.5$ μm. Table 10.4 shows the MATLAB code "nonlin_hol_AF1951_exp," which uses nonlinear back-propagation to reconstruct the input field.

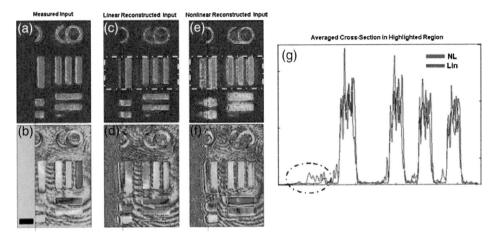

Figure 10.13 Numerically reconstructed input fields: (a)–(b) Measured input intensity and phase; (c)–(d) reconstructed input using linear digital holography; and (e)–(f) reconstructed input using nonlinear digital holography (scale bar = 200 μm). Note, for instance, the appearance of enhanced blue regions in (e) as compared with (c). (g) Averaged cross-sections of highlighted regions in panels (c) and (e). The nonlinear reconstruction shows a clear enhancement of the field of view of 15%.[14]

10.3 Coherence Holography

Thus far the book has primarily discussed various aspects of DH where the hologram is recorded by the interference of two coherent beams or waves and then reconstructed by a coherent wave. This section presents a holographic reconstruction method based on illuminating a hologram with a spatially incoherent beam. In coherence holography (CH), an object recorded in a hologram is reconstructed as the distribution of a complex spatial coherence function rather than as the distribution of the complex optical field that represents the reconstructed image, as is the case in conventional holography. In other words, CH reconstructs the image as the degree of spatial coherence between a pair of points, of which one serves as a reference point R and the other as a probe point P on the object to be reconstructed.[18,19] This section discusses an optical geometry for the direct visualization of the reconstructed coherence image, along with some experimental results. CH is projected to have many applications in optical coherence tomography and profilometry.

Coherence holography is based on the analogy between the diffraction integral and the formula of mutual intensity in the Van Cittert–Zernike theorem.[20,21] The theorem states that under certain conditions the Fourier transform of the mutual coherence function of a distant, incoherent source is equal to its complex visibility, which implies that the wavefront from a spatially incoherent source will appear mostly coherent at large distances. The situation is similar to throwing a bunch of pebbles in the water: the diverging wavefronts, which initially appear to be totally uncorrelated close to the

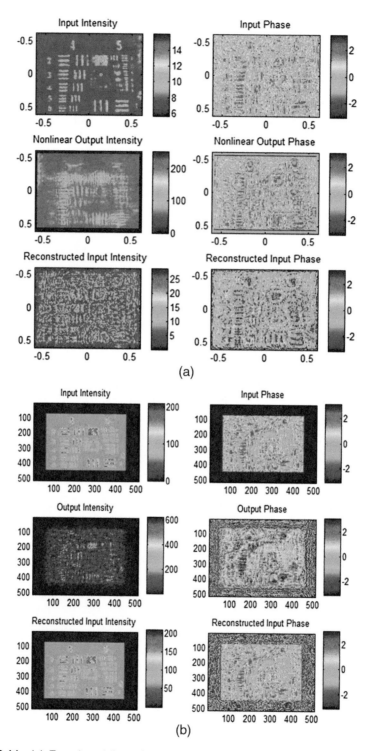

Figure 10.14 (a) Experimental results and (b) simulation. (Top row) Input intensity and phase, (middle row) output intensity and phase, (lower row) reconstructed intensity and phase using Eq. (10.26).[13]

Table 10.4 MATLAB code "nonlin_hol_AF1951_exp.m" uses nonlinear back-propagation to reconstruct the input field (see Fig. 10.14).

```
1    %%Nonlinear holography
2    clc;clear all; close all;
3    Nd=512;
4    %Load output intensity and phase
5    I1=imread('4c.bmp');          %3c
6    I1=double(rgb2gray(I1));
7    P1=imread('4g.bmp');          %3g
8    P1=double(rgb2gray(P1));
9    maxval=pi; minval=-pi;
10   P1 = P1 - min(P1(:));         %Phase
11   %Normalize the phase
12   P1= (P1/range(P1(:)))*(maxval-minval);
13   P1 = P1 + minval;
14   [Ny,Nx]=size(I1);
15   I1=padarray(I1,[floor((Nd-Ny)/2)...
16   floor((Nd-Nx)/2)],0,'both');
17   P1=padarray(P1,[floor((Nd-Ny)/2)...
18   floor((Nd-Nx)/2)],0,'both');
19   [Ny,Nx]=size(I1);
20   %Initialize parameters
21   L=1.222;
22   d=10;                         %Propagation distance in mm
23   dz=0.065;
24   zpoints=round(d/dz);
25   gamma=1*10^-4; %Kerr nonlinearity dn=-gamma*intensity
26   lambda0=0.532*10^-3;          %Wavelength in mm
27   k0=2*pi/lambda0;
28   dx=L/Nx;
29   n=[-Nx/2:1:Nx/2-1];
30   x=n*dx;
31   y=x;
32   [X,Y]=meshgrid(x,y);
33   a=pi./dx;
34   kx=[-a:2*a/Nx:a-2*a/Nx];ky = kx;
35   [KX,KY]=meshgrid(kx,ky);
36   no=2.3; %Refractive index.
37   %%Nonlinear.
38   f=sqrt(I1).*exp(i.*P1);
39   Ff=fftshift(fft2(f));         %Fourier transform of the
40                                 %complex amplitude
41   u=Ff;
42   %Linear propagation
43   D=exp(-i*dz*(KX.^2/(no+0.07)+KY.^2/no)/(2*k0));
44   for m=1:1:zpoints
45   u=u.*D;
46   v=(ifft2(fftshift(u)));
47   N=exp(-i*gamma.*abs(v).^2.*dz);      %Nonlinear propagation
48   v=N.*v;
49   u=fftshift(fft2(v));
50   end
51   If=v;
52   %%Compare with reconstructed from paper
53   Ip=imread('4d.bmp');
```

(continued)

Table 10.4 (*Continued*)

```
54   Ip=double(rgb2gray(Ip));
55   pp=imread('4h.bmp');
56   pp=double(rgb2gray(pp));
57   maxval = pi;minval = -pi;
58   pp = pp - min(pp(:));
59   pp = (pp/range(pp(:)))* (maxval-minval);
60   pp = pp + minval;
61   IP=padarray(I1,[ floor((Nd-Ny)/2)...
62   floor((Nd-Nx)/2)],0,'both');
63   PP=padarray(P1,[ floor((Nd-Ny)/2)...
64   floor((Nd-Nx)/2)],0,'both');
65   fp=sqrt(Ip).*exp(i.*pp);
66   figure
67   subplot(321)
68   imagesc(x,y,abs(fp))
69   %colormap(gray(256))
70   %axis square
71   title('Input Intensity'); colorbar
72   subplot(322)
73   imagesc(x,y,angle(fp))
74   title('Input Phase'); colorbar
75   %colormap(gray(256))
76   %axis square
77   subplot(323)
78   imagesc(x,y,I1)
79   %colormap(gray(256))
80   title('Nonlinear Output Intensity');colorbar
81   %axis square
82   subplot(324)
83   imagesc(x,y,P1)
84   %colormap(gray(256))
85   title('Nonlinear Output Phase'); colorbar
86   %axis square
87   subplot(325)
88   imagesc(x,y,abs(If))
89   %colormap(gray(256))
90   %axis square
91   title('Reconstructed Input Intensity '); colorbar
92   subplot(326)
93   imagesc(x,y,angle(If));
94   title('Reconstructed Input Phase'); colorbar
95   %colormap(gray(256))
96   %axis square
```

source(s), finally coagulate to form a distinct diverging wavefront some distance away.

If we consider the case of phase-conjugate reconstruction in conventional holography, the recording and reconstruction beam of light is highly coherent both temporally and spatially. Consider the following: a reference beam is a spherical wave diverging from a point source R of the form

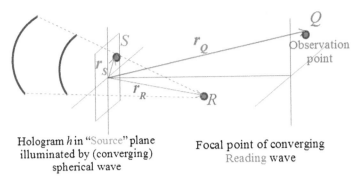

Hologram h in "Source" plane
illuminated by (converging)
spherical wave

Focal point of converging
Reading wave

Figure 10.15 Optical fields reconstructed from a conventional hologram with a phase-conjugated reference beam.[18]

$$E_R(\mathbf{r}_s) = \frac{\exp(-jk_0|\mathbf{r}_s - \mathbf{r}_R|)}{|\mathbf{r}_s - \mathbf{r}_R|}. \qquad (10.27)$$

If the hologram is reconstructed by illuminating it with a reading wave that is the phase conjugate $E_R^*(\mathbf{r}_s)$ of the reference, as shown in Fig. 10.15, the reconstructed optical field at an arbitrary observation point Q is given by

$$\begin{aligned}
E_p(\mathbf{r}_Q,\mathbf{r}_S) &= \iint h(\mathbf{r}_S) E_R^*(\mathbf{r}_S) \frac{\exp(-jk_0|\mathbf{r}_Q - \mathbf{r}_S|)}{|\mathbf{r}_Q - \mathbf{r}_S|} d\mathbf{r}_S \\
&= \iint h(\mathbf{r}_S) \frac{\exp[-jk_0(|\mathbf{r}_Q - \mathbf{r}_S| - |\mathbf{r}_R - \mathbf{r}_S|)]}{(|\mathbf{r}_Q - \mathbf{r}_S| \cdot |\mathbf{r}_R - \mathbf{r}_S|)},
\end{aligned} \qquad (10.28)$$

where $h(\mathbf{r}_S)$ is the amplitude transmittance of the hologram function.

In statistical optics, the mutual intensity between two points Q and R is then determined by the Van Cittert–Zernike theorem, which can be written as[20–22]

$$J(\mathbf{r}_Q,\mathbf{r}_S) = \iint I_I(\mathbf{r}_S) \frac{\exp[-jk_0(|\mathbf{r}_Q - \mathbf{r}_S| - |\mathbf{r}_R - \mathbf{r}_S|)]}{(|\mathbf{r}_Q - \mathbf{r}_S| \cdot |\mathbf{r}_R - \mathbf{r}_S|)} d\mathbf{r}_S, \qquad (10.29)$$

where $I_I(\mathbf{r}_S)$ is the intensity distribution of the spatially incoherent source, and $|\mathbf{r}_Q - \mathbf{r}_S|$ and $|\mathbf{r}_R - \mathbf{r}_S|$ are the distances from a point S on the source to the points Q and R. Note that Eq. (10.29) has a form similar to Eq. (10.28).

If a hologram whose intensity transmittance is proportional to the recorded intensity is illuminated with quasi-monochromatic, spatially incoherent light with a temporal coherence length larger than the longitudinal depth of the 3D object, then an optical field will be generated for which the mutual intensity between observation point Q and reference point R is equal to the optical field that would be reconstructed if the hologram with the

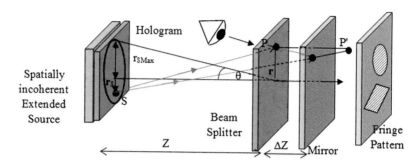

Figure 10.16 Direct visualization of a coherence image reconstructed from a coherence hologram. The coherence image is directly observable as the contrast and the phase of a fringe pattern.[18]

same amplitude transmittance $h(\mathbf{r}_S) \propto I_I(\mathbf{r}_S)$ were illuminated with a phase conjugate of the reference beam. The hologram now represents the irradiance distribution $I(\mathbf{r}_S)$ of a quasi-monochromatic, spatially incoherent extended source, and the recorded fringe intensity during reconstruction depends on this irradiance distribution (and thus on the hologram function). Although the recording of a coherent hologram is like that of a conventional hologram, the reconstruction is performed by illuminating the hologram with quasi-monochromatic, spatially incoherent light. Coherence holography records the fringe intensity and reconstructs the spatial coherence function (SCF).

Because the reconstructed image is encoded in the spatial coherence of the field and cannot be directly observed, the distribution of the spatial coherence function can be visualized as the contrast and the phase distribution of interference fringes by using an appropriate interferometer, such as a Michelson or a Fizeau interferometer. In the Fizeau interferometer arrangement shown in Fig. 10.16, the light from each point source S on the incoherently illuminated hologram is reflected from the beamsplitter and the mirror and then produces an interference fringe pattern of a Fresnel zone plate (FZP), with its central axis normal to the beamsplitter and passing through the source point S at $\mathbf{r}_S$. The interference fringe intensity at point P is observed as a result of intensity-based superposition of many FZPs weighted by the irradiance of the hologram, as given by[18]

$$I(\mathbf{r},\Delta z) \propto \int I_S(\mathbf{r}_S)\left\{1 + \cos\left[k\left(\frac{\Delta z}{2}\right)\frac{|\mathbf{r}-\mathbf{r}_S|^2}{z} + \alpha(\Delta z)\right]\right\}d\mathbf{r}_S$$

$$= \int I_S(\mathbf{r}_S)d\mathbf{r}_S\{1 + |\mu(\mathbf{r},\Delta z)|\cos[\alpha(\Delta z) - \beta(\mathbf{r},\Delta z)]\}, \quad (10.30)$$

where $\alpha(\Delta z)$ is the initial phase of the FZP fringe, and $\mu(\mathbf{r},\Delta z)$ is a complex degree of coherence given by

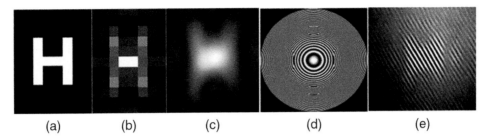

(a)　　　　(b)　　　　(c)　　　　(d)　　　　(e)

Figure 10.17 (a) Object; (b) image reconstructed from the phase-only hologram; (c) modulus of the spatial coherence function; (d) coherent hologram representing a spatially incoherent source distribution; (e) experimentally reconstructed coherent image visualized as a fringe contrast.[18]

$$\mu(\mathbf{r},\Delta z) = |\mu(\mathbf{r},\Delta z)| \exp[-j\beta(\mathbf{r},\Delta z)]$$

$$= \frac{\int I_S(\hat{\mathbf{r}}_S) \exp\left\{-jk_0\Delta z \tan^2\theta \left|\frac{\mathbf{r}}{r_{Smax}} - \hat{\mathbf{r}}_S\right|^2\right\} d\hat{\mathbf{r}}_S}{\int I_S(\hat{\mathbf{r}}_S) d\hat{\mathbf{r}}_S}, \qquad (10.31)$$

where $\hat{\mathbf{r}}_S = \mathbf{r}_S/r_{Smax}$ is a position vector normalized with the size of the hologram r_{Smax}, and $\tan\theta = r_{Smax}/z$, with θ being the half angle subtended by the hologram, as shown in Fig. 10.16.

Therefore, the complex degree of coherence is given by the Fresnel transform of the incoherently illuminated hologram. If a Fresnel hologram were recorded with coherent light for an object at an average distance $\bar{z} = z^2/2\Delta z$ from the hologram and then illuminated with spatially incoherent light from behind, a set of interference fringe patterns will be observed on the beamsplitter whose fringe contrast and phase represent the field amplitude and the phase, respectively, of the original object recorded with coherent light.

Figure 10.17(a) shows an object (a letter H) formed by 4×5 pixels on an SLM. Using a spatial light modulator (SLM), the generated Fresnel phase-only hologram, with the parameters $\Delta z = 1$ mm and $\tan(\theta) = 0.15$, is shown in Fig. 10.17(d). First, if the hologram is reconstructed numerically with simulated coherent light, then the phase-only reconstruction causes the image to be blurred, as shown in Fig. 10.17(b). According to the proposed principle of a coherent hologram, the brightness of the blurred image of the letter H will be transformed into the fringe visibility when the hologram is illuminated with spatially incoherent light. The hologram is then displayed on the SLM and illuminated with an extended beam from a HeNe laser through a rotating ground-glass diffuser that destroys spatial coherence. Figure 10.17(e) shows a fringe pattern recorded on a CCD camera. Note that the fringes exhibit a high contrast in the region that corresponds to the bright part of the numerically reconstructed image of Fig. 10.17(b). When these fringes are analyzed by the Fourier transform technique,[22] the fringe contrast is obtained and then displayed as a brightness distribution. As seen in Fig. 10.17(c), the contrast of

Table 10.5 Comparison between different types of holography.[23–29]

Technique	Recording	Input	Reconstruction	Output
Conventional holography	Spatially coherent	Amplitude transmittance	Coherent	Optical field
Coherent holography	Spatially coherent	Fringe intensity distribution	Incoherent	SCF
Michelson stellar interferometry	Spatially incoherent	SCF	Numerically	Fringe intensity distribution
Incoherent holography	Spatially incoherent (split and recombine)	Irradiance FZP	Coherent	Optical field
Gamma holography	Spatially incoherent	SCF	Incoherent	SCF

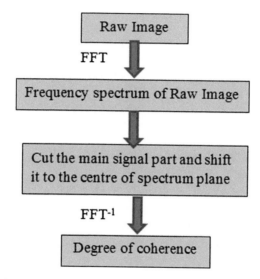

Figure 10.18 Flowchart of the coherence holography technique.

the fringes observed in the image reconstructed from the incoherently illuminated coherent hologram has good correspondence to the brightness of the image numerically reconstructed from the coherently illuminated hologram.

In summary, the intensity (rather than amplitude) transmittance of the hologram is made proportional to the recorded interference fringe intensity. The hologram represents the irradiance distribution of a spatially incoherent extended source. Although the recording of a coherent hologram is like that of a conventional hologram, the reconstruction is performed by illuminating the hologram with quasi-monochromatic, spatially incoherent light. The CH process records the fringe intensity and reconstructs the SCF; the reconstructed image encoded in the SCF cannot be observed directly. Table 10.5 compares several different holographic techniques; their illuminating, recording, and reconstruction beams; and the input and output type of information recorded. Figure 10.18 shows the flowchart of the MATLAB script code "my_coherence2.m" (shown in Table 10.6) used to find the degree

Table 10.6 MATLAB code "my_coherence_2.m," showing a typical CH example to find the degree of coherence shown in Fig. 10.19.

```
1    %Coherence holography program
2    clc;clear all;
3    %%%%%%%%%%%%%%%%%Raw Image%%%%%%%%%%%%%%%%%%%%%%%
4    Object=imread('2.tif');
5    Object=double(Object(:,:,1));
6    Object=imresize(Object,[ 700 700]);
7    figure (1)
8    imagesc(Object);
9    colormap(gray(256))
10   title({ 'Coherence image visualized as',
11   'a fringe contrast:Raw Image'})
12   saveas(gcf,'fig19a.tif');
13   %%%%%%%Frequency Spectrum of Raw Image%%%%%%%
14   Object_ft=fftshift(fft2(Object));
15   Object_ft=Object_ft/max(max(Object_ft));
16   figure(2);
17   colormap(gray(256))
18   imagesc(log(abs(Object_ft)));
19   title('Frequency Spectrum of Raw Image');
20   saveas(gcf,'fig19b.tif');
21   %%%%%%%%Coherence Function of Object%%%%%%
22   %Cut the main signal part and shift it to the
23   %center of spectrum plane
24   Object_ft_cut=zeros(16,16);
25   for m=1:16
26   for n=1:16
27   Object_ft_cut(m,n)=Object_ft(m+357,n+318);
28   end
29   end
30   Object_ft_cut_move=zeros(700,700);
31   for m=1:16
32   for n=1:16
33   Object_ft_cut_move(m+350-8,n+350-8)=...
34   Object_ft_cut(m,n);
35   end
36   end
37   figure(3);
38   colormap(gray(256))
39   imagesc(log(abs(Object_ft_cut_move)));
40   title('Object Frequency Spectrum');
41   saveas(gcf,'fig19c.tif');
42   Coherence=ifft2(Object_ft_cut_move);
43   figure(4);
44   colormap(gray(256))
45   imagesc(abs(Coherence));
46   title('Coherence Function of Object');
47   saveas(gcf,'fig19d.tif');
48   figure(5)
49   mesh(abs(Coherence)/max(abs(Coherence(:))))
50   xlabel('x-axis(pixel)');ylabel('y-axis(pixel)')
51   zlabel('Degree of Coherence');axis ij
```

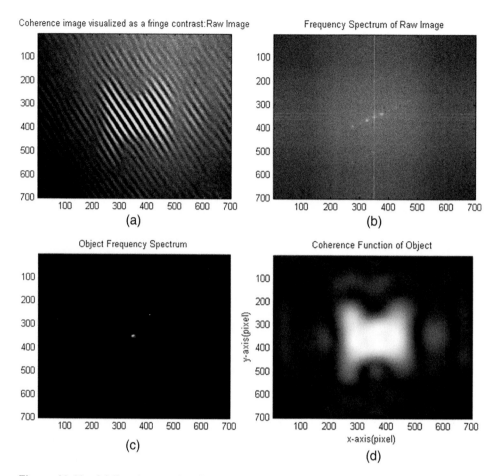

Figure 10.19 (a) Raw image visualized as a fringe contrast of the letter H, as in Fig. 10.17; (b) the spectrum; (c) the cropped and shifted spectrum; and (d) the degree of coherence.

of coherence of a typical example. Figure 10.19(a) shows the raw image visualized as a fringe contrast; Fig. 10.19(b) shows the spectrum; Fig. 10.19(c) shows the cropped and shifted spectrum; and Fig. 10.19(d) shows the degree of coherence.

10.4 Polarization Imaging Using Digital Holography

This section discusses polarization imaging techniques that utilize digital holographic recording and reconstruction techniques to quantitatively determine the polarization state of an object's reflected or transmitted wavefront. These techniques include both sequential and "one-shot" recording and reconstruction techniques that use orthogonally polarized reference waves to achieve a state-of-polarization (SOP) image resolution on the order of ~ 1 μm. Another topic includes polarization multiplexing for intensity imaging techniques to reduce laser speckle.

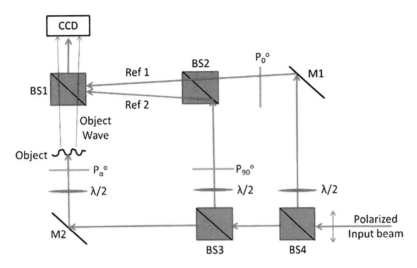

Figure 10.20 Off-axis configuration for one-shot capture using two orthogonally polarized reference beams, each with a small angular offset. Adapted from Colomb.[31]

The SOP of the object wave can be determined by using two orthogonally polarized reference waves and then numerically reconstructing the amplitude and phase for each polarization separately.[30,31] The simplest method records one hologram using the first polarization state and then a second hologram using the orthogonal polarization state. Each hologram is reconstructed separately; the phases are subsequently compared to determine the SOP of the object wave. It is also possible for both holograms to be recorded simultaneously using the "one-shot" method, which employs an off-axis configuration to spatially separate each reconstruction region in the image, as shown in Fig. 10.20. In this configuration, orthogonal polarizations prevent unintended interference between each of the reference waves during recording.[31] The one-shot method can be advantageous in some instances when only a single exposure is possible (e.g., a moving object), although it is optically and computationally more complex than recording two sequential holograms.[31]

Following the derivation and notation of Yokota et al.[32], the intensity I_H of the interference pattern between the object wave $E_O(x,y)$ and the reference wave $E_R(x,y)$ at the CCD recording plane (x,y) is given by

$$I_H(x,y) = \sum_{\beta=x,y} |E_{R\beta}(x,y)|^2 + |E_O(x,y)|^2$$
$$+ \sum_{\beta=x,y} E_{R\beta}(x,y) E_O^*(x,y) + \sum_{\beta=x,y} E_{R\beta}^*(x,y) E_O(x,y), \qquad (10.32)$$

where the first two terms are the zero order, the third term is the real image, and the fourth term is the virtual image.

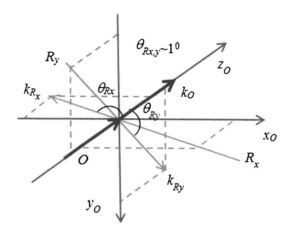

Figure 10.21 Off-axis geometry at incidence on the CCD. The x_O,y_O plane is parallel to the CCD camera. Both R_y in the y_O,z_O plane and R_x in the x_O,z_O plane come from different spatial directions.[31]

The amplitude and phase of the object wave at the CCD can be expressed by the Jones vector:

$$E_O(x,y) = \begin{bmatrix} A_{Ox}(x,y) \exp[j\phi_{Ox}(x,y)] \\ A_{Oy}(x,y) \exp[j\phi_{Oy}(x,y)] \end{bmatrix}. \tag{10.33}$$

The x and y directions represent the orthogonal horizontal and vertical linear polarization states, respectively. For simplification, the spatial dependence of the polarization state will be implied from this point onward; thus, the (x,y) notation will subsequently be suppressed. According to Fig. 10.21,

$$
\begin{aligned}
E_{Rx}(x,y,z,t) &= |E_{Rx}| \exp[j(k_{Rx} \cdot \vec{r} - \omega t + \phi_{Rx})] \\
&=> E_{Rx}(x,y) = A_{Rx} \exp[j(\phi_{Rx} + k_{Rx} \sin(\theta_{Rx})x)],
\end{aligned}
\tag{10.34}
$$

where $\vec{k}_{Rx} \cdot \vec{r} = k_{Rx} \sin(\theta_{Rx})x + 0y + k_{Rx} \cos(\theta_{Rx})z$, $|E_{Rx}| = A_{Rx}$. The polarization states of the reference waves, propagating at some small angle θ_R relative to the CCD normal, can be described by

$$E_{Rx}(x,y) = \begin{bmatrix} A_{Rx}(x,y) \exp[j\phi_{Rx}(x,y) + k \sin(\theta_{Rx})x] \\ 0 \end{bmatrix}, \tag{10.35a}$$

$$E_{Ry}(x,y) = \begin{bmatrix} 0 \\ A_{Ry}(x,y) \exp[j\phi_{Ry}(x,y) + k \sin(\theta_{Ry})x] \end{bmatrix}. \tag{10.35b}$$

Using the Jones vector expressions (and the β subscript to represent the x or y polarizations), the recorded intensity $I_{H\beta}$ is given by

$$I_H(x,y) = A_O^2 + \sum_{\beta=x,y} A_{R\beta}^2(x,y)$$

$$+ \sum_{\beta=x,y} A_{O\beta} \exp[j\phi_{O\beta}]A_{R\beta} \exp[-j(\phi_{R\beta} + k\,\sin(\theta_{R\beta})x)]$$

$$+ \sum_{\beta=x,y} A_{O\beta} \exp[-j\phi_{O\beta}]A_{R\beta} \exp[j(\phi_{R\beta} + k\,\sin(\theta_{R\beta})x)], \qquad (10.36)$$

where $A_O^2 = A_{Ox}^2 + A_{Oy}^2$ is the total object beam intensity. The first two terms represent the zeroth-order diffraction and are generally not of any interest. The third and fourth terms represent the real and virtual images of the reconstructed object, respectively.

The hologram is reconstructed using the Fresnel transform, as previously discussed in Chapter 4, and described in Yokota et al.[32] The reconstruction distance is chosen to be either $+z$ or $-z$ (which focuses the real or virtual image, respectively), where z is the optical distance from the physical object to the CCD camera. Because focusing one image defocuses the other image, it is important to spatially separate these terms in the object reconstruction with an appropriate choice of reference tilt angle θ_R (typically on the order of $\sim$1 deg).

For a reference wave of the form $R_D(x,y) = \exp[jk\,\sin(\theta_{Rx})x]$, the complex field of the reconstructed object field at the image plane I at a distance z is

$$E_{I\beta}(x,y,z) = \exp\left[\frac{j\pi}{\lambda z}(x^2 + y^2)\right]$$

$$\times \iint R_D \cdot I_{H\beta} \exp\left[\frac{j\pi}{\lambda z}(x^2 + y^2)\right] \exp\left[-\frac{j\pi}{\lambda z}(x\xi + y\eta)\right] dx dy. \qquad (10.37)$$

The hologram is then reconstructed separately for each orthogonal polarization state, yielding the following Jones vectors for each object wave that corresponds to the third term in Eq. (10.36) (real image):

$$E_{Ox}(\xi,\eta, -z) = \begin{bmatrix} A_{Rx}(\xi,\eta)A_{Ox}(\xi,\eta)\exp[j(\phi_{Ox}(\xi,\eta) - \phi_{Rx}(\xi,\eta))] \\ 0 \end{bmatrix}, \qquad (10.38a)$$

$$E_{Oy}(\xi,\eta, -z) = \begin{bmatrix} 0 \\ A_{Ry}(\xi,\eta)A_{Oy}(\xi,\eta)\exp[j(\phi_{Oy}(\xi,\eta) - \phi_{Rx}(\xi,\eta))] \end{bmatrix}. \qquad (10.38b)$$

The reference waves are typically chosen to have equal amplitudes $A_{Rx}(\xi,\eta) = A_{Ry}(\xi,\eta)$ such that the ellipticity (amplitude ratio) or azimuth angle $\alpha(\xi,\eta)$ is given by

$$\tan(\alpha(\xi,\eta)) = |A_{Oy}(\xi,\eta)|/|A_{Ox}(\xi,\eta)|,$$

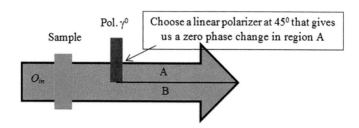

Figure 10.22 Insertion of a known polarization device (linear polarizer at angle γ) into the object beam. Region A becomes the area used to perform phase correction/calibration, whereas region B contains the object wave of interest.[32]

whereas the phase difference due to the orthogonal polarization states is given by

$$\Delta\phi(\xi,\eta) = \phi_{Oy}(\xi,\eta) - \phi_{Ox}(\xi,\eta) - \Delta\phi_R(\xi,\eta), \tag{10.39}$$

where $\Delta\phi_R(\xi,\eta) = \phi_{Ry}(\xi,\eta) - \phi_{Rx}(\xi,\eta)$ is an error term due to polarization switching of the reference wave (e.g., phase drift, etc.) and must be measured from a known polarization reference state. To this end, some part of the "object" must contain a well-behaved polarization component (e.g., a linear polarizer, etc.) such that the part of each reconstructed hologram contains a known polarization state. A measurement of the mean phase difference over the area A (see Fig. 10.22) of the known polarization state directly gives $\Delta\phi_R(\xi,\eta)$ because $\phi_{Oy}(\xi,\eta) = \phi_{Ox}(\xi,\eta)$.

The reference phase is subsequently added to the phase calculation to yield the absolute phase as

$$\begin{aligned}\Delta\phi_c(\xi,\eta) &= \phi_{Oy}(\xi,\eta) - \phi_{Ox}(\xi,\eta) - \Delta\phi_R(\xi,\eta) + \Delta\phi_R(\xi,\eta) \\ &= \phi_{Oy}(\xi,\eta) - \phi_{Ox}(\xi,\eta). \tag{10.40}\end{aligned}$$

The geometry required to implement this correction is straightforward and can be performed by inserting a known polarizer into part of the object beam, as shown in Fig. 10.22.

Because $\alpha(\xi,\eta)$ and $\Delta\phi_c(\xi,\eta)$ are computed pixel by pixel, using the polarization ellipse geometry of Fig. 10.23, the total polarization state of the object can then be calculated in terms of the principal axis and ellipticity angles, ψ and χ, respectively, over the entire object reconstruction:

$$\psi(\xi,\eta) = \frac{1}{2}\tan^{-1}[\tan(2\alpha(\xi,\eta))\cos(\Delta\phi_c(\xi,\eta))], \tag{10.41a}$$

$$\chi(\xi,\eta) = \frac{1}{2}\sin^{-1}[\sin(2\alpha(\xi,\eta))\sin(\Delta\phi_c(\xi,\eta))]. \tag{10.41b}$$

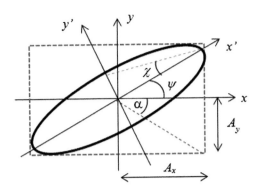

Figure 10.23   Geometry of the polarization ellipse.[32]

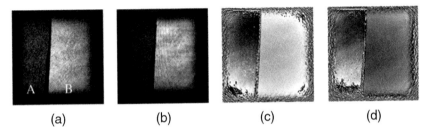

    (a)   (b)   (c)   (d)

Figure 10.24   Hologram reconstruction of the HWP: (a) intensity hologram for $|A_x|$, (b) intensity hologram for $|A_y|$, (c) phase hologram of ϕ_x, and (d) phase hologram of ϕ_y. Region A includes the 45-deg reference polarizer, and region B is the HWP under test, using the geometry of Fig. 10.22.[31]

Following a similar derivation from Nomura and Javidi[33] and Nomura et al.,[34] the Stokes parameters of the object wave can be shown to be

$$
S = \begin{bmatrix} S_0(\xi,\eta) \\ S_1(\xi,\eta) \\ S_2(\xi,\eta) \\ S_3(\xi,\eta) \end{bmatrix} = \begin{bmatrix} A_{0x}^2(\xi,\eta) + A_{0y}^2(\xi,\eta) \\ A_{0x}^2(\xi,\eta) - A_{0y}^2(\xi,\eta) \\ 2A_{0x}^2(\xi,\eta) \cdot A_{0y}^2(\xi,\eta) \cdot \cos \Delta\phi_c(\xi,\eta) \\ 2A_{0x}^2(\xi,\eta) \cdot A_{0y}^2(\xi,\eta) \cdot \sin \Delta\phi_c(\xi,\eta) \end{bmatrix}, \qquad (10.42)
$$

where A_{ox} and A_{oy} denote the horizontal and vertical components, respectively, of the electric field of a reconstructed object wave.

    Using the techniques described above, a half-wave plate (HWP) was imaged in Colomb et al.[31] using the one-shot configuration in a transmissive geometry to determine the polarization state of the object wave. The hologram reconstructions are shown in Fig. 10.24. Region A consists of a linear polarizer oriented at 45 deg, used for a phase reference, whereas region B contains the HWP under test. The amplitude ratio (ellipticity) angle α is found by dividing region B of Fig. 10.24(b) by that of Fig. 10.24(a) (pixel by pixel) and computing the inverse tangent; $\Delta\phi$ is found by subtracting Fig. 10.24(c) from Fig. 10.24(d) (again, over region B, pixel by pixel).

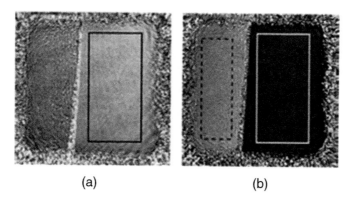

(a)   (b)

Figure 10.25 SOP images of the HWP: (a) computed amplitude ratio angle α and (b) computed phase difference $\Delta\phi$. The solid rectangle denotes the area of interest in region B, whereas the dashed rectangle denotes the area averaged over region A to determine the phase error $\Delta\phi_R$.[31]

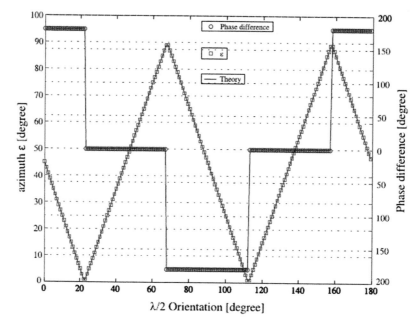

Figure 10.26 SOP measurements compared to theoretical values for the HWP under test.[31]

The average phase error $\Delta\phi_R$ is similarly computed from region A using the reference polarization. The resulting SOP images are shown in Fig. 10.25.

The HWP was rotated 180 deg in 1-deg increments, and the SOP measurements illustrated in Figs. 10.24 and 10.25 were repeated for each rotation increment to fully characterize the HWP over all relevant angles. The measured SOP for each angle (computed from the hologram reconstructions) is compared to the theoretical performance in Fig. 10.26 after correction for phase error $\Delta\phi_R$. The measured SOP using this method is in good agreement

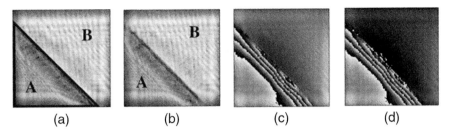

(a)   (b)   (c)   (d)

Figure 10.27 Hologram reconstructions of the QWP at 0-deg rotation: (a) intensity hologram for $|A_x|$, (b) intensity hologram for $|A_y|$, (c) phase hologram of ϕ_x, and (d) phase hologram of ϕ_y. Region A includes the 45-deg reference polarizer, and region B is the QWP under test, using the geometry of Fig. 10.20.[32]

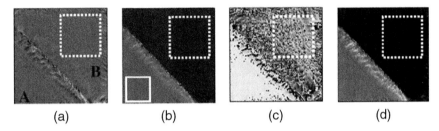

(a)   (b)   (c)   (d)

Figure 10.28 SOP images of the QWP at 0-deg rotation: (a) computed angle α, (b) computed phase difference $\Delta\phi$, (c) principal ellipse angle Ψ, and (d) ellipticity χ. The dashed rectangle denotes the region B area of interest, whereas the solid rectangle denotes the area averaged over region A to determine the phase error $\Delta\phi_R$.[32]

with the theoretical SOP for the HWP, with a mean α (ellipticity) error of approximately 1 deg and a mean $\Delta\phi$ error of ~ 5 deg. The greatest errors occurred when the object wave SOP was either linear vertical or linear horizontal, producing near-zero interference with the orthogonally polarized reference wave. At these four specific angles, the orthogonal reference hologram encodes almost no information, so the phase cannot be accurately reconstructed, and the algorithm returns a random phase (thus greatly increasing the error at these angles). The mean $\Delta\phi$ error of 5 deg is primarily due to the large errors introduced at these specific angles, whereas the mean $\Delta\phi$ error is closer to 1 deg when far from these specific angles. (See Colomb et al.[31] for a thorough discussion and error analysis.)

A very similar procedure using a quarter-wave plate (QWP) was performed in Kuroda et al.[30] by a separate research group. In this instance, the QWP was illuminated by a 45-deg linearly polarized beam, with a 45-deg linear polarizer inserted in the object beam to provide a reference polarization. The QWP was rotated 180 deg in 10-deg increments. The hologram reconstructions and SOP measurements for 0-deg rotation are shown in Figs. 10.27 and 10.28, respectively.

Following the same procedure described earlier, the QWP measurements can be compared to their theoretical values in Fig. 10.29. Note that for

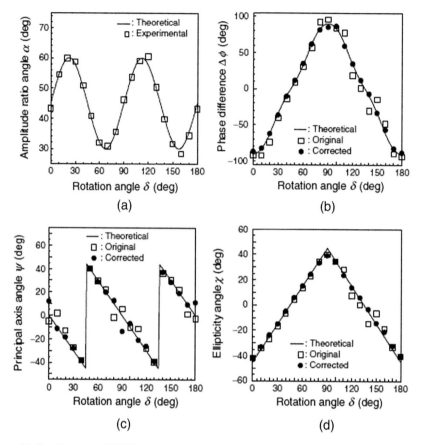

Figure 10.29 Computed SOP measurements compared to theoretical values for the QWP under test: (a) amplitude ratio angle α, (b) phase difference $\Delta\phi$, (c) principal axis ψ, and (d) ellipticity χ.[32]

rotation angles of 0 deg, 90 deg, and 180 deg, the object wave is circularly polarized, which leads to a poorly defined principal axis angle ψ. Therefore, the error in ψ is relatively large ($\sim$5.5 deg) due to the inclusion of these specific angles, whereas the error in $\Delta\phi$ and χ is approximately 2.5 deg.[32] It can be inferred from the SOP measurements of both the HWP and QWP that when the device under test is well known, it becomes possible to predict which orientation angles will produce the largest error; however, this is not generally true for an unknown test object.

After establishing the accuracy of these techniques, they can then be applied to image the polarization states of transmissive objects, as in Colomb et al.,[35] in which the birefringence of a bent fiber is calculated via holographic polarization imaging through a microscope objective (MO). The use of a MO has become a standard technique in digital holography to yield spatial resolutions on the order of 1 μm in the holographic reconstruction.[31,35] Figure 10.30 shows the amplitude and phase holographic reconstructions (for each orthogonal polarization state) for both the unbent and bent fiber

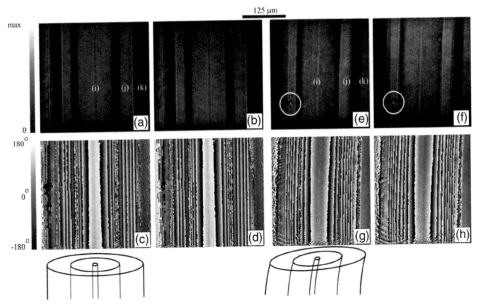

Figure 10.30 Amplitude and phase reconstructions for the (a)–(d) unbent and (e)–(h) bent fiber. The fiber regions are labeled as the (i) fiber core and cladding, (j) cover, and (k) index-matching fluid. The circled point denotes a small dust particle on the sample.[35]

viewed through a $20 \times$ MO (0.5 NA) with an effective spatial resolution of $\sim$2 μm.

Figure 10.31 reveals the azimuth and phase SOP images of the unbent and bent fibers, whereas Fig. 10.32 illustrates the average phase profile along the direction perpendicular to the fiber axis. The phase difference for the unbent fiber is not constant, but rather it exhibits small variations due to internal stresses in the fiber resulting from the manufacturing process.[35] The right side of the coating also has a large phase difference relative to the left side ($\sim$40 deg), which is due to residual stress from winding the fiber after fabrication. For the bent fiber, a relatively smooth phase gradient can be seen in the direction perpendicular to the fiber axis in the core/cladding region. The compressed region of the fiber exhibits a larger refractive index than the rarified region, corresponding to a smaller phase difference for higher compression, as shown in Fig. 10.32. This effect can also be seen in the cover region of the fiber in Fig. 10.32, albeit to a lesser degree. The accuracy of this technique is compared with a standard measurement technique in Colomb et al.[35] and found to be accurate within a standard deviation of $\sim$2 deg.

Polarization imaging via DH can also be performed on 3D objects in a reflective geometry by again using two holograms in which the reference wave and object wave polarizations are orthogonal, as in Nomura and Javidi[33] and Nomura et al.[34] In the recording geometry described by Nomura et al.,[34] a QWP is used to introduce a fixed $\pi/2$ phase shift between the horizontal and

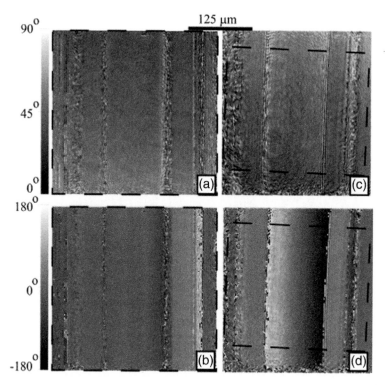

Figure 10.31 The SOP images of the unbent and bent fibers over the dotted region of interest with an effective spatial resolution of ~2 μm for an (a) unbent fiber ellipticity α, (b) unbent fiber phase Δφ, (c) bent fiber ellipticity α, and (d) bent fiber phase Δφ.[35]

vertical reference waves, thus suppressing the need for a calibration object to be inserted in the object beam. A die is used first as an unpolarized object and then subsequently placed behind spatially separated orthogonal polarizers (i.e., the "polarized" die) for polarimetric imaging, as shown in Fig. 10.33.

Holograms of both the unpolarized and polarized die were recorded, and the Stokes parameters were calculated pixel by pixel (in a manner similar to that previously described), shown in Figs. 10.34 and 10.35 for both the unpolarized and polarized die, respectively.

The intensity in each figure is normalized such that white and black correspond to the intensity maximum and minimum, respectively. As expected, the images of the unpolarized die do not reveal any well-defined polarization states, with S_1, S_2, and S_3 essentially randomly distributed across the image. Note that the S_1 image reveals some small difference in the magnitude of the s- and p- polarized reflections across the unpolarized die. However, the polarized die allows the polarization states to be imaged, with the S_0 and S_1 states appearing as expected given the orientation of the orthogonal polarizers. The S_1' "state" is shown for illustration purposes only and is given by $S_1' = A_{0y}^2(\xi,\eta) - A_{0x}^2(\xi,\eta)$. It is not clearly stated in Nomura et al.[34] what the S_2 and S_3 states shown in Fig. 10.35 reveal about the object,

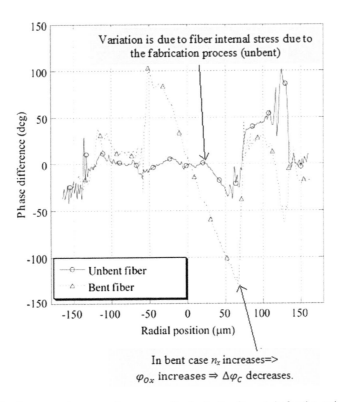

Figure 10.32 Average phase profile perpendicular to the fiber axis for the unbent and bent fibers. The core/cladding region of the bent fiber exhibits a linearly decreasing slope with an increasing refractive index.[35]

Figure 10.33 Die test object: (a) unpolarized configuration and (b) behind orthogonal polarizers.[33]

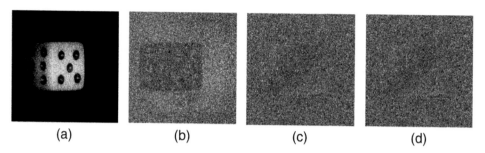

Figure 10.34 Normalized Stokes parameter images of an unpolarized die: (a) S_0, (b) S_1, (c) S_2, and (d) S_3.[34]

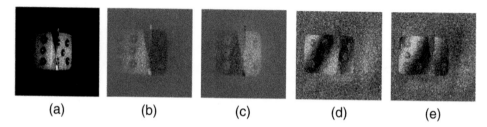

Figure 10.35 Normalized Stokes parameter images of a polarized die: (a) S_0, (b) S_1, (c) S_1', (d) S_2, and (e) S_3.[34]

except that they "make suggestions about the polarimetric information of the object," to illustrate that DH is a viable method for polarimetric imaging of 3D objects. Nomura and Javidi[33] show that the addition of such polarimetric information can greatly increase discrimination when used for pattern recognition (e.g., autocorrelation) among images of 3D objects.

Stokes vector imaging of the Newport logo using orthogonal polarizers has been performed by the authors, in a manner similar to that shown in Fig. 10.33, with the corresponding MATLAB code (shown in Table 10.7) used to generate Figs. 10.36–10.38. The Newport logo was recorded twice—once each with linear s- and p-polarized reference beams. The linear polarization angle was rotated 90 deg using a HWP, such that the phase offset is fixed at $\pi/2$. Figure 10.36 shows the individual reconstructions of the s- and p-polarized holograms, Fig. 10.37 illustrates the Stokes parameters, and Fig. 10.38 illustrates the azimuthal and ellipticity angles of the polarization ellipse using the geometry of Fig. 10.23.

Note that if the Stokes parameters are normalized on a pixel-by-pixel basis, the resulting intensity image of Fig. 10.37(a) would be unity at every pixel, thus revealing no useful information. Additionally, phase and speckle noise can dramatically alter the "true" polarization value when evaluated on a pixel-by-pixel basis. For this reason, it is difficult to quantitatively determine the Stokes parameter for any given pixel, although the qualitative reconstructions still reveal a great deal of polarimetric information about the object.

Table 10.7 MATLAB code "Stokes_parameters.m" uses holograms recorded with orthogonal polarizations to determine the Stokes vectors of the object wave (shown in Figs. 10.36–10.38).

```
1   %This example uses holograms recorded with
2   %orthogonal polarizations to determine the
3   %Stokes vectors of the object wave
4   format compact
5   close all;clc;
6   load Saved_Raw_holo1.mat %variable name hraw1
7   load Saved_Raw_holo2.mat %variable name hraw2
8   %Reconstruction parameters
9   d = 0.41;
10  lambda = 514.5e-9;
11  dx = 6.7e-6;
12  %Reconstruct the holograms
13  h1 = myFresnel(hraw1,d,lambda,dx);        %TM, p-polarized.
14  %illumination,vert
15  h2 = myFresnel(hraw2,d,lambda,dx);        %TE, s-polarized.
16  %illumination,horiz
17  figure(1)
18  imagesc(abs(h1))
19  axis square
20  colormap gray
21  title('p-Polarized Object Reconstruction')
22  axis([ 1 300 300 700])
23  figure(2)
24  imagesc(abs(h2))
25  axis square
26  colormap gray
27  title('s-Polarized Object Reconstruction')
28  axis([ 1 300 300 700])
29  %%Compute the polarization phase difference
30  phir = pi/2;                 %Fixed/known reference angle
31                    %for this recording configuration
32  phi1p = angle(h1)+phir;      %Add fixed ref. phase shift
33  phi2p = angle(h2);
34  phic = phi1p-phi2p;
35  %Wrap 2pi, if needed
36  phic(find(phi1p<phi2p))=phic(find(phi1p<phi2p))+2*pi;
37  figure(1)
38  imagesc(phic)
39  title('\Delta\phi_c')
40  axis([ 1 300 300 700])
41  axis square
42  colormap jet
43  %%Compute the Stokes vectors
44  S0 = abs(h1).^2+abs(h2).^2;     %S0->total intensity
45  S1 = abs(h1).^2-abs(h2).^2;     %S1->diff. between
46                             %s- and p-polarizations
47  S2 = 2*abs(h1).*abs(h2).*cos(phic); %S2->diff. between
48                             %45-deg polarizations
49  S3 = 2*abs(h1).*abs(h2).*sin(phic);   %S3->diff.
50                                %between RHC-LHC.
51  %Normalize the Stokes vectors to a range of [ 0,1] .
52  %This normalizes each vector to itself, which is
53  %not strictly correct.
```

(continued)

Table 10.7 (*Continued*)

```
54  S0 =(S0 - min(min(S0)))./(max(max(S0))-min(min(S0)));
55  S1 =(S1 - min(min(S1)))./(max(max(S1))-min(min(S1)));
56  S2 =(S2 - min(min(S2)))./(max(max(S2))-min(min(S2)));
57  S3 =(S3 - min(min(S3)))./(max(max(S3))-min(min(S3)));
58  %Degree of polarization (using normalized param.)
59  p = sqrt(S1.^2+S2.^2+S3.^2)./S0;       %Should always be
60                                         %p <= 1
61  p_max = max(max(p(find(p < inf))));    %Find the highest
62                                         %non-inf. value
63  p(find(p == inf)) = p_max;       %Replace divide by zeros
64                                   %with p_max.
65  %This fix should introduce minimal error into the
66  %degree of polarization p.
67  %Polarization ellipse angles.
68  Psi=0.5.*atan(S2./S1);       %Azimuthal(orientation) angle
69  Chi=0.5.*asin(S3./S0);       %Ellipticity angle
70  figure(2)
71  imagesc(S0.^.25)
72  %logim(S0,1.5)
73  title('S0, Total Intensity')
74  axis square
75  colormap gray
76  axis([ 1 300 300 700])
77  figure(3)
78  imagesc(S1.^2)
79  %logim(S1,.5)
80  title('S1, Diff. Between s- and p-polarizations')
81  axis square
82  colormap gray
83  axis([ 1 300 300 700])
84  figure(4)
85  imagesc(S2.^2)
86  %logim(S2,-1.5)
87  title({ 'S2, Difference between +45^o,'
88  'and -45^o polarizations'})
89  axis square
90  colormap gray
91  axis([ 1 300 300 700])
92  figure(5)
93  imagesc(S3.^2)
94  %logim(S3,1.5)
95  title({ 'S3, Difference Between RHC',
96  'and LHC polarizations'})
97  axis square
98  colormap gray
99  axis([ 1 300 300 700])
100  Psi = 0.5.*atan(S2./S1);     %Azimuthal angle
101  Chi = 0.5.*asin(S3./S0);     %Ellipticity angle
102  figure(7)
103  imagesc(Psi.^2)
104  title('\Psi, Azimuthal (Orientation) Angle')
105  axis square
106  colormap gray
107  axis([ 1 300 300 700])
108  figure(8)
109  imagesc(abs(Chi))
```

(continued)

Table 10.7 *(Continued)*

```
110  title('\chi, Ellipticity Angle')
111  axis square
112  colormap gray
113  axis([ 1 300 300 700] )
114  %%Find Stokes "vector" for a given point (x,y)
115  x = 155;
116  y = 621;
117  %Alternate (equivalent) definition of Stokes
118  %parameters
119  I = abs(h1).^2+abs(h2).^2;
120  Q = abs(h1).^2-abs(h2).^2;
121  U = 2.*real(h1.*conj(h2));
122  V = -2.*imag(h1.*conj(h2));
123  %Normalize each vector to itself (not exactly
124  %correct)
125  I = (I - min(min(I)))./(max(max(I))-min(min(I)));
126  Q = (Q - min(min(Q)))./(max(max(Q))-min(min(Q)));
127  U = (U - min(min(U)))./(max(max(U))-min(min(U)));
128  V = (V - min(min(V)))./(max(max(V))-min(min(V)));
129  %Normalize to the total intensity.
130  %This method will not produce a full "image" of the
131  %Stokes vectors because
132  %normalizing to S0 at each pixel will produce a
133  %uniform matrix of ones.
134  %However, it is interesting to view this on a
135  %point-by-point basis. Note
136  %also that normalizing in this manner is not
137  %strictly correct because the
138  %intensity relationships between the two holograms
139  %are not necessarily equal.
140  I = I./I;
141  Q = Q./I;
142  U = U./I;
143  V = V./I;
144  sprintf('Stokes vector at point (%u,%u)',x,y)
145  S_alternate =[ I(y,x) Q(y,x) V(y,x) U(y,x)]'
146  %Order is row-by-col, or (y,x)
147  p = sqrt(S_alternate(2)^2+S_alternate(3)^2+...
148  S_alternate(4)^2)/S_alternate(1)
```

Polarization multiplexing can be applied to DH to increase the SNR by reducing laser speckle. The goal is not to quantify the individual polarization states (as previously described) but to capture many different polarization images and average them to reduce the overall image speckle in the intensity reconstruction. In Rong et al.,[36] a circularly polarized illumination beam is combined with a rotating linearly polarized reference beam to capture multiple holograms, with each reconstruction ideally exhibiting an independent speckle pattern. In this configuration, the linearly polarized reference beam will only interfere with the corresponding component of the circularly polarized object beam. Holograms using this configuration were recorded for each 20-deg rotation of the reference beam. Ideally, by averaging *N*

p-Polarized Object Reconstruction   s-Polarized Object Reconstruction

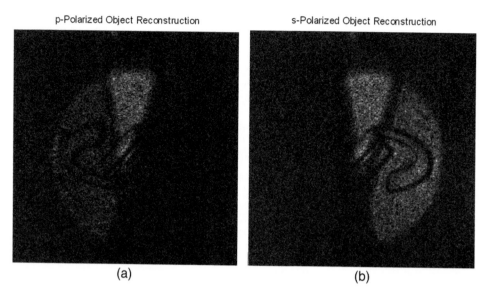

(a)   (b)

Figure 10.36 (a) *p*-polarized and (b) *s*-polarized reconstruction of the Newport logo. The logo was polarized by placing it behind orthogonal polarizers in a manner similar to Fig. 10.33.

independent speckle patterns, the overall speckle contrast should be reduced by a factor of $1/\sqrt{N}$, where the speckle contrast c is defined as the standard deviation of the speckle image divided by the mean intensity.

Figure 10.39 qualitatively illustrates the speckle reduction obtained by this method, and Fig. 10.40 reveals that this method somewhat underperforms the theoretically expected result. It can be inferred from this result (Fig. 10.40) that the separate speckle patterns arising from different rotation angles are not independent but rather partially correlated. Further analysis[36] determines that a rotation angle of at least 30 deg between successive holograms is required for the speckle correlation to reach approximately zero for this object, although it is noted that, in general, the required angle will vary greatly from object to object based on individual object properties. Subtle changes in polarization may result in significantly different speckle realizations due to the nature of laser speckle; therefore, it is not generally necessary to use fully orthogonal polarizations to generate sufficiently different speckle realizations.

A similar speckle-reduction experiment was performed by the authors; the MATLAB code shown in Table 10.8 was used to generate Figs. 10.41–10.42. Note that for this die object, the degree of polarization rotation required to yield independent speckle patterns is much greater (~90 deg, rather than ~30 deg, as in Rong et al.[36]), which results in a lower overall speckle-contrast reduction. Obviously, for this technique, rotation angles are limited to a range between 0 deg and 360 deg; therefore, the smaller the increment between rotation angles required to generate independent speckle patterns is, the more independent patterns that are available for speckle reduction. Perhaps less

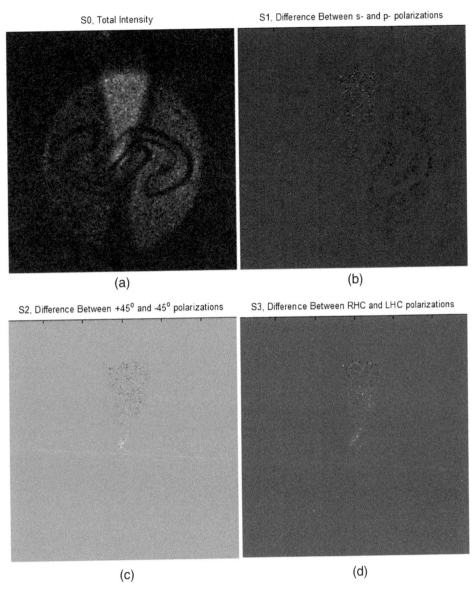

Figure 10.37 (a) S_0 reconstruction, representing total intensity; (b) S_1 reconstruction, representing the difference between *s*- and *p*-polarizations; (c) S_2 reconstruction, representing the difference between 45-deg polarizations (which is approximately zero here, as expected); and (d) the S_3 reconstruction, representing the difference between RHC and LHC polarizations (which is also essentially zero here, as expected).

obviously, it should be noted that, in this case, linear polarization states rotated 180 deg produce different speckle patterns because a wave plate was used to perform polarization rotation, such that two seemingly identical polarization states (e.g., 0 deg and 180 deg) in fact carry different Berry's phases and are therefore unique polarization states.

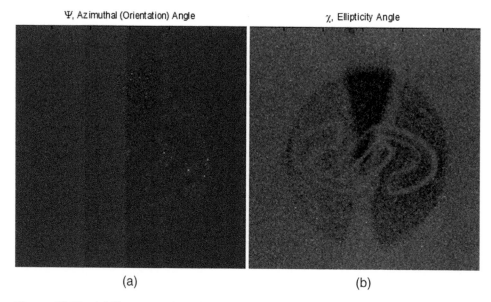

(a)   (b)

Figure 10.38 (a) Reconstruction of the azimuthal angle ψ and (b) the ellipticity angle χ using the geometry of polarization ellipse in Fig. 10.23.

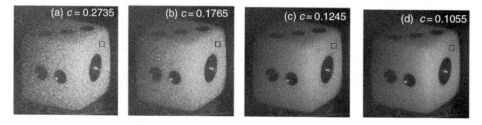

Figure 10.39 Qualitative evaluation of speckle contrast reduction for averaging (a) a single hologram, (b) three holograms, (c) nine holograms, and (d) 18 holograms at 20-deg increments. The inset value c denotes the speckle contrast.[36]

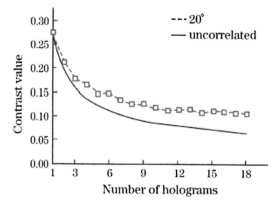

Figure 10.40 Measured speckle contrast versus the number of holograms (20-deg rotation increments), compared to the ideal contrast for uncorrelated speckle patterns.[36]

Table 10.8 MATLAB code "Speckle_reduction.m" multiplexes several holograms recorded at different polarization angles to reduce the speckle of the overall hologram (see Figs. 10.41–10.42).

```
1   %This example multiplexes several holograms recorded
2   %at different
3   %polarization angles to reduce the speckle of the
4   %overall hologram
5   format compact
6   %close all
7   %clear all
8   %clc;
9   %Reconstruction parameters:
10  d = 0.246;
11  lambda = 514.5e-9;
12  dx = 6.7e-6;
13  %Reconstruct all of the holograms, at all angles
14  %(15-deg increments)
15  load Saved_Raw_holo_0deg;
16  h0 = abs(myFresnel(hraw1,d,lambda,dx));
17  h0 = h0(210:730,660:1024);
18  figure(2)
19  imagesc(h0)
20  axis square
21  %%
22  load Saved_Raw_holo_15deg;
23  h15 = abs(myFresnel(hraw1,d,lambda,dx));
24  h15 = h15(210:730,660:1024);
25  h15 = h15.*(mean2(h0)/mean2(h15));
26  load Saved_Raw_holo_30deg;
27  h30 = abs(myFresnel(hraw1,d,lambda,dx));
28  h30 = h30(210:730,660:1024);
29  h30 = h30.*(mean2(h0)/mean2(h30));
30  load Saved_Raw_holo_45deg;
31  h45 = abs(myFresnel(hraw1,d,lambda,dx));
32  h45 = h45(210:730,660:1024);
33  h45 = h45.*(mean2(h0)/mean2(h45));
34  load Saved_Raw_holo_60deg;
35  h60 = abs(myFresnel(hraw1,d,lambda,dx));
36  h60 = h60(210:730,660:1024);
37  h60 = h60.*(mean2(h0)/mean2(h60));
38  load Saved_Raw_holo_75deg;
39  h75 = abs(myFresnel(hraw1,d,lambda,dx));
40  h75 = h75(210:730,660:1024);
41  h75 = h75.*(mean2(h0)/mean2(h75));
42  load Saved_Raw_holo_90deg;
43  h90 = abs(myFresnel(hraw1,d,lambda,dx));
44  h90 = h90(210:730,660:1024);
45  h90 = h90.*(mean2(h0)/mean2(h90));
46  load Saved_Raw_holo_105deg;
47  h105 = abs(myFresnel(hraw1,d,lambda,dx));
48  h105 = h105(210:730,660:1024);
49  h105 = h105.*(mean2(h0)/mean2(h105));
50  load Saved_Raw_holo_120deg;
51  h120 = abs(myFresnel(hraw1,d,lambda,dx));
52  h120 = h120(210:730,660:1024);
```

(continued)

Table 10.8 (*Continued*)

```
53  h120 = h120.* (mean2(h0)/mean2(h120));
54  load Saved_Raw_holo_135deg;
55  h135 = abs(myFresnel(hraw1,d,lambda,dx));
56  h135 = h135(210:730,660:1024);
57  h135 = h135.* (mean2(h0)/mean2(h135));
58  load Saved_Raw_holo_150deg;
59  h150 = abs(myFresnel(hraw1,d,lambda,dx));
60  h150 = h150(210:730,660:1024);
61  h150 = h150.* (mean2(h0)/mean2(h150));
62  load Saved_Raw_holo_165deg;
63  h165 = abs(myFresnel(hraw1,d,lambda,dx));
64  h165 = h165(210:730,660:1024);
65  h165 = h165.* (mean2(h0)/mean2(h165));
66  load Saved_Raw_holo_180deg;
67  h180 = abs(myFresnel(hraw1,d,lambda,dx));
68  h180 = h180(210:730,660:1024);
69  h180 = h180.* (mean2(h0)/mean2(h180));
70  load Saved_Raw_holo_195deg;
71  h195 = abs(myFresnel(hraw1,d,lambda,dx));
72  h195 = h195(210:730,660:1024);
73  h195 = h195.* (mean2(h0)/mean2(h195));
74  load Saved_Raw_holo_210deg;
75  h210 = abs(myFresnel(hraw1,d,lambda,dx));
76  h210 = h210(210:730,660:1024);
77  h210 = h210.* (mean2(h0)/mean2(h210));
78  load Saved_Raw_holo_225deg;
79  h225 = abs(myFresnel(hraw1,d,lambda,dx));
80  h225 = h225(210:730,660:1024);
81  h225 = h225.* (mean2(h0)/mean2(h225));
82  load Saved_Raw_holo_240deg;
83  h240 = abs(myFresnel(hraw1,d,lambda,dx));
84  h240 = h240(210:730,660:1024);
85  h240 = h240.* (mean2(h0)/mean2(h240));
86  load Saved_Raw_holo_255deg;
87  h255 = abs(myFresnel(hraw1,d,lambda,dx));
88  h255 = h255(210:730,660:1024);
89  h255 = h255.* (mean2(h0)/mean2(h255));
90  load Saved_Raw_holo_270deg;
91  h270 = abs(myFresnel(hraw1,d,lambda,dx));
92  h270 = h270(210:730,660:1024);
93  h270 = h270.* (mean2(h0)/mean2(h270));
94  load Saved_Raw_holo_285deg;
95  h285 = abs(myFresnel(hraw1,d,lambda,dx));
96  h285 = h285(210:730,660:1024);
97  h285 = h285.* (mean2(h0)/mean2(h285));
98  load Saved_Raw_holo_300deg;
99  h300 = abs(myFresnel(hraw1,d,lambda,dx));
100 h300 = h300(210:730,660:1024);
101 h300 = h300.* (mean2(h0)/mean2(h300));
102 load Saved_Raw_holo_315deg;
103 h315 = abs(myFresnel(hraw1,d,lambda,dx));
104 h315 = h315(210:730,660:1024);
105 h315 = h315.* (mean2(h0)/mean2(h315));
106 load Saved_Raw_holo_330deg;
```

(*continued*)

Table 10.8 (*Continued*)

```
107  h330 = abs(myFresnel(hraw1,d,lambda,dx));
108  h330 = h330(210:730,660:1024);
109  h330 = h330.*(mean2(h0)/mean2(h330));
110  load Saved_Raw_holo_345deg;
111  h345 = abs(myFresnel(hraw1,d,lambda,dx));
112  h345 = h345(210:730,660:1024);
113  h345 = h345.*(mean2(h0)/mean2(h345));
114  load Saved_Raw_holo_360deg;
115  h360 = abs(myFresnel(hraw1,d,lambda,dx));
116  h360 = h360(210:730,660:1024);
117  h360 = h360.*(mean2(h0)/mean2(h360));
118  %%
119  figure(1)
120  imagesc(h0)
121  axis square
122  title('Single hologram, 0^o')
123  colormap gray
124  H_3x60 = (h0+h60+h120)./3;
125  H_7x60 = (h0+h60+h120+h180+h240+h300+h360)./7;
126  figure(2)
127  imagesc(H_3x60)
128  axis square
129  title('3 Holograms, seperated by 60^o')
130  colormap gray
131  H_2x90 = (h0+h90)./2;
132  H_3x90 = (h0+h90+h180)./3;
133  H_5x90 = (h0+h90+h180+h270+h360)./5;
134  H_2x45 = (h0+h45)./2;
135  H_4x45 = (h0+h45+h90+h135)./4;
136  H_6x45 = (h0+h45+h90+h135+h180+h225)./6;
137  H_9x45 = (h0+h45+h90+h135+h180+h225+...
138  h270+h315+h360)./9;
139  H_6x30 = (h0+h30+h60+h90+h120+h150)./6;
140  H_13x30 = (h0+h30+h60+h90+h120+h150+h180+...
141  h210+h240+h270+h300+h330+h360)./13;
142  figure(3)
143  imagesc(H_6x30)
144  axis square
145  title('6 Holograms, seperated by 30^o')
146  colormap gray
147  %Calculate for 15-deg increments
148  H_3x15 = (h0+h15+h30)./3;
149  H_6x15 = (h0+h15+h30+h45+h60+h75)./6;
150  H_9x15=(h0+h15+h30+h45+h60+h75+h90+h105+h120)./9;
151  H_12x15 = (h0+h15+h30+h45+h60+h75+h90+...
152  h105+h120+h135+h150+h165)./12;
153  H_15x15 = (h0+h15+h30+h45+h60+h75+h90+...
154  h105+h120+h135+h150+h165+h180+ h195+h210)./15;
155  H_18x15 = (h0+h15+h30+h45+h60+h75+h90+h105+...
156  h120+h135+h150+h165+h180+...
157  h195+h210+h225+h240+h255)./18;
158  H_21x15 = (h0+h15+h30+h45+h60+h75+h90+...
159  h105+h120+h135+h150+h165+h180+...
160  h195+h210+h225+h240+h255+h270+h285+h300)./21;
```

(*continued*)

Table 10.8 (*Continued*)

```
161  H_25x15 = (h0+h15+h30+h45+h60+h75+h90+h105+...
162  h120+h135+h150+h165+h180+...
163  h195+h210+h225+h240+h255+h270+h285+h300...
164  +h315+h330+h345+360)./25;
165  figure(4)
166  imagesc(H_25x15)
167  %imagesc(h180)
168  axis square
169  title('25 Holograms, seperated by 15^o' )
170  colormap gray
171  %%Compare standard deviations of speckle.
172  %Speckle contrast equals (sigma)/(mean intensity).
173  %Calculate for 15-degree increments.
174  c_1 = std2(h0(100:350,145:225))/...
175  mean2(h0(100:350,145:225))
176  c_3 = std2(H_3x15(100:350,145:225))/...
177  mean2(H_3x15(100:350,145:225))
178  c_6 = std2(H_6x15(100:350,145:225))/...
179  mean2(H_6x15(100:350,145:225))
180  c_9 = std2(H_9x15(100:350,145:225))/...
181  mean2(H_9x15(100:350,145:225))
182  c_12 = std2(H_12x15(100:350,145:225))/...
183  mean2(H_12x15(100:350,145:225))
184  c_15 = std2(H_15x15(100:350,145:225))/...
185  mean2(H_15x15(100:350,145:225))
186  c_18 = std2(H_18x15(100:350,145:225))/...
187  mean2(H_18x15(100:350,145:225))
188  c_21 = std2(H_21x15(100:350,145:225))/...
189  mean2(H_21x15(100:350,145:225))
190  c_25 = std2(H_25x15(100:350,145:225))/...
191  mean2(H_25x15(100:350,145:225))
192  c_3x60 = std2(H_3x60(100:350,145:225))/...
193  mean2(H_3x60(100:350,145:225))
194  c_7x60 = std2(H_7x60(100:350,145:225))/...
195  mean2(H_7x60(100:350,145:225))
196  c_6x30 = std2(H_6x30(100:350,145:225))/...
197  mean2(H_6x30(100:350,145:225))
198  c_13x30 = std2(H_13x30(100:350,145:225))/...
199  mean2(H_13x30(100:350,145:225))
200  c_2x45 = std2(H_2x45(100:350,145:225))/...
201  mean2(H_2x45(100:350,145:225))
202  c_4x45 = std2(H_4x45(100:350,145:225))/...
203  mean2(H_4x45(100:350,145:225))
204  c_6x45 = std2(H_6x45(100:350,145:225))/...
205  mean2(H_6x45(100:350,145:225))
206  c_9x45 = std2(H_9x45(100:350,145:225))/...
207  mean2(H_9x45(100:350,145:225))
208  c_2x90 = std2(H_2x90(100:350,145:225))/...
209  mean2(H_2x90(100:350,145:225))
210  c_3x90 = std2(H_3x90(100:350,145:225))/...
211  mean2(H_3x90(100:350,145:225))
212  c_5x90 = std2(H_5x90(100:350,145:225))/...
213  mean2(H_5x90(100:350,145:225))
214  X_deg = 0:15:360;
```

(continued)

Table 10.8   (*Continued*)

```
215  X15 = [ 1 3 6 9 12 15 18 21 25] ;
216  B15 = [ c_1 c_3 c_6 c_9 c_12 c_15 c_18 c_21 c_25] ;
217  X30 = [ 1 6 13] ;
218  B30 = [ c_1 c_6x30 c_13x30] ;
219  X45 = [ 1 2 4 6 9] ;
220  B45 = [ c_1 c_2x45 c_4x45 c_6x45 c_9x45] ;
221  X60 = [ 1 3 7] ;
222  B60 = [ c_1 c_3x60 c_7x60] ;
223  X90 = [ 1 2 3 5] ;
224  B90 = [ c_1 c_2x90 c_3x90 c_5x90] ;
225  N = 1:1:25;
226  Bn = c_1.* (1./sqrt(N));
227  plot(X15,B15,'b')
228  hold on
229  plot(X30,B30,'r')
230  plot(X45,B45,'m')
231  plot(X60,B60,'c')
232  plot(X90,B90,'g')
233  plot(N,Bn,'-k')
234  plot(X15,B15,'bo')
235  plot(X30,B30,'ro')
236  plot(X45,B45,'mo')
237  plot(X60,B60,'co')
238  plot(X90,B90,'go')
239  hold off
240  title({ 'Speckle Reduction via',
241  'Polarization Multiplexing'})
242  legend('15^o Increments',' 30^o Increments',...
243  '45^o Increments',' 60^o Increments',...
244  '90^o Increments',' Theoretical Limit')
245  xlabel('Number of Measurements')
246  ylabel('Speckle Contrast, \c/I')
```

(a)   (b)   (c)

Figure 10.41   Intensity reconstructions using polarization multiplexing to reduce the speckle contrast for (a) die object imaged at a single polarization angle ($c = 0.55$), (b) die object imaged at six angles with 30-deg separation ($c = 0.33$), and (c) die object imaged at 25 angles with 15-deg separation ($c = 0.22$). The speckle contrast was measured in the relatively uniform central portion of each image.

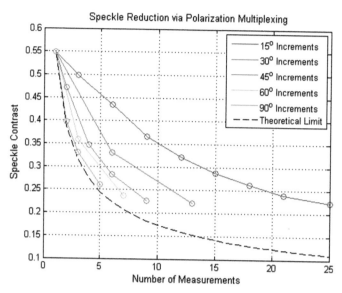

Figure 10.42 Degree of speckle reduction for the die object of Fig. 10.41 using various combinations of polarization angles. The degree of speckle reduction is shown for a given number of measurements. Note that measurements that do not follow the theoretical curve exist because the speckle patterns are not truly independent. This data implies that, for this object, only measurements made with 90-deg polarization rotation increments produce fully independent (i.e., zero correlation) speckle patterns.

References

1. W. Choi, C. Fang-Yen, K. Badizadegan, S. Oh, N. Lue, R. R. Dasari, and M. S. Feld, "Tomographic phase microscopy," *Nature Methods* **4**(9), 717–719 (2007).
2. A. Barty, K. A. Nugent, A. Roberts, and D. Paganin, "Quantitative phase tomography," *Opt. Comm.* **175**(4–6), 329–336 (2000).
3. M. R. Teague, "Image formation in terms of the transport equation," *J. Opt. Soc. Am. A* **2**(11), 2019–2026 (1985).
4. M. R. Teague, "Deterministic phase retrieval: a Green's function solution," *J. Opt. Soc. Am.* **73**(11), 1434–1441 (1983).
5. N. Streibl, "Phase imaging by the transport equation of intensity," *Opt. Comm.* **49**(1), 6–10 (1984).
6. J. Lee, J. Ku, L. Waller, and G. Barbastathis, "Transport of intensity imaging applied to quantitative optical phase tomography," *Topical Meeting in Digital Holography and Three-Dimensional Imaging*, Tokyo, Japan (May 2011).
7. M. Krenkel, M. Bartels, and T. Salditt, "Transport of intensity phase reconstruction to solve the twin image problem in holographic x-ray imaging," *Opt. Exp.* **21**(2), 2220–2235 (2013).
8. F. Roddier and C. Roddier, "Wavefront reconstruction using Fourier transforms," *Appl. Opt.* **30**(11), 1325–1327 (1991).

9. C. Roddier and F. Roddier, "Wavefront reconstruction from defocused images and the testing of ground-based optical telescopes," *J. Opt. Soc. Am. A* **10**(11), 2277–2287 (1993).

10. C. Zuo, Q. Chen, W. Qu, and A. Asundi, "High-speed transport-of-intensity phase microscopy with an electrically tunable lens," *Opt. Exp.* **21**(20), 24060–24075 (2013).

11. T. C. Nguyen, G. Nehmetallah, A. Darudi, and P. Soltani, "3D High Speed Characterization of Phase And Amplitude Objects Using The Transport of Intensity Equation," Three-Dimensional Imaging, Visualization, and Display, Baltimore, MD (April 2015).

12. A. Darudi, J. Amiri, P. Soltani, and G. Nehmetallah, "Experimental verification of reconstruction of two interfering wavefronts using the transport of intensity equation," Three-Dimensional Imaging, Visualization, and Display, Baltimore, MD (April 2015).

13. C. Barsi, W. Wian, and J. W. Fleischer, "Imaging through nonlinear media using digital holography," *Nat. Phot.* **3**(4), 211–215 (2009).

14. C. Barsi and J. W. Fleischer, "Increased field of view via nonlinear digital holography," *Lasers and Electro-Optics and Quantum Electronics and Laser Science Conf.*, San Jose, CA (May 2010).

15. A. Goy and D. Psaltis, "Digital reverse propagation in focusing Kerr media," *Phys. Rev. A* **83**(3), 031802 (2011).

16. I. Yamaguchi and T. Zhang, "Phase-shifting digital holography," *Opt. Lett.* **22**(16), 1268–1270 (1997).

17. G. Nehmetallah and P. P. Banerjee, "Numerical modeling of $(D+1)$-dimensional solitons in a sign-alternating nonlinear medium using an adaptive fast Hankel split step method," *J. Opt. Soc. Am. B* **22**(10), 2200–2207 (2005).

18. M. Takeda, W. Wang, Z. Duan, and Y. Miyamoto, "Coherence holography," *Opt. Exp.* **13**(23), 9629–9635 (2005).

19. M. Takeda, "Coherence holography: A tutorial review," *Topical Meeting in Digital Holography and Three-Dimensional Imaging*, Tokyo, Japan (May 2011).

20. J. W. Goodman, *Statistical Optics*, 2nd Ed., John Wiley & Sons, Hoboken, NJ (2015).

21. C. W. McCutchen, "Generalized source and the van Cittert–Zernike theorem: a study of the spatial coherence required for interferometry," *J. Opt. Soc. Am.* **56**(6), 727–733 (1966).

22. M. Takeda, H. Ina, and S. Kobayashi, "Fourier-transform method of fringe-pattern analysis for computer-based topography and interferometry," *J. Opt. Soc. Am.* **72**(1), 156–160 (1982).

23. W. H. Lee, "Sampled Fourier transform hologram generated by computer," *Appl. Opt.* **9**(3), 639–643 (1970).

24. D. Leseberg and O. Bryngdahl, "Computer-generated rainbow holograms," *Appl. Opt.* **23**(14), 2441–2447 (1984).

25. F. Wyrowski, R. Hauck, and O. Bryngdahl, "Computer-generated holography: hologram repetition and phase manipulation," *J. Opt. Soc. Am. A* **4**(4), 694–698 (1987).

26. D. Leseberg and C. Frère, "Computer-generated holograms of 3D objects composed of tilted planar segments," *Appl. Opt.* **27**(14), 3020–3024 (1988).

27. B. R. Brown and A. W. Lohmann, "Complex spatial filtering with binary masks," *Appl. Opt.* **5**(6), 967–969 (1966).

28. A. W. Lohmann and D. P. Paris, "Binary Fraunhofer holograms generated by computer," *Appl. Opt.* **6**(10), 1739–1748 (1967).

29. J. P. Waters, "Holographic image synthesis utilizing theoretical methods," *Appl. Phys. Lett.* **9**(11), 405–407 (1968).

30. K. Kuroda, Y. Matsuhashi, R. Fujimura, and T. Shimura, "Theory of polarization holography," *Opt. Rev.* **18**(5), 374–382 (2011).

31. T. Colomb, E. Cuche, F. Montfort, P. Marquet, and C. Depeursinge, "Jones vector imaging by use of digital holography: Simulation and experimentation," *Opt. Comm.* **231**(1–6), 137–147 (2004).

32. M. Yokota, Y. Terui, and I. Yamaguchi, "Analysis of polarization state by digital holography with polarization modulation," *Opt. Rev.* **13**(6), 405–409 (2006)

33. T. Nomura and B. Javidi, "Object recognition by use of polarimetric phase-shifting digital holography," *Opt. Lett.* **32**(15), 2146–2148 (2007).

34. T. Nomura, B. Javidi, S. Murata, E. Nitanai, and T. Mumata, "Polarization imaging of a 3D object by use of on-axis phase-shifting digital holography," *Opt. Lett.* **32**(5), 481–483 (2007).

35. T. Colomb, F. Dürr, E. Cuche, F. Marquet, H. Limberger, R. Salathé, and C. Depeursinge, "Polarization microscopy by use of digital holography: application to optical-fiber birefringence measurements," *Appl. Opt.* **44**(21), 4461–4469 (2005).

36. L. Rong, W. Xiao, F. Pan, S. Liu, and R. Li, "Speckle noise reduction in digital holography by use of multiple polarization holograms," *Chinese Opt. Lett.* **8**(7), 653–655 (2010).

Chapter 11

Progress in Stereoscopic, Head-Mounted, Multiview, Depth-Fused, Volumetric, and Holographic 3D Displays

11.1 Introduction to 3D Displays

There is often confusion among the general public between holograms and the type of contemporary 3D images seen in movie theaters, in which viewers from each side of the theater see the same image on the screen. As astonishing as these 3D effects are, the technologies used are typically based on either polarization stereoscopy (the technique currently used in cinemas and 3D television), digital image fusion [in the case of CNN's election night "hologram" (see https://www.youtube.com/watch?v=thOxW19vsTg)], or 2D semitransparent screens (for musion, see http://www.musion.co.uk/). These techniques have little to do with holography, which is based on the reproduction of not only the amplitude but also the phase of light by diffraction. These 3D images can have depth but are typically filmed from a single perspective. On the other hand, for a viewer moving around a hologram, the appearance of the object changes continuously and smoothly as the viewer's perspective changes, as if the object is real. A standard 3D movie camera (which actually uses two cameras) captures light scattered from an object at two different angles, one for each eye, from a single perspective. However, in the real world, light reflects from objects at an infinite number of angles. For a 3D television viewing experience to be maximally realistic, it must be autostereoscopic (requiring no glasses), present continuous parallax (rather than just stereopsis), and realistically represent other perceptual depth cues, such as proper visual accommodation (focusing) and vergence. The display technology most likely able to offer these features is holographic television.[1] Some recent 3D display technologies, though not necessarily holographic, have been commercialized due to the increasing demand from the public for autostereoscopic 3D TVs, 3D games, and mobile devices equipped with 3D displays. This chapter systematically reviews various 3D display technologies. Byoungho Lee et.al.[2] and Jason Geng[3] have recently published excellent review articles concerning many state-of-the-art 3D display technologies, which will be summarized in this chapter.

Section 11.1 discusses the characteristics of an optimal 3D display, depth cues related to the human visual system, and classification of 3D display systems. Section 11.2 address traditional binocular stereoscopic 3D displays (requiring glasses), followed by head-mount stereoscopic displays in Section 11.3. In Section 11.4, autostereoscopic 3D display technologies are discussed; these techniques are divided into four main categories:

(a) multiview 3D displays,
(b) depth-fused 3D displays,
(c) volumetric 3D displays, and
(d) digital holographic displays.

A detailed analysis of each category is discussed. Section 11.5 compares several different 3D display techniques. Finally, Section 11.6 addresses commonly misunderstood nonholographic and non-3D displays. Figure 11.1 shows a top-level flowchart of the different 3D display techniques, as suggested in Geng.[3]

11.1.1 Characteristics of an optimal 3D display

Traditional 2D display devices include cathode ray tubes (CRTs), liquid crystal devices (LCDs), LED-backlit LCD displays, digital light processing (DLP), and plasma displays. Even with the help of sophisticated software, all of these 2D displays have an inherent problem, which is a lack of adequate representation of 3D images and depth cues when trying to represent a 3D object. Figure 11.2(a) shows three views of the Perth "impossible triangle" sculpture from different angles. As the view rotates, a Penrose triangle appears to form. Figure 11.2(b) shows an impossible cube (left), Penrose stairs (middle), and Oscar Reutersvärd's optical illusion (right), which all have one thing in common: they are nonphysical objects that can be displayed on a 2D screen. As mentioned earlier, a perfect 3D display should mimic all of the depth cues of the human visual system.

11.1.2 Display-technology depth cues related to the human visual system

To visualize 3D images, the human visual system utilizes two primary types of depth cues: physical and psychological. Only the real 3D objects affect the physical cues, whereas the psychological cues can be invoked by 3D or 2D images. Physiological cues are not enough to fully evoke the perception of 3D objects. Thus, information extracted from 2D displays will not be of a satisfactory quality unless physiological as well as psychological cues are provided by the 3D displays.

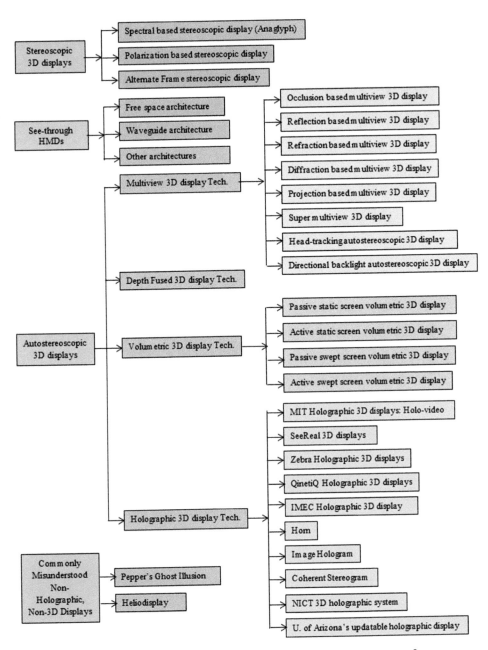

Figure 11.1   Classification of different 3D display technologies.[3]

The physiological depth cues are as follows:

- **Vergence:** The angle between the line of sight of two eyes when fixating on a specific point on the 3D object [see Fig. 11.3(a)].
- **Accommodation (focusing):** The change of the curvature of the eye lens to create a sharp image on the retina [see Fig. 11.3(b)].

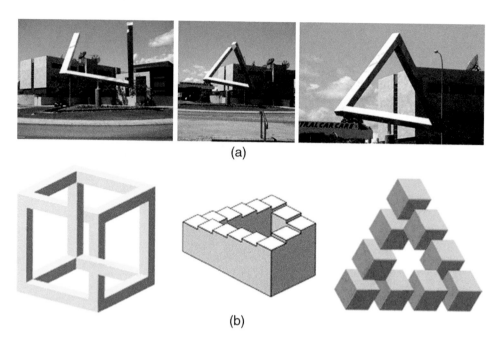

Figure 11.2 (a) Views of the Perth "impossible triangle" from different angles. As the view rotates, a Penrose triangle appears to form. (b) An impossible cube (left), Penrose stairs (middle), and Oscar Reutersvärd's optical illusion (right).[3]

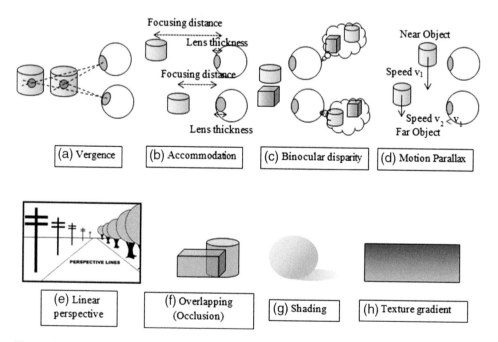

Figure 11.3 The physical depth cues include (a) vergence, (b) accommodation, (c) bipolar disparity, and (d) motion parallax. The psychological depth cues include (e) linear perspective, (f) overlapping (occlusion), (g) shading, and (h) texture gradient.[2]

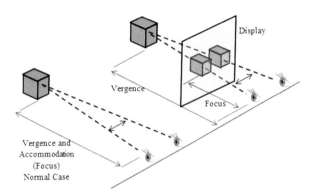

Figure 11.4 Conflict between vergence and accommodation.

- **Binocular disparity or stereopsis:** The most important depth cue for the human visual system, binocular disparity, occurs when depth information is acquired from the parallax effect of two images when viewed from the right and left eye [see Fig. 11.3(c)]. Most of the early 3D displays were based on this depth cue. Stereoscopic and autostereoscopic displays rely primarily on binocular disparity. Autostereoscopic displays, unlike stereoscopic displays, provide stereopsis without needing extra glasses. Other displays, such as volumetric-based displays, may include other physiological depth cues, although volumetric displays typically introduce other physiological limitations, such as the inability to render specularities and occlusions. One drawback of both stereoscopic and autostereoscopic displays is the possible discomfort and eye fatigue that some viewers experience due to the vergence–accommodation conflict, shown in Fig. 11.4. Vergence is mostly satisfied in stereoscopic displays, but accommodation is always on the 3D display plane, which is on a different plane than the convergence distance most of the time. Some other sources of eye fatigue are due to crosstalk and vertical disparity between the right and left eye. Other 3D display technologies—such as volumetric and holographic 3D displays, which support most of the depth cues (although texture or shading might not be possible)—may be a better choice to solve the issue of viewer discomfort.
- **Motion parallax:** A perceptual effect that, within a specific scene relative to the observer, makes closer objects appear to move faster than farther objects. A comparison of this relative motion provides the depth cue [see Fig. 11.3(d)].

The psychological depth cues are as follows:

- **Linear perspective:** The appearance that parallel lines intersect at some point on the horizon. This phenomenon can be seen while driving on a road or looking at electric poles in a row [see Fig. 11.3(e)].

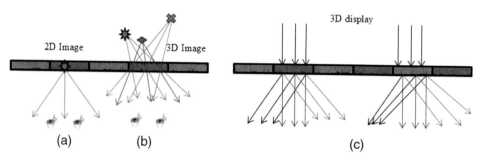

Figure 11.5 (a) A 3D image compared to (b) a 2D version. (c) In a typical holographic stereogram (left), a hogel emits light in multiple directions with the same wavefront curvature but different intensities. In a diffraction-specific coherent panoramagram (right), both the intensity and curvature can vary with direction, eliminating the accommodation–convergence mismatch and providing smooth motion parallax with fewer views.[5]

- **Overlapping (occlusion):** The interpretation of the human visual system that occluded objects are located farther than clear objects [see Fig. 11.3(f)].
- **Shading:** The variation of light intensity on the surface of the object, as well as the shadow that an object casts on another object, provides details about the 3D depth of the objects and their respective distances from the viewer [see Fig. 11.3(g)].
- **Texture gradient:** The 3D shape of an object can be inferred through its texture gradient and its surface roughness [see Fig. 11.3(h)].

Note that most of these depth cues are related to distance.[2-4] As a general trend, the effects of psychological depth cues are relatively insensitive to the distance of the object from the viewer, whereas the strength of physiological depth cues tends to decrease with increasing distances.

All of the pixels in a 2D display emit the same amount of light intensity in all directions (omnidirectional); therefore, the scene is independent of the position of the viewer, and 2D displays are incapable of providing the 3D depth cues expected by the human visual system, as shown in Fig. 11.5(a). This limitation led researchers to devise 3D pixels called volumetric picture elements (voxels) or holographic picture elements (hogels) that are directional. As an example, in a typical holographic stereogram [Figure 11.5(b)], a hogel emits light in multiple directions with the same wavefront curvature but different intensities. In a diffraction-specific coherent panoramagram [discussed in Chapter 8 and illustrated in Fig. 11.5(c)], both the intensity and phase curvature can vary with direction, which eliminates the accommodation–convergence mismatch and provides smooth motion parallax with fewer views.

11.2 Stereoscopic 3D Displays

All stereoscopic 3D display techniques require the viewer to wear special eye glasses to induce binocular disparity and convergence by projecting two different (right eye and left eye) images to the viewer [see Fig. 11.3(c)]. The 3D

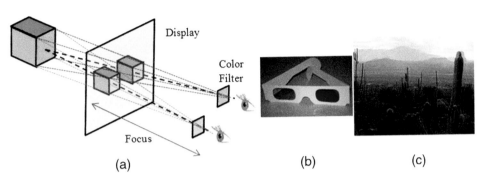

Figure 11.6 (a) Anaglyph stereoscopic 3D display system, (b) typical anaglyph glasses, and (c) typical anaglyph stereo image.[3]

display contains two images of a 3D scene recorded from two different perspectives. Any stereoscopic technique should be able to separate these two images and deliver the right image to the right eye and the left image to the left eye. Three techniques are typically used by the industry to perform this stereoscopic separation:

(a) spectral, color, or anaglyph;
(b) polarization (spatial or frame modulation); and
(c) time multiplexing.

11.2.1 Spectral-based stereoscopic display (anaglyph)

Spectral (anaglyph) stereoscopic 3D visual effects are created by encoding each eye's image using chromatically opposite (complementary) colors—typically red and cyan, as shown in Fig. 11.6(a). Thus, a typical anaglyph 3D image, as shown in Fig. 11.6(c), contains two chromatically opposite, filtered colored images, one for each eye. As shown in Fig. 11.6(b), the anaglyph eyeglasses will filter out one of the unintended images reaching each eye. The visual cortex of the brain fuses the integrated stereoscopic image into a 3D scene. Anaglyph eyeglasses are made of chromatically opposite colors such as red and cyan or green and magenta, as shown in Fig. 11.7. For example, the red filter passes red, and the cyan filter reflects red. One of the drawbacks of such a technique is chromatic adaptation.

11.2.2 Polarization-based stereoscopic display

This technique relies on polarization instead of color to induce binocular disparity,[2] as shown in Fig. 11.8(a). The original implementation projects two images at the same time onto the same screen using orthogonal polarizing filters (usually at 45 deg and 135 deg), as shown in Fig. 11.8(b). The viewer uses polarized eyeglasses with identical orthogonal polarizations as the two polarized images on the screen. Each polarizer passes light that corresponds to the same polarization state of the image on the screen while rejecting the

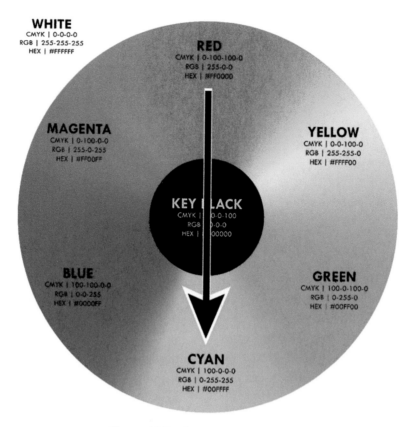

Figure 11.7 Complementary colors.

orthogonal polarization state. The 3D binocular disparity effect is then induced due to the ability of the polarizing filters to isolate the left or right eye images.

One major drawback of this process is that viewers must keep their head as horizontal as possible with respect to the screen or else there will be crosstalk between the left and right eye as the polarizers mounted in the eyeglasses rotate out of alignment, which causes discomfort under prolonged viewing. A relatively simple solution to fix this issue of limited head movement uses circularly polarized images with opposite handedness, rather than linear polarization, as shown in Fig. 11.8(c). Due to reflection from the screen, the viewer eyeglasses must contain analyzing filters with opposite handedness, i.e., left circularly polarized light reflected from the polarization maintaining screen will be blocked by the right circularly polarized filter, and vice versa. The analyzing filter is shown in Fig. 11.8(d). Left circularly polarized light falls on a QWP, which transforms it to a linear polarization at 45 deg, and is then followed by a linear polarizer (LP) with its axis mounted at 45 deg. The same logic holds for the other eye but in the orthogonal direction. Rotating both the QWP and the LP by the same angle does not change the operation of the analyzing filter, and thus the viewer's head may tilt and still maintain binocular disparity.

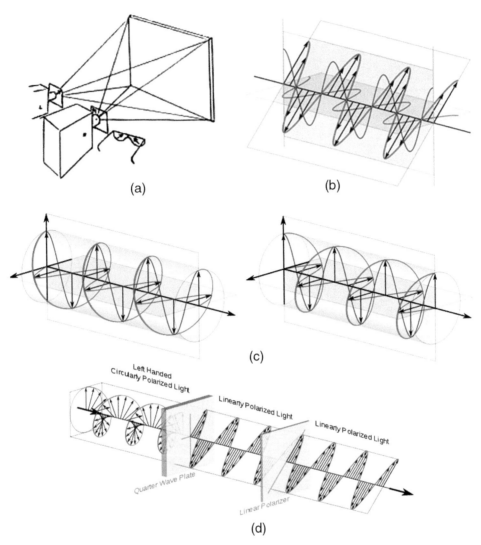

Figure 11.8 (a) Polarization stereoscopic 3D display system, (b) 45-deg linearly polarized light, (c) circularly polarized light, and (d) left circularly polarized light passing through an analyzer.

There are currently two stereoscopic 3D display systems that use polarization eyeglasses:

    (a) a spatial modulation or patterned retarder (PR)[6], and
    (b) a frame modulation or active retarder (AR), or a shutter in panel (SIP).[7]

A. Spatial modulation or patterned retarder (PR)

In this technique, the 3D display contains two interleaved images, one for each eye, at the same time. Every other row is either right or left circularly polarized light through a phase retardation of π, as shown in Fig. 11.9.

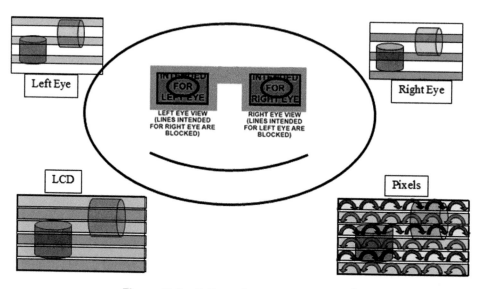

Figure 11.9   Patterned retarder technology.[2]

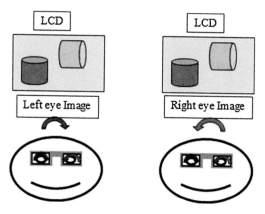

Figure 11.10   Active retarder technology.[2]

B. Frame modulation or active retarder (AR), or shutter in panel (SIP)

In this technique, instead of interlacing a single frame with two orthogonal polarizations, the right and the left circularly polarized images are displayed sequentially in two consecutive frames and are eventually separated by the passively polarized eyeglasses. The frame speed should be more than 120 frames per second (fps), or 60 fps for each polarization, for this technique to be effective. The 3D display should be synchronized with a time-sequential polarization modulator. One drawback of this technique is that it is more expensive because it is composed of two LCD panels.

11.2.3 Alternate-frame stereoscopic display

Time-multiplexed (alternate-frame) 3D display technology employs two active liquid crystal (LC) shutters. These LC shutters, mounted on the left and right

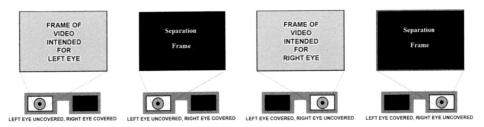

Figure 11.11 Alternate-frame, LC-shutter 3D display technology.

eye, open and close sequentially in synch with the 3D display left-eye and right-eye frame, respectively. The human visual system can merge stereo images separated by a minimum of 20 fps because of its persistence property, so the observer experiences binocular disparity and convergence. The alternate-frame LC shutter system is shown in Fig. 11.11. The LC eyeglasses are synchronized with the 3D display via a specific wireless communication protocol at a frame rate of 120 fps (240 fps if the separation frames are included). A separation black frame is usually employed before switching to the other eye due to the progressive-scan technology of the LCD.

One common advantage of all of the polarization-based stereoscopic display techniques is the high quality and low cost. The major drawback is the need to wear eyeglasses, which some viewers find uncomfortable.

11.3 Head-Mounted Displays (HMDs)

Most of the head-mounted-display devices consist of two displays, one mounted in front of each eye, to provide the binocular disparity between images. A typical HMD device is shown in Fig. 11.12. There are two general types of HMD: opaque and semi-transparent (often called "transparent" or "look-through"). Opaque HMDs are generally used to "immerse" the user in a virtual environment and do not allow the user to view anything beyond the imagery displayed on the HMD. Examples of this type of opaque HMD include the Oculus Rift VR® and night-vision goggles. Semi-transparent HMDs are generally used for "augmented reality" applications, in which HMD imagery is viewed on a semi-transparent screen against the backdrop of reality. This type of HMD is often used to display information or symbols/cues pertaining to some aspect of the reality currently being viewed. Examples of semi-transparent HMDs include Google Glass and the helmet-mounted cuing systems used in some fighter aircraft.

When designing a HMD, there are several fundamental considerations which must be addressed:[8,9]

- Does the HMD device need to be essentially transparent, semi-transparent, or opaque, given the specific target audience and application?

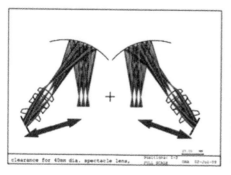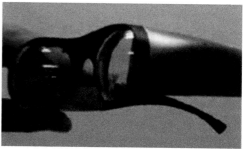

Figure 11.12 "Bug-eye"-type, purely reflective see-through combiners from ODA Labs.[10]

- Augmented-reality HMDs should have the potential to provide relevant information that can enhance typical daily activities from work to entertainment.
- To what degree should the augmented reality provided by the HMD mimic the real world? Should the images be made indistinguishable from a real visual experience, or should they distinctly stand out against the real-world background? Either way, augmented reality should combine virtual and real physiological experiences to provide a well-constructed, intuitive image to the observer.
- Ideally, the HMD device should be relatively nonintrusive, similar to wearing sunglasses or medical eyeglasses; however, this feature will often be limited by the desired HMD functionality (e.g., night-vision goggles, etc.).

A transparent optical head-mounted display (OHMD) should be capable of reflecting projected images while simultaneously allowing the viewer to see through it.

Various techniques have been used to produce see-through HMDs, which typically employ an optical combiner to combine the real-world and virtual imagery presented to the viewer. Optical combiners can be divided into two main categories:

(a) **Free-space-based architecture**: 45-deg flat combiner architectures, less-than-45-deg flat combiners, curved combiners, array or cascaded combiners, and freeform total-internal-reflection (TIR) combiners.

(b) **Waveguide-based architecture**: cascaded mirror combiners (reflective waveguide), diffractive coupler extractors via slanted diffraction grating elements or surface relief modulation, holographic coupler extractors [using holographic optical elements (HOEs)], and dynamic extractors.

Most of these techniques can be summarized according to their functionalities, as shown in Fig. 11.13.[10] Figure 11.14 shows different 45-deg flat combiner architectures in the vertical direction (see products

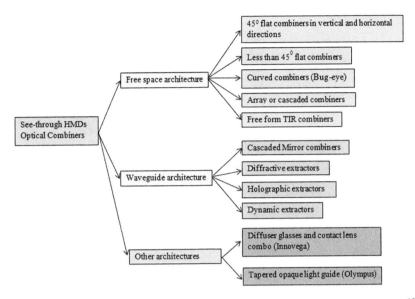

Figure 11.13 Different optical combiner technologies for see-through HMDs.[10]

from Vuzix, Inc., Laster Technologies, and Olympus) and the horizontal direction (Google Glass). Figure 11.15 shows different free-space architectures. Figures 11.15(a) and 11.15(b) show less-than-45-deg flat combiners. Figures 11.15(c) and 11.15(d) show curved combiner architectures (ODA Labs bug-eye combiner, Laster Technologies, Occulus Rift occlusion, and Sony HMZ T2 3D glasses). Figures 11.15(e) and 11.15(f) show array or cascaded combiner architectures, and Fig. 11.15(g) shows freeform TIR combiner architectures (Verizon/Kopin's Golden-i and Canon).[10]

Guided-space architectures are shown in Fig. 11.16. Figure 11.16(a) shows cascaded-mirror combiner architectures, such as the Epson Moverio light-guide tilted-mirror combiner, Lumus LOE cascaded dichroic mirrors, and the Optinvent light-pipe arrayed-prisms architecture. Figure 11.16(b) shows a diffractive coupler extractor architecture, such as the Vuzix/Nokia waveguide diffractive combiner. Figure 11.16(c) shows a holographic coupler extractor architecture, such as the Sony reflective holographic combiner and the Konica/Minolta volume holographic combiner, and Fig 11.16(d) shows a dynamic extractor architecture.[10] Finally, some other architectures are also available, such as a diffuser-glasses-and-contact-lens combination (Innovega) and a see-through HMD that uses a tapered light guide and 45-deg mirror combiner (Olympus). Table 11.1 compares different combiner techniques for HMDs.[10]

Looking to the future, there are many design aspects that currently limit the success of the HMD technology that should be addressed:

- field of view,
- brightness,
- resolution,

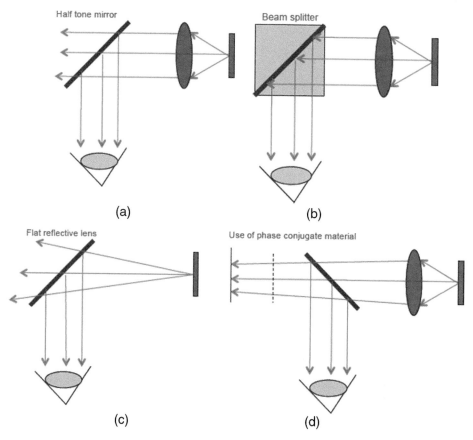

Figure 11.14 Free-space 45-deg flat combiners architectures: (a) halftone mirror, (b) beamsplitter, (c) flat reflective miror, and (d) phase conjugate material.[10]

- battery power,
- weight and compactness,
- tether,
- human factor problems, and
- accommodation of all visual cues that contribute to depth perception.

11.4 Autostereoscopic 3D Displays

There exist three main categories of autostereoscopic 3D display technologies:[2,3] multiview, volumetric, and holographic.

11.4.1 Multiview 3D display technology

11.4.1.1 Introduction to different multiview systems

One of the main objectives of an autostereoscopic 3D display is to mimic (as close as possible) the continuously distributed reflected light from physical 3D objects. Because implementing an infinite number of views is extremely difficult, an approximation using a finite but large number of views is sought,

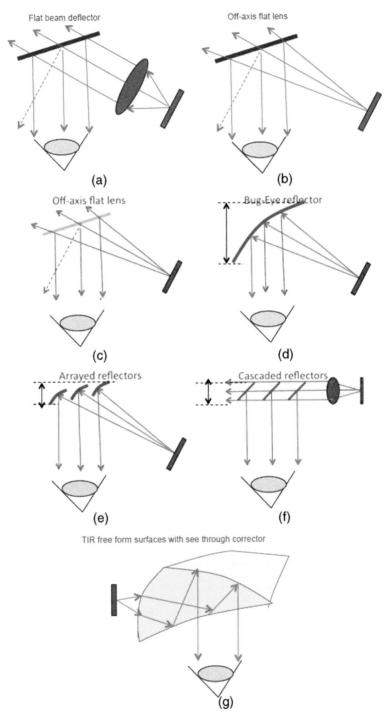

Figure 11.15 Free-space architectures: (a)–(b) less-than-45-deg flat combiners, (c)–(d) curved combiners, (e)–(f) array or cascaded combiners, and (g) freeform TIR combiners.[10]

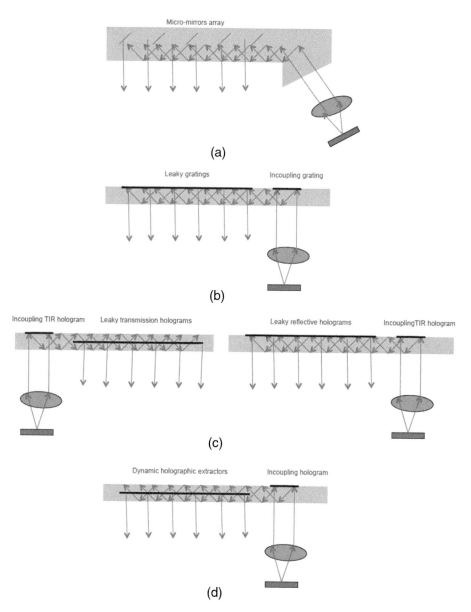

Figure 11.16 Guided-space architectures: (a) cascaded mirror combiners, (b) diffractive coupler extractors, (c) holographic coupler extractors, and (d) dynamic extractors.[10]

as shown in Fig. 11.17(a). The number of views needed is determined by the required angular resolution or visual acuity (VA), which is defined as

$$VA = \frac{1}{(H/D) \times (180/\pi) \times 60} = \frac{1}{1 \text{ arc min}},$$

where H is the height of a display pixel (or feature of a letter), and D is the distance between the viewer and the display (6 m is a standard used to account

Table 11.1 Comparison between different combiner techniques for HMDs.[10]

Combiner Architecture	Size	Eye Box	Field of View	Other	Examples
Flat combiner 45 deg	Thick	Medium	Medium	Traditional design	Vuzix/Google
Curved combiner	Thick	Large	Large	Bug-eye design	ODA Labs, Laster Technologies
Phase conjugate material	Thick	Medium	Medium	Very bulky	ODA Labs
Cascaded prism/mirror	Variable	Medium to large	Medium	Louver effect	Lumus, Optinvent
Freeform TIR	Medium	Large	Medium	Bulky glass combiner	Canon, Verizon
Diffractive combiner	Very thin	Very Large	Medium	Haze and parasitic effects	Nokia, Vizux
Holographic wave-guide combiner	Very thin	Medium to large in horizontal direction	Medium	Requires volume holographic elements	Sony
Holographic light-guide combiner	Medium	Small in vertical direction	Medium	Requires volume holographic elements	Konica/ Minolta
Combination diffuser/contact lens	Thin	Very large	Very large	Requires contact lens	Innovega
Tapered opaque light guide	Medium	Small	Small	Image can be relocated	Olympus

for infinity), as shown in Fig. 11.17(b). The term "20/20 vision" is based on the ability to resolve a 1.75-mm feature 20 feet (6 m) away. Note that a horizontal-parallax-only (HPO) multiview 3D display system is easier to achieve than the full parallax, as well as more applicable, because horizontal motion parallax (i.e., the viewer's head moves horizontally) and binocular disparity or stereopsis are the most important depth cues of the human visual system. Vertical parallax is only needed if the viewer's head moves vertically, which is unlikely in most cases.

The following sections discuss the different techniques used for 3D multiview display systems that can produce different images at different viewer angular positions and induce the binocular and motion parallax depth-cue sensations of the human visual system.[3,11]

11.4.1.2 Occlusion-based system

The basic principle behind all occlusion-based multiview 3D display systems is that, due to the parallax effect, each eye will see only part of the image on the screen while the other part is blocked by a certain barrier. Therefore, each eye will see different images consisting of even or odd columns of pixels, thus stimulating the binocular disparity or stereopsis effect. The barrier can range from single to multiple slits, it can be stationary as well as time sequential, and it can be behind or in front of the screen, as well as a combination of the above categories.

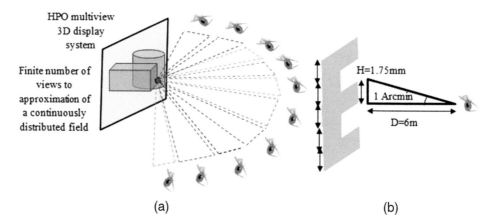

(a)   (b)

Figure 11.17 (a) Horizontal-parallax-only multiview 3D display system.[3] (b) Angular resolution or visual acuity.

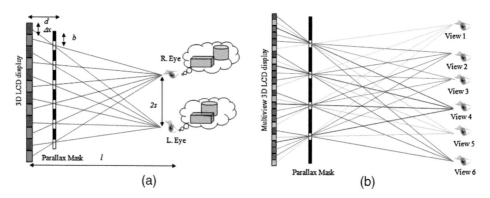

(a)   (b)

Figure 11.18 Parallax barrier HPO autostereoscopic 3D display: (a) two views and (b) multiview.[3]

A. An occlusion-based multiview 3D display using a parallax barrier HPO autostereoscopic 3D display

In this technique, shown in Fig. 11.18(a),[12] a mask consisting of a vertical grid is placed in front of the screen at a distance d (to be determined) in such a way that every other vertical column is visible only to one eye, and thus a parallax masking effect is achieved. If the viewer distance from the screen is considered to be l, the pixel size to be Δx, and the eye separation to be s, then the mask distance d and the period of the barrier b can be computed with basic geometry to be

$$d = \frac{l\Delta x}{(s + \Delta x)}, \qquad b = \frac{2\Delta x(l - d)}{l}. \qquad (11.1)$$

Note that the barrier pitch and its distance from the screen should be adjustable because they depend on the viewer distance l. Figure 11.18(b)

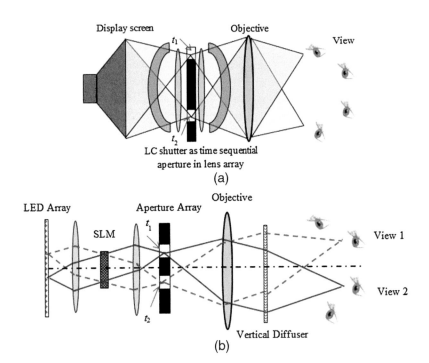

Display screen   Objective

View

t_1

LC shutter as time sequential
aperture in lens array

(a)

Objective

LED Array   Aperture Array

SLM t_1 View 1

View 2

t_2

Vertical Diffuser

(b)

Figure 11.19 Time-sequential multiview 3D display using (a) a high-speed CRT and (b) a switchable LED array.[3]

shows a multiview version of Fig. 11.18(a). As a rule of thumb, an array of vertical masks whose pitch b is n times the pixel pitch Δx of the display panel renders n views. A 2D display mode can be obtained by displaying a transparent parallax barrier. Several disadvantages arise from such a 3D display system, namely

(a) reduced illumination due to the barrier;
(b) reduced resolution by a factor of n for an n multiview system;
(c) a "picket fence" effect appears through dark vertical lines;
(d) image flipping due to misalignment, where images intended for the left eye are seen by the right eye, and vice versa; and
(e) diffraction degradation due to the limited aperture size in a multiview system.

B. An occlusion-based multiview 3D display that uses a time-sequential aperture

This technique is shown in Fig. 11.19.[13] At a given time t_1, only one shutter transmits light, and the rest are opaque. The early version of such a system relied on a high-speed CRT display (~1000 Hz). The shutters are made of ferroelectric LC acting as fast moving apertures. Each image in the time sequence appears at a different position, depending on the synchronized ON/OFF status of the LC shutter, thus ensuring that the correct projection is displayed in the corresponding view zone. Another advanced version of this approach relies on switchable LED arrays acting as light sources instead of a high-speed CRT.[14] These LEDs can be switched at a high frame rate. At any given time t_1, only one LED is on, and the rest are off. The light emitted by each LED is focused using an optical lens setup and a spatial light modulator (SLM), which can be a LCD, liquid crystal on silicon (LCOS), or a digital light processor (DLP). In its turn, the SLM modulates the light beam, which is then projected using lenses to an array of LC apertures. Each LED corresponds to a certain aperture in the array. The last step projects the light from each aperture into a vertical diffuser with a corresponding viewer angle, as shown in Fig. 11.19(b).

It is worth mentioning that some of the advantages of the time-sequential scheme, unlike the parallax barrier methods, are the ability to provide full resolution for each view, the simplicity of the design and calibration, and the low cost because there is no need for multiple LCDs. The main disadvantages are the limited FOV and the fact that the number of views is determined by the speed of the SLM. For example, a 1000-Hz SLM displaying an image at 25 fps results in ~40 unique viewing angles.[3]

C. An occlusion-based multiview 3D display that uses a moving slit in front of the display

This device is similar to the previous display, in principle, although a physical slit is moved rather than using an LC shutter. Each time the slit is moved, the display shows a new set of multiplexed image columns.[15] A fourth example of an occlusion-based multiview 3D display uses an innovative design to increase the FOV to 360 deg by using a rotating cylinder parallax barrier and rotating LED arrays in the opposite direction, as shown in Fig. 11.20.

11.4.1.3 Refraction-based system

The basic principle behind most refraction-based multiview 3D displays is the lenticular lens technology, which is optically analogous to a parallax barrier mask but more efficient because it is transparent. The lenticular lens array distributes the light coming from the pixels of the display to multiple

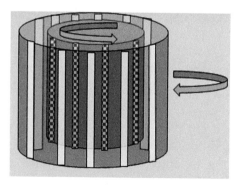

Figure 11.20   Cylindrical, parallax barrier multiview 3D display system.[3]

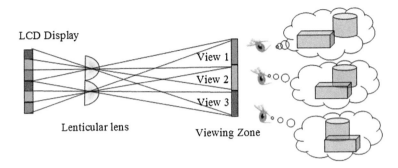

Figure 11.21 An HPO spatial multiplex multiview 3D display with three views using a lenticular lens sheet in front of a 2D LCD screen.[3]

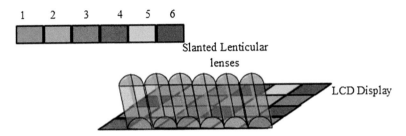

Figure 11.22 An HPO spatial multiplex multiview 3D display with three views using a slanted lenticular lens sheet in front of a 2D LCD screen.[3]

viewpoints. Therefore, light from specific pixels is magnified and transferred to specific observer positions. These viewers located at different viewpoints observe different images, thus providing the binocular disparity, convergence, and motion parallax depth cues for the visual system.

A. One-dimensional lenticular sheet

This technique is shown in Fig. 11.21.[16] The lenticular lens sheet consists of an array of plano-convex cylindrical lenses. In certain specific positions, viewers can see stereo images from the spatially multiplexed screen; the viewer may also experience motion parallax when changing position. The main advantages of such a system are low cost and high optical efficiency, whereas the main disadvantages are crosstalk between views, the "picket fence" effect, alignment issues, and the limited resolution, which is divided by *n* for an *n* multiview 3D display system.

B. Slanted lenticular layer on a LCD

This technique, shown in Fig. 11.22,[17] was developed to improve the resolution by distributing the loss of resolution into the vertical and the horizontal direction through the contribution of nearby views, which reduces image flipping and crosstalk.

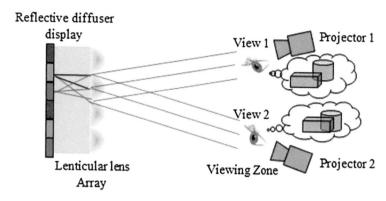

Figure 11.23 Refraction-based multiview 3D display using multiple projectors with a lenticular sheet array.[3]

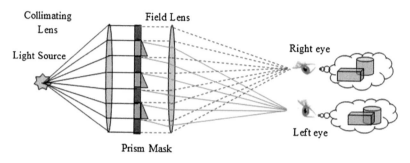

Figure 11.24 Refraction-based multiview 3D display using a prism mask.[3]

C. Multiple projectors with a reflective lenticular sheet array

In this technique, shown in Fig. 11.23,[18] each projector holds an image of a separate view. Light from the projectors passes the lenticular lens array twice. Light in the forward pass is diffused in that direction because the lenticular lens array is in the vertical direction, but it is focused in the horizontal direction on the diffuser screen. On the backward propagation, the lenticular lens array will focus back the image in the same original horizontal direction. The main advantage of such an approach is that there is no reduction of the resolution per view angle. The main disadvantage is the cost when a projector is needed per view.

D. Prism mask and single light source

In this technique, shown in Fig. 11.24,[19] every other column consists of RGB pixels that correspond to a column of either the left or the right image. The purpose of the prisms is to refract light to different viewing zones.

E. LC lens technology

As shown in Fig. 11.25,[20–23] LC-based lens technology enables the lenticular multiview 3D display system to be an electrically switchable 2D/3D display.

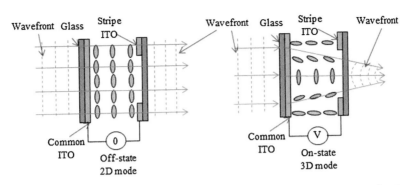

Figure 11.25 Refraction-based multiview 3D display employing LC lens technology.[2,3]

Due to the geometry of the electrodes, the electric field in the middle of the LC cell is much smaller than that of the edge of the cell, thus creating a nonuniform distribution of the tilt angle of the LC director axis; a refractive index profile is thus created because of this effect. This refractive-index profile creates a lensing effect and, when mounted in front of the SLM, will refract the beam in different directions, similar to the lenticular lens array.

The main advantage of such a system is that it is electrically controlled, which maintains the original resolution in the case of the 2D display mode. One of the disadvantages of such a system is the crosstalk that occurs between the different views, resulting in image degradation. This type of display is an active research area, and many techniques have been proposed to fix some of these issues.[24]

F. Integral imaging

This technique is based on integral photography, as shown in Fig. 11.26.[25–27] To obtain full parallax instead of HPO, as provided by the lenticular-based multiplex techniques, the cylindrical lenses are replaced with hemispheres or convex lenses. The image in this technique consists of multiple 2D images of the same scene captured using a large number of small convex lenses, known as the fly's eye lens sheet. Each of these lenslets captures a different view of the same scene from a different angle or perspective. Integral imaging involves two steps:

(a) the capture (pick up) stage, where each of the lenslets records a different elemental image of the 3D object, and
(b) the replay (display) stage, in which the display panel holding the different elemental images is positioned before the fly's eye lens sheet.

Due to these lenslets, the refracted light from each image point is directed at a specific viewing zone, and a spatial reconstruction of the 3D object is created in front of the lens array. Therefore, the observer perceives different compositions of image points at different points of view, invoking the parallax sensation. There are different configurations of integral imaging systems

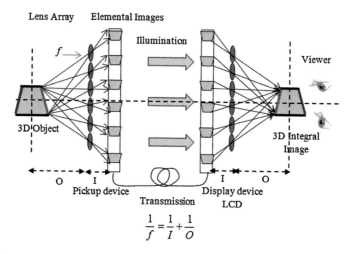

Figure 11.26 Refraction-based multiview 3D display employing integral imaging technology.[27]

according to the distance between the display holding the elemental images and the lenslet array.[2] The distance between the display and the lens sheet can be at the focal plane of the lenslets, thus called the focal display mode. If the distance is greater or smaller than the focal plane distance, then the system is in real/virtual mode. In integral imaging, the same fly's eye lens sheet is used in both steps, and the image must be inverted for orthoscopic depth rendition.[28,29]

Some of the advantages of integral-imaging-based 3D displays are

(a) a bare-eyed viewer,
(b) autostereoscopic images from continuous viewpoints,
(c) full-color and real-time 3D images within a certain viewing angle,
(d) both horizontal and vertical parallaxes (full parallax, or FP), and
(e) incoherent illumination in the pick-up process.

Some of the disadvantages are

(a) a narrow viewing zone,
(b) limited depth of field,
(c) relatively poor resolution, and
(d) the pseudoscopic problem.

The pseudoscopic problem occurs because the directions of the pick-up device (object recording) and the display device (image reconstruction) are opposite each other. Objects that are closer to the pick-up device are closer to the display device or farther from the observer; therefore, the integrated image is observed with a reversed depth perspective. Because integral imaging is a current research topic, researchers are trying to find solutions to these disadvantages by reducing the NA of the lens array or modulating the binary amplitude of the lenslet array.[30] Finally, a solution for the pseudoscopic inconvenience is to change the display mode by providing elemental images that are rotated by 180 deg with respect to their center, which is known as the virtual mode.[27]

G. Moving lenticular sheet

This technique involves moving a lenticular lens array sheet at a high speed to provide different viewing directions of high-speed images displayed on the LCD panel.[31,32] Therefore, there is a one-to-one correspondence between each position of the lenticular lens array, the displayed image on the screen, and a particular viewing direction. The major drawback of such a system is the precise motion control of the lens array sheet, where a constant scanning speed should be maintained for high-quality images.

11.4.1.4 Reflection-based system

A reflection-based autostereoscopic 3D display based on beamsplitter technology is shown in Fig. 11.27.[33] In this particular setup, two LCDs and two light sources are needed to project the left and the right image to the designated left and right eyes, thus inducing binocular parallax. The two images are combined using a half mirror or a beamsplitter. The collimating lenses are used to direct the light in the appropriate direction.

11.4.1.5 Diffraction-based system

A. Diffractive optical element (DOE) 3D display technology

In this technique, pixels pertaining to adjacent perspective views are grouped in arrays of partial pixels.[34,35] Diffraction gratings are placed in front of each partial pixel; these gratings direct the incident illumination to a specific

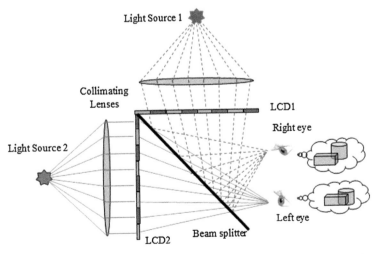

Figure 11.27 Refraction-based autostereoscopic 3D display employing beamsplitter technology [3].

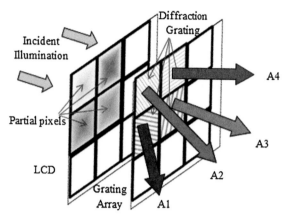

Figure 11.28 Diffraction-based autostereoscopic 3D display employing DOE technology.[3,35]

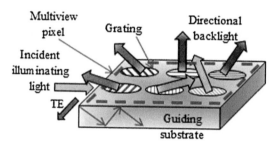

Figure 11.29 Diffraction-based autostereoscopic 3D display employing diffractive optics.[3,37]

image's viewing zone (first-order diffraction, A1 to A4 in Fig. 11.28). Current HOE technology yields images ~1.5 inches in diameter. Other, more-advanced techniques integrate image modulation and diffraction of light simultaneously within a single high-resolution SLM.[36]

B. Directional backlight based on a diffractive grating

Full parallax, directional-backlight 3D displays with wide viewing angles can be generated using SLM-based LC displays, as shown in Fig. 11.29.[37] A TE-polarized light source illuminates a glass waveguide. As in any waveguide, light can be coupled in or out of the waveguide using either prisms or a diffraction grating, which is the case in this design. These diffraction gratings are etched on the surface and then scatter the light in different directions, depending on the grating pattern, resulting in a multiview system with a full parallax and a 90-deg viewing angle.

C. Holographic-optical-element model

This model uses a HOE, which comprises at least two sets of interleaved regions, such that light incident on each set of regions is directed to a specific

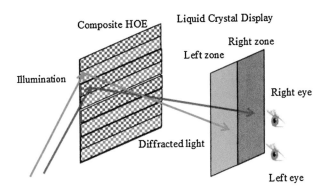

Figure 11.30 Diffraction-based autostereoscopic 3D display employing the HOE approach.[38,39]

viewing zone. The HOE is typically incorporated in a display device such as a stereoscopic display device. The two eyes see separate pictures, which may combine through stereopsis to show an image in three dimensions. In general, HOEs model the properties of conventional optical elements, such as lenses, through holographic methods. An HOE contains no image information by itself, but it is used to diffract incident modulated light. The first diffraction-based autostereoscopic 3D display employing the HOE approach (Fig. 11.30[38]) was prototyped by Richmond Holographic Studios, Ltd. and Realty Vision, Ltd.

The HOE is an integral part of the modified LCD. It consists of a hologram of an evenly diffused plane that is rastered so as to direct light from alternating lines to specified viewing zones. Outside the stereoscopic viewing zone, viewers experience 2D images. The stereo zone can be made to follow the observer's head movement by moving a light source. Some of the advantages of HOE-based systems are that they are transparent and flexible (permitting freedom in designing the shape of a system), and they are very thin and lightweight. This technique is likely to become very useful in future mobile devices.

11.4.1.6 Projection-based system

A. 360-deg rotating screen and a high-speed projector

This device consists of a high-speed projector and an anisotropically diffusing spinning mirror, is shown in Fig. 11.31.[40] The first step generates 2D images from 360-deg surrounding directions; these images are then projected in the display device toward the corresponding viewing angles in the 360-deg surrounding directions, generating a 360-deg HPO view. The major disadvantage of such a technique is the rotating mirror, which limits the display size.

B. Holografika system

The approach used by HoloVizio technology is different from traditional stereoscopic, multiview, volumetric, and holographic systems that can provide

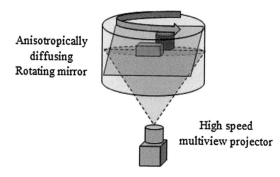

Figure 11.31 Projection-based multiview 3D display using a rotating screen with a high-speed projector.[3,40]

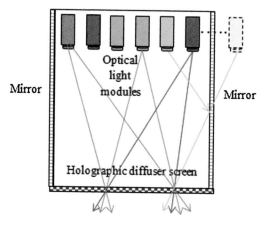

Figure 11.32 Holografica illumination light beam generated by the optical modules hits the vertical diffuser screen at various angles.[3,43]

different images in multiple directions. A major drawback of traditional autostereoscopic multiview 3D displays, such as parallax barrier or lenticular systems, is the limited number of rays (3D resolution). This limited resolution produces a continuous view only within a narrow FOV. Viewers will experience jumps when leaving and entering neighboring viewing zones, degrading the 3D viewing experience.

On the other hand, the Holografica system provides continuous motion and binocular parallax for a wide FOV zone for several viewers.[41–43] Current Holografica camera array systems consist of several cameras (>25, capturing ~20 million light rays) connected to a 30-MPixel HoloVizio system (HoloVizio 720RC). This system is supported by sophisticated software that can capture and display images in real time. Offline operation, such as storage and playback, is also feasible.

Current Holografica systems use a specially arranged array of optical light modules and a holographic vertical diffuser screen, as shown in Fig. 11.32. The screen can be a refractive or diffractive diffuser; its function is to scatter light in the vertical direction while leaving the horizontal direction unaltered. The illuminating light beams generated in the optical modules (array of projectors) hit the vertical diffuser screen points in various angles. Each pixel of the holographic screen emits light beams of different color and intensity in various directions. With appropriate software control, light beams diffracting from the pixels propagate in multiple directions, as if they were emitted from the points of 3D objects at the right spatial locations. Therefore, the holographic screen makes the necessary optical transformation to combine these beams into a meaningful, continuous 3D image. Each optical light module provides a thin slit of images to each viewer in the horizontal direction. For a meaningful view in a certain direction, the software performs image mosaicing from the different image slits provided by the different projectors.

Note that the horizontal angle is very critical to control in such a system. If the horizontal angle is too wide, the FOV will decrease, and a shadowing effect will appear in the images for objects that are farther from the screen, due to overlapping regions. If the horizontal angle is too narrow, then the image will suffer from inhomogenities degrading its quality. Also, an inverse geometry can be achieved by applying side mirrors in the display design, which enhances the FOV by collecting all light beams from the modules through reflection (thus increasing the apparent number of modules). Overall, the system is compact in terms of number of computers and provides superior image quality, resolution, and frame rate compared to other traditional systems.

C. Lenticular mirror sheet

This technique uses a projector and a lenticular reflective mirror array as a reflective screen, as shown in Fig. 11.33.[44] The projector creates an image on each of the lenticular strips; as a result of the curvature of the lenticular lenses, the reflected beam is reflected in different but calibrated directions, creating the different multiview perspectives.

D. Double-layered parallax barrier

This technique is an extension of the parallax barrier HPO autostereoscopic 3D display discussed in Section 11.4.1.2. In this case, a double parallax barrier and a multiprojector array are employed, as shown in Fig. 11.34.[45] Each

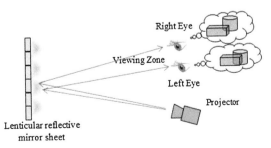

Figure 11.33 Projection-based multiview 3D display with a lenticular mirror sheet.[3]

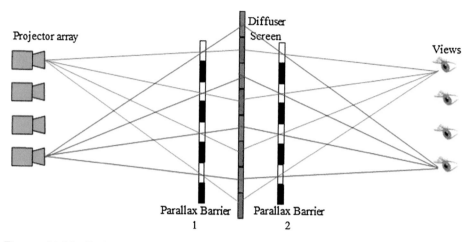

Figure 11.34 Projection-based multiview 3D display with a double-layered parallax barrier.[3]

projector produces one image per view. The first barrier is used to direct the projected image from each projector to a specific location on the diffuser screen. The second barrier, which is situated symmetrically opposite the first barrier with respect to the diffuser screen, controls the viewing direction. As a result of this arrangement, different viewers in different locations see different perspectives of the images, invoking motion and binocular parallax cues.

11.4.1.7 Super multiview (SMV) 3D display

As mentioned earlier, two major disadvantages among traditional autostereoscopic 3D displays are the accommodation–convergence conflict and the limited resolution. In the former, viewers experience visual fatigue, and in the latter, viewers will experience jumps when leaving and entering neighboring viewing zones, degrading the 3D viewing experience. SMVs try to solve these two shortcomings in traditional multiview displays where the horizontal viewing zone width is reduced to less than the diameter of the eye pupil (~1.5 mm in bright light and 8 mm in dim light) guaranteeing smooth motion parallax and at the same time solving the accommodation convergence conflict.

An early SMV display was designed for a windshield display application [Fig. 11.35(a)].[46,47] The SMV display combines a slanted lenticular lens array and a projection lens. A flat transreflective mirror acting as an optical combiner was also used to exclude the prewarping issue in the system.[2] As shown in Fig. 11.35(b), a projection lens is used to image the viewing zone of a slanted lenticular lens array. Note that the width of the entire viewing zone is reduced, and thus the pitch of each viewing zone is reduced to less than the diameter of the pupil of an eye, as needed for a SMV display. The early prototype provided 36 viewing zones with a pitch of 3.61 mm for each zone, demonstrating a continuous motion parallax for a 3D virtual image located

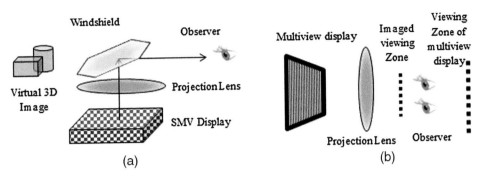

Figure 11.35 Multiview 3D display system that adopts SMV technology: (a) conceptual diagram of a system configuration and (b) implementation of a SMV feature where the pitch of each viewing zone is reduced by a projection lens.[2]

5–50 m from the observer.[47] Also demonstrated was the possibility to focus on the 3D images, which solves the accommodation–convergence conflict for the 3D images produced by the prototype display.

11.4.1.8 Head-tracking autostereoscopic 3D display

Because the viewer's position with respect to an autostereoscopic display is important, the head-tracking autostereoscopic 3D display techniques are intended to adaptively optimize the display based on the position of the viewer's eyes to produce the best 3D experience from a viewer's perspective. HELIUM3D is one of the many multiviewer, laser-based, head-tracking 3D autostereoscopic displays designed for this purpose;[48,49] Fig. 11.36 is a simplified schematic diagram. HELIUM3D is a projection-type display wherein images are created in a light engine and transferred to a viewing screen by a relay lens system, which contains a SLM. As shown in Fig. 11.36(a), L1 is the light-engine projection lens, and L2 is a field lens that concentrates the light emanating from L1 to a second projection lens L3. A horizontal diffuser situated behind L2 spreads the real image of L1 across the whole width of L3. Thus, L3 transfers the image that exists on L2 to the superlens screen assembly. A SLM is situated behind the L3 lens that controls the light input to the screen. A real image is produced by the SLM in the viewing field, and the images of the transmitting regions form the exit pupils.[50] Therefore, exit pupils in the HELIUM3D display are formed by allowing light to pass through clear apertures in the SLM. These pupils are effectively focused at the viewers' eyes by the screen. The superlens screen assembly contains a Gabor superlens that comprises two sets of microlens arrays that have different imaging properties compared to conventional lenses, as shown in Fig. 11.36(b). In this type of lenses, input and output ray angles remain on one side of the normal to the lens surface, and image distances become less as the object distance is reduced.[51] The purpose of the superlens screen in the display is to effectively magnify and focus an image of the SLM into the viewing field so that it fills the complete width.[50]

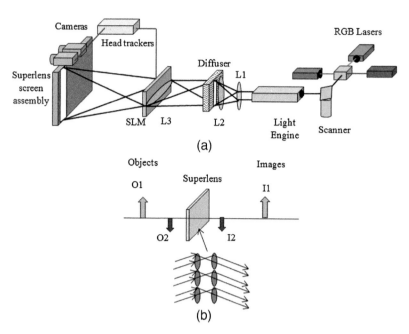

Figure 11.36   (a) HELIUM3D schematic diagram of the display. The projector is illuminated with a horizontally scanned white beam, which produces a scanned image column on L2 that is transferred to the screen via L3. Multiple exit pupils are formed dynamically by controlling the light directions with a SLM during the period of a horizontal scan. The pupil tracker uses digital cameras and custom software to acquire and track the user's eye pupil locations and serves as the dynamic feedback for adjusting the exit pupil locations. (b) Gabor superlens showing the unique image-formation properties.[49]

Finally, other head-tracked displays that operate on a different principle to HELIUM3D have been developed by the European MUTED project.[50] In these types of displays, the left and right images are produced on a direct-view LCD. Also, the conventional backlight is replaced with steering optics that can produce multiple pairs of exit pupils that track the positions of the viewers' eyes under the control of a multiuser head tracker.

11.4.1.9 Directional-backlight autostereoscopic 3D display

These systems rely on fast LCD displays and innovative directional-backlight techniques that provide time-dependent multiview regions without sacrificing the resolution. These systems are time-multiplexed techniques because the backlight sequentially projects the directional lighting. Full resolution is achieved using these systems because time-sequential left and right images are displayed quickly enough to avoid the perception of flicker.

A. 3M directional-backlight system

One of these directional-backlight devices was invented by 3M;[52] the schematic is shown in Fig. 11.37. The 3D display is provided with a backlight to make the image noticeable to the viewer. The backlight includes a

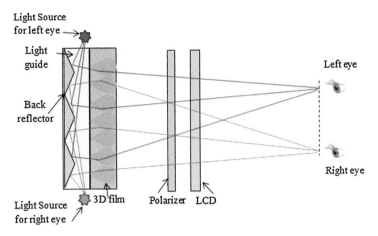

Figure 11.37 Directional-backlight autostereoscopic 3D display design by 3M.[3,52]

polarizer, a 3D redirecting film, a light guide, first and second light-source assemblies (LEDs), and a back-reflector. The 3D redirecting film consists of a nanometer-scale lenticular structure. Only one of the LED light sources is on at any given time, and the back reflector and the light guide ensure that the light is directed to the corresponding eye by synchronizing with the image displayed on the LCD. Therefore, the left light source is synchronized with the display of the left image on the LCD, and the right light source with the right image. The display consists of a LC panel that has individual pixels arranged in a matrix that defines an active area of the panel. The pixels are individually addressable by a controller, which synchronizes the light source with the panel to form any desired RGB in a subpixel-format image. The refresh rate of the LCD panel is 120 Hz, making the refresh rate of the 3D display system 60 Hz.

B. Sony switchable 2D/3D directional-backlight system

Another directional-backlight device was invented by Sony;[53,54] the design schematic is shown in Fig. 11.38.

The 3D display system can be switched between 2D and 3D, depending on whether the 2D backlight or the 3D source light is on. The light guide acts as a parallax barrier in this case. In the 3D mode, the light bounces back and forth in the light guide and is scattered when it hits the scattering regions (which act like the slits in a parallax-based barrier design). The scattered light that is reflected back to the LCD produces the multiview effect if it is synchronized with the image displayed on the LCD. When the 3D light source is switched off and the backlight is switched on, the display will be in 2D mode.

C. Multidirectional backlight unit (BLU) and an LCD panel

This technique, shown in Fig. 11.39(a), is similar to the lenticular-based multiview 3D displays discussed in Section 11.4.1.3. The drawback of the lenticular-based multiview autostereoscopic 3D displays that use a spatial

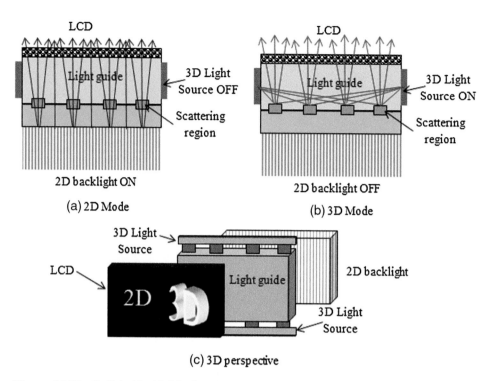

Figure 11.38 Switchable 2D/3D directional-backlight autostereoscopic display design by Sony.[3,53,54]

multiplex design is the inverse correlation between the number of viewpoints n and the resolution of the 3D image in the resulting spatial distribution. This correlation divides the resolution by the same number of views n. In this system, the resolution problem is resolved by using the time-sequential operation.[55] The system consists of a directional BLU and a fast LCD. The BLU consists of a lens array and light sources situated at the front focal plane of the lens array; thus, the output light is collimated in different directions depending on the position of the light source. Beam steering is feasible if the light-source position changes.

Figure 11.39(a) shows four light sources per lens; thus, four collimated beams can be obtained in four different directions. The light sources are controlled by changing the position of the white pixels in the LCD module using customized software. This same software also controls the LCD panel, ensuring that the images are displayed in synchronization with the locations of the line light sources in the LCD module steering the light to the appropriate viewpoint direction. Figure 11.39(b) describes the operational principles of this system consisting of four sequences. When the first set of line light sources 1 are on and the image 1 is simultaneously displayed on the LCD panel, the viewer can only see the images of 1 at viewpoint 1. The images of 2, 3, and 4 are also displayed on the LCD panel but are not visible due to the operation of the LCD module. Therefore, for an observer whose left and right eye are

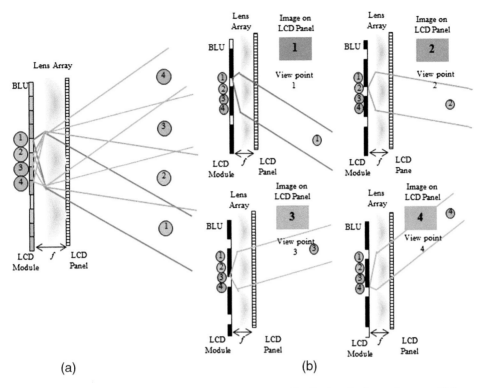

Figure 11.39 Directional-backlight autostereoscopic 3D display design using a multidirectional backlight unit (BLU).[55]

located at adjacent viewpoints (and if the sequential images on the LCD panel correspond to the left and right eye images), the viewer will experience 3D. Note that the LCD panel as well as the directional BLU should change fast enough to provide the 3D sensation in the viewer due to the afterimage or persistence effect. As an example, for a 240-Hz LCD panel, four views can be multiplexed with a full 60-Hz temporal resolution.

11.4.2 Depth-fused 3D display technology

A depth-fused display (DFD) is an autostereoscopic 3D display technology that does not suffer from the drawbacks of stereoscopic 3D display systems. A DFD provides a 3D depth experience to an observer using 2D images on two or more overlapping transparent screens.[56] The 3D image depth is obtained by combining the luminance of two 2D images displayed at different depths, as shown in Fig. 11.40(a). A DFD is a visually comfortable 3D display because it can satisfy not only binocular disparity, convergence, and accommodation but also motion parallax for a small observer displacement. Experimental studies show that an accommodation cue to fused depth perception is free from the visual fatigue problems of stereoscopic displays.[57]

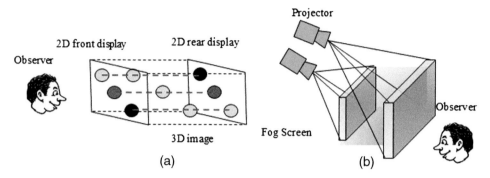

Figure 11.40 (a) General schematic and (b) 3D display adopting the DFD technique to visualize a 3D image with a diffusive screen.[2,61]

For the DFD to work, the observer must be positioned such that the 2D images displayed on the transparent screens are superposed. The depth can be deciphered from the superposed 2D images pixel by pixel by varying the luminance of each pixel of one 2D image with respect to the other. A particular pixel is perceived by the observer to be "near" if more luminance is assigned to it on the frontal screen. In contrast, if more luminance is assigned to a certain pixel on the back screen, this pixel will be perceived as "far" from the observer.

Another equally valid explanation of the mechanism of perceiving continuous depth with changing pixel luminance between the front and rear 2D images is that the human visual system is trying to solve the binocular matching problem. After failing to solve this problem by using high-spatial-frequency components of the image, the human visual system resorts to the low-spatial-frequency components of the image. When the luminance ratio between the front and rear images changes, this behavior results in a continuous change in the disparity of the low-spatial-frequency components, which indicates that the perceived depth can be continuously changed by changing the luminance ratio.[58–60]

A system that introduces a DFD to visualize a 3D image with a diffusive screen is shown in Fig. 11.40(b).[61] This system adopts two fog screens for diffusive screens. The two superposed projected images render a 3D volume between two screens. Earlier versions of DFD displays were limited to a single fixed viewpoint of a DFD. This system overcomes that drawback by using a head-tracking system. Therefore, this technique can provide a 3D virtual image mediated to the real world. However, the range in which a 3D virtual image can be expressed is limited to the range between the two screens, and the use of a diffusive screen affects the quality of a real-world scene.

11.4.3 Volumetric 3D display technology

Section 11.4.1 discussed several multiview system techniques that are capable of providing 3D images to different viewers in different directions. On the other hand, the volumetric techniques discussed in this section attempt to display a real volumetric 3D image in a 3D space. The pixels in traditional 2D images are now called voxels. The location of the voxels in the 3D space should mimic the real original position of the 3D scene and, when illuminated, reflect light in all directions toward any viewer located in any direction. These voxels should be selectively addressed at any location for the volumetric 3D display system to work. Therefore, these displays are superior to multiview 3D technologies because they can invoke the physical and the psychological depth cues of our visual system.

11.4.3.1 Passive static-screen display

Three examples of such a technique are discussed in this subsection:

(a) 3D two-step upconversion display (either solid state or gas medium),
(b) 3D volumetric display using passive optical scatterers, and
(c) plasma-based 3D volumetric display (to create visible image in air).

A. Solid-state and gas-medium 3D two-step upconversion display

This technique is based on the two-step upconversion process in which two beams of infrared lasers are used to excite the material to an excited energy state from which visible fluorescence may be emitted, as shown in Fig. 11.41(a). In such a 3D display system, each voxel should be selectively addressed by two laser beams, as shown in Fig. 11.41(b). These voxels should only be activated at the intersection of two laser beams; thus, the chosen material must permit the two-photon absorption process. Typical solid state materials are rare-earth materials doped into a glass medium, such as ZBLAN

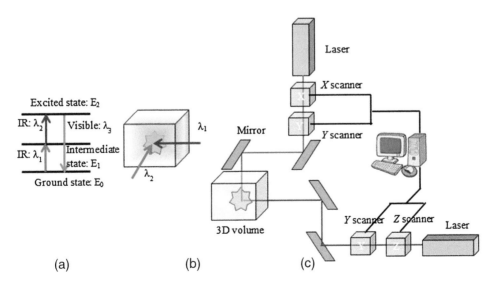

(a)   (b)   (c)

Figure 11.41 Solid state 3D upconversion display: (a) energy diagram, (b) voxel addressing, and (c) imaging configuration.[3,67]

(ZrF4-BaF2-LaF3-AlF3-NaF).[3,62,63] Challenges involved with these types of displays are scalability and the ability to display a full-color gamut.

Another type of materials used for static volumetric 3D displays are gaseous vapors, such as mercury vapor,[64] iodine monochloride vapor,[65] and rubidium vapor.[66,67] Some organic dyes in liquid or polymeric solutions can also serve as 3D display media.[68] A gaseous material is easy to produce, fills the allotted 3D volume, and has a refractive index that is close to air, so there will be minimal distortion of the generated images. However, most of the gases used in this kind of display are toxic and must be kept in a chamber at high pressure. An experimental 3D display system using the two-step excitation of fluorescence in rubidium vapor is shown in Fig. 11.41(c).[67] The two beams from the two lasers are scanned using xy scanning mirrors to produce a vector scan and thus create an image.

B. 3D volumetric display using passive optical scatterers

A relatively recent low-cost technology called laser-induced damage (LID) can accurately embed a desired point cloud of passive optical scatterers in a solid block of glass or plastic.[69,70] Each scatterer is a physical crack in the block of glass created by focusing a laser beam at a specific location. When the crack is illuminated by ambient, it will be barely visible; however, when it is illuminated by a focused source, it glows brightly (see Fig. 11.42). The grid of scatterers in each horizontal xy plane is offset from the other planes to ensure that the illuminating source can address each point in the cloud. Therefore, no two stacks overlap each other with respect to the light-source projection rays illuminating the cube from the z direction.

There are several ways to illuminate the scatterers. One way involves an orthographic light engine that uses a DLP projector, planar mirror, and Fresnel lens to convert the DLP projector into an orthographic projector. The Fresnel lens thus converts diverging rays into parallel rays along the z direction, which are then focused onto the designated scatterers, as shown in Fig. 11.42(a).[71] Orthographic projection allows the use of point clouds without resolution biases

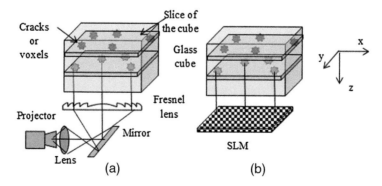

Figure 11.42 Optical layout of 3D display using passive optical scatterers using (a) a projector and (b) a SLM.[3,71]

and with relatively easy display calibration. When the projector projects time-varying images, the 3D surface appears dynamic. Another method of illumination uses a high-resolution SLM, as shown in Fig. 11.42(b). Varying the illuminated pixel pattern on the SLM varies the location of the voxels that are illuminated. Note that each LID crack is ~ 0.18 mm wide and ~ 0.21 mm long, which limits the resolution of the system.

Because these types of displays render a 3D image in a physical volume, the 3D image invokes the binocular parallax, motion parallax, and accommodation depth cues. Some of the advantages of this technology:

(a) there are no moving parts,
(b) it can be full color,
(c) there is no need for glasses (autostereoscopic), and
(d) because the image is displayed in a 3D volume, multiple observers can view the content from a wide range of directions simultaneously.

One limitation of this technology, which is inherent to most volumetric displays, is that view-dependent effects, such as specularities and occlusions, cannot be rendered.

C. Plasma-based 3D volumetric display used to form visible image in air

A focused infrared laser beam induces breakdown in air at that location, bringing the gas into a high-density plasma state and causing a localized flash of light. An impact noise is also generated due the same effect. When the IR laser beam is focused by the condenser lens at a certain point in the air, a plasma state at that specific point occurs, and a flash of light is generated that viewers can see from a remote location. The setup is shown in Fig. 11.43.[72] The laser source is a Q-switched Nd:YAG or a CO_2 infrared laser. This IR beam is not subject to absorption or scattering caused by atmosphere and can propagate a far distance. The scanning device consists of a rotational mirror and an oscillating mirror that scan the beam in the xy direction. A driving device moves the condensing optical lens that collects the infrared beam along the propagation direction. The controlling system coordinates the laser source, the scanning system, the driving device, and the input image system,

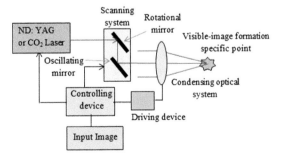

Figure 11.43 Schematic of a plasma-based 3D volumetric display for forming a visible image in air.[72]

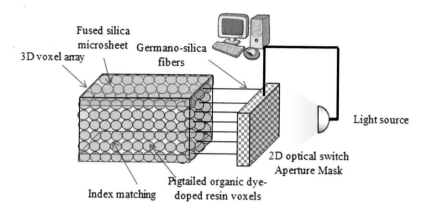

Figure 11.44 Diagram of a volumetric display, illustrating the pigtailed voxels and the structurally supportive fused-silica microsheets.[3,73]

whose output should be projected in the air. In a typical system,[72] the laser pulsewidth is ~10 ns, the repetition frequency is 20 Hz, and the energy density of the pulse beam is 10 mJ/pulse. When this pulse beam is focused on a spot with a 0.1-mm beam diameter, a peak output of $\sim 10^{10}$ W/cm^2 is obtained.

11.4.3.2 Active static-screen display

Four examples of such technique are discussed in this subsection:

    (a) fiber-optic-based volumetric 3D display;
    (b) volumetric 3D LED display;
    (c) solid state, multiplanar, volumetric 3D display; and
    (d) volumetric 3D display with dust as the participating medium.

A. Fiber-optic-based volumetric 3D display

The fiber-optic-based volumetric 3D display, shown in Fig. 11.44,[73] uses a controllable light source and a 3D array of voxels doped with a fluorescent dye. Optical fibers guide light from the source elements to the voxels which, in their quiescent state, are transparent. The voxels and fibers are immersed in a refractive index-matching liquid to avoid refraction artifacts. The image is controlled by an SLM. The ensemble of all activated 3D voxels results in a 3D image in real physical space. This system is very impressive from an engineering perspective, but implementing it is complex and expensive compared to other approaches that use passive light scatterers.

B. Volumetric 3D LED display

This type of volumetric 3D display uses matrices of LEDs.[74] A schematic of this technique is shown in Fig. 11.45.[75] In addition to the scalability issue of

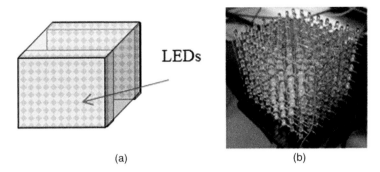

(a) (b)

Figure 11.45 (a) Schematic of a volumetric 3D LED display, and (b) an experimental module.[75]

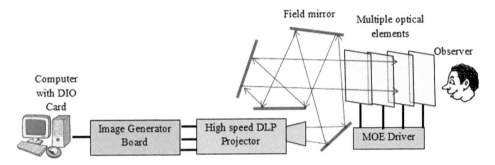

Figure 11.46 Schematic diagram of the DepthCube solid state, multiplanar, volumetric 3D display system.[76]

the previous technique, this technique has an additional limitation—the occlusion introduced by the opacity of the LEDs.

C. Solid state, multiplanar, volumetric 3D display

The DepthCube is a commercial 3D display system that is based on the static multiplanar volumetric display technology and uses a stack of 20 scattering and voltage-switchable LCD sheets illuminated in sequence by a high-speed digital projector.[76,77] The LCD sheets are transparent when no voltage is applied and become scattering when voltage is applied. The schematic of this design is shown in Fig. 11.46. The key point for this 3D display system to work is to synchronize the 2D image section of the original 3D physical image on the projector and the LCD sheet corresponding to the 3D location. Although this display produces compelling 3D content, it is expensive because it uses a high-speed light engine and electrically controlled LCD scatterers. Also, one limitation of this technology is the low brightness due to the short exposure time.

D. Volumetric 3D display with dust as the participating medium

Researchers from New York University[76] proposed using dust particles suspended in air to project 3D images. The system scans the dust particles using

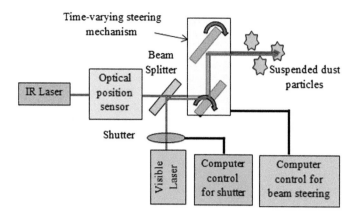

Figure 11.47 Volumetric 3D display with dust as the participating medium.[78]

an infrared time-of-flight detector to find the locations of the particles and then use a visible light-scanning beam to illuminate the appropriate particles that correspond to the original 3D physical image.[78] A schematic of the system is shown in Fig. 11.47; it consists of an IR laser; a switchable visible-light laser; a beamsplitter; a computer control for switching the visible light laser; a time-varying optical-beam-steering mechanism; a computer control for time-varying optical beam steering; a linear, infrared-sensitive optical position sensor; and suspended dust particles in the air.

11.4.3.3 Passive swept-screen display

This section discusses several autostereoscopic volumetric display techniques wherein a periodically time-varying 2D image is used to scan out a volume of space periodically at a frequency higher than the eye can resolve to eliminate flicker. Depth-perception cues, such as binocular disparity and motion parallax, are invoked due to the human-vision persistence effect, and a 3D image will be perceived. The 2D image will be generated on a passive projection screen (the next section, the image will be generated on an emissive panel screen). The screen can be of any shape (rectangular, circular, helical, etc.) and rotates on an axis to create the depth effect in synchronization with the 2D projected image. On the other hand, the screen can be fixed but viewed using an oscillating mirror, creating the illusion that the image is oscillating. The rotating screen scans the 3D volume in order to create the 3D image.[79] Five examples of such a technique are discussed in this subsection:

    (a) high-brightness CRT projection,
    (b) varifocal 3D display techniques,
    (c) laser projection on a helical screen,
    (d) Perspecta optical projection system, and
    (e) multiplanar, helical-screen volumetric 3D display.

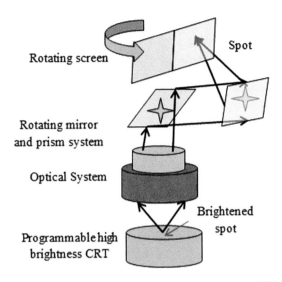

Rotating screen

Spot

Rotating mirror
and prism system

Optical System

Brightened
spot

Programmable high
brightness CRT

Figure 11.48 High-brightness CRT projection.[3,80]

A. High-brightness CRT projection

ITT Laboratories developed one of the early approaches of this display type. The system consists of a programmed high-brightness CRT whose spots are optically relayed to a translucent rotating screen located in a glass cylinder, as shown in Fig. 11.48. The rotating screen is driven by a motor that turns at ~20 rps to reduce flicker.[80,81]

B. Varifocal 3D display technique

The varifocal techniques are based on the changing focal length of a membrane producing a virtual image field much larger than the physical membrane vibration. These techniques are not technically volumetric, but they share a lot of the characteristics with the volumetric 3D display technique. A thin, flat aluminized plastic sheet mounted on an airtight frame can be pneumatically modified (by decreasing or increasing the static air pressure) to form a concave or convex mirror. A change of curvature also changes the focal length of the mirror; this phenomenon can be exploited when creating an autostereoscopic 3D display system, as shown in Fig. 11.49.[82] In this system, a thin, aluminized Mylar mirror film is driven by an acoustic drive, such as a loudspeaker. If the mirror film is stretched enough, small amplitude oscillations will change the mirror's surface curvature accordingly.

An observer views the sequence of images displayed on the CRT through the reflection of the synchronized variable curvature of the mirror film. Thus, when the curvature of the mirror that is in synchronization with the displayed image on the CRT changes, the position of the reflected image changes, creating a 3D autostereoscopic image in a transparent stack of 2D images.

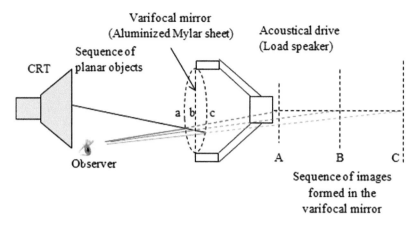

Figure 11.49 Varifocal mirror for 3D volumetric imaging.[82]

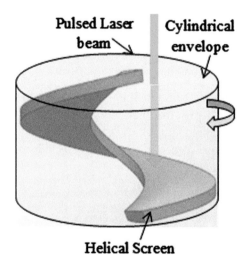

Figure 11.50 Laser projection on a helical screen.[87]

A notable limitation of this 3D display system is its limited FOV, determined by the virtual display volume and the reflective surface coverage. This system does not provide a 360-deg view of the image.

A computer-driven 3D display that uses this varifocal system is the SpaceGraph 3D Display.[83] Another varifocal system, known as the XYZ Scope, employs a lens rotating about its diameter instead of a vibrating mirror film.[84] The operating principle is that the rotating lens causes aberrations as the viewer moves out of the center axis of the lens, creating the 3D effect.

C. Laser projection on a helical screen

A system based on laser projection on a helical screen is shown in Fig. 11.50.[85–87] When the scanned laser beam hits any position on the helix, light will be scattered, creating a visible illuminated spot (voxel). As the helical screen rotates, it sweeps a cylindrical envelope and renders a 3D volumetric display. The device contains polygonal mirrors, acousto-optic modulator deflectors, and galvanometers to scan the laser beam. Synchronization between the laser pulse and the rotating helix determines the location of the illuminated voxel within the display.

An advanced extension of the helical screen volumetric imager is the FELIX 3D Display, which has a portable setup, advanced software, and projection techniques.[88,89] Another related system uses a scanned laser beam to illuminate a motorized, rotating oblique disc or helical surface (the latter is known as the OmniView 3D Display). Another helix approach employs a CRT projector instead of a laser source.[90] In this system, an anamorphic lens is used to correct for the focal distance variations of the different points on the helical surface. Finally, laser-based volumetric 3D displays that employ a helical surface with reflective and translucent screens have been suggested.[91] This system was equipped with a high-performance acousto-optic scanning system, leading to higher image resolutions.

D. Perspecta optical projection system

In this system, illustrated by Fig. 11.51,[92] a projection lens focuses the light beam from a SLM or a DLP through an annular shaft of a DC motor. The motor rotates the back-end optics (i.e., projection lens and mirrors) about an axis, as shown in Fig. 11.51 for scanning purposes. The illuminating light beam directed by the projection lens hits the three mirrors consecutively; the

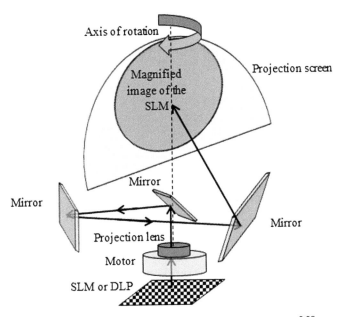

Figure 11.51 Perspecta optical projection system.[3,92]

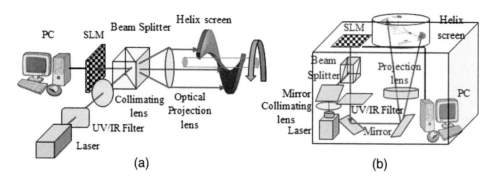

Figure 11.52 (a) First embodiment of the SLM/Helix 3D display. (b) A version of the portable volumetric 3D display unit and optics layout with the rear-projection system configuration.[3,93]

mirrors fold in such a way that the light is limited to the projection screen. The image formed on the projection screen is a magnified version of the image on the SLM. A typical image area diameter is ~10 inches, corresponding to ~20 × magnification of the image at the SLM. The SLM image resolution is 768 × 768 pixels.

E. Multiplanar, helical-screen volumetric 3D display

This technique is autostereoscopic and requires no special eyewear. The 3D image is perceived to be floating in true 3D space, just as if the real object were there. Figure 11.52(a) shows a schematic of the SLM Helix 3D volumetric display.[93–97] Illuminating light is produced by a light source, such as a laser. The beam then passes through a UV and IR cut-off filter, a collimating lens, and then a polarized beamsplitter. The light is then reflected to a high-frame-rate SLM that displays images provided by a computer at a rate of thousands of frames per second. Only the light that corresponds to pixels that are turned on will reflect back toward the beamsplitter, whereas the others will not. The patterned reflected light is then projected to a rotating helix screen by an optical projection lens. The patterned beam hits the helical screen, intersecting it at different heights in different locations and forming a volumetric 3D image.

In order for this system to work, the rotation of the helical screen must be synchronized with the pattern displayed on the SLM device. The resulting images are displayed in the 3D volume at a rate faster than 20 Hz, thus allowing the human visual system to fuse the images into a volumetric 3D image. Another compact portable configuration is shown in Fig. 11.52(b). Note that the surface of the helix is made of a semi-transparent material. Half of the light impinging on it will be transmitted, and the rest will be reflected. Therefore, light spots projected by the SLM will be diffused and can be viewed from both sides of the helical screen, which makes it a 360-deg-type system.

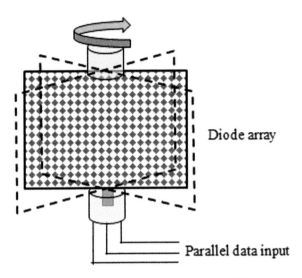

Figure 11.53   Rotating LED array.[3,99]

11.4.3.4 Active swept-screen display

Two examples of such a technique are discussed in this subsection:

(a) rotating LED array and
(b) rotating phosphorous disk in a CRT.

A. Rotating LED array

This technique is based on a matrix of xy addressable electroluminescent light sources mounted on a panel that rotates within a certain confined volume.[98] A system where the 2D matrix consists of LEDs is shown in Fig. 11.53.[99] The resolution of these types of systems depends on the LED packing density, the pulse rate, and the speed of rotation.[100–103]

B. Rotating phosphorous disk in a CRT

This system employs a rotating phosphorous-coated screen in vacuum, with a controlled electron beam striking its surface, as shown in Fig. 11.54. A 3D image can be achieved by controlling the scanning mechanism of the electron beam.[104] A more-advanced volumetric display that uses the same principle is called the cathode ray sphere (CRS).[105–107]

The rotating screen is coated with a phosphorous material, ensuring high efficiency and low persistence to avoid trails caused by the rotation of the screen. The screen rotates at ~ 15 Hz, where images are refreshed during one rotation. The dead-zone issue with these types of systems is solved by using multiple electron guns positioned to ensure distinct dead zones. Color can be incorporated in these systems by coating both sides of the rotating screen with a different phosphorous material.[105]

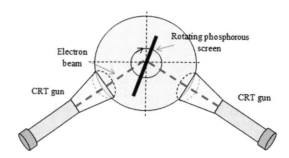

Figure 11.54   Plane view of a 3D CRT display system that uses two electron guns and a planar screen.[105]

11.4.4 Holographic 3D display technology

There exist two major trends for holographic display technology, analog and digital. With regards to the former, a group at Bell Laboratories in 1966 captured a holographic interference fringe pattern on a vidicon and transmitted it to a CRT, where it was photographed. The resulting transparency was then illuminated by a laser to reconstruct the image.[108] In 1972, a CBS team used a similar technique but replaced the transparency with a reusable PTP material, similar to the one discussed in Chapter 1, to create a phase hologram.[109] In the 1990s, several groups used LC light modulators designed for projectors, with laser illumination as displays for analog real-time holographic display systems.[110,111]

Digital holographic display systems have two major differences from the analog version. The first is the preference of multiview camera arrays rather than coherent light and interference to capture a scene capture—lenslet arrays can be attached to single sensors, which permits the digital capture of integral images. Digital holograms can be either computed from 3D computer graphic models, or they can be holographic stereograms generated from sets of parallax 2D views. The latter approach is typically used in current holographic display systems.[112]

One way the holographic video system works is that these systems produce diffraction fringes. These fringes can diffract the light passing through them in predictable ways. The effect of light reflecting from a 3D object can be simulated with a dense array of fringe patterns, where each one bends light in a different direction.[113] However, computing a "true" hologram of a 3D scene is a very demanding process because each point in the scene contributes to each point in the hologram, and the resulting calculations grow quickly as the hologram becomes larger. Therefore, practical real-time holovideo computation does not simulate the physics of light interference; however, the diffraction patterns that will create a desired light field are obtained by assembling precomputed basis functions and modulating them with the scene content. One way to do that is to generate a holographic multiview stereogram by using parallax views from a camera array or by rendering a large number of parallax views of a scene. The intensities of these views are then used to modulate the amplitude, point-by-point, of a set of precomputed chirped diffraction patterns, which act as light emitters on a plane whose intensity/wavefront curvature can be controlled in each direction. These patterns are then summed together to create the hologram. The following section briefly discusses the different types of spatial light modulators and then explains some of the current holographic-based 3D display techniques.

11.4.4.1 Spatial light modulators (SLMs)

One of the most important components in holographic-based 3D displays is the SLM. SLMs can modulate the illuminating light and can be controlled electronically or optically. In the latter case, a coherent light source writes a certain pattern on the SLM, and another light source is modulated by the SLM. In the former case, electric signals are converted into an interference pattern that can be electrically written on each pixel using a computer. Typical SLM technologies are

(a) LCDs,
(b) LCoS devices,
(c) optically addressed LCDs (OALCDs),
(d) digital micromirror devices (DMDs),
(e) holographic polymer-dispersed liquid crystals (PDLCs), and
(f) acousto-optic modulators (AOMs).

The major requirements of SLMs are a high refresh rate, high transmittance, high efficiency, small pixel size, and the ability to form large arrays because the number of pixels represents the space–bandwidth product, which represents the resolution of the system. The ultimate size of the pixel should approach the optical wavelength because the diffraction angle is inversely proportional to the size of the pixel. As an example, a pixel size of one-half of a micron results in a diffraction angle of $\sim$60 deg.[114]

A. LCD

Since their inception,[115] LCs have exhibited many useful features due to their anisotropic nature that make them very suitable for display technologies. LCs react differently to different light sources and can be modulated electrically and magnetically.[116] Twisted nematic and ferroelectric LC-based SLMs are no different from those currently used in LCD TV technology. Interference fringe patterns can also be written on the LC SLM pixels. Holographic techniques rely on modulating the amplitude, the phase, or both. LC-based SLMs can either change the amplitude or the phase of the illuminating beam.

A twisted nematic LC cell is shown in Fig. 11.55. An LC cell consists of LC molecules sandwiched between two glass slides. During manufacture, the glass slides are rubbed in two perpendicular directions to produce

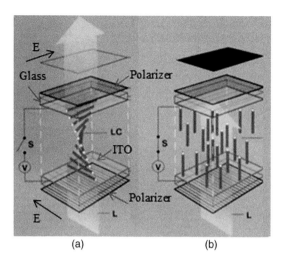

(a)   (b)

Figure 11.55 (a) Twisted unbiased and (b) biased LC cell.

microscopic grooves in the glass; these grooves induce the LC to twist [shown in Fig. 11.55(a)] as the LC molecules attempt to align with the grooves. A film of indium-tin oxide (ITO) conducting layer is usually deposited on the glass slides, thus enabling the cell to be electrically biased. If two crossed polarizers are inserted on either side of the cell, then a linearly polarized light with electric field E parallel to the grooves of the first slide (also parallel to the transmission axis of the first polarizer) will emerge 90-deg rotated with respect to the input beam but also parallel to the grooves of the second slide (and to the transmission axis of the second polarizer). In effect, the polarization of the beam rotates along with the LC rotation. This is the ON state of the LC cell. If a bias voltage is applied, as in Fig. 11.55(b), the nematic LC molecules will be aligned along the propagation direction of the optical beam (or along the electrostatic field of the bias voltage) and will no longer exhibit a particular rotational alignment. Because the input polarization did not change and the LC is no longer well aligned to rotate the polarization, the beam will be blocked by the second polarizer, thus achieving amplitude modulation.

Liquid-crystal cells can also operate as phase modulators by utilizing the dielectric anisotropy of the LC molecules, as shown in Fig. 11.56. A LC cell whose molecules are not twisted is used when modulating the phase. The retardation angle $\Delta\phi$ is given by the birefringence $\Delta n = n_e - n_o$, vacuum wavelength λ, and thickness of the sample d as $\Delta\phi = 2\pi\Delta nd/\lambda$. The value for the refractive index of the ordinary beam n_o passing through the cell is unaffected by the applied field, whereas the value for the extraordinary beam n_e increases with voltage (due to dielectric coupling of the director with the field) if the LC mixture is of negative dielectric anisotropy. Note that phase modulation is usually preferable over amplitude modulation because it does not require additional polarization optics that reduce the optical efficiency of the device.

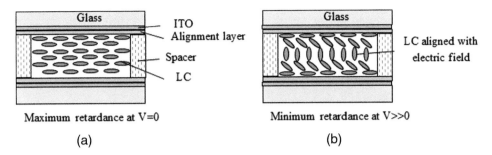

Figure 11.56 Liquid crystal variable retarder illustrating molecular alignment (a) without and (b) with applied voltage (drawing not to scale).

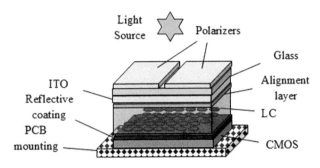

Figure 11.57 LCoS schematic.

B. LCoS devices

Like regular transmissive-type, LC-based SLMs, LCoS SLMs can modulate the amplitude, phase and/or polarization by using different configurations in the initial LC alignment and polarization elements. This can be performed in reflection mode using a mirror, as shown in Fig. 11.57. The voltage is applied between the back of the mirror and the ITO on the top, thus changing the orientation of the LC molecules (and the retardation in the case of phase modulation, for example). The main advantage of LCoS technology is the high fill factor, better optical efficiency, and smaller pixel size than transmissive displays, which makes it suitable for holographic applications.

C. Optically addressed LCDs (OALCDs or OASLMs)

OALCDs (often called OASLMs, see Fig. 11.58) optically control the phase or amplitude modulation of the reading beam by employing another writing beam that illuminates the backside of the device to modulate (in 2D) the refractive index in the LC film. The writing beam is converted into a voltage that will bias the LC layer. The major advantage of such a system is the absence of discrete pixels, which produces no higher diffraction orders and results in a very high optical efficiency. However, the current disadvantage of such a technique is the low spatial resolution.

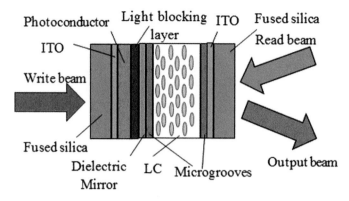

Figure 11.58 OASLM schematic.

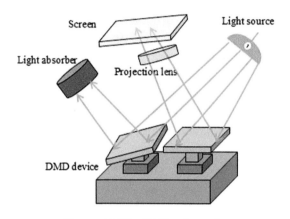

Figure 11.59 DMD schematic.

D. Mirror-based devices

This technology is based on an array of micromirrors that can be tilted or translated by an electromechanical system. Mirror tilt can modulate the amplitude of the reflected beam, as shown in Fig. 11.59, and obviously (vertically) translated mirrors will modulate the phase. A major advantage of such a technique is that reflection efficiency is close to 100%, contrary to LC-based devices, which suffer from absorption. Mirror-based devices typically allow very fast switching as well [20 kHz for the Texas Instruments Digital Light Processing (DLP) technology], which permits time multiplexing of images. Micromirrors make possible many other device architectures as well, such as the Grating Light Valve™ (GLV™) developed at Stanford University, in which an array of deformable (i.e., vertical translation) micromirror "ribbons" is used to create a dynamically controllable diffraction grating that controls both the amplitude and phase of the reflected beam.

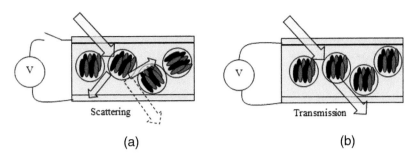

Figure 11.60 Dichroic PDLC: (a) OFF state and (b) ON state.

E. Holographic PDLCs

Liquid-crystal droplets in a polymer matrix is the focus of much current research. These droplets are fabricated by dispersing LC nanoscale droplets in photopolymer films. Polymer-dispersed liquid crystal (PDLC) is a new technology used for display systems. There are many droplets with different configurations and orientations in a typical PDLC cell. When an electric field is applied to the cell, the molecules within the droplets align along the electric field, which induces a change in the scattering characteristics of the PDLC and the refractive index between these droplets and the surrounding medium, as shown in Fig. 11.60. The change in the scattering characteristics also changes the light passing through the sample; thus, the cell acts as a light switch. The major advantage of such a technology is its low cost, high resolution, and fast modulation. The major disadvantage is the high bias voltage involved compared to a LCD.

F. Acousto-optical modulators (AOMs)

In an AO cell, the incident light interacts with an acoustic wave. An AO modulator uses the traveling acoustical wave coming from a piezoelectric transducer to modulate the properties of the transmitted optical beam, as shown in Fig. 11.61. This interaction is due to an RF-driven acoustic wave that acts as a phase grating traveling through the crystal, where the acoustic wavelength is dependent on the frequency of the RF signal. The incident laser beam interacting with the phase grating will be diffracted into many orders. AO SLMs are used in holographic displays, as discussed in the following section.

11.4.4.2 MIT holographic 3D displays: holovideo

A horizontal-parallax-only (HPO) Scophony-style holographic display system called "Mark I" was built at MIT's Media Lab in 1989. The basic principle of this technique involves computing the fringe patterns of 3D scenes through simulation. The fringes in each pattern will diffract the light passing through them in a predictable way, such that the effect of light scattering from a 3D object can be simulated after a dense array of fringe patterns is acquired. These fringes are displayed using an AOM to modulate a RGB light

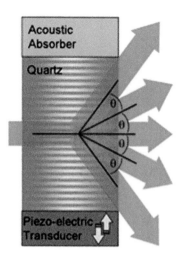

Figure 11.61 AO cell.

consisting of three separate lasers. The AOM is mechanically raster scanned using a rotating polygon to produce the 3D image. The volume of the hologram is only 25 cubic millimeters with 15 deg of viewing angle at 20 fps.[117] The Mark I system [shown in Fig. 11.62(a)] can support monochromatic or full-color display of holographic imagery.

The second generation of the MIT holovideo 3D display (Mark II) uses an 18-channel AOM and a bank of scanning mirrors instead of a rotating polygon. The volume of the hologram is 150 mm × 75 mm × 150 mm with a 30-deg viewing angle [shown in Fig. 11.62(b)].[118]

In the third generation, the AOM was replaced by a surface acoustic wave (SAW) device referred to as the guided-wave scanner (GWS), which employs acoustic waves traveling on the surface of the crystal.[119] The material used is $LiNbO_3$ instead of TeO_2, where acoustic frequencies modulating the incident light reach well into the GHz range. Also, the horizontal scanning elements were replaced by HOEs. This system's 3D volume is 80 mm × 60 mm × 80 mm with a 24-deg viewing angle and 30-Hz frame rate, shown in Fig. 11.62(c).

In 2005, the same group presented a new system that can capture visual information using off-the-shelf electronics, send it over the Internet to a holographic display, and update the image at rates approaching those of feature films.[120] This system uses a 15-fps data-capture device (Kinect® camera designed for Microsoft's Xbox gaming system). The light intensity of each image pixel and its original distance from the camera is fed to a PC and then transmitted over the Internet. On the receiving end, a PC with commercial GPUs computes the diffraction patterns.[121,122] The Mark III is used to display the 3D image.[123,124] This system begins with a computed 3D model of a moving object; diffraction patterns that reconstruct the different intensities for each of the different angles are then created and combined into a single video output.

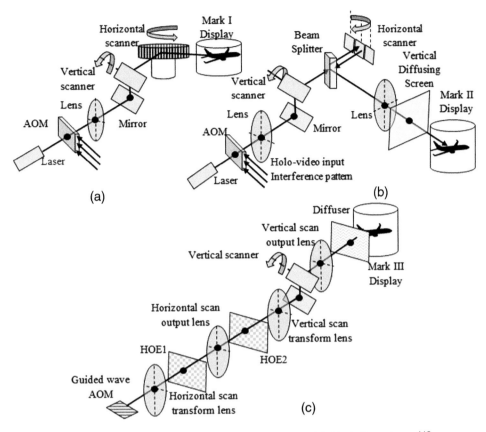

Figure 11.62 MIT's (a) Mark I, (b) Mark II, and (c) Mark III systems.[119]

After the computation is complete, the output is fed to the SLM. Finally, to reconstruct the image, light from a set of lasers that strike the modulator scatters (as if it were reflecting from the object at different angles) before reaching the screen. The new device is compact, fast, and can process high-resolution holograms. The holostereogram is computationally simple but suffers from the accommodation–convergence mismatch problem.

In 2011, the same MIT group developed the diffraction-specific coherent panoramagram (DSCP), a new form of stereogram that is slightly more computationally complex than the 2005 version but can still be computed in real time without the accommodation–convergence mismatch that affected previous versions. In the DSCP system, the views are generated from a graphics model; thus, the distance to each point in each of the parallax views is known. On the other hand, for real imagery, it is necessary to use range-sensing cameras, which are currently available. In the DSCP, the basis functions multiplied by the view intensities are selected not only based on angle but also on the 3D location of points in the parallax views, with the result that the wavefront curvature can be varied, thus preserving the correct accommodation cues (see Fig. 11.5). The advantage of having the correct wavefront curvatures is that smooth motion parallax is possible with many fewer views than in a regular stereogram. Instead of the hundreds of camera positions that a typical HPO stereogram would require for the appearance of continuous parallax, the DSCP works well with one-tenth that number.

The Object-Based Media Group at the MIT Media Lab has transmitted intensity and depth images from the Microsoft Kinect® range-finding camera over a computer network to a PC, which converted the images to HPO DSC panoramagrams in real time at 15 fps.[121] The resulting holograms have also been displayed on a 30-fps display based on AO light modulation. Note that it is possible to create a hologram from a single range-finding camera, but there will be missing/occluded regions when the viewer looks far to the left or right of the original camera viewpoint. Active range-finding cameras (such as the Kinect®), which project infrared patterns (i.e., structured light) onto the scene, pose problems when more than one is used simultaneously because they interfere with one another, but multiple devices can be used if the angle between them is large enough.

11.4.4.3 SeeReal 3D displays

An innovative approach to 3D holographic-based displays was invented by SeeReal Technologies.[125] They concluded that for a certain viewer it is only necessary to reconstruct the part of the diffracted wavefront emitted by the 3D object that hits the viewer's eyes, as opposed to reconstructing the full diffracted wavefront of the entire 3D scene, which makes the holographic approach more computationally feasible. Therefore, only the wavefront in a certain window (called the "observer window") is reconstructed.[116] This window is typically located at the Fourier plane of the hologram with a size comparable to the eye pupil. Each eye of the observer has a different window that is generated either by spatial or temporal multiplexing.

The key for this technology to work is to track the observer's eyes in real time via eye-tracking systems that use two CCD cameras. A typical schematic (shown in Fig. 11.63) shows a collimated laser beam illuminating an SLM that carries a hologram that reconstructs a point of the 3D image. A typical system has a pixel size of 50 μm × 50 μm. The spread angle is

$$\theta_{sp} \approx \frac{\lambda}{\Delta x} = \frac{0.5 \ \mu m}{50 \ \mu m} = 0.01 \ \text{rad} = 0.57 \ \text{deg},$$

which generates an observer-window size of ∼20 mm at a distance of 2 m. Note that without this approach, a 1-μm pixel is necessary to produce a 3D scene 1 m in diameter at a 2-m distance.

11.4.4.4 Zebra holographic 3D displays

This type of holographic 3D display is based on the full-parallax light field principle.[126,127] Figure 11.64 illustrates the basics of the holographic display technology. The 3D input data of a scene captured by a 3D camera is

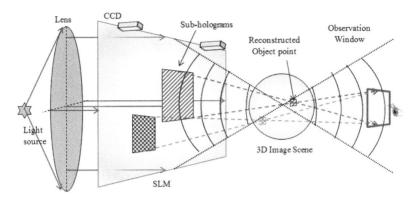

Figure 11.63 SeeReal holographic display system featuring a reconstructed 3D scene that comprises the object points and the observer eye. Each object point is encoded in a subhologram, the position and the size of which is determined by the position of the point and the virtual viewing window (VW). The entire hologram is generated by a summation of the subholograms. The drawing shows the wavefront information that is generated in the conventional approach (black) and the essential wavefront information (red) that is actually needed at a VW.[116,125]

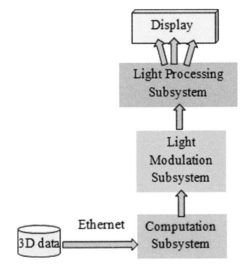

Figure 11.64 Zebra holographic display architecture.[127]

transferred to the display system using an ethernet connection. The display system consists of three parts:

(a) the computation subsystem used to convert the data into holographic data (hogel generation),

(b) the light modulation subsystem that converts the holographic data into photons (SLMs), and

(c) the light processing subsystem that performs light guiding and processing.

The emitted light from the last stage provides the 3D image. The output holographic image is produced in real time and possesses all of the depth cues of the physical object, which enables the 3D images displayed on a PC monitor to appear as dynamic, 3D holograms in real time. A typical size of the 3D image of the Zebra system is approximately $30 \, \text{cm(H)} \times 45 \, \text{cm(L)} \times 45 \, \text{cm(W)}$.

Advantages of this system include the following:[127]

- Autostereoscopic: all depth cues are satisfied with full motion parallax (continuous viewing without jitter).
- Full parallax.
- Real time.
- Supports RGB with a wide color gamut (bright).
- Fully interactive and includes live video content.
- Wide field of view.
- High resolution.
- Easily linked to a PC via an ethernet connection.
- Supports industry-standard 3D graphics APIs, such as OpenGL.
- Compatible with a wide range of visualization and graphics applications.
- Interactive via a front-end software application.

11.4.4.5 QinetiQ holographic 3D displays

QinetiQ has developed a 3D display technology based on an active tiling system.[128–130] The system consists of the following block subsystems:

(a) A high-frame-rate electrically addressed SLM (EASLM) similar to Fig. 11.57 that can display the CGH interference patterns quickly;

(b) replication optics that project multiple smaller versions of the CGH interference patterns displayed by the EASLM onto optically addressed SLMs (OASLMs), similar to Fig. 11.58;

(c) a OASLM subsystem that stores and displays the CGH patterns;

(d) a reading optics subsystem that displays the 3D holographic image; and

(e) a control subsystem that synchronizes the different components of the system, as shown in Fig. 11.65.

In a typical QinetiQ system, the EASLM is a 1-Megapixel LCoS device operating at 2500 fps (see Fig. 11.57). The replication optics are made of DOEs and some refractive optics that result in a 5×5 replication.[129] A typical system allows multiple channels to be assembled and produce a continuous output modulation plane, each of which consists of 26 million pixels. This tiling system can reach a pixel density of 2.2×10^6 pixels/cm^2, which renders a display volume density of 2.4×10^9 pixels/m^3. The system supports color and is scalable with full parallax.[116]

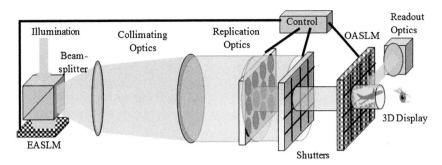

Figure 11.65 QinetiQ holographic 3D display.[116,129]

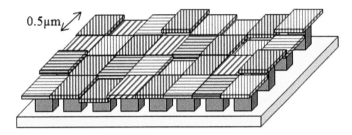

Figure 11.66 Schematic of a 2D array comprising millions of individually programmable DNDs.[114]

11.4.4.6 IMEC holographic 3D display

In CGH, diffractive pixels are programmed to render a holographic fringe that recreates the 3D scene. Each diffractive pixel contributes to all of the 3D voxels, and thus the 3D scene is actually distributed evenly over the whole array of diffractive pixels. In other words, high-definition 3D holographic displays must have billions of individually controlled submicron diffractive pixels to achieve high-definition images with a wide field of view.[114]

The previous techniques are primarily based on LCD and LCoS technologies. Using the current fabrication techniques, these technologies reached the scaling limits at ~2–4 μm per pixel, limiting the viewing angle to ~15 deg. The holographic 3D display system developed by the Interuniversity Microelectronics Centre (IMEC) in Belgium uses a SiGe microelectromechanical systems (MEMS) chip that can hold 10^9 diffractive nanodevices (DNDs) with an average size around one-half of a micron, which yields a much wider viewing angle.[131] IMEC is expecting to design the ultimate 3D display with a 60-deg diffraction angle and a high-definition visual experience. Figure 11.66 shows a variable-focal-length lens that uses micromirrors.[114]

11.4.4.7 HOlographic ReconstructioN (HORN)

The current incarnation of HORN is a special-purpose clustered computing system for electroholography that uses CGH through field programmable gate

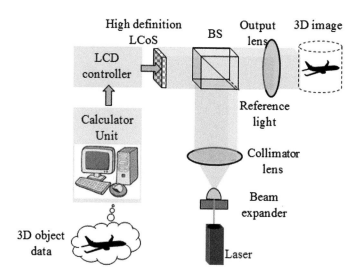

Figure 11.67 HORN optical system.[132]

arrays (FPGAs) and double-data-rate synchronous dynamic random access memory (DDR-SDRAM) modules.[132–137] There have been several versions of this system since 1993, the latest of which is HORN-6.[137] Figure 11.67 shows the 3D-based holographic optical system used for HORN-6.

The system consists of the following steps:

(a) capturing the 3D object data and saving it on a PC,
(b) generating the CGH fringe patterns using the HORN unit,
(c) displaying these fringes using a high-definition LCoS device and a controller,
(d) reading the LCoS device using a readout reference beam, and
(e) reconstructing the 3D image using an output lens.

Note that in order to reduce the computational complexity in the HORN-6 unit, the Fresnel-hologram-generation algorithm is approximated using a LUT, as discussed in Chapter 8. This system is capable of computing fringe patterns of $\sim 5 \times 10^4$ object points in real time (20 fps).

11.4.4.8 Image hologram

This type of holographic 3D display reduces computational complexity by reducing the size of the recorded object through imaging with a lens.[138–141] If the image distance r is closer to the hologram plane (LCoS), then the calculation area is smaller because the diffraction angle is smaller, and thus a point on the object contributes to a smaller area of the hologram. Therefore, only the part of the diffracted beam that passes through a virtual window placed on the viewer's eyes need be calculated, as shown in Fig. 11.68(a). When the object point (object point 2) is placed closer to the hologram

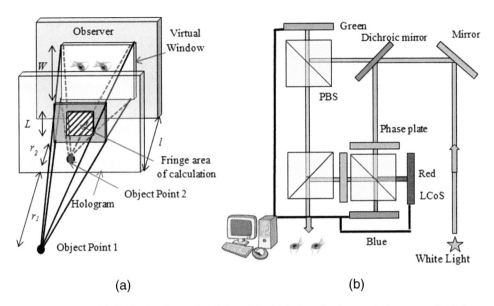

(a)   (b)

Figure 11.68 (a) Optical schematic of the virtual window for image hologram calculation, and (b) diagram showing how to separate and combine color components.[139]

through imaging (object point 1), the complexity of the calculation is significantly reduced.

The necessary calculation of the length L of the fringe pattern intensity defined in Eq. (8.14) is determined by $L = |r| \cdot W/(r + l)$, where l is the distance from the hologram plane to the virtual window, W is the size of the virtual window, and r is the distance from the hologram plane to the object point.[139] Therefore, the calculation time could be reduced by decreasing the distance between the object image point and the hologram plane, and increasing the distance between the hologram plane and the virtual window. The developed system has 1408×1058 pixels with a 10.4-μm separation width. The number of object points is 3000, and a typical computing time is 60 ms. The system uses a white LED as the light source, which means it can support color, as well. Figure 11.68(b) shows a diagram of how to separate and combine color components.

11.4.4.9 Coherent stereogram

In traditional CGH, an object is often considered to consist of several cross-sections. The contributions from the cross-sections at the hologram plane are calculated and then summed to determine the light amplitude propagating from the object to the hologram plane. One of disadvantages of the traditional technique is the large number of computations required to construct a hologram of an object with a wide view angle. Holographic stereograms are produced by computing (or ray tracing) the geometrical projections and then optically interfering with a reference beam. The first step of the stereogram

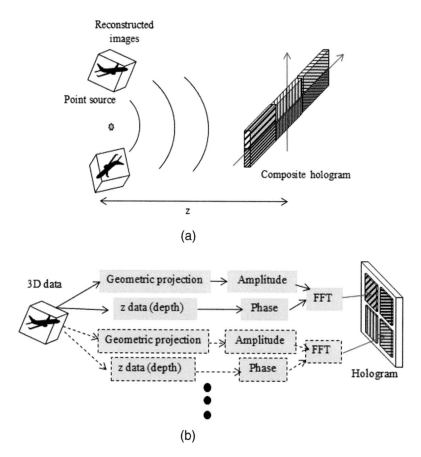

Figure 11.69 (a) Optical setup for 3D image reconstruction from the composite hologram using a point source. (b) Schematic block diagram of the phase-added stereogram. A geometric projection and DFT operation produce fringe patterns in a small region of the hologram.[146]

technique computes a sequence of perspective projections of the 3D object, and their Fourier transform holograms. In the second step, the computed holograms are arranged in the order of viewpoints and assembled to produce a final composite hologram.[142] One way to reconstruct the 3D image involves illuminating the elementary holographic stereograms with a point source, leading to virtual images in the plane of the point source because it is a Fourier transform hologram [shown in Fig. 11.69(a)]. When each of these holograms is illuminated by the point source, a certain perspective corresponding to a viewpoint can be seen as an observer's head moves. Thus, binocular and motion parallax are experienced as the observer views the 3D image. Holographic stereograms can be used to calculate a CG hologram with fewer computations.[143–148] Computer-graphics techniques, such as shading and image mapping, can also be applied to CG holograms generated by holographic stereograms.

Other, more-advanced but related techniques are the phase-added stereogram (PAS) and compensated phase-added stereogram (CPAS). The PAS is synthesized by applying a phase mask to the 2D parallax image used in the holographic stereogram.[146] The algorithm to compute fringe patterns from 3D data using the PAS is shown in Fig. 11.69(b). The quadratic phase terms are calculated from the depth of the 3D object and are applied to the 2D parallax image calculated through the GPU. The Fourier transform of the generated image produces the patterns to be recorded on a small area of the hologram. Note that in traditional CGH the Fourier transform size in pixels must be the same size as the hologram. In PAS, DFTs are performed by producing fringes in small areas of the hologram plane, which reduces the calculation enormously.

As indicated in Fig. 11.69, the hologram plane is divided into small regions in the calculation algorithm, and thus parallel processing can be used for high-speed hologram generation. Phase-added stereogram techniques result in better-quality reconstruction and are attractive because they can be implemented using GPUs. Currently, 1-Megapixel holograms can be generated at real time (30 fps) for objects of up to 10,000 points.[116,149–154]

11.4.4.10 NICT 3D holographic system

Integral imaging and holography are spatial image-reconstruction techniques because they reproduce light rays (just like when an actual object exists in space). Whereas integral imaging [discussed in Section 11.4.1.3 (F)] reproduces light rays from the object, holography reproduces light rays more accurately.

NICT is a holographic 3D display system that uses both integral imaging and electronic holography. The system consists of three units: a 3D acquisition unit, a computational unit, and an electroholographic display unit.[116,155,156] The acquisition unit uses integral photography to capture a scene using a high-resolution camera equipped with a microlens array.[25] The computational unit generates a hologram from the captured image. The electroholographic display unit displays the computed hologram on three LCD SLMs (one for each color). The different images are then reconstructed if the SLMs carrying the holograms are illuminated by three different lasers (RGB). The advantage of such a system is the ability to capture and reconstruct 3D scenes in real time. Color holographic images with a viewing angle up to 15 deg have been reproduced.

11.4.4.11 University of Arizona's updatable holographic display

A groundbreaking advance in the fabrication of holographic displays occurred when the Arizona group reported an updatable holographic 3D display based on PR polymers capable of recording and displaying new images every few minutes.[157,158] Later in 2010, the same group modified the PR polymers to reduce the recording and displaying time for new images to

2 seconds.[159] A typical PR polymer is a mixture of PATPD/CAAN:FDCST: ECZ:PCBM (49.5:30:20:0.5 wt%). The display size reported was 4×4 inches; diffraction efficiency was high (close to 90%) and could be recorded within a few seconds, viewed for several hours without the need for refreshing, and could be completely erased and updated with new images when desired.[157] The optical setup is shown in Fig. 11.70(a), and the image processing, recording, display and erasing steps are shown in Fig. 11.70(b). Unlike a pixel, which emits the same amount of light at all angles, the holographic element or "hogel" (which is actually composed of a group of pixels representing a modulated grating) can emit different intensities in different directions. This is the basis of the holographic stereogram. Hogel generation in holographic stereography can be performed at the video rate and does not require much computational power, as opposed to the CG holograms previously discussed.

This system works as follows: First, 2D perspective views of the object of interest are generated from a 3D computer model. The 2D perspectives can also be generated using methods such as magnetic resonance imaging, computer-assisted tomography, confocal microscopy, or aerial and satellite imaging. The perspectives are then divided or "sliced" into multiple 2D image planes. The image planes are reorganized using a computer algorithm into 2D matrices (the hogel data), which are then uploaded to a SLM. The SLM is illuminated with a 532-nm laser beam to display the hogel data in sequence with the translation stages and an electro-optic laser shutter. The laser beam modulated by the SLM (object beam) illuminates the predefined hogel area on the polymer device. A coherent reference beam simultaneously illuminates the same area, which facilitates the recording of the hogel through interference with the object beam and the photorefractive effect. After one hogel is recorded, the shutter turns off the lasers, the polymer device is translated to the next hogel position, and new hogel data are uploaded to the SLM. The holographic display is viewed using light from an expanded, low-power HeNe (633 nm) laser beam in a transmission geometry.

This method uses HPO imaging because humans perceive depth using horizontally offset eyes. HPO recording helps significantly reduce the number of hogels in a 3D display, resulting in shorter total writing times. For larger, full-parallax displays, a combination of short pulsed recording and thermal fixing can be used, which is a future route for holographic 3D display development.

Angular multiplexing is used to achieve a multicolor holographic 3D display. Up to three different holograms are written in the material at different angles and read out with different colored LEDs (red-green-blue for full color). The three holograms are recorded simultaneously so the recording speed for the colored holograms is the same as for the monochromatic holograms. A full-parallax system has also been developed, along with a 3D telepresence setup; see Blanche et al.[159]

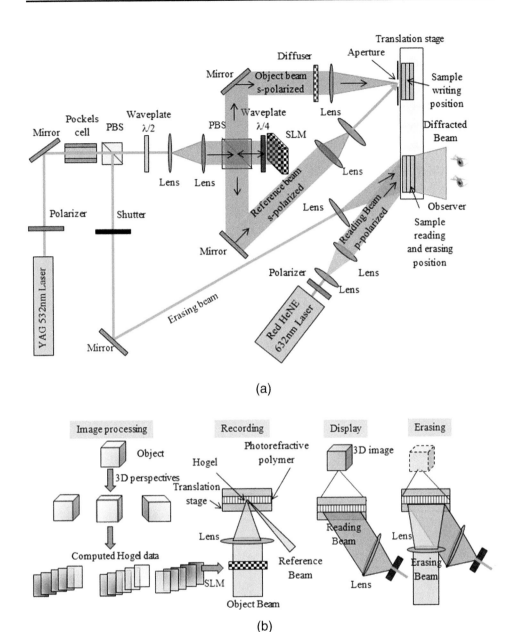

Figure 11.70 (a) 3D holographic display optical setup, (b) image processing, hologram recording, and display. The 2D perspective views of the object are generated using a 3D computer model or a video camera moving on tracks around the object. The perspective images are reorganized (hogel data) and uploaded to the SLM. The SLM modulates the object beam, which is focused onto the photorefractive polymer and recorded in the Fourier transform geometry. The completed display can be viewed using a reading beam. The result is realistic 3D imagery with parallax and depth. The holograms can be erased by uniform illumination at the writing wavelength.[157,158]

11.5 Comparison of the Different 3D Display Techniques

This section lists the advantages and disadvantages of the general categories of 3D display techniques discussed in this chapter.

A. Stereoscopic-based 3D displays

Advantages:

- Supports all of the psychological depth cues.
- Supports convergence.
- Supports binocular disparity.
- Compatible with 3D and 2D display.
- High resolution.
- Scalable.
- Simple optical systems.
- Real-time interactivity and animation.
- Low cost.

Disadvantages:

- Lack of motion parallax.
- Lack of accommodation.
- No natural three-dimensional viewing (without glasses)
- Accommodation–convergence conflict.

B. Autostereoscopic multiview techniques[160]

Advantages:

- Simultaneous 3D viewing by several viewers.
- Supports convergence.
- Supports binocular disparity and motion parallax (limited).
- Supports all of the psychological depth cues.
- High resolution.
- Compatible with 3D and 2D display.
- Scalable.
- Simple optical systems.
- Real-time interactivity and animation.
- Low cost (for some implementations, e.g., parallax barrier).

Disadvantages:

- No natural three-dimensional viewing (accommodation-convergence conflict).
- No continuous parallax.
- Head tracking is necessary for wide-angle viewing by one user.
- Brightness reduction (for occlusion-based displays).
- High cost (for some implementations, e.g., with head tracking).

- Presence of positions where viewers perceive 3D images in pseudoscopy (reverse depth vision). This phenomenon occurs accidentally, but quite frequently, in stereo displays when the inputs are switched (i.e., the left image is sent to the right eye, and vice versa). For two-channel video, this situation is easy to fix by switching the video cables.

C. Volumetric imaging techniques

Advantages:

- True 3D imaging experience (all physiological depth cues are satisfied).
- Full parallax.
- No head tracking.
- Real-time interactivity and animation.

Disadvantages:

- Limited support for psychological depth cues, such as occlusion, shading, and texture.
- Presence of rotating or vibrating mechanical assemblies.
- Presence of complicated optical systems.
- Impossibility of using a very large volume display.
- Use of rare and expensive materials (for static volume displays).
- Large dimensions and weight of the whole system.
- Huge amount of data.
- Difficulty of making a "live" color image.
- Display generally requires a darkened or shaded room.
- High cost.

D. Electroholographic technique

Advantages:

- True 3D imaging experience (all physiological and psychological depth cues are satisfied).
- Full parallax.
- No head tracking needed.

Disadvantages:

- Uses coherent or special metal-halide light sources.
- Complicated optical system.
- Complicated electronic system.
- Huge amount of data.
- Low resolution of 3D images.
- Difficulty to receive full-color images.
- Difficulty to make large-size displays.
- Difficulty to realize real-time interactivity and animation.
- Difficulty to reproduce texture.
- High cost.

E. Integral imaging technique (classified as autostereoscopic multiview refraction-based 3D technology)

Advantages:

- True 3D imaging experience (all physiological and psychological depth cues are satisfied).
- Continuous parallax, both horizontal and vertical, in each viewing zone.
- Possibility of simultaneous viewing by several viewers.
- Simple optical setup.
- Absence of a huge amount of spatial data.
- Real-time interactivity and animation.
- Possibility of using both 3D and 2D display.
- Adaptability for large screen formats.
- Low cost.

Disadvantages:

- Limited viewing angle.
- Insufficient depth of 3D scene at present time due to the small resolution of CCDs and displays.
- Head tracking may be necessary for wide-angle vision by one user.
- Distortion of the 3D scene in lateral viewing zones.
- Pseudoscopy (PS), or reversed depth perception, can be solved by various methods—conversion methods from PS to orthoscopic (OR)—and have been proposed by many research groups.[161]

Figure 11.71 shows a simplified diagram comparing the most famous techniques of 3D imaging: integral imaging [Fig. 11.71(a)], multiview display [Fig. 11.71(b)], holographic display [Fig. 11.71(c)], and see-through HMD [Fig. 11.71(d)].

Note that integral imaging samples a ray field from the ray source locations. On the other hand, multiview display systems sample a ray field from predetermined views, as shown in Figs. 11.71(a) and 11.71(b).[2] This sampled ray field is then reconstructed when an autostereoscopic display operates. As for holography-based techniques, the entire analog field is recored and reconstructed, which is challenging when using DMDs. See-through HMDs contain a mixture of both real-world and virtual 3D images. This technology is a still a topic of research and development, with significant issues still to be resolved, such as the occlusion problem. Without occlusion of the real-world scene, a reconstructed 3D virtual image will suffer from excess or inappropriate translucence.[2]

It is hoped that significant progress will be made in the next few years toward overcoming some of these disadvantages as commercial 3D displays become more widely available in the market.

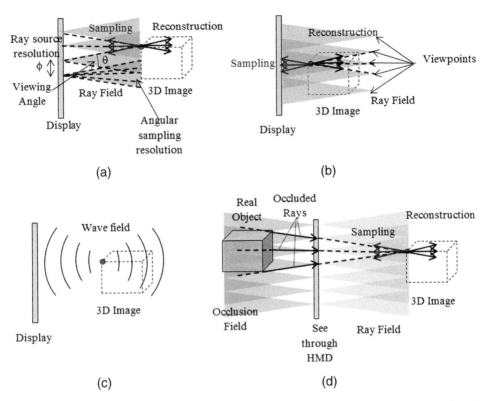

Figure 11.71 Sampling and reconstruction processes of outlined technologies: (a) integral imaging, (b) multiview display, (c) holography, and (d) see-through HMD.[2]

11.6 Commonly Misunderstood Nonholographic, Non-3D Displays

The great majority of 2D display technologies are generally not relevant to this discussion of 3D stereoscopic and holographic displays. However, while most 2D display technologies are generally well known to the public, there are some that are frequently misunderstood and often mislabeled as "holograms" or thought to produce 3D images when, in fact, they simply employ clever applications of 2D optical principles. Two of the most frequently encountered technologies in this category concern the so-called Pepper's ghost illusion and the Heliodisplay.

11.6.1 Pepper's ghost illusion

The Pepper's ghost illusion was developed by the 19th-century engineer Henry Dircks, although it is named after John Henry Pepper, who popularized the effect in 1862 during a production of Charles Dicken's play *The Haunted Man*. This illusion allows a semi-transparent ghost-like figure to appear on stage to perform with the actors and has since been frequently employed in theaters, theme parks, museums, television, and cinema. This is the illusion

Figure 11.72 Illustration of the Pepper's ghost illusion during the 1862 production of Charles Dicken's play *The Haunted Man*. © Archive Photos/Getty Images.

which recently ignited widespread amazement during the 2012 Coachella Valley Music and Arts Festival, in which the deceased rapper Tupac Shakur was projected on stage to "perform" with live artists. The popular media widely, and incorrectly, described this effect as a "hologram."

The Pepper's ghost illusion makes use of the low reflection coefficient of clear glass. A clear sheet of glass or Plexiglas is placed between the stage and the audience, with the "ghost" actor positioned in a hidden room out of sight of the audience. The glass and the ghost actor are positioned such that the partial reflection of the actor is seen by the audience as if it were originating from among the live actors onstage, as shown in Fig. 11.72. This effect can be produced using several alternate geometries, sometimes employing mirrors rather than transparent glass; in modern times, the ghost actor is often digitally projected. Although this effect is often mistaken to be a hologram, it is simply a partial reflection of a real object. If the image source is an actual 3D object (e.g., an actor, as in Fig. 11.72), then the reflection will preserve all 3D cues, as if the 3D object were viewed directly (i.e., a reflection of a 3D image from a mirror does not eliminate 3D cues). However, if the image source is a 2D digital projection, as is often the case for modern implementations of Pepper's ghost, then the reflected image will also be 2D, without parallax, disparity, or any other 3D cues not originally present in the source image.

The Pepper's ghost illusion has recently been implemented in the Dreamoc™ line of commercial displays by Realfiction. This display consists of three separate top-mounted 2D displays that are reflected from three corresponding panes of glass, arranged in a "pyramid" configuration, as shown in Fig. 11.73. The use of three separate displays enables the projection

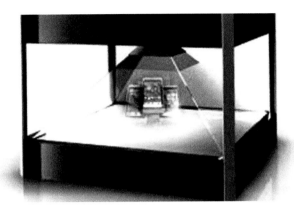

Figure 11.73 Example of the Pepper's ghost image produced by the Dreamoc™ display. In this case, the three display devices are embedded in the top of the device and project down toward the angled glass viewing "surface." © Realfiction.

of three different sides of an object (if the appropriate display content is available), although this display is not necessarily a 3D display if the source is 2D imagery, as previously discussed. However, if "3D" displays are used as the top-mounted source displays, it may be possible to reproduce some 3D cues, as determined by the choice of 3D source display. Although Realfiction advertises this technology as "holographic," and it is widely perceived by the public to be such, no principles of holography are involved.

11.6.2 Heliodisplay

The Heliodisplay is a predominantly 2D/3D, nonvolumetric, mid-air display invented by Chad Dyner and commercialized by IO2 Technology in 2003. The device uses a relatively small number of atomized particles suspended in the bulk of pre-existing air to form a "screen" to display a bottom-/rear-projected 2D image. The device creates a temperature difference in the air directly above it, causing condensation in the air. These air particles are converted into atom-sized particles and are re-emitted upward through a dozen metal plates within the device. These particles, approximately the size of printer ink droplets, are held together by surface tension and form a cloud that can act as a screen for a traditionally projected image. Changes to the molecular properties of this cloud can also change the qualities of the image, such as brightness and sharpness. The block diagram of such a mechanism is shown in Fig. 11.74.

Figure 11.75 shows the top view of the multisource optical setup of the device. Image projection uses a high-frame-rate LCD, or digital light processing (DLP) unit, collimating optics, and a beamsplitter. The two beams are then directed toward a multifaceted rotating scanner that redirects the beam toward multiple sources. An optical chopper or electronic shutter is used to create consecutive images, similar to a conventional reel-to-reel movie projector moving through its frames. Further anamorphic and keystone optical assemblies correct for off-axis projection to ensure that the projection

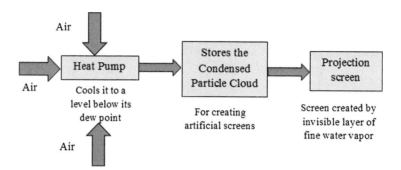

Figure 11.74   Block diagram of the Heliodisplay mechanism.

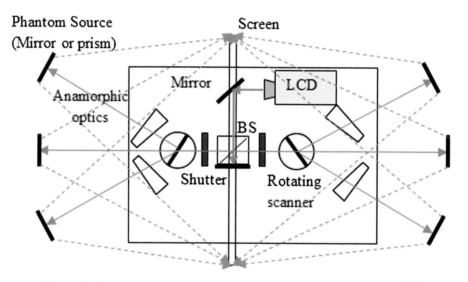

Figure 11.75   Top view of the multisource optical setup of the device.[162]

beams illuminating the particle cloud are focusing the same image from each source at the same location on the particle cloud screen.

Although the Heliodisplay is capable of displaying 3D content, the display remains nonvolumetric, therefore the 3D content would be more accurately described as stereoscopic content. The system allows for multiple viewing and dual viewing (back and front) when combined with two light sources. However, because this is a free-space display, it is possible for viewers to interact directly with the mid-air image; it can operate as a sort of mid-air "touchscreen" when used with an IR laser and tracking camera. This technology differs from a fog screen because the mid-air Heliodisplay "screen" remains effectively transparent, displaying images such as those shown in Fig. 11.76. Although IO2 Technology advertises this technology as "holographic," and it is widely perceived by the public to be such, no principles of holography are involved.[162]

Figure 11.76 Example mid-air image produced by Heliodisplay; the device is embedded in the table.

The system has many advantages:

(a) no screen is needed to project images;
(b) light weight;
(c) nothing added to the air;
(d) does not create fog, so no other electronics are affected by the device;
(e) viewing area is 150 deg; and
(f) no special glasses are required.

The systems' disadvantages are that it needs controlled lighting (less visible in bright light), and wind and bright light interfere with image visibility.

References

1. V. M. Bove, Jr., "What is holographic television, and will it ever be in my living room?" *Proc. SMPTE Int. Conf. on Stereoscopic 3D for Media and Entertainment* (2010).
2. J. Hong, Y. Kim, H-J. Choi, J. Hahn, J-H. Park, H. Kim, S-W. Min, N. Chen, and B. Lee, "Three-dimensional display technologies of recent interest: principles, status, and issues," *Appl. Opt.* **50**, H87–H115 (2011).
3. J. Geng, "Three-dimensional display technologies," *Adv. Opt. Photonics* **5**, 456–535 (2013).
4. D. M. Hoffman, A. R. Girshick, K. Akeley, and M. S. Banks, "Vergence–accommodation conflicts hinder visual performance and cause visual fatigue," *J. Vis.* **8**(3), 1–30 (2008).
5. V. M. Bove, Jr., "Live holographic TV: From misconceptions to engineering," *Proc. SMPTE Int. Conf. on Stereoscopic 3D for Media and Entertainment* (2011).

6. H. Kang, S.-D. Roh, I.-S. Baik, H.-J. Jung, W.-N. Jeong, J.-K. Shin, and I.-J. Chung, "A novel polarizer glasses-type 3D displays with a patterned retarder," *SID International Symposium Digest of Technical Papers (Society for Information Display)*, Vol. **41**, pp. 1–4 (2010).

7. S.-M. Jung, Y.-B. Lee, H.-J. Park, S.-C. Lee, W.-N. Jeong, J.-K. Shin, and I.-J. Chung, "Improvement of 3D crosstalk with over-driving method for the active retarder 3D displays," *SID International Symposium Digest of Technical Papers (Society for Information Display)*, Vol. **41**, pp. 1264–1267 (2010).

8. O. Cakmakci and J. Rolland, "Head-worn displays: a review," *J. Disp. Technol.* **2**, 199–216 (2006).

9. D. Cheng, Y. Wang, H. Hua, and M. M. Talha, "Design of an optical see-through headmounted display with a low f-number and large field of view using a free-form prism," *Appl. Opt.* **48**, 2655–2668 (2009).

10. B. Kress and T. Starner "A review of head-mounted displays (HMD) technologies and applications for consumer electronics," *Proc. SPIE* **8720**, 87200A (2013).

11. S. Pastoor and M. Wöpking, "3D displays: a review of current technologies," *Displays* **17**, 100–110 (1997).

12. T. Peterka, R. L. Kooima, D. J. Sandin, A. Johnson, J. Leigh, and T. A. DeFanti, "Advances in the Dynallax solid-state dynamic parallax barrier autostereoscopic visualization display system," *IEEE Trans. Vis. Comp. Graph.* **14**, 487–499 (2008).

13. N. Dodgson, "Autostereoscopic 3D displays," *Computer* **38**(8), 31–36 (2005).

14. T. Kanebako and Y. Takaki, "Time-multiplexing display module for high density directional display," *Proc. SPIE* **6803**, 68030P (2008).

15. D. S. St. John, "Holographic color television record system," U.S. patent 3,813,685 (May 28, 1974).

16. W. Hess, "Stereoscopic picture," U.S. patent 1,128,979 (February 16, 1915).

17. C. van Berkel and J. A. Clarke, "Characterization and optimization of 3D-LCD module design," *Proc. SPIE* **3012**, 179 (1997).

18. W. Matusik and H. Pfister, "3D TV: a scalable system for real-time acquisition, transmission, and autostereoscopic display of dynamic scenes," *ACM Trans. Graph.* **23**, 814–824 (2004).

19. A. Schwerdtner and H. Heidrich, "Dresden 3D display (D4D)," *Proc. SPIE* **3295**, 203 (1998).

20. G. J. Woodgate and J. Harrold, "A new architecture for high resolution autostereoscopic 2D/3D displays using freestanding liquid crystal microlenses," *SID International Symposium Digest of Tech. Papers (Society for Information Display)*, Vol. **36**, pp. 378–381 (2005).

21. H.-K. Hong, S.-M. Jung, B.-J. Lee, H.-J. Im, and H.-H. Shin, "Autostereoscopic 2D/3D switching display using electric-field-driven LC lens (ELC lens)," *SID International Symposium Digest of Technical Papers (Society for Information Display)*, Vol. **39**, pp. 348–351 (2008).

22. C.-W. Chen, Y.-C. Huang, and Y.-P. Huang, "Fast switching Fresnel liquid crystal lens for autostereoscopic 2D/3D display," *SID International Symposium Digest of Technical Papers (Society for Information Display)*, Vol. **41**, pp. 428–431 (2010).

23. A. Takagi, T. Saishu, M. Kashiwagi, K. Taira, and Y. Hirayama, "Autostereoscopic partial 2D/3D switchable display using liquid-crystal gradient index lens," *SID International Symposium Digest of Technical Papers (Society for Information Display)*, Vol. **41**, pp. 436–439 (2010).

24. Y.-P. Huang, C.-W. Chen, T.-C. Shen, and J.-F. Huang, "Autostereoscopic 3D display with scanning multielectrode driven liquid crystal (MeD-LC) lens," *3D Res.* **1**, 39–42 (2010).

25. G. Lippmann, "Épreuves réversibles. Photographies intégrales," *C. R. Acad. Sci.* **146**, 446–451 (1908).

26. H. Takahashi, H. Fujinami, and K. Yamada, "Holographic lens array increases the viewing angle of 3D displays," *SPIE Newsroom* (June 6, 2006).

27. A. Stern and B. Javidi, "3D image sensing, visualization, and processing using integral imaging," *Proc. IEEE* **94**, 591–607 (2006).

28. T. Okoshi, *Three-Dimensional Imaging Techniques*, Academic Press, New York (1976).

29. S. Pastoor and M. Wöpking, "3D displays: a review of current technologies," *Displays* **17**, 100–110 (1997).

30. H. Liao, T. Dohi, and K. Nomura, "Autostereoscopic 3D display with long visualization depth using referential viewing area based integral photography," *IEEE Trans. Vis. Comp. Graph.* **17**, 1690–1701 (2011).

31. O. S. Cossairt, M. Thomas, and R. K. Dorval, "Optical scanning assembly," U.S. patent 7,864,419 (June 8, 2004).

32. E. Goulanian and A. F. Zerrouk, "Apparatus and system for reproducing 3D images," U.S. patent 7,944,465 (May 17, 2011).

33. G. J. Woodgate, D. Ezra, J. Harrold, N. S. Holliman, G. R. Jones, and R. R. Moseley, "Observer tracking autostereoscopic 3D display systems," *Proc. SPIE* **3012**, 187 (1997).

34. M. W. Jones, G. P. Nordin, J. H. Kulick, R. G. Lindquist, and S. T. Kowel, "Liquid crystal display based implementation of a real-time ICVision holographic stereogram display," *Proc. SPIE* **2406**, 154–164 (1995).

35. T. Toda, S. Takahashi, and F. Iwata, "Three dimensional (3D) video system using Grating Image," *Proc. SPIE* **2406**, 191–198 (1995).

36. E. Schulze, "Synthesis of moving holographic stereograms with high resolution spatial light modulators," *Proc. SPIE* **2406**, 124 (1995).

37. D. Fattal, Z. Peng, T. Tran, S. Vo, M. Fiorentino, J. Brug, and R. G. Beausoleil, "A multidirectional backlight for a wide-angle glasses-free three-dimensional display," *Nature* **495**, 348–351 (2013).

38. D. Trayner and E. Orr, "Autostereoscopic display using holographic optical elements," *Proc. SPIE* **2653**, 65 (1996).

39. E. M. Orr and D. J. Trayner, "Holographic Optical Element," patent WO9302372 by Richmond Holographic Studios, Ltd and RealtyVision, Ltd, (2002).

40. A. Jones, I. McDowall, H. Yamada, M. Bolas, and P. Debevec, "Rendering for an interactive 360° light field display," SIGGRAPH paper 40 (2007).

41. T. Balogh, "Method and apparatus for displaying three-dimensional images," U.S. Patent 6, 201, 565, EP 0900501, (Feb 04, 1997).

42. T. Balogh, "The HoloVizio system," *Proc. SPIE* **6055**, 60550U (2006).

43. T. Balogh, T. Forgacs, T. Agocs, E. Bouvier, F. Bettio, E. Gobbetti, and G. Zanetti, "A large scale interactive holographic display," IEEE VR2006, Virginia, USA.

44. C. H. Krah, "Three-dimensional display system," U.S. patent 7,843,449 (November 30, 2010).

45. Y.-H. Tao, Q.-H. Wang, J. Gu, and W.-X. Zhao, "Autostereoscopic three dimensional projector based on two parallax barriers," *Opt. Lett.* **34**, 3220–3222 (2009).

46. Y. Takaki, Y. Urano, S. Kashiwada, H. Ando, and K. Nakamura, "Super multiview windshield display for longdistance image information presentation," *Opt. Express* **19**, 704–716 (2011).

47. Y. Takaki and N. Nago, "Multiprojection of lenticular displays to construct a 256-view super multiview display," *Opt. Express* **18**, 8824–8835 (2010).

48. P. Surman, R. S. Brar, I. Sexton, and K. Hopf, "MUTED and HELIUM3D autostereoscopic displays," in *IEEE International Conference on Multimedia and Expo (ICME)*, pp. 1594–1599 (2010).

49. H. Urey, E. Erden, and P. Surman, "State of the Art in Stereoscopic and Autostereoscopic Displays," *Proc. IEEE* **99**(4), (2011).

50. R. S. Brar, "Head Tracked Multi User Autostereoscopic 3D Display Investigations," Ph.D. Thesis, Imaging and Displays Research Group Faculty of Technology, De Montfort University, Leicester, UK (2012).

51. C. Hembd, R. Stevens, and M. Hutley, "Imaging Properties of the Gabor Superlens," European Optical Society, Topical Meetings Digest Series: 13 "Microlens Arrays", NPL Teddington, May 15-16 1997, pp. 101–104, (1997).

52. J. C. Schultz and M. J. Sykora, "Directional backlight with reduced crosstalk," U.S. patent application 2011/0285927 A1 (May 24, 2010).

53. M. Minami, K. Yokomizo, and Y. Shimpuku, "Glasses-free 2D/3D switchable display," in *SID Symposium Digest of Technical Papers*, pp. 468–471 (2011).

54. M. Minami, "Light source device and display," U.S. patent application 2012/0195072 A1 (August 2, 2012).

55. H. Kwon and H. J. Choi, "A time-sequential multiview autostereoscopic display without resolution loss using a multidirectional backlight unit and a LCD panel," *Proc. SPIE* **8288**, 82881Y (2012).

56. S. Suyama, Y. Ishigure, H. Takada, K. Nakazawa, J. Hosohata, Y. Takao, and T. Fujikao, "Apparent 3D image perceived from luminance-modulated two 2D images displayed at different depths," *Vision Res.* **44**, 785–793 (2004).

57. Y. Ishigure, S. Suyama, H. Takada, K. Nakazawa, J. Hosohata, Y. Takao, and T. Fujikado, "Evaluation of visual fatigue relative in the viewing of a depth-fused 3D display and 2D display," in *Proceedings of International Display Workshops (Society for Information Display)*, pp. 1627–1630 (2004).

58. H. Kuribayashi, M. Date, S. Suyama, and T. Hatada, "A method for reproducing apparent continuous depth in a stereoscopic display using" Depth-fused 3D" technology," *J. Soc. Info. Display* **14**(5), 493–498 (2006).

59. H. Takada, S. Suyama, and K. Nakzawa, "A new 3D display method using 3D visual illusion produced by overlapping two luminance division displays," *IEICE Trans. Elect.* **E88**–C(3), 445–449 (2005).

60. H. Takada, S. Suyama, K. Hiruma, and K. Nakazawa, "A Compact Depth-Fused 3D LCD," *SID Symp. Digest Tech Papers (58.2)*, pp. 1526–1529, (2003).

61. C. Lee, S. DiVerdi, and T. Höllerer, "Depth-fused 3D imagery on an immaterial display," *IEEE Trans. Vis. Comp. Graph.* **15**, 20–32 (2009).

62. E. A. Downing, "Method and system for three-dimensional display of information based on two photon upconversion," U.S. patent 5,684,621 (November 4, 1997).

63. E. A. Downing, "A solid-state three-dimensional upconversion display," *Nonlinear Optics: Materials, Fundamentals, and Applications*, 409–411, (1994).

64. R. Zito, Jr., "Rate Analysis of Multiple-Step Excitation in Mercury Vapor," *J. App. Phys.* **34**(5), 1535–1543 (1963).

65. R. H. Barnes, C. E. Moeller, J. F. Kircher, and C. M. Verber, "Two-step excitation of fluorescence in iodine monochloride vapor," *Appl. Phys. Lett.* **24**(12), 610–612 (1974).

66. I. I. Kim, E. Korevaar, and H. Hakakha, "Three-dimensional volumetric display in rubidium vapor," *Proc. SPIE* **2650**, 274–284 (1996).

67. E. J. Korevaar and B. Spiver, "Three dimensional display apparatus," U.S. patent 4,881,068 (November 14, 1989).

68. A. Rapaport, K. Ayrault, E. St. Mattew-Daniel, and M. Bass, "Visible light emission from dyes excited by simultaneous absorption of two different frequency beams of light," *Appl. Phys. Lett.* **74**, 329–331 (1999).

69. R. M. Wood, *Laser-Induced Damage of Optical Materials*, Institute of Physics (2003).

70. I. N. Troitski, "Laser-Induced Image Technology (Yesterday, Today, and Tomorrow)," *Proc. SPIE* **5664**, 293–301 (2005).

71. S. K. Nayar and V. N. Anand, "3D volumetric display using passive optical scatterers," *Computer* **40**(7), 54–63 (2007).

72. M. Momiuchi and H. Kimura, "Device for forming visible image in air," U.S. patent 7,533,995 (May 19, 2009).

73. D. L. MacFarlane, "Volumetric three-dimensional display," *Appl. Opt.* **33**(31), 7453–7457 (1994).

74. D. Wyatt, "A volumetric 3D LED display" (MIT, 2005), http://web.mit.edu/6.111/www/f2005/projects/wyatt_Project_Design_Presentation.pdf.

75. http://www.3d-display-info.com/tags/volumetric-displays

76. A. Sullivan, "A solid-state multiplanar volumetric display," *SID Digest* **58**(3), 354–356 (2003).

77. A. Sullivan, "DepthCube solid-state 3D volumetric display," *Proc. SPIE* **5291**, 279–284 (2004).

78. K. Perlin and J. Han, "Volumetric display with dust as the participating medium," US patent application 20040218148 to New York Univ., Patent and Trademark Office, (2004).

79. K. Langhans, D. Bezecny, D. Homann, D. Bahr, C. Vogt, C. Blohm, and K.-H. Scharschmidt, "New portable FELIX 3D display," *Proc. SPIE* **3296**, (1998).

80. M. Hirsch, "Three dimensional display apparatus," U.S. patent 2,967,905 (January 13, 1958).

81. 3D Display from ITT Labs, "New display gives realistic 3D effect," Aviation Week, 66–67 (October 31, 1960).

82. E. G. Rawson, "Vibrating varifocal mirrors for 3D imaging," *IEEE Spectrum*, pp. 37–43, (September 1969).

83. D. F. McAllister (Ed.), *Stereo Computer Graphics and Other True 3D Technologies*, (pp. 230–246, Princeton University Press, Princeton, New Jersey, 1993).

84. J. Fajans, "Three-dimensional display," *Proc. SPIE* **199**, 23–28 (1979).

85. R. D. Williams and D. Donohoo, "Image Quality Metrics for Volumetric Laser Displays," *Proc. SPIE* 1457, (1991).

86. D. Bahr, K. Langhans, M. Gerken, C. Vogt, D. Bezecny, and D. Homann, "FELIX: A volumetric 3D laser display," *Proc. SPIE* **2650**, 265–273 (1996).

87. K. Langhans, D. Bezecny, D. Homann, D. Bahr, C. Vogt, C. Blohm, and K.-H. Scharschmidt, "New portable FELIX 3D display," *Proc. SPIE* **3296**, 24–30 (1998).

88. D. Bahr, K. Langhans, D. Bezecny, D. Homann, and Carsten Vogt, "FELIX: a volumetric 3D imaging technique," *Proc. SPIE* **3101**, 202–210 (1997).

89. K. D. Linsmeier, "Raumbilder auf dreidimensionalem monitor," Spektrum der Wissenschaft, pp. 24–25, January (1996).

90. R. Morton, "Three-dimensional display system," U.S. patent 4,922,336 (May 1 1990).

91. M. Lasher, P. Soltan, W. Dahlke, N. Acantilado, and M. McDonald, "Laser-projected 3D volumetric displays," *Proc. SPIE* **2650**, 285–295 (1996).

92. R. Dorval, M. Thomas, and J. Bareau, "Volumetric three dimensional display system," U.S. patent 6,554,430 B2, (Apr. 29, 2003).

93. J. Geng, "A volumetric 3D display based on a DLP projection engine," *Displays* **34**, 39–48 (2013).

94. J. Geng, "Method and apparatus for high resolution three dimensional display," U.S. patent 6,064,423 (May 16, 2000).

95. J. Geng, "Method and apparatus for an interactive volumetric three dimensional display," U.S. patent 7,098,872 (August 29, 2006).

96. J. Geng, "Method and apparatus for an interactive volumetric three dimensional display," U.S. patent 6,900,779 (May 31, 2005).

97. J. Geng, "Method and apparatus for generating structural pattern illumination," U.S. patent 6,937,348 (August 30, 2005).

98. R. J. Schipper, "Three-dimensional display," U.S. patent 3,097,261 (July 9, 1963).

99. E. P. Berlin, Jr., "Three-dimensional display," U.S. patent 4,160,973 (July 10, 1979).

100. D. G. Jansson, E. P. Berlin, I. Straus, and J. Goodhue, "A three-dimensional computer display," *Computer Graphics in CAD/CAM Systems, Annual Conference*, Cambridge, April (1979).

101. R. D. Williams and D. Donohoo, "Image Quality Metrics for Volumetric Laser Displays," *Proc. SPIE* 1457, (1991).

102. D. Solomon, "Volumetric imaging launches graphics into a 3D world," *Photonics Spectra*, pp. 129–134, June (1993).

103. T. F. Budinger, "An analysis of 3D display strategies," *Proc. SPIE* **507**, 2–8 (1984).

104. R. D. Ketchpel, "CRT provides three-dimensional displays," *Electronics*, November (1962).

105. B. G. Blundell, A. J. Schwarz, and D. K. Horrell, "Cathode ray sphere: a prototype system to display volumetric three dimensional images," *Opt. Eng.* **33**(1), 180–186 (1994).

106. B. G. Blundell, A. J. Schwarz, and D. K. Horrell, "Volumetric three-dimensional display systems: their past, present and future," *Eng. Sci. Ed. J.*, 196–200, Oct. (1993).
107. B. G. Blundell, "Three dimensional display system," U.S. patent 5,703,606 (December 30, 1997).
108. L. H. Enloe, J. A. Murphy, and C. B. Rubinstein, "Hologram transmission via television," *Bell Syst. Tech. J.* **45**, 335–339 (1966).
109. R. J. Doyle and W. E. Glenn, "Remote real-time reconstruction of holograms using the Lumatron," *Appl. Opt.* **11**, 1261–1264 (1972).
110. K. Sato, K. Higuchi, and H. Katsuma, "Holographic television by liquid-crystal device," *Proc. SPIE* **1667**, 19–31 (1992).
111. N. Hashimoto, K. Hoshino, and S. Morokawa, "Improved real-time holography system with LCDs," *Proc. SPIE* **1667**, 2–7 (1992).
112. V. M. Bove, Jr., "Live holographic TV: From misconceptions to engineering," *Proc. SMPTE Int. Conf. on Stereoscopic 3D for Media and Entertainment* (2011).
113. V. M. Bove, Jr., Q. Y. J. Smithwick, J. Barabas, and D. E. Smalley, "Is 3D TV preparing the way for holographic TV?," *Proc. 8th International Symposium on Display Holography* (2009).
114. R. Stahl and M. Jayapala, "Holographic displays and smart lenses," *Optik Photonik* **6**, 39–42 (2011).
115. F. Reinitzer, "Beitrge zur kenntniss des cholesterins," *Wiener Monatschr, Fur Chem.*, vol. **9**, pp. 421–441, (1888).
116. F. Yaras, H. Kang, and L. Onural, "State of the Art in Holographic Displays: A Survey," *J. Disp. Tech.* **6**(10), 443–454 (2010).
117. P. St. Hilaire, S. A. Benton, M. Lucente, M. L. Jepsen, J. Kollin, H. Yoshikawa, and J. Underkoffler, "Electronic display system for computational holography," *Proc. SPIE* **1212**, 174–182 (1990).
118. P. St. Hilaire, "Scalable optical architectures for electronic holography," Ph.D. dissertation, Program in Media Arts and Sciences, MIT, Cambridge, MA (1994).
119. D. E. Smalley, Q. Y. J. Smithwick, and J. V. Michael Bove, "Holographic video display based on guided-wave acousto-optic devices," *Proc. SPIE* **6488**, 64880L (2007).
120. V. M. Bove, Jr., W. J. Plesniak, T. Quentmeyer, and J. Barabas, "Real-time holographic video images with commodity PC hardware," *Proc. SPIE* **5664**, 5664A (2005).
121. J. Barabas, S. Jolly, D. E. Smalley, and V. M. Bove, Jr., "Diffraction specific coherent panoramagrams of real scenes," *Proc. SPIE* 7957 (2011).
122. J. Barabas, Q. Y. J. Smithwick, and V. M. Bove, Jr., "Evaluation of rendering algorithms for presenting layered information on holographic displays," *SID Symposium Digest of Technical Papers*, **41**, 1233–1236 (2010).

123. Q. Y. J. Smithwick, D. E. Smalley, V. M. Bove, Jr., and J. Barabas, "Progress in holographic video displays based on guided-wave acousto-optic devices," *Proc. SPIE* 6912, (2008).

124. T. Quentmeyer, "Delivering Real-Time Holographic Video Content with Off-the-Shelf PC Hardware," (MS thesis) (2004).

125. R. Haussler, S. Reichelt, N. Leister, E. Zschau, R. Missbach, and A. Schwerdtner, "Large real-time holographic displays: from prototypes to a consumer product," *Proc. SPIE* **7237**, 72370S (2009).

126. M. Klug, T. Burnett, A. Fancello, A. Heath, K. Gardner, S. O'Connell, and C. Newswanger, "A scalable, collaborative, interactive light-field display system," *SID Symposium Digest of Technical Papers* Vol. **44**(1), pp. 412–415 (2013).

127. Mark Lucente, "The first 20 years of holographic video–and the next 20," *SMPTE 2nd Annual International Conference on Stereoscopic 3D for Media and Entertainment of Motion Picture and Television Engineers (SMPTE)*, June (2011).

128. M. Stanley, M. A. Smith, A. P. Smith, P. J. Watson, S. D. Coomber, C. D. Cameron, C. W. Slinger, and A. D. Wood, "3D electronic holography display system using a 100 mega-pixel spatial light modulator," *Proc. SPIE* **5249**, 297 (2004).

129. M. Stanley et al., "A novel electro-optic modulator system for the production of dynamic images from giga-pixel computer generated holograms," *Proc. SPIE* **3956**, 13 (2000).

130. C. Slinger, C. Cameron, and M. Stanley, "Computer-generated holography as a generic display technology," *IEEE Computer* **38**(8), 46–53 (2005).

131. IMEC Holographic Display, http://www.imec.be/ScientificReport/SR2010/2010/1159126.html.

132. Y. Ichihashi, H. Nakayama, T. Ito, N. Masuda, T. Shimobaba, A. Shiraki, and T. Sugie, "HORN-6 special-purpose clustered computing system for electroholography," *Opt. Express* **17**, 13895–13903 (2009).

133. T. Ito, N. Masuda, K. Yoshimura, A. Shiraki, T. Shimobaba, and T. Sugie, "Special-purpose computer HORN-5 for a real-time electro-holography," *Opt. Express* **13**, 1923–1932 (2005).

134. T. Shimobaba, S. Hishinuma, and T. Ito, "Special-purpose computer for holography HORN-4 with recurrence algorithm," *Comput. Phys. Comm.* **148**, 160–170 (2002).

135. T. Shimobaba, N. Masuda, T. Sugie, S. Hosono, S. Tsukui, and T. Ito, "Special-purpose computer for holography HORN-3 with PLD technology," *Comput. Phys. Comm.* **130**, (2000).

136. T. Ito, H. Eldeib, K. Yoshida, S. Takahashi, T. Yabe, and T. Kunugi, "Special-purpose computer for holography HORN-2," *Comput. Phys. Comm.* **93**, 13–20 (1996).

137. T. Ito, T. Yabe, M. Okazaki, and M. Yanagi, "Special-purpose computer HORN-1 for reconstruction of virtual image in three dimensions," *Comput. Phys. Comm.* **82**, 104–110 (1994).

138. T. Hamano and H. Yoshikawa, "Image-type CGH by means of e-beam printing," *Proc. SPIE* **3293**, 2– (1998).

139. T. Yamaguchi, G. Okabe, and H. Yoshikawa, "Real-time image plane full-color and full-parallax holographic video display system," *Opt. Eng.* **46**, 125801 (2007).

140. T. Yamaguchi and H. Yoshikawa, "Real time calculation for holographic video display," *Proc. SPIE* **6136**, 61360T (2006).

141. H. Yoshikawa, T. Yamaguchi, and R. Kitayama, "Real-time generation of full color image hologram with compact distance look-up table," in OSA Tech. Dig. Digital Holography and Three-Dimensional Imaging, paper DWC4 (2009).

142. T. Yatagai, "Stereoscopic approach to 3D display using computer-generated holograms," *Appl. Opt.* **15**, 2722–2729 (1976).

143. H. Kang, T. Yamaguchi, H. Yoshikawa, S. C. Kim, and E. S. Kim, "Acceleration method of computing a compensated phase-added stereogram on a graphic processing unit," *Appl. Opt.* **47**, 5784–5789 (2008).

144. H. Kang, T. Fujii, T. Yamaguchi, and H. Yoshikawa, "Compensated phase-added stereogram for real-time holographic display," *Opt. Eng.* **46**, 095802 (2007).

145. H. Y. J. Tamai, "Faster computation of subsampled coherent stereogram," *J. Inst. Television Eng. Japan* **50**, 1612–1615 (1996).

146. M. Yamaguchi, H. Hoshino, T. Honda, and N. Ohyama, "Phase-added stereogram: Calculation of hologram using computer graphics technique," *Proc. SPIE* **1914**, 25 (1993).

147. H. Yoshikawa and H. Kameyama, "Integral holography," *Proc. SPIE* **2406**, 226 (1995).

148. H. Kang, "Quality Improvements of the coherent holographic stereogram for natural 3D display and its applications," Ph.D. dissertation, Nihon University, Tokyo, Japan (2008).

149. H. Kang, F. Yaras, and L. Onural, "Graphics processing unit accelerated computation of digital holograms," *Appl. Opt.* **48**(34), H137–H143, (2009).

150. F. Yaras, H. Kang, and L. Onural, "Real-time phase-only color holographic video display system using LED illumination," *Appl. Opt.* **48**(34), H48–H53 (2009).

151. H. Kang, F. Yaras, L. Onural, and H. Yoshikawa, "Real-time fringe pattern generation with high quality," in *OSA Tech. Dig. Digital Holography and Three-Dimensional Imaging*, paper DTuB7 (2009).

152. F. Yaras, H. Kang, and L. Onural, "Real-time multiple SLM color holographic display using multiple GPU acceleration," in *OSA Tech.*

Dig. Digital Holography and Three-Dimensional Imaging, paper DWA4 (2009).

153. H. Kang, F. Yaras, and L. Onural, "Quality comparison and acceleration for digital hologram generation method based on segmentation," in *Proc. IEEE 3DTV Conf.: The True Vision—Capture, Transmission and Display of 3D Video*, (2009).

154. F. Yaras, H. Kang, and L. Onural, "Real-time color holographic video display system," in *Proc. IEEE 3DTV Conf.: The True Vision—Capture, Transmission and Display of 3D Video*, (2009).

155. H. Sasaki, K. Yamamoto, Y. Ichihashi, and T. Senoh "Image Size Scalable Full-parallax Coloured Three-dimensional Video by Electronic Holography," *Sci. Rep.* **4**, 4000 (Feb. 2014).

156. N. Inoue, M. Kawakita, and K. Yamamoto, "200-inch glasses-free 3D display and electronic holography being developed at NICT," *Conference on Lasers and Electro-Optics/Pacific Rim Kyoto Japan*, WO1-1, June 30- July 4, (2013).

157. P. A. Blanche et al., "An updatable holographic display for 3D visualization," *J. Display Technol.* **4**(4), 424–430 (2008).

158. S. Tay et al., "An updatable holographic three-dimensional display," *Nature* **451**, 694–698 (2008).

159. P. A. Blanche et al., "Holographic three-dimensional telepresence using large-area photorefractive polymer," *Nature* **468**, 80–83 (2010).

160. http://users.auth.gr/~iantonio/HOME3DTechnologies.html

161. J. H. Jung, J. Kim, and B. Lee, "Solution of pseudoscopic problem in integral imaging for real-time processing," *Opt. Lett.* **38**, 76–78 (2013).

162. B. G. Blundell, "Method and system for free-space imaging display and interface," U.S. patent 20040001182 A1 (Jan 1, 2004).

Appendix
Additional MATLAB Functions

This appendix contains additional MATLAB function headers, which are necessary to implement the example code provided in the body of the text. The actual codes are found on the CD-ROM.

```
1    function [Dr,Dr_phase,Slice,Slice_phase,Vol,...
2    Vol_phase] = myDiffraction(Object,...
3    Propagation_distance,wavelength,...
4    Object_pixel_size, Diffraction_Increment,...
5    Diffraction_start,Slice_location,...
6    Calculate_volume)
7    %This file will load a diffraction object and calculate
8    %the mid-to-far-field diffraction pattern using the
9    %Fresnel-Kirchoff integral. This is most easily done by
10   %using the 'myFresnel' function to propagate the object
11   %some distance.
12   %If desired, a phase can be added to the object before
13   %propogation. The Fresnel number F will be calculated
14   %to verify that F≪1 so that the Fresnel integral is
15   %accurate.
16   % (>1 Fresnel to Rayleigh-Sommerfeld) (≪1 Fraunhouffer)
17   % (1 geo)
18   %Note that for the Fresnel number calculation, the
19   %characteristic object size is assumed to be around
20   %1/10 of the overall matrix size. This should be
21   %reasonable for most objects.
22   %
23   %FUNCTION INPUTS:
24   %Object: The object may be complex (i.e., already
25   %contains phase information). The object should already
26   %be a. mat file format (i.e., a standard matrix).
27   %The object matrix is assumed to be SQUARE.
28   %
29   %Propagation_distance: Distance in meters. The total
30   %distance should be less than 1 meter, or the
31   %computation will become too large and crash MATLAB.
32   %There will be an error message if this happens.
33   %
```

(continued)

Appendix   (*Continued*)

```
34  %wavelength: Simulated illumination wavelength in
35  %meters.
36  %
37  %Object_pixel_size: In meters (typically around
38  %10e-6 meters, or 10 um).
39  %
40  %Diffraction_Increment: Distance between the diffraction
41  %planes, in meters.
42  %PHASE ANGLES SHOULD NOW BE CALCULATED EXTERNALLY
43  %Horizontal_phase_angle: Adds a phase tilt to the
44  %object, in radians.
45  %Vertical_phase_angle: Adds a phase tilt to the object,
46  %in radians.
47  %%%
48  %Diffraction_start: Begin calculating the diffraction
49  %from this plane.
50  %Default is to begin at zero (at the aperture).
51  %
52  %Slice_location: Where to put the slice to view the
53  %side view of the diffraction profile. Defaults to
54  %the center of the image if set to zero.
55  %
56  %FUNCTION OUTPUTS
57  %Dr: Diffraction reconstruction at the final
58  %propagation distance in the (x,y) plane.
59  %
60  %Slice: The side-view of the diffraction, in the (y,z)
61  %plane.
62  %
63  %Slice_phase: The side-view of the phase.
64  %
65  %Vol and Vol_phase: The volume of all diffraction planes
66  %calculated, scaled by 50% to manage memory overflow
67  %issues.
```

```
1   function [S] = myDrawCircle(Bitmap_size,radius,...
2   shift_x,shift_y)
3   %Written by Logan Williams
4   %2 April 2013
5   %This functin draws a circle of ones on a background
6   %of zeroes.
7   %Bitmap_size in pixels, nxn format.
8   %Radius in pixels.
9   %A shift in x and y direction shifts the center of
10  %the circle in pixels.
```

```
11  function [Hr] =...
12  myFresnel(hologram,reconstruction_distance,...
13  wavelength,pixel_size,in_line,phase_mask,...
14  scale_factor,pad_size)
15  %%Written by Logan Williams, 4/27/2012 (version 1).
16  %%Added padding capability on 7/14/2012.
17  %%Fixed image crop errors for nonsquare holos on
18  %11/14/2013.
19  %%Fixed scale factor greater than one on 6/8/2013.
20  %%Final version updated 1/28/2014.
21  %
```

(*continued*)

Appendix   (*Continued*)

```
22   %%This function reconstructs a hologram using a
23   %Fresnel transform
24   %%and returns the reconstructed complex image matrix.
25   %
26   %%reconstruction_distance in meters.
27   %%Wavelength in meters.
28   %%Pixel size in meters (pixels are assumed to be
29   %square).
30   %
31   %%If in_line is set to 1, the hologram will rescale
32   %with distance about the zero order (use full for
33   %inline
34   %holograms)defaults to 0.
35   %%NOTE: reconstruction_dist must be positive for
36   %in_line
37   %scaling to work.
38   %
39   %%phase_mask should be the same size as the hologram.
40   %%If either one is not square, they will be cropped to
41   %square if a scalar value is entered for phase_mask,
42   %%a constant array of that value is used (i.e., uniform
43   %phase, plane wave).
44   %
45   %%scale_factor will change the size of the original
46   %hologram.
47   %%scale_factor should go above 1 now (updated 7 May
48   %2013).
49   %%Increasing the scale factor will dramatically improve
50   %the reconstruction
51   %%results when in the very near field (without extra
52   %padding).
53   %%scale_factor defaults to 1.
54   %%Reducing the scale factor too low (<1/2 or so) will
55   %begin vignetting the image significantly, losing the
56   %higher spatial freq. info. due to resampling losses.
57   %%For very large CCD arrays, scale the image down.
58   %%For very-near-field holograms, scale the image up.
```

```
1    function [S] =...
2    myLensPhase_f(Bitmap_size,focal_length,...
3    wavelength,dx,shift_x,shift_y)
4    %Written by Logan Williams
5    %4 April 2013
6    %This function computes a complex bitmap representing
7    %the phase of a lens.
8    %The phase is computed by giving a bitmap size, with
9    %pixels of size dx,
10   %and a focal length and wavelength.
11   %Bitmap_size in pixels, nxn format.
12   %Focal length in meters.
13   %dx is the pixel scale in meters per pixel (i.e., 10e-6=
14   %10 um/pixel).
15   %Wavelength in meters.
16   %A shift in x and y direction shifts in pixels (units of
17   %dx).
```

(*continued*)

Appendix *(Continued)*

```
1    function [S] = ...
2    myTiltPhase(Bitmap_size,horizontal_phase_angle,...
3    vertical_phase_angle)
4    %Written by Logan Williams
5    %This function applies a phase tilt in x and y to a
6    %bitmap input object.
7    %Vertical and horizontal phase angles in radians.
```

```
1    function [del_phi_filtered] = ...
2    myDHIfilter(del_phi,filter_size)
3    %Written by Logan Williams
4    %October 2013
5    %
6    %This function performs mean filtering of the hologram
7    %phase difference using the method described by Kries,
8    %pg 275. It should remove salt-and-pepper phase noise
9    %without softening the 2pi phase edges, so phase
10   %unwrapping should still be able to work after this
11   %type of filter.
12   %
13   %IMPORTANT NOTE: Precaution must be taken to ensure
14   %this works correctly!
15   %When sin and cos are used to filter in this manner,
16   %MATLAB will double the frequency of the wrapped
17   %del_phi while also changing the total phase
18   %variation from [-pi pi] to [-pi/2 +pi/2].
19   %This will not unwrap correctly with PUMA unless the
20   %full range is restored to [-pi pi] by multiplying
21   %the filtered result by 2. Then unwrap using PUMA.
22   %The resulting unwrapped absolute phase will
23   %now be too great by a factor of 2; thus, the PUMA
24   %result must now be divided by 2. This will yield
25   %the correct unwrapped phase after filtering. I have
26   %verified this method using several simulations.
27   %
28   %Example of proper use:
29   %%MUST multiply by 2 for PUMA
30   %del_phi_filt =(myDHIfilter(del_phi,7).*2);
31   %%unwrapped phase will be 2x
32   %doubled_unwph = puma_ho(del_phi_filt);
33   %%divide the doubled result by 2
34   %correct_unwph = doubled_unwph./2;
35   %
36   %INPUTS: the del_phi phase map and the size of
37   %the mean-filter grid.
38   %
39   %del_phi is the phase difference interferogram.
40   %filter_size = 3; -> this produces a symmetric
41   %3x3 filter grid.
```

```
1    function [data_out] = Display3d(data_in, threshold,...
2    smoothing, alpha_value)
3    %Written by Logan Williams, 5/10/2012
4    %This function will display a 3D volume using
5    %isosurface while performing simple thresholding.
6    %The threshold is a percentage of the maximum value
```

(continued)

Appendix   (*Continued*)

```
7    %and should vary between zero and one.
8    %Smoothing will be Gaussian smoothing. The value of
9    %smoothing must conform to the smooth3 function,
10   %which requires odd integer values greater than one.
11   %Setting smoothing to zero will disable smoothing.
12   %alpha_value is the percentage of transparency
13   %between 0 and 1, with 1 = opaque and 0 = transparent.
```

```
1    function [N] = myFast_Rigid3D(k1,thx,thy,thz,tx,ty,tz)
2    %Image Registration - 3D Rigid body Transformation
3    %Jeny Rajan, Chandrashekar P.S
4    %This program is for rigid-body transformation of 3D
5    %objects.
6    %Input variables:
7    %k1 - Input array (X*Y*Z)
8    %thx,thy,thz - rotation angle theta (in degrees) along
9    %x, y, and z axis respectively.
10   %tx,ty,tz - translation along x, y, and z.
11   %Code modified by Rola Aylo and Logan Williams
12   % (Dec 2013, March 2014)
13   %The modification removes the for loops from the
14   %original code to operate
15   %directly on the matrices. This speeds the code up by
16   %approximately a
17   %factor of 12x.
```

```
1    function [Ps,Pr] = myInterferogram(h1,h2)
2    %Input = complex field of already-reconstructed
3    %holograms.
4    %Output = the phase interferogram between the two
5    %holograms.
6    %This function will output the digital interferogram
7    %computed using two
8    %different methods. The primary difference in the
9    %results of the two
10   %methods is a pi phase shift in the fringe locations.
```

```
1    function [S] =...
2    myLensPhase(Bitmap_size,phase_angle,...
3    shift_x,shift_y)
4    %Written by Logan Williams
5    %2 April 2013
6    %This functin draws a circle of ones on a background
7    %of zeroes.
8    %Bitmap_size in pixels, nxn format.
9    %Radius in pixels.
10   %A shift in x and y direction shifts the center of the
11   %circle in pixels.
```

```
1    function [Output_Volume] =...
2    myLoftAndRotate(input_matrix,scale_factor,angle)
3    %written by Logan Williams, 5/10/2012
4    %This function will accept a 2D or 3D input matrix
5    %and loft it along the z axis to make it a cube.
6    %If the angle is set to a nonzero value, the matrix
```

(*continued*)

Appendix   (*Continued*)

```
7    %will also be rotated using the rigid3D function.
8    %THIS FUNCTION ONLY WORKS CORRECTLY FOR MATRICIES THAT
9    %ARE SQUARE IN X AND Y. There is no error checking
10   %to enforce this requirement.
11   %If the matrix is already a 3D volume but not a cube,
12   %this function will loft it along the z axis to make
13   %it a cube by lofting the space between the original
14   %planes of the matrix (WRITTEN BUT NOT TESTED YET).
15   %input_matrix should already be square, or it will not
16   %loft to a cube.
17   %scale_factor should be less than one to avoid memory
18   %overruns. Defaults to one if no scale factor is given.
19   %Angle is in degrees, defaults to zero if no angle is
20   %given. The rotation will only be in the xz plane.
21   %If some other rotation plane is desired,
22   %call this function to loft with an angle of zero,
23   %then call rigid3D afterward for arbitrary rotation.
24   %The input matrix is converted to single to minimize
25   %memory use.
```

```
1    function N=rigid3D(k1,thx,thy,thz,tx,ty,tz);
2    %Image Registration - 3D Rigid body Transformation
3    %Jeny Rajan, Chandrashekar P.S
4    %This program is for rigid-body transformation of 3D
5    %objects.
6    %Input variables
7    %k1 - Input array (X*Y*Z).
8    %thx,thy,thz - rotation angle theta (in degrees) along
9    %x, y, and z axis, respectively.
10   %tx,ty,tz - translation along x, y, and z.
```

```
1    function [S] = ...
2    myDrawRectangle(Bitmap_size,size_x,size_y,...
3    shift_x,shift_y)
4    %Written by Logan Williams
5    %2 April 2013
6    %This functin draws a rectangle of ones on a
7    %background of zeroes.
8    %Bitmap_size in pixels, nxn format.
9    %size_x: size of x dimension in pixels.
10   %size_y: size of y dimension in pixels.
11   %A shift in x and y direction shifts the center
12   %of the rectangle in pixels.
```

```
1    function [S] =...
2    myDrawTriangle(Bitmap_size,size,shift_x,shift_y)
3    %Written by Logan Williams
4    %2 April 2013
5    %This functin draws a "right isosceles triangle" of ones
6    %on a background of zeroes.
7    %Bitmap_size in pixels, nxn format.
8    %size: length of the base in pixels.
9    %A shift in x and y direction shifts the center of the
10   %rectangle in pixels.
```

Index

Dr. Georges Nehmetallah is currently an Assistant Professor in the EECS department at the Catholic University of America. From 2011–2012, he was at the University of Dayton as a Research Professor; prior to that, he was a Postdoctoral Researcher and Research Engineer with the University of Dayton. He received his Ph.D. in ECE from the University of Dayton in 2006. He has served as a PI and a Co-PI for several SBIR and STTR Phase-I and Phase-II projects for the Air Force, Army, and DARPA, and he was one of the 11 out of over 500 people who received the Army SBIR Achievement Award in 2011. His research interests are in 3D imaging, digital holography, and metamaterials. He has authored a book chapter on soliton stabilization and published more than 70 refereed journal papers, review articles and conference proceedings. Nehmetallah is the recipient of the Newport Spectra-Physics Research Excellence Award (2005), SPIE Educational Scholarship in Optical Science and Engineering (2005), and the 2014 Burns Fellowship Award at CUA. He is a reviewer for *Applied Optics, Chinese Optics Letters, and the Journal of the Optical Society of America B*. He is a member of OSA and SPIE.

Dr. Rola Aylo is currently a technical advisor at Oblon in the electrical patent prosecution group, where she is involved in the preparation and prosecution of patent applications. Prior to her current position, she worked at the University of Dayton as a Research Associate (2010–2012) in their electro-optics program, then as a lecturer in the EECS department at the Catholic University of America (2013). Aylo has published more than 20 refereed journal papers and conference proceedings in the areas of optical design, metamaterial applications to sensors technology, and nanoparticle dispersed-liquid-crystal cell fabrication and characterization, which was part of a Phase I and Phase II DARPA-sponsored project from 2009–2012. She is the recipient of the SPIE Newport Spectra Research Excellence Award (2009), the Dayton Area Graduate Studies Institute (DAGSI) Scholarship (2008–2009), and the University of Dayton Innovation Incentive Graduate Research Assistantships (2007).

Dr. Logan Williams is a senior research engineer at the United States Air Force School of Aerospace Medicine, Aeromedical Research Division, at Wright-Patterson AFB, Ohio, where he conducts visual perception and visual task performance research. He previously served in the Air Force Research Laboratory, Warfighter Readiness Research Division, where he lead multiple lines of research in various fields, such as human effectiveness, immersive training environments, visual-display system design, and distributed simulation for aircrew training; he has also served as the lead systems engineer for F-16, A-10, and KC-135 aircrew training systems. Williams has almost two decades of experience in analog and digital circuit design, networked control systems, optical and electro-optical system design, computer programming, and physics-based modeling and simulation. He has earned a Ph.D. in electro-optics, M.E. and B.S. degrees in electrical engineering, and a B.S. in physics. He is an active member of SPIE.